MINISTRY OF DEFENCE (NAVY)

BR 45(1)

Admiralty
Manual of Navigation

Volume I
Revised 1987
Superseding the edition of 1964

LONDON
HER MAJESTY'S STATIONERY OFFICE
1987

© Crown copyright 1987

First published 1956
New edition 1987

ISBN 0 11 771468 2

BR 45(1)

Admiralty
Manual of Navigation

Volume I
Revised 1987
Superseding the edition of 1964

March 1987

By Command of the Defence Council

MINISTRY OF DEFENCE
Directorate of Naval Warfare
D/DNW/102/3/14/2

Preface

The 1987 edition of the *Admiralty Manual of Navigation* consists of five volumes:

Volume I comprises General Navigation (Position and Direction, Projections, Charts and Publications, Chartwork, Fixing, Tides and Tidal Streams, Navigational Errors, Relative Velocity, etc.), Coastal Navigation and Pilotage.

Volume II is the text book of ocean navigation and nautical astronomy.

Volume III includes chapters on Radio Aids, Navigational Instruments, Logs and Echo Sounders, Gyros and Magnetic Compasses, Automated Navigation and Radar Plotting Systems, Traffic Separation and Control. Volume III is published in 'six bound parts to allow revised editions to be produced at frequent intervals.

Volume IV is a loose-leaf book, classified Restricted, containing data and information on navigation, fleetwork and shiphandling that is of particular concern to the Royal Navy, and is not therefore available to the press or public. This volume also includes chapters on new navigational practices and equipment which will eventually be incorporated into Volumes I, II and III as appropriate.

A series of supplements to Volume IV, classified Restricted, are also published. Each supplement contains manoeuvring and acceleration/deceleration data for a specific warship class based on first of class trials.

Volume V is published in six bound parts and comprises exercises in the use of tables and other publications (with extracts). These exercises include Astronomical, Great Circle, Tidal and Tidal Streams, Time and Chronometer, and Relative Velocity questions.

Volumes I, II and III are complementary volumes and together cover all aspects of marine navigation. The material need not be studied sequentially. For example, when Coastal Navigation and Pilotage in Volume I are being considered, the relevant chapters in Volume III on Radio Aids and Echo Sounders should be studied at the same time.

Theory and practice are contained in each volume at a level up to and including the highest level of marine navigation — Royal Naval Specialist Navigating Officers, Master Mariners, etc. Where possible, the more advanced subjects and mathematical proofs not required by the general reader have been incorporated into appendices at the end of the particular volume. The mathematics in the appendices presupposes that the reader is familiar with the more common formulae used in plane and spherical trigonometry, and with the differential and integral calculus, and has a knowledge of statistics, particularly probability theory — all these to GCE 'A' level standard.

Volume I has been prepared by Lieutenant Commander A. G. Dunne Royal Navy of the Naval Staff Author Section of the Directorate of Naval Warfare.

Thanks are due to the following, who have provided advice and assistance in the production of Volume I:

> The Navigation Section, School of Maritime Operations, HMS *Mercury*.
> Britannia Royal Naval College, Dartmouth.
> The Hydrographic Department, Ministry of Defence.
> The Admiralty Compass Observatory, Slough.
> The Naval Operational Command Systems Group, ARE Portsdown.
> The RN Hydrographic School, HMS *Drake*.
> The Directorate of Naval Analysis, Ministry of Defence.
> The Marine Division of the Department of Transport.
> The Royal Institute of Navigation.
> The Nautical Institute.
> The Honourable Company of Master Mariners.
> The General Council of British Shipping (GCBS) and, through the GCBS, the Deep Sea Cargo Division of The Peninsular and Oriental Steam Navigation Company and Furness Withy (Shipping) Ltd.
> The College of Maritime Studies, Warsash, Southampton.
> The Department of Maritime Studies, City of London Polytechnic.
> The Department of Maritime Studies, Liverpool Polytechnic.
> The Department of Maritime Science, Plymouth Polytechnic.
> The Department of Nautical Science, South Tyneside College.

Acknowledgements are also due to the Department of Transport, Marine Division, for permission to use the extracts from Merchant Shipping Notices M854 and M1102, and from Statutory Instrument 1982 No. 1699, *Merchant Shipping (Certification and Watchkeeping) Regulations 1982;* and to the International Chamber of Shipping, for permission to use the extracts from the ICS *Bridge Procedures Guide* (1977).

Contents

CHAPTER 1
Position and Direction on the Earth's Surface

Navigation is the process of planning and carrying out the movement of transport of all kinds from one place to another — at sea, in the air, on land or in space. The navigation of ships and all waterborne craft is called *marine* navigation to distinguish it from navigation in other surroundings, and it is marine navigation that is dealt with in this book and its companion volumes, which together comprise a new edition of the *Admiralty Manual of Navigation.*

The last thirty years have seen great advances in navigational techniques. Man has landed on the moon. Spacecraft are exploring the outer regions of the solar system. The new techniques developed for space navigation have benefited marine navigation: detailed study of the first satellites in orbit around the Earth has led to the development of a world-wide navigation satellite system which can tell a ship's navigator his position with an accuracy of a few hundred metres. Automated computer-assisted navigational systems enable the navigator to maintain a continuous and accurate track and to avoid collisions. Hand-held calculators and desk-top computers enable him to reckon courses and distances around the globe with great precision, taking into account the true shape of the Earth.

The principles of marine navigation remain unchanged by new techniques; therefore the treatment of the subject in this manual has been designed to re-state the principles while reflecting the latest methods.

Volume I deals with the essentials of marine navigation — position and direction on the Earth's surface, map projections, charts and publications, chartwork, tides, coastal navigation and pilotage. Summaries of plane and spherical trigonometry, proofs of formulae, etc. may be found in the appendices at the back of the book.

This opening chapter introduces the basic terms dealing with position and direction on the Earth's surface.

POSITION ON THE EARTH'S SURFACE

The Earth

The Earth is not a perfect sphere; it is slightly flattened, the smaller diameter being about 24 miles less than the larger. The Earth's shape is known as an oblate spheroid (Fig. 1–1) with greatest (*a*) and least (*b*) radii of approximately 3444 and 3432* international nautical miles. The Earth turns about its shortest

* These figures are taken for the International (1924) Spheroid, which is explained in Chapter 3.

diameter PP_1, called the *axis*, the extremities of which are called the *poles*.

An oblate spheroid is a figure traced out by the revolution of a semi-ellipse such as PWP_1, in Fig. 1–1, about its minor axis PP_1. The successive positions of PWP_1 are called *meridians*. The meridian passing through Greenwich is called the *prime meridian*. The circle traced out by W is called the *equator*.

The Earth revolves about its axis PP_1 in the direction shown by the arrow. The direction of revolution is called *east*, the opposite direction *west*. The *North Pole* is on the left and the *South Pole* on the right of the observer facing east.

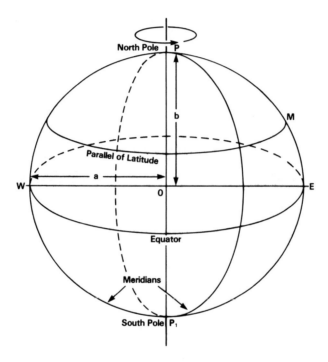

Fig. 1–1.   The Earth, an oblate spheroid

Latitude and longitude

A position on the Earth's surface is expressed by reference to the plane of the equator and the plane of the prime meridian. The *latitude* of a place (also called the geodetic, geographical or true latitude) is the angle which the perpendicular to the Earth's surface at the place makes with the plane of the equator. It is measured from 0° to 90° north or south of the equator. Fig. 1–2 shows a meridional section of the spheroid. The latitude of point M is the angle MLE (ϕ), where L is the point of intersection of the perpendicular to the Earth's surface at M and the plane of the equator OE.

Planes parallel to the plane of the equator joining all places of the same latitude are known as *parallels of latitude*. They are also known as *small circles* (*see* page 9).

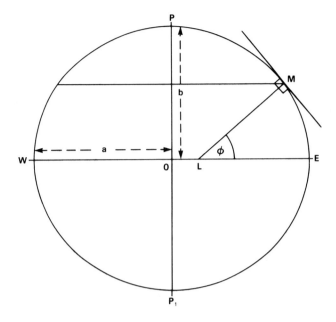

Fig. 1–2.   Latitude of a place

The *longitude* of a place is the angle between the plane of the prime (Greenwich) meridian and the meridian of the place measured from 0° to 180° east or west of Greenwich (Fig. 1–3).

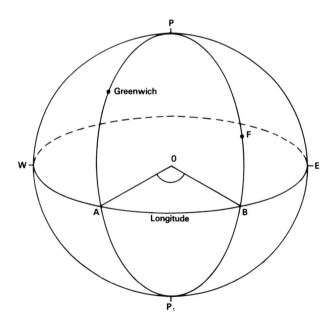

Fig. 1–3.   Longitude of a place

In Fig. 1–3 the longitude of F is the arc AB = angle AOB (east).

The position of a place may therefore be expressed in latitude and longitude. For example, the Central Signal Station Flagstaff, Portsmouth Dockyard, is in latitude 50 degrees 47 minutes 57 seconds north of the equator and in longitude 1 degree 6 minutes 32 seconds west of Greenwich.

The position may be recorded as follows:

$$50°47'57''N \qquad 50°47'.95N \qquad +\ 50°.79917$$
$$\textit{or} \qquad\qquad \textit{or}$$
$$1°06'32''W \qquad 1°06'.53W \qquad -\ \ 1°.10889$$

The third method of recording shown above is for use in a calculator, +ve signs being used for N latitudes and E longitudes, −ve signs for S latitudes and W longitudes.

Difference of latitude, longitude

The *difference of latitude* (d.lat) between two places is the arc of the meridian between the two parallels of latitude. When a ship is proceeding from one place to another, d.lat is named north or south according to whether the parallel of the destination is north or south of the parallel of the place of departure. In Fig. 1–4 the d.lat between F and T is the same as the d.lat between G and T, where GF is the parallel of latitude through F.

$$\text{d.lat from } F \text{ to } T = \text{angle } GDT \text{ (south)} = \text{lat } F - \text{lat } T$$

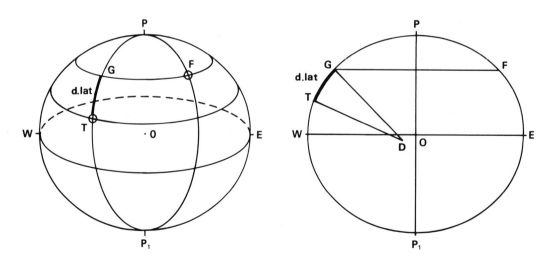

Fig. 1–4.   d.lat

The *difference of longitude* (d.long) between two places is the smaller arc of the equator between their meridians. When a ship is proceeding from one place to another, d.long is named east or west according to whether the meridian of the destination is east or west of the meridian of the place of departure. In Fig. 1–5 the d.long from F to T = arc BA = angle BOA (west) = angle FPT (the angle at the pole between the meridians of the two places).

Fig. 1–5.   d.long

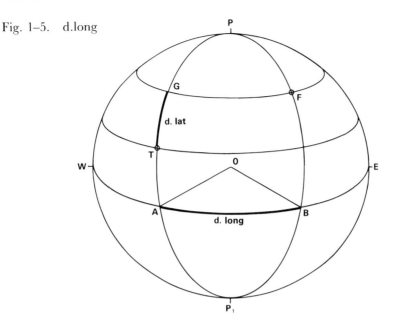

Calculation of d.lat and d.long

The rule for finding the d.lat and the d.long is as follows:

Same names: Subtract   Opposite names: Add

If, when using this rule, the sum of the longitudes exceeds 180°, this sum is subtracted from 360° to find the smaller angle and the name is reversed.

EXAMPLES

Find the d.lat and d.long between:

1. Portsmouth (F): (50°48′N, 1°07′W) and New York (T): (40°40′N, 74°00′W).
2. Malta (F): (35°53′N, 14°31′E) and Gibraltar (T): (36°07′N, 5°21′W).
3. Sydney (F): (33°52′S, 151°13′E) and Honolulu (T): (21°18′N, 157°52′W).

1.	lat *F* 50°48′N	long *F* 1°07′W
	lat *T* 40°40′N	long *T* 74°00′W
	d.lat 10°08′S	d.long 72°53′W
2.	lat *F* 35°53′N	long *F* 14°31′E
	lat *T* 36°07′N	long *T* 5°21′W
	d.lat 0°14′N	d.long 19°52′W
3.	lat *F* 33°52′S	long *F* 151°13′E
	lat *T* 21°18′N	long *T* 157°52′W
	d.lat 55°10′N	d.long 309°05′W

subtract from 360°

d.long   50°55′E

The sea mile

The sea mile is the length of one minute of arc (1′) measured along the meridian in the latitude of the position. This is illustrated in Fig. 1–6.

If *M* is the place on the Earth's surface and *C* the centre of curvature at *M*, and *AMB* is an arc of the meridian subtending an angle of 1′ at *C*, then *AMB* is the length of the sea mile at *M*.

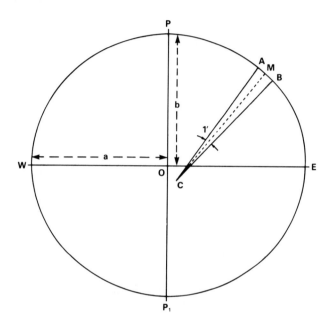

Fig. 1–6.   The sea mile

On Admiralty charts on the Mercator projection (*see* Chapter 4), the latitude graduations form a scale of sea miles.*

Except on charts, where the symbol M is used, the sea mile is denoted by ′, which is the symbol for a minute of arc. Thus, 10′.8 means 10.8 sea miles. The symbol is always placed before the decimal point.

The length of the sea mile

The radius of curvature in the meridian increases as *M* moves from the equator to the pole; thus, the distance subtended by 1′ of arc also increases. The length of the sea mile[†] is shortest at the equator (1842.9 m) and longest at the poles (1861.7 m), with a mean value of 1852.3 m at 45° latitude. Its length is tabulated in *Spheroidal Tables* (NP 240), published by the Hydrographer of the Navy.

The formula for the length of 1′ of arc is given in Chapter 3 and its derivation in Appendix 5.

---

* It is a common but mistaken practice for mariners to refer to a *sea mile* as a *nautical mile*. The British Standard Nautical Mile was discarded in 1970.

[†] For the International (1924) Spheroid, *see* Chapter 3.

One-tenth of a sea mile is known as a *cable*, which varies between 184.3 m and 186.2 m according to latitude. A cable approximates to 200 yards, a convenient measure frequently used at sea for navigational purposes.

The geographical mile

The geographical mile is the length of 1′ of arc measured along the equator (i.e. 1′ of longitude). As the equator is a circle the length of the geographical mile is the same at all parts of the equator and is equal to (*a* sin 1′ of arc), where *a* is the radius of the equator. For the International (1924) Spheroid, its value is 1855.4 m.

The international nautical mile

This is a standard fixed length of 1852 m. Its correct abbreviation is the term *n mile*. Distances given in the *Admiralty Distance Tables* and in *Ocean Passages of the World* are in international nautical miles.

The statute mile

The statute or land mile is the unit of distance of 1760 yards or 5280 feet (1609.3 m).

The knot

In navigation, it is convenient to have a fixed or standard unit for measuring speed. This unit is one international nautical mile (1852 m) per hour and is called a *knot*, abbreviated to *kn*.

In normal practice, the errors arising from using international nautical miles instead of sea miles are very small (less than 0.5%). Sometimes, however, it is necessary to determine the error and this is set out in Appendix 5.

Linear measurement of latitude and longitude

The linear latitude of a place is the length of the arc of the meridian between the equator and that place. It is measured in *sea miles* north or south of the equator. This is illustrated in Fig. 1–7.

If point *M* is in latitude 60°N, then:

$$\text{angle } MLW = 60°$$
$$= 60 \times 60 \text{ minutes of arc} = 3600′$$

The linear latitude of *M* is 3600 sea miles north of the equator.

If a place M_1 is situated 1800 sea miles south of the equator, its latitude is

$$\frac{1800′}{60} \text{ or } 30°S.$$

The linear longitude of a place is the smaller arc of the equator between the prime meridian and the meridian of the place. Along the equator it is measured in *geographical miles* (*see* above) east or west of the prime meridian. This is illustrated in Fig. 1–8.

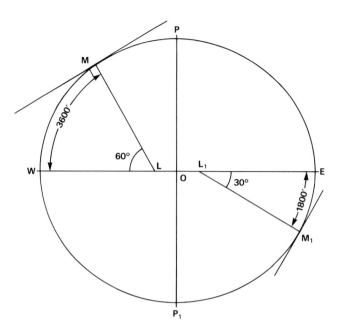

Fig. 1–7.   Linear measurement of latitude

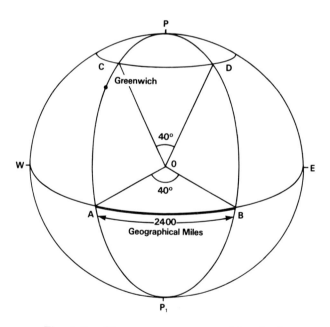

Fig. 1–8.   Linear measurement of longitude

If point B is 40°E of the prime meridian PAP_1, the angle AOB is 40°, the arc AB of the equator is 40° = 40 × 60 = 2400 minutes of arc along the equator, i.e. 2400 geographical miles.

It will be seen from Fig. 1–8 that the distance on the Earth's surface between any two meridians is greatest at the equator and diminishes until it is zero at the poles, where all the meridians meet. The linear distance of a degree of longitude on the surface of the Earth varies approximately with the cosine of the latitude. (The error in assuming that the length of a degree of longitude varies *directly* with the cosine of the latitude lies between zero at the equator and 0.34% at latitude 89° for the International (1924) Spheroid.)

The precise formulae for the length of 1′ of latitude and 1′ of longitude are given in Chapter 3.

The Earth as a sphere

Although the shape of the Earth is that of an oblate spheroid, for most purposes of navigation it may be assumed to be a sphere, with radius equal to the mean of the greatest and least radii and measuring approximately 3440 international nautical miles.* A sphere is the figure formed by rotating a semi-circle about its diameter.

Any plane through the centre of the sphere cuts the surface in what is known as a *great circle*. Any plane which cuts the surface of the sphere, but does not pass through the centre, is called a *small circle* (Fig. 1–9). Thus, when the Earth is regarded as a sphere, meridians of longitude become semi-great circles joining (but not passing through) the poles cutting the equator at right angles. The equator is a great circle but all other parallels of latitude are small circles.

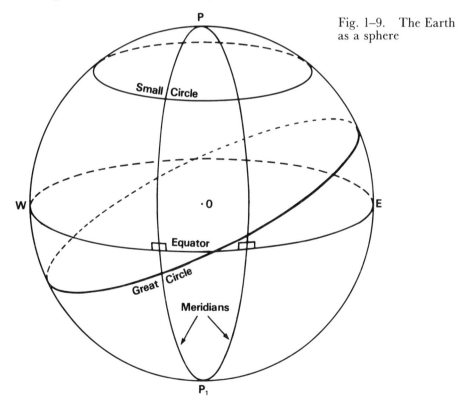

Fig. 1–9. The Earth as a sphere

---

* This figure is taken from the International (1924) Spheroid, which has mean radius
$$\frac{2a + b}{3} = 6,371,229.3 \text{ m}$$

The great circle is important in navigation because it gives the shortest distance between two points. It is also the path taken by an electro-magnetic radiation near the Earth's surface (radio, radar, light, etc.).

Using the mean radius for the sphere derived from the International (1924) Spheroid, the length of 1′ of arc on the meridian or on the equator equals 1853.3 m. This distance approximates very closely to the length of the international nautical mile of 1852 m. The Earth may therefore be treated, without appreciable error, as a sphere where 1′ of latitude is considered equal to 1 n mile anywhere on the surface. (The errors introduced by assuming a spherical Earth based on the international nautical mile are not more than 0.5% for latitude, 0.2% for longitude.) On the equator 1′ of arc of longitude also equals one n mile. This means that linear latitude and linear longitude may now be measured in the same units, n miles.

DIRECTION ON THE EARTH'S SURFACE

True direction

The true direction between two points on the Earth's surface is given by the great circle between them; it is expressed in terms of the angle between the meridian and the great circle (angle *PFT* in Fig. 1–10(a)).

True north

True north is the northerly direction of the meridian and is the reference from which true bearings and courses are measured.

True bearing

The true bearing of an object is the angle between the meridian and the direction of the object.

In Figs 1–10 and 1–11 the true bearing of *T* from *F* is given by the angle *PFT*, where *PF* is the meridian through *F* and *FT* is the great circle joining *F* to *T*.

PFT is measured clockwise from 000° to 360°. In Fig. 1–10 *T* bears 030° from *F*: in Fig. 1–11 *T* bears 330° from *F*.

Over short distances the great circle may be drawn as a straight line without appreciable error, as in Figs 1–10(b) and 1–11(b). The error varies with the latitude and the bearing.

Position of close objects

It is often convenient to indicate the position of an object by its bearing and distance from a known or key position, rather than by latitude and longitude. A shoal, for example, might be described as being 239°, 7 miles from a certain lighthouse.

True course

True course is the direction along the Earth's surface in which the ship is being steered (or intended to be steered). It is measured by the angle between the meridian through the ship's position and the fore-and-aft line, clockwise from 000° to 360°.

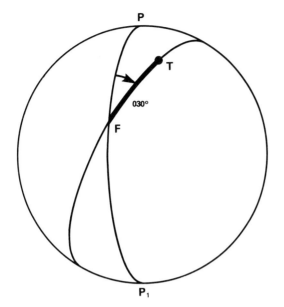

Fig. 1–10(a) True bearing—small bearing—great circle

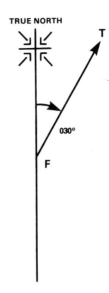

Fig. 1–10(b) True bearing—small bearing—straight line

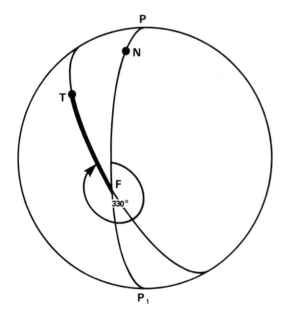

Fig. 1–11(a) True bearing—large bearing—great circle

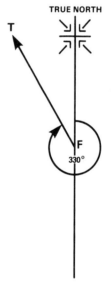

Fig. 1–11(b) True bearing—large bearing—straight line

True course is not to be confused with *heading* (or *ship's head*), which is the instantaneous direction of the ship and is thus a constantly changing value if the ship yaws across the course due to the effect of wind, sea and steering errors.

The compass

The navigational compass is an instrument which provides the datum from which courses and bearings may be measured. There are two principal types of compass—the gyro-compass and the magnetic compass. (These instruments are described in detail in Volume III.) The general principles of the two types of compass are set out below with an explanation as to how true courses and bearings may be obtained from them.

The gyro-compass

This instrument is a rapidly spinning wheel or gyroscope, the axis of which is made to point along the meridian towards true north. Courses and bearings which are measured using a gyro-compass are true provided there is no error in the compass, and are measured clockwise from 000° to 360°.

Error of the gyro-compass

For a number of reasons the gyro-compass will not always point exactly towards true north. Any error must be known before the compass may be used as an accurate reference. Details of how the error may be found are given in Chapter 9.

The degree of accuracy of gyro-compasses used in the Royal Navy is such that the maximum error is of the order of $\frac{1}{2}$° at the equator and 1° at latitude 60°. However, in a number of commercial compasses the error may exceed this by one or two degrees.

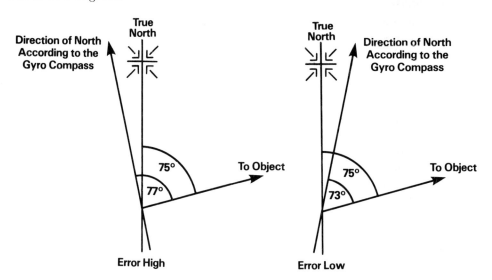

Fig. 1–12(a)   Gyro error high   Fig. 1–12(b)   Gyro error low

If the gyro bearing of an object is 077°, while its true bearing is known to be 075°, then it can be seen from Fig. 1–12(a) that the gyro is reading 2° *high*; similarly, if the gyro bearing is 073°, as in Fig. 1–12(b), the gyro is reading 2° *low*. In order to obtain the true bearing, a gyro error *high* must be *subtracted* from the gyro bearing, and a gyro error *low* must be *added* to the gyro bearing. The suffixes G or T may be used to denote Gyro or True courses and bearings respectively.

The magnetic compass

This instrument may be considered as a bar magnet freely suspended in the horizontal plane and acted upon by the Earth's magnetic field and the magnetic properties of the ship.

The Earth may be considered as a gigantic magnet. Magnetic lines of force emanate from a position near King George V Land in Antarctica known as the South Magnetic Pole. These lines of force follow approximate semi-great circle paths to the North Magnetic Pole, north of Bathurst Island in the Canadian Arctic. These magnetic poles are not stationary but are continually moving over a largely unknown path in a cycle of some hundreds of years.

The magnetic meridian

A freely suspended magnetic compass needle acted upon by the Earth's magnetic field alone will lie in the vertical plane containing the line of total force of the Earth's magnetic field. This vertical plane is known as the *magnetic meridian*. Magnetic meridians, however, do not necessarily point towards the magnetic poles because the Earth's magnetic field is irregular. In addition, the magnetic poles are not 180° apart; thus, it is rare for the magnetic needle to point towards the magnetic pole.

Magnetic north

Magnetic north is the name given to the direction in which the 'north' end of a magnetic needle, suspended so as to remain horizontal, would point when subject only to the influence of the Earth's magnetism. It is the northerly direction of the magnetic meridian.

Variation

Variation is the angle between the geographic (true) and magnetic meridians at any place. It is measured east or west from true north; in Fig. 1–13 the variation at F is 20° west.

Variation has different values at different places and is gradually changing. Its value at any place may be found from the chart which gives the variation for a certain year together with a note of the annual change. The navigator must always allow for this annual change.

Variation may also be obtained from special *isogonic* charts on which all places of equal variation are joined by *isogonic* lines and known as *isogonals* (not to be confused with magnetic meridians, which are lines of force).

Deviation, compass north

If a magnetic compass is put in a ship, the presence of iron, steel or electrical equipment will cause the magnetic compass to deviate from the magnetic meridian. The angle between the magnetic meridian (magnetic north) and the direction in which the needle points (compass north) is called the *deviation*. It is measured east or west from magnetic north.

The magnetic field of the ship changes direction and amount, in part, as the

Fig. 1–13.   Variation

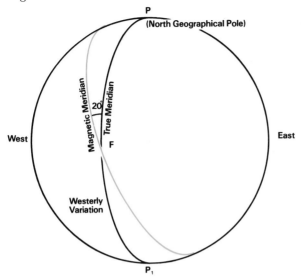

ship alters course. Consequently the deviation is different for different compass courses.

In practice, the deviation in a ship's magnetic compass is reduced to a minimum by the use of permanent magnets and soft-iron correctors. The residual deviation is found by swinging the ship through 360° and tabulating that residual deviation for the various compass headings. (Both these procedures are explained in detail in Volume III.)

The residual deviation may be tabulated as in Table 1–1.

Table 1–1.   Deviation table*

COMPASS HEADING		BEARING OF DISTANT OBJECT		DEVIATION
		MAGNETIC (FROM CHART)	COMPASS (OBSERVED)	
N	(000 °)	236°M	237$\frac{1}{2}$°C	1$\frac{1}{2}$°W
NNE	(022$\frac{1}{2}$°)	236°M	237$\frac{3}{4}$°C	1$\frac{3}{4}$°W
NE	(045 °)	236°M	237$\frac{3}{4}$°C	1$\frac{3}{4}$°W
ENE	(067$\frac{1}{2}$°)	236°M	237$\frac{1}{2}$°C	1$\frac{1}{2}$°W
E	(090 °)	236°M	237 °C	1 °W
ESE	(112$\frac{1}{2}$°)	236°M	236$\frac{1}{2}$°C	$\frac{1}{2}$°W
SE	(135 °)	236°M	235$\frac{1}{2}$°C	$\frac{1}{2}$°E
SSE	(157$\frac{1}{2}$°)	236°M	235 °C	1 °E
S	(180 °)	236°M	234$\frac{1}{2}$°C	1$\frac{1}{2}$°E
SSW	(202$\frac{1}{2}$°)	236°M	234 °C	2 °E
SW	(225 °)	236°M	234 °C	2 °E
WSW	(247$\frac{1}{2}$°)	236°M	234$\frac{1}{4}$°C	1$\frac{3}{4}$°E
W	(270 °)	236°M	234$\frac{3}{4}$°C	1$\frac{1}{4}$°E
WNW	(292$\frac{1}{2}$°)	236°M	235$\frac{1}{4}$°C	$\frac{3}{4}$°E
NW	(315 °)	236°M	236 °C	NIL
NNW	(337$\frac{1}{2}$°)	236°M	237 °C	1 °W

* The standard forms used in the Royal Navy to record deviation (S374A, Record of Observations for Deviation, and S387, Table of Deviation) are tabulated every 22$\frac{1}{2}$° to facilitate the calculation of the various compass coefficients (*see* Volume III). Intervals of 10° or 20° may be used if so desired.

It may also be shown in the form of a curve where deviation is plotted against the compass heading. This is shown in Fig. 1–14.

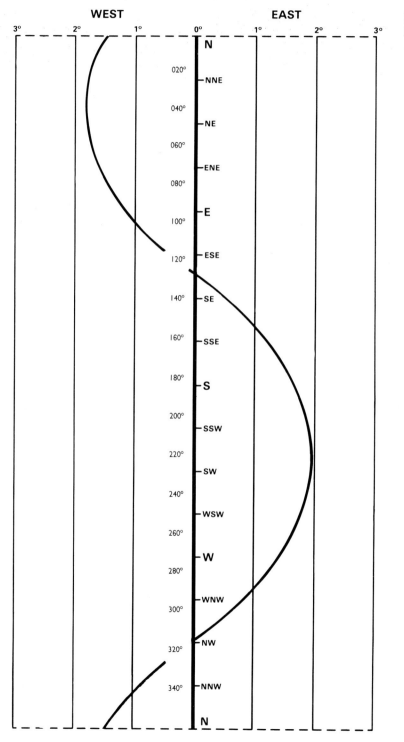

Fig. 1–14.
Deviation curve

Intermediate values for deviation may be found by interpolation from the tables or inspection of the curve. For example, the deviation for 260° compass heading may be found to be $1\frac{1}{2}°$E.

Magnetic and compass courses and bearings

Magnetic courses and bearings are measured clockwise from 000° to 360° from magnetic north (the magnetic meridian) and are given the suffix M, e.g. 075°M. They differ from true courses and bearings by the variation. This is illustrated in Fig. 1–15.

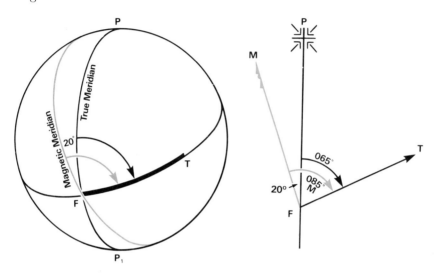

Fig. 1–15.   Magnetic courses and bearings

The magnetic bearing of *T* from *F* (angle *MFT*) is 085°M, while the true bearing of *T* from *F* (angle *PFT*) is 065°. The difference is the variation, 20°W.

Compass courses and bearings are measured clockwise from 000° to 360° from compass north, and are given the suffix C, e.g. 195°C. They differ from true courses and bearings by the amount of variation for the place and the deviation for the compass heading. This is illustrated in Fig. 1–16.

The compass bearing of *T* from *F* (angle *CFT*) is 055°C, whereas the magnetic bearing (angle *MFT*) is 065°M and the true bearing (angle *PFT*) is 045°. Angle *MFC* is the deviation, 10°E, angle *PFM* is the variation, 20°W.

Graduation of older magnetic compass cards

There may still be some older magnetic compass cards* at sea which are divided into four quadrants of 90°, the angles being measured from north and south to east and west. For example, the bearing 137°M would be shown as S43°E.

---

* Even older cards may still be found which are divided into four quadrants by the cardinal points, north, east, south, west. Each quadrant is divided into eight equal parts, the division marks being called *points:* each point has a distinctive name—north, north by east, north north east and so on. There are 32 points in the whole card.

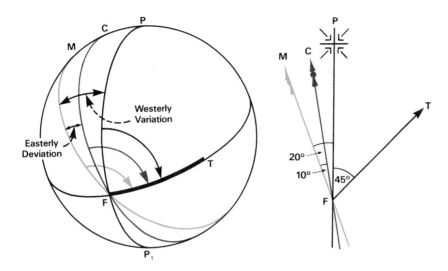

Fig. 1–16. Magnetic and compass bearings

Practical application of compass errors

All charts have what are known as compass *roses* printed on them. When there are two concentric rings, the outer ring represents the true compass and the inner the magnetic compass, as shown in Fig. 1–17. Some small-scale charts have only the true compass rose; others also have an indication of the amount of magnetic variation.

On the north–south line of the magnetic rose is written the variation, the year for which it is correct, and its rate of change.

Before he can use this magnetic rose for laying off the compass bearing or the compass course, the navigator must apply both the deviation and the change in variation.

Conversion of magnetic and compass courses and bearings to true

The following rule should be applied for the conversion of magnetic or compass courses and bearings to true:

Easterly variation and deviation are *added* or applied *clockwise*.
Westerly variation and deviation are *subtracted* or applied *anti-clockwise*.

This rule may be memorised by the mnemonic *CADET:*

C	AD	E	T
Compass	Add	East	True

i.e. when converting from compass to true, add east, subtract west and vice versa.

An alternative mnemonic which may be used is:

Error West, Compass Best.
Error East, Compass Least.

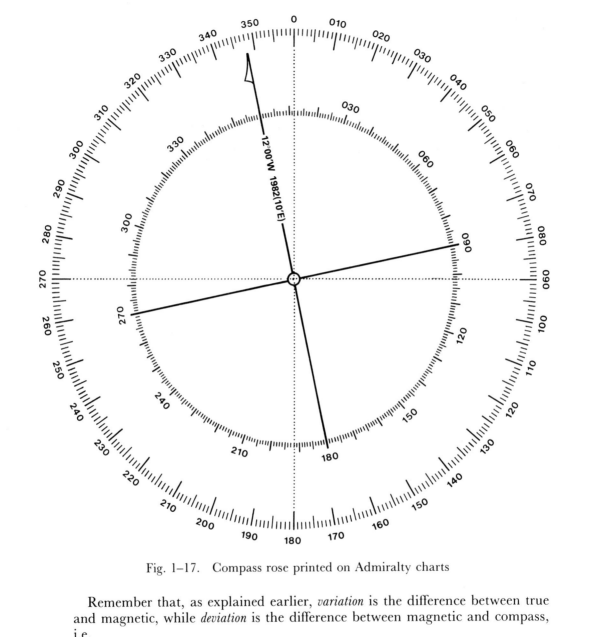

Fig. 1–17. Compass rose printed on Admiralty charts

Remember that, as explained earlier, *variation* is the difference between true and magnetic, while *deviation* is the difference between magnetic and compass, i.e.

$$\text{True} \pm \text{Variation} = \text{Magnetic}$$
$$\text{Magnetic} \pm \text{Deviation} = \text{Compass}$$

There are two methods available for laying off the compass course or bearing.

Method 1

Deviation (for the compass course steered) and variation (corrected to date) are applied to the compass course or bearing in accordance with the above rule to obtain the true course or bearing. The parallel ruler is then placed at the true reading on the true rose.

Method 2

The parallel ruler is placed on the given compass bearing or course on the magnetic rose. It is then slewed through a small angle in accordance with the above rule to allow for:

1. The change in variation to bring it up to date.
2. The deviation for the compass course being steered.

The algebraic sum (+ve for east, −ve for west) of the deviation and the change in variation is called the *rose correction*.

These two methods are illustrated by the following example.

EXAMPLE

A ship is steering 260°C. Variation from the chart was 12°W in 1982, decreasing 10′ annually. The compass bearing of an object is 043°C. Using the deviation from Fig. 1–14, what is the true course and how would the bearing be plotted using the above two methods? The year is 1985.

Variation in 1982	12 °W
Change in variation 1982–1985: 3 × 10′E	$\frac{1}{2}$°E
Variation in 1985	$11\frac{1}{2}$°W
Deviation for 260°C heading	$1\frac{1}{2}$°E
Compass heading	260 °C
Deviation	+ $1\frac{1}{2}$°E
Magnetic heading	$261\frac{1}{2}$°M
Variation	− $11\frac{1}{2}$°W
True course	250 °

Plotting the bearing

Method 1

Compass bearing	043 °C
Deviation	+ $1\frac{1}{2}$°E
Magnetic bearing	$044\frac{1}{2}$°M
Variation	−$11\frac{1}{2}$°W
True bearing to be plotted	033 °

For any particular compass heading, it will be evident that the combined effect of deviation and variation may be applied as a *total error correction*.

In this case, total error correction = $+1\frac{1}{2}$°E − $11\frac{1}{2}$°W = −10°W. To convert to true while on heading 260°C, all compass bearings should be reduced by 10°.

The application of compass error in one step avoids a very common mistake, that of taking out the deviation for the compass bearing of the object instead of the compass course of the ship.

Method 2

Place the parallel rule on the magnetic rose in the direction 043°M. Slew through a total rose correction of +2° clockwise ($\frac{1}{2}$° clockwise to allow for the easterly change of variation and $1\frac{1}{2}$° clockwise to allow for the easterly deviation). Plot the bearing on the magnetic rose, 045°M. As magnetic north on the compass rose is offset 12° to the west (*see* Fig. 1–17), it will be immediately apparent that 045°M is the same as 033°T, the true bearing.

To find the compass course from the true course

The mnemonic *CADET* is used in the reverse direction, i.e.

True to compass, add west, subtract east

There is, however, a small complication. Before the navigator can find his compass course he must know the deviation, but he cannot find his deviation until he knows his compass course. He therefore enters the deviation table with the magnetic course in lieu of compass course and, particularly if the deviation is large, makes a second calculation to get the exact deviation.

For example:

True course	260 °
Variation	+ 10 °W
Magnetic course	270 °M
Deviation (for 270°M)	− $1\frac{1}{4}$°E
Approx. compass course	$268\frac{3}{4}$°C

If the navigator enters the deviation table with this approximate course of $268\frac{3}{4}$°C, he will see that the correct deviation to use is nearer $1\frac{1}{2}$°E than $1\frac{1}{4}$°E, giving a revised compass course of $268\frac{1}{2}$°C.

Checking the deviation

If a compass bearing is taken of an object which has a known true bearing and if the variation is also known, then the deviation may be found and compared with that obtained from the deviation table. The various methods of checking the deviation are given in Chapter 9.

In practice within the Royal Navy, the deviation of a magnetic compass providing the primary means of navigation should remain within 2° of the residual deviation obtained at the time of the swing over a period of several months, whilst that for a magnetic compass providing a secondary means of navigating (or a primary means of steering) should remain within 5° over a similar period.

EXAMPLE

By calculation, the sun's true bearing is 230°, the compass bearing is 235°C, variation 12°W. What is the deviation?

True bearing	230	°
Variation	+ 12	°W
Magnetic bearing	242	°M
Deviation	± ?	
Compass bearing	235	°C

Clearly deviation is −7° and since, true to compass, east is subtracted, the devation is 7°E.

Relative bearings

The line of reference is the fore-and-aft line of the ship, i.e. the ship's course. Bearings are relative to this line and are measured from the bow from 0° to 180° on each side. Starboard bearings are Green, port bearings are Red.

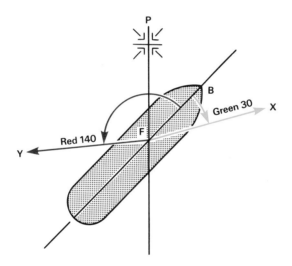

Fig. 1–18.   Relative bearings

Relative bearings may also be measured clockwise from 000° to 360° from the fore-and-aft line of the ship and are given the suffix Rel, e.g. 135° Rel.

In Fig. 1–18 the bearing of *X* is Green 30 (030° Rel), that of *Y* Red 140 (220° Rel). If the ship is steering 045°, the true bearing of *X* is 075°, and of *Y* 265°. Alternatively, *X* could be said to be 30° on the starboard bow, *Y* 40° on the port quarter.

The expressions *on the bow, on the beam,* and *on the quarter* without any specified number of degrees or points mean respectively 45° (4 points), 90° (8 points), 135° (12 points) from ship's head.

CHAPTER 2
The Sailings (1)

The sailings are terms used to describe the various mathematical methods of finding course and distance from one place on the Earth's surface to another. The various sailings are:

1. Parallel sailing.
2. Plane sailing.
3. Mean and corrected mean latitude sailing.
4. Traverse sailing.
5. Mercator sailing.
6. Great-circle sailing.
7. Composite sailing.

All these sailings are described in this chapter. Mercator sailing is, however, covered in detail in Chapters 4 and 5, while the finding of the vertex and the composite track in great-circle sailing are set out in Chapter 5.

The rhumb line

The first five sailings all use the *rhumb line*, a curve drawn on the Earth's surface cutting all the meridians at the same angle (Fig. 2–1). A ship steering a constant course is moving along a rhumb line.

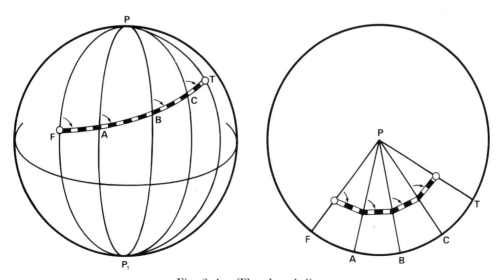

Fig. 2–1.   The rhumb line

The equator, parallels of latitude and meridians of longitude are special cases of rhumb line. Along the equator and parallel of latitude, the rhumb line of constant course is 090° or 270°, whilst along the meridian it is 000° or 180°. Other rhumb lines, crossing the meridian at a constant angle, spiral towards the pole and are often referred to as *loxodromes*.

Departure

Departure is the distance made good in an east–west direction in sailing from one place to another along a rhumb line.

PARALLEL SAILING

If (Fig. 2–2) a ship is travelling along the equator from A to B, the departure and d.long are equal.

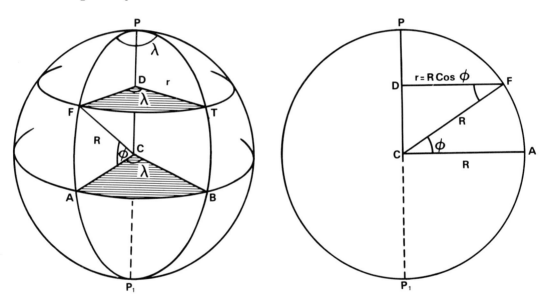

Fig. 2–2(a)   The arc of a parallel of latitude

Fig. 2–2(b)   Alteration of the arc with a change of latitude

When the ship is travelling along any other parallel of latitude ϕ, FT, the d.long λ, is still AB, but the distance FT is numerically less than the d.long.

The nearer the parallel is to the pole — in other words, the higher the latitude — the shorter FT becomes. But the d.long does not alter. The relationship between distance and d.long may be found as follows.

The radius r of the circle of latitude ϕ is $R \cos \phi$, where R is the radius of the sphere.

The distance FT along the parallel of latitude

$$= r\lambda, \text{ where } \lambda \text{ is in radians}$$
$$= R\lambda \cos \phi$$
$$= AB \cos \phi$$
$$= \lambda \cos \phi, \text{ where } \lambda \text{ is in minutes}$$
$$= \text{d.long (in minutes) cos latitude}$$

i.e.   departure = d.long cos latitude   ... **2.1**

For the perfect sphere, the distance along a parallel of latitude in minutes of latitude is equal to the d.long, expressed in minutes of arc, multiplied by the cosine of the latitude.

Parallel sailing is thus a method of converting the departure along a parallel of latitude into longitude, assuming the Earth is a sphere.

If, for example, the latitude of the parallel is 40°N and the longitudes of F and T are 15°E and 60°E respectively, the d.long is 45° or, in minutes of arc along the equator, 2700′.

$$FT = 2700' \cos 40° = 2068'.3$$

Had the latitude been 60°N instead of 40°N, the distance along this new parallel would have been 2700′ cos 60°, i.e. 1350′.

PLANE SAILING

When a ship travels along any rhumb line other than a parallel of latitude or a meridian of longitude, her d.lat, departure, distance and course may be considered as forming a plane right-angled triangle (Fig. 2–3).

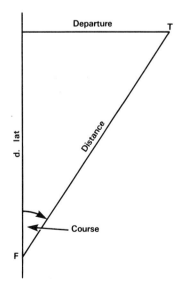

Fig. 2–3.   d.lat/departure/distance

Various formulae may be deduced from this triangle:

$$\text{departure} = \text{distance}\sin\text{course} \qquad \ldots \textbf{2.2}$$

$$\text{d.lat} = \text{distance}\cos\text{course*} \qquad \ldots \textbf{2.3}$$

By dividing **(2.2)** by **(2.3)**:

$$\frac{\text{departure}}{\text{d.lat}} = \tan\text{course} \qquad \ldots \textbf{2.4}$$

Plane sailing is thus a method of solving the relationship between d.lat, departure, distance and course. It does not involve d.long except indirectly (*see* page 28).

Proof of the plane sailing formulae

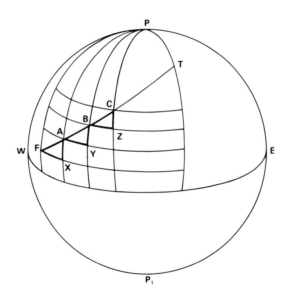

Fig. 2–4.   The division of the rhumb line

In Fig. 2–4, let the rhumb line *FT* be divided into a large number *n* of equidistant parallels of latitude cutting the rhumb line in *F*, *A*, *B*, *C*, etc. Let the meridians through the points cut the parallels of latitude in *X*, *Y*, *Z*, etc.

In the small triangles *FAX*, *ABY*, *BCZ*, etc. the angles *FXA*, *AYB*, *BZC* are right angles. The angles *FAX*, *ABY*, *BCZ* are all equal, being equal to the course. The sides *AX*, *BY*, *CZ* are all equal.

The triangles are therefore equal in all respects and, as they are very small, may be considered as plane right-angled triangles.

---

* When using formula **(2.3)** to find the distance, there is a fundamental weakness in the formula as the course approaches 90° because small errors in the course introduce large errors in the distance. Formula **(2.2)** should be used instead.

In the triangle *FAX*:

$$AX = FA \cos \text{course}$$
$$\therefore nAX = nFA \cos \text{course}$$
$$\therefore \text{d.lat} = \text{distance} \cos \text{course} \qquad \qquad \dots (2.3)$$
$$FX = FA \sin \text{course}$$
$$nFX = nFA \sin \text{course}$$
$$\therefore \text{departure} = \text{distance} \sin \text{course} \qquad \qquad \dots (2.2)$$

Dividing **(2.2)** by **(2.3)**:

$$\tan \text{course} = \frac{\text{departure}}{\text{d.lat}} \qquad \qquad \dots (2.4)$$

MEAN AND CORRECTED MEAN LATITUDE SAILING

There are two methods by which a ship may determine her latitude and longitude after travelling along a rhumb line other than in a north–south or east–west direction. One of these methods uses the mean or corrected mean latitude, the other uses Mercator sailing (described later).

Consider the rhumb line *FT* in Fig. 2–5. The departure is greater than *HT*, the departure along the parallel through *T*, and less than *FG*, the departure along the parallel through *F*.

The departure from *F* to *T* must therefore equal the departure along a parallel lying somewhere between *FG* and *HT*. Let this parallel be *UV*.

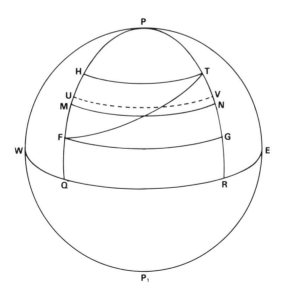

Fig. 2–5. The mean and corrected mean latitude

Provided that the d.lat between *F* and *T* is fairly small and, the latitudes of *F* and *T* are not too high, this departure is *approximately* equal to the arc of the parallel *MN*, which has as its latitude the mathematical mean between *F* and *T*.

This latitude is referred to as the *mean latitude*. In these particular circumstances *MN* and *UV* are almost identical.

If *QR* is the d.long between *F* and *T*:

since $MN = QR \cos QM$ (formula **2.1**)

then, for the sphere:

departure = d.long cos (mean latitude)   ...**2.5**

This formula is not accurate mathematically except when *F* and *T* are on the same parallel of latitude. In practice, its accuracy depends on how close *T* is to *F*. Such a formula should not be used for distances exceeding 600′.

If the latitudes of *F* and *T* are on each side of the equator and also within 10° of latitude of the equator, the departure may be taken as the d.long without appreciable error. (The maximum error in departure cannot exceed 0.4%.)

The true or *corrected mean latitude* between *F* and *T* is given by *UV*. It is frequently referred to in nautical tables and navigational publications as the middle latitude.*

For the sphere, it may be shown (*see* Appendix 3) that the latitude *L* of *UV*, may be found from the following formulae:

$$\sec L = \frac{7915.7045}{\text{d.lat (mins of arc)}} \left[\log_{10} \tan \left(45° + \frac{T°}{2} \right) - \log_{10} \tan \left(45° + \frac{F°}{2} \right) \right]$$

...**2.6**

or:

$$\sec L = \frac{\text{DMP}}{\text{d.lat (minutes of arc)}} \quad (\textit{see} \text{ Chapter 4})$$ ...**2.7**

EXAMPLE 1

A ship steams from position F in latitude 30°N, longitude 40°W to a point T in latitude 34°N, longitude 36°W. Determine the departure, course and distance.

d.lat = 4°N = 240′N

d.long = 4°E = 240′E

mean lat = $\frac{1}{2}$ (30° + 34°)N = 32°N

From formula **(2.5)**:

dep = 240′ cos 32°E = 203′.53E

From formula **(2.4)**:

$$\tan \text{course} = \frac{\text{dep}}{\text{d.lat}}$$

course = 040°.3

From formula **(2.3)**:

distance = d.lat sec course = 240′ sec 040°.3 = 314′.68

---

* Throughout the *Admiralty Manual of Navigation*, the term *corrected mean latitude* is used in preference to middle latitude.

The corrected mean latitude may be found from formula **(2.6)**:

$$\sec L = \frac{7915.7045}{240'} \left[\log_{10} \tan \left(45° + \frac{34°}{2} \right) - \log_{10} \tan \left(45° + \frac{30°}{2} \right) \right]$$

$$L = 32°.033158 \ (32°02')$$
$$\text{dep} = 203'.46$$
$$\text{course} = 040°.3$$
$$\text{distance} = 314'.64$$

The difference in distance (0.013%) is so small that the mean latitude may be used without appreciable error.

EXAMPLE 2

A ship in position F, 70°N, 20°W, steers a course of 020° for a distance of 600 miles. What is her latitude and longitude at the end of the run?

From formula **(2.3)**:
$$\text{d.lat} = 600' \cos 20°N$$
$$= 563'.81557N$$
$$= 9°.3969262 = 9° 23'.8N$$
$$\text{lat } T = 79° 23'.8N$$

From formula **(2.2)**:
$$\text{dep} = 600' \sin 20°E = 205'.21209E$$
$$\text{mean lat} = 74°.6984631N \ (74° 41'.9N)$$

From formula **(2.5)**:
$$\text{d.long} = 205'.21209 \sec 74°.6984631E$$
$$= 777'.61623E = 12° 57'.6E$$
$$\text{long } T = 7° 02'.4W$$

From formula **(2.6)**:
$$\sec L = \frac{7915.7045}{563'.81557} (\log_{10} \tan 84°.698463 - \log_{10} \tan 80°)$$
$$L = 75°.197922 \ (75° 11'.9N)$$

From formula **(2.5)**:
$$\text{d.long} = 205'.21209 \sec 75°.197922$$
$$= 803'.23871E$$
$$= 13°.387312E = 13° 23'.2E$$
$$\text{long } T = 6° 36'.8W$$

The discrepancy in longitude is 25'.6E, i.e. 4.7 miles.

The discrepancy in position (0.8% of the distance) at the end of the run illustrates the danger of using the mean latitude in high latitudes, even though the distance is only 600 miles.

Although the computation of the longitude using the corrected mean latitude is an accurate one, it is for the sphere. If one wishes to compute accurately the rhumb-line position taking into account the spheroidal shape of the Earth, another method should be used. This is described in Chapter 5.

TRAVERSE SAILING

Traverse sailing is the term given to the combination of plane sailing solutions when there are more than two courses. The various legs of the ship's track are the hypotenuses of a series of plane sailing triangles (*see* Fig. 2–4). The individual d.lats and departures may be found using formulae **(2.2)** to **(2.4)** and the d.long using formula **(2.5)**.

The traverse table in *Norie's Nautical Tables* solves the d.lat/departure/ distance/course plane triangles for any distance up to 600′. Instructions for the use of these tables are given in the explanation. The tables may also be used to solve the d.long by means of formula **(2.5)** by treating the course as mean latitude, d.lat as departure and distance as d.long.

A pocket calculator with the normal trigonometric ratios is quicker and more accurate to use than the traverse table and, if a calculator with a co-ordinate conversion is available, it should be possible to read off d.lat and departure directly using Cartesian (x, y) co-ordinates. Using a calculator avoids the need to interpolate between sets of figures as when using the traverse table.

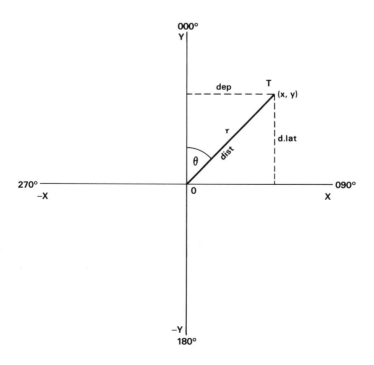

Fig. 2–6.   Polar, Cartesian, co-ordinates of a position

In Fig. 2–6 the position of T may be defined in polar (r, θ) or Cartesian (x, y) co-ordinates where:

$$r = \text{distance}$$
$$\theta = \text{course}$$
$$x = \text{departure*}$$
$$y = \text{d.lat*}$$

EXAMPLE

A ship in position 45° 25′N, 15° 05′W at 0900 steers the following courses and speeds. What is her position at 1315?

TIME	COURSE	SPEED
0900–0946	045°	15 knots
0946–1015	312°	$16\frac{1}{2}$ knots
1015–1122	217°	$14\frac{3}{4}$ knots
1122–1247	103°	17 knots
1247–1315	190°	15 knots

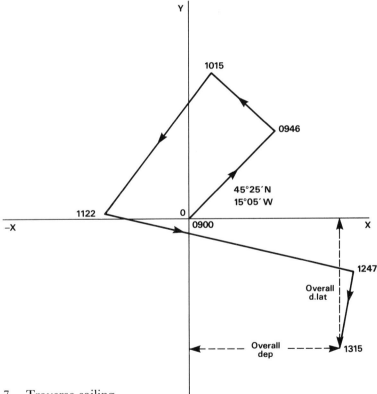

Fig. 2–7. Traverse sailing

* When carrying out polar to Cartesian conversion using a calculator, d.lat appears as x and departure as y because of the difference between mathematical and navigational conventions on the initial line from which angles are measured. In navigational notation, course is measured clockwise from the north–south line, while in mathematical notation, angle is measured anti-clockwise from the east–west line.

Table 2–1.   Traverse sailing

TIME	COURSE θ	SPEED	DISTANCE r	TRAVERSE TABLE			CALCULATOR	
				COURSE	DEP	D.LAT	DEP x ORD	D.LAT y ORD
0900–0946	045°	15 kn	11'.5	N45°E	8'.13E	8'.13N	8'.132	8'.132
0946–1015	312°	$16\frac{1}{2}$ kn	7'.975	N48°W	5'.96W	5'.33N	−5'.927	5'.336
1015–1122	217°	$14\frac{3}{4}$ kn	16'.471	S 37°W	9'.91W	13'.16S	−9'.912	−13'.154
1122–1247	103°	17 kn	24'.083	S 77°E	23'.46E	5'.42S	23'.466	−5'.417
1247–1315	190°	15 kn	7'.0	S 10°W	1'.22W	6'.89S	−1'.216	−6'.894
					14'.5E	12'.01S	+14'.543 (E)	−11'.997 (S)

mean lat 0900–1315:   45°19'.0N

d.long (formula **2.5**):   20'.7E

position at 1315:   45°13'.0N

                   14°44'.3W

MERCATOR SAILING

As mentioned on page 27, Mercator sailing provides a method of determining position after travelling along a rhumb line other than in a north–south or east–west direction. It is similar to plane sailing but uses difference of meridional parts (DMP) instead of d.lat and d.long instead of departure.

Meridional parts are a feature of the Mercator projection on which the great majority of small-scale Admiralty navigational charts are based and are discussed at length in Chapter 4. The calculations involved in Mercator sailing are set out in Chapter 5.

SPHERICAL GREAT-CIRCLE AND COMPOSITE SAILING

The great circle

A straight line is the shortest distance between two points and, when the two points lie on the surface of a sphere, the arc of the great circle joining them is the curve that most nearly approaches the straight line, because it has the greatest radius and therefore the least curvature. The shorter arc of the great circle joining two places on the Earth's surface is thus the shortest route between them. In Fig. 2–8 *FT* is such an arc and its length is the shortest distance between the two points *F* and *T* on the Earth's surface. *PF* and *PT* are arcs of the meridians passing through *F* and *T* and are also arcs of great circles. The triangle *PFT* is therefore a spherical triangle, and the problem of finding the shortest distance between two points is the problem of finding the length of the side opposite the pole in this triangle.

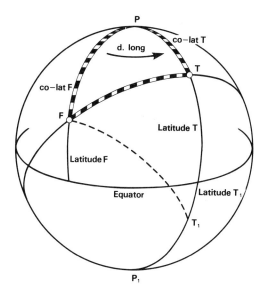

Fig. 2–8.   The great circle

The navigator very often requires to know the *true bearing* of one point from another. The true bearing of T from F is the angle between the meridian through F and the great circle joining F and T, measured clockwise from the meridian — that is, the angle *PFT*. This angle represents the initial course to be steered by a ship sailing on a great circle from F to T. Radio waves also travel along great circles near the Earth's surface, and the angle *PFT* is thus the bearing of T from F as it would be given by MFDF (Figs 2–9(a) and 2–9(b)).

In Fig. 2–9(a) at any intermediate point G, between F and T, the true bearing of T is the angle *PGT*, and this is not equal to the angle *PFT*. To an observer moving along the great circle from F to T, the true bearing of T changes continuously. Only when T is close to F may this change be neglected. The area of the Earth's surface traversed by FT is then sufficiently small to be considered as a plane or flat surface, on which great circles appear as straight lines.

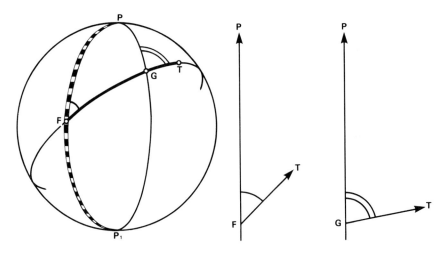

Fig. 2–9(a)   Great-circle bearings   Fig. 2–9(b)   Initial and final great-circle courses

Great-circle distance and bearing

The length of the side FT (Fig. 2–8) and the true bearing *PFT* are found by solving the spherical triangle *FPT*. In this triangle the angle *FPT* is clearly the d.long between F and T. The lengths of the sides PF and PT depend upon the latitudes of F and T. When these latitudes have the same name — both F and T are north in Fig. 2–8 — PF is ($90°$ − latitude F) and PT is ($90°$ − latitude T). The distance ($90°$ − latitude) is known as the *co-latitude* of the place concerned.

When the destination is in the opposite hemisphere — T_I has south latitude in Fig. 2–8 — the length of the side PT_I is ($90°$ + latitude T_I). Therefore:

For latitudes of the same name:

$$PF = 90° - \text{latitude } F = \text{co-latitude } F$$
$$PT = 90° - \text{latitude } T = \text{co-latitude } T$$
$$\text{angle } FPT = \text{d.long}$$

For latitudes of the opposite name:

$$PF = 90° - \text{latitude } F = \text{co-latitude } F$$
$$PT_I = 90° + \text{latitude } T_I$$
$$\text{angle } FPT_I = \text{d.long}$$

When F is also in southern latitudes, as in Fig. 2–10, the same relations hold if P_I is substituted for P, so that for either hemisphere:

$$PF = 90° \pm \text{lat } F$$
$$PT = 90° \pm \text{lat } T$$

the sign being determined by the name of the pole and by the latitude of the place (*same names, subtract; opposite names, add*).

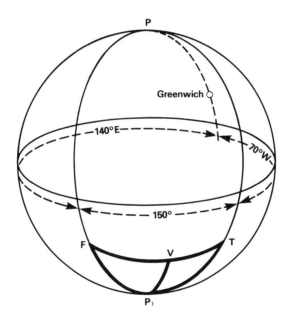

Fig. 2–10.   The solution of the spherical triangle and the vertex

Great-circle sailing

If a ship followed the great-circle track she would have to change course continually. In practice, the great-circle track is divided into suitable lengths, successive points on the great circle being joined to form a succession of rhumb lines. This is known as *approximate great-circle sailing*, or simply *great-circle sailing*.

Fig. 2–11 illustrates any such approximate great circle. The navigator would alter course at A, B and C and he would choose the lengths FA, AB, etc. to suit his convenience. FA for example, might be a twelve-hour run or when a suitable meridian is crossed, e.g. 10°W, 20°W, 30°W, 40°W and so on.

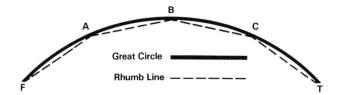

Fig. 2–11.   Great-circle and rhumb-line tracks

The vertex

The point at which a great circle most nearly approaches the pole is called the *vertex* (of that great circle) — *V* in Fig. 2–10. At this point, the great circle ceases to approach the pole and begins to curve away. It must therefore cut the meridian through the vertex at right angles. The method of finding this position involves the use of right-angled spherical triangles, and is described in Chapter 5.

The composite track

Since the great-circle track between two places not on the equator passes nearer to the pole than does the rhumb-line track, the ship may be carried into the ice region. When ice is likely to be encountered, the great-circle track must therefore be modified to avoid such high latitudes, while remaining the shortest possible safe track. This modified track is known as the *composite track*, and is formed by two great-circle arcs joined by an arc of the limiting or 'safe' parallel of latitude.

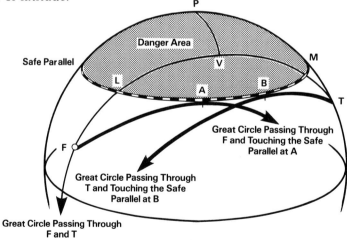

Fig. 2–12.   The composite track

In Fig. 2–12 *FLVMT* is the great circle joining *F* and *T*. Latitudes higher than the *parallel* of *LM* are assumed to be dangerous. The ship cannot, therefore, follow the great-circle arc *LVM*. Nor would she go from *F* to *L*, along to *M* and then down to *T*. The shortest route she can take is *FABT*, where *FA* and *BT* are great-circle arcs tangential to the safe parallel at *A* and *B*.

FABT is thus the composite track in this example. It is the shortest route because, if *L* and *M* are taken as any points on the parallel outside the part *AB*, (*FL* + *LA*) is greater than *FA* and (*BM* + *MT*) is greater than *BT*. Moreover, since *A* is the point nearest the pole on the great circle of which *FA* is an arc, any other great circle from *F* to a point between *A* and *B* would cut the parallel between *L* and *A* and so carry the ship into danger.

The calculation of the composite track is set out in Chapter 5.

Solution of spherical great-circle problems

Six methods are considered altogether for solving spherical great-circle problems. Table 2–2 lists the methods and their applicability to finding the distance and the course/bearing.

Table 2–2.   Solving great-circle problems

METHOD	DISTANCE	COURSE/ BEARING
Cosine	×	×
Sine		×
Haversine	×	
Sight reduction tables (NP 401)	×	×
Half log haversine		×
ABC tables (*Norie's*)		×

The cosine method is very suitable for use with a pocket calculator and is described below. The sine method may be used to cross-check the cosine solution and may also be used to determine the course or bearing. Both the cosine and the sine formulae are set out in Appendix 2. Although the sine formula is ambiguous, this ambiguity is easily resolved in most cases, and the calculation is simpler than the cosine method. An example is given below.

The haversine and half log haversine methods are set out in Appendix 2. The sight reduction and ABC methods are set out in Volume II.

The calculation of great-circle courses and distances taking into account the spheroidal shape of the Earth is set out in Chapter 5.

The cosine method

Great-circle distance

$$\cos FT = \cos FP \cos PT + \sin FP \sin PT \cos FPT$$
$$\cos \text{distance} = \cos (90° \pm \text{lat } F) \cos (90° \pm \text{lat } T)$$
$$+ \sin (90° \pm \text{lat } F) \sin (90° \pm \text{lat } T) \cos \text{d.long} \qquad \ldots \textbf{2.8}$$

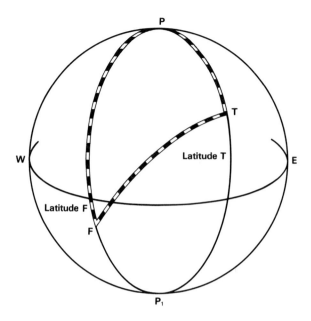

Fig. 2–13.   Solution of spherical great-circle problems

The sign is determined by the name of the pole and the latitude of the place (*same names, subtract; opposite names, add*).

In Fig. 2–13 F and T are on opposite sides of the equator; thus, the latitude of F would be added and that of T subtracted.

When F and T are both on the same side of the equator, formula **(2.8)** resolves into:

$$\cos \text{distance} = \sin \text{lat } F \sin \text{lat } T + \cos \text{lat } F \cos \text{lat } T \cos \text{d.long} \qquad \ldots \textbf{2.9}$$

This basic formula **(2.9)** may also be used to cover the contrary case by making any opposite (to the elevated pole) latitude negative. In Fig. 2–13 $\sin \text{lat } (-F)$ and $\cos \text{lat } (-F)$ would be used.

Formula **(2.9)** may be modified as follows:

$$\cos \text{distance} = (\tan \text{lat } F \tan \text{lat } T + \cos \text{d.long}) \cos \text{lat } F \cos \text{lat } T$$

$$\ldots \textbf{2.10}$$

Great-circle course/bearing

$$\cos PT = \cos FP \cos FT + \sin FP \sin FT \cos PFT$$

$$\cos PFT = \frac{\cos PT - \cos FP \cos FT}{\sin FP \sin FT}$$

$$= \frac{\cos (90° \pm \text{lat } T) - \cos (90° \pm \text{lat } F) \cos FT}{\sin (90° \pm \text{lat } F) \sin FT} \qquad \ldots \textbf{2.11}$$

In Fig. 2–13 the latitude of T would be subtracted and that of F added.

When F and T are both on the same side of the equator, formula (2.11) resolves into:

$$\cos \text{ initial course} = \frac{\sin \text{ lat } T - \sin \text{ lat } F \cos \text{ distance}}{\cos \text{ lat } F \sin \text{ distance}} \qquad \ldots 2.12$$

EXAMPLE

A ship steams from position F (45°N, 140°E) to T (65°N, 110°W). Find the great-circle distance and the initial course by the cosine method, and also the initial course by the sine method.

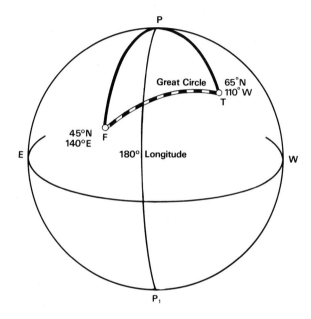

Fig. 2–14.   A great-circle problem

A great-circle distance

The cosine method

$$\cos \text{ distance} = \sin \text{ lat } F \sin \text{ lat } T$$
$$+ \cos \text{ lat } F \cos \text{ lat } T \cos \text{ d.long} \qquad \ldots (2.9)$$
$$= \sin \text{ lat } 45° \sin \text{ lat } 65°$$
$$+ \cos \text{ lat } 45° \cos \text{ lat } 65° \cos 110°$$
$$= 0.53864837 \text{ (by pocket calculator)*}$$

G.C. distance $= 57°.408325 = 3444'.5$

---

* In this and subsequent examples using the sailings, the final answer is usually rounded off to the nearest degree for course and 0.1 mile for distance. This is the degree of precision to which the practical navigator usually works these problems at sea, as governed by the accuracy of the equipment available. However, so that the student may follow the examples given using his own electronic calculator, the workings are normally shown to six or more decimal places.

The initial course

The cosine method

$$\cos \text{ initial course} = \frac{\sin \text{lat } T - \sin \text{lat } F \cos \text{distance}}{\cos \text{lat } F \sin \text{distance}} \qquad \ldots \textbf{(2.12)}$$

$$= \frac{\sin \text{lat } 65° - \sin \text{lat } 45° \cos 57°.408325}{\cos \text{lat } 45° \sin 57°.408325}$$

$$= \frac{0.52542587}{0.59575915} = 0.88194343$$

initial course = N28°.122305E = 028°

sine rule check:

$$\frac{\sin 57°.408325}{\sin 110°} = \frac{\sin 25°}{\sin 28°.122305} = 0.8966024$$

The sine method

$$\frac{\sin FT}{\sin FPT} = \frac{\sin PT}{\sin PFT}$$

$$\sin PFT = \frac{\sin PT \sin FPT}{\sin FT}$$

$$\sin \text{ initial course} = \frac{\sin (90° \pm \text{lat } T) \sin \text{d.long}}{\sin \text{distance}} \qquad \ldots \textbf{2.13}$$

$$= \frac{\cos \text{lat } T \sin \text{d.long}}{\sin \text{distance}}$$

$$= \frac{\cos 65° \sin 110°}{\sin 57°.408325} = 0.47135526$$

$$PFT = \text{N28°.122305E or N151°.87769E}$$

In this case the ambiguity is easily resolvable, as the great-circle course from F to T must lie to the north of east. Thus:

initial course = 028°

CHAPTER 3
An Introduction to Geodesy

Goedesy is that branch of mathematics concerned with large areas in which allowance must be made for the curvature of the Earth's surface. As the accuracy to which a ship may now be navigated world-wide is governed by this irregular shape, a general understanding of geodesy is necessary. This chapter introduces the navigator to this subject.

DEFINITIONS AND FORMULAE

The oblate spheroid

As already mentioned in Chapter 1, the Earth is an oblate spheroid rotating about its shortest diameter which is the polar axis, PP_1 in Fig. 3–1.

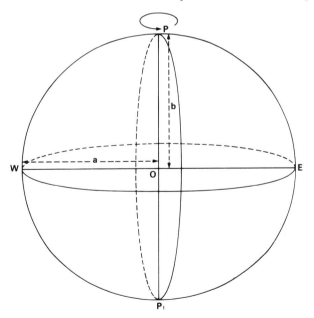

Fig. 3–1.   The oblate spheroid

The flattening of the Earth

The polar radius b is somewhat less than the equatorial radius a; thus, the Earth may be considered as being 'flattened' in the polar regions.

The flattening or ellipticity of the Earth may be defined by a quantity f where:

$$f = \frac{a - b}{a}$$ ... **3.1**

The eccentricity

When a point M (Fig. 3–2) moves so that its distance from a fixed point S (the focus) is always in a constant ratio e (less than unity) to its perpendicular distance from a fixed straight line AB (the directrix), the locus of M is called an ellipse of eccentricity e.

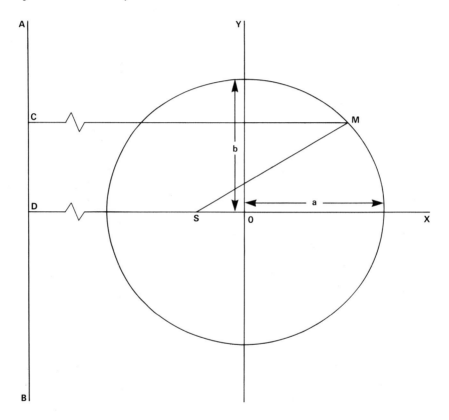

Fig. 3–2.   The eccentricity of the ellipse

In Fig. 3–2:

$$MS = eMC$$

e may be defined in terms of a and b by the formula:

$$e = \left(\frac{a^2 - b^2}{a^2} \right)^{1/2}$$ ... **3.2**

From formula (**3.1**):

$$e = (2f - f^2)^{1/2}$$ ... **3.3**

Geodetic and geocentric latitudes

Fig. 3–3 shows a meridional section of the spheroid. M is a point on the meridian PAP_1, and MK is the tangent to the meridian at M. If the normal to this tangent LM cuts OA in L, the angle MLA is called the geodetic latitude of M, and denoted by ϕ.

The angle MOA is called the geocentric latitude of M and is denoted by θ.

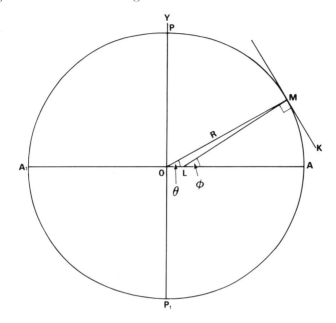

Fig. 3–3.   Geodetic and geocentric latitudes

ϕ and θ are connected by the formula (*see* Appendix 5):

$$\tan \theta = \frac{b^2}{a^2} \tan \phi \qquad \qquad \textbf{...3.4}$$

$$= (1 - f)^2 \tan \phi \qquad \qquad \textbf{...3.5}$$

$$= (1 - e^2) \tan \phi \qquad \qquad \textbf{...3.6}$$

The difference between the geodetic and geocentric latitudes is zero at the equator and the poles and has a greatest value when $\phi = 45°$. For the International (1924) Spheroid the greatest value is about 11.6 minutes of arc.

The parametric latitude

Fig. 3–4 shows a meridional section of a spheroid WPE; its polar axis is OP and its shape and size are defined by the radii $OE = a$, and $OP = b$. WBE is the meridional section of a sphere with centre O, polar axis OB and radii $OE = OB = a$. M is a point on the spheroid with geodetic latitude ϕ. HM is parallel to OP and produced to cut the circle WBE at U. The radius OU makes an angle β with the X axis.

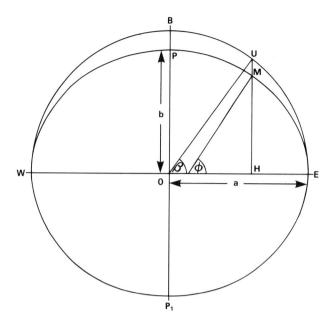

Fig. 3–4.   Parametric latitude

It may be shown (Appendix 5) that:

$$\tan \beta = \frac{b}{a} \tan \phi \qquad \ldots \textbf{3.7}$$

The angle β is known as the *parametric* or *reduced latitude* of the point M. This parametric latitude is frequently used in long distance calculations on the spheroid (*see* Chapter 5).

The length of one minute of latitude

As indicated on page 6, the length of the sea mile varies between the equator and the poles because of the changing radius of curvature.

The length of 1 minute of latitude may be found from the formula $\rho d\phi$, where ρ is the radius of curvature in the meridian and $d\phi$ is a small increase (measured in radians) in the geodetic latitude ϕ (Fig. 3–5). It may be shown (Appendix 5) that:

$$\rho = \frac{a(1 - e^2)}{(1 - e^2 \sin^2 \phi)^{3/2}} \qquad \ldots \textbf{3.8}$$

When $d\phi$ is equal to 1 minute of arc:

$$1' \text{ of latitude} = \frac{a(1 - e^2)}{(1 - e^2 \sin^2 \phi)^{3/2}} \sin 1' \qquad \ldots \textbf{3.9}$$

$$\text{when} \qquad \phi = \text{zero}$$

$$1' \text{ of latitude at the equator} = a(1 - e^2) \sin 1' \qquad \ldots \textbf{3.10}$$

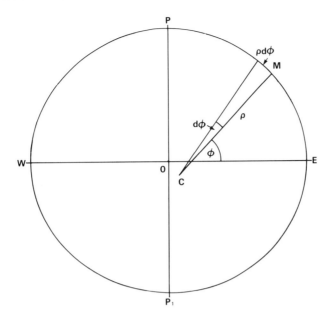

Fig. 3–5.   The length of one minute of latitude

The length of one minute of longitude

As indicated on page 7:

$$1' \text{ of longitude at the equator } = a \sin 1' \qquad \qquad \ldots \mathbf{3.11}$$

At latitude ϕ:

$$1' \text{ of longitude } = \frac{a \cos \phi}{(1 - e^2 \sin^2 \phi)^{1/2}} \sin 1' \qquad \ldots \mathbf{3.12}$$

The geodesic

In the same way that a great-circle gives the shortest distance between two points on a sphere, a *geodesic* is the shortest line between two points on the spheroidal Earth.

Geodetic datum

In geodesy there are two kinds of datum: a *horizontal datum*, e.g. the Ordnance Survey of Great Britain (1936) Datum, from which basis the latitude and longitude of a place may be determined taking into account the spheroidal shape of the Earth; a *vertical datum*, e.g. Ordnance Datum (Newlyn), to which heights are referred.

THE DETERMINATION OF POSITION ON THE SPHEROID

Anyone at the Central Signal Station Flagstaff in Portsmouth Dockyard knows where he is in relation to his geographical surroundings. However, to inform someone else in another place, for example the Falkland Islands, of that position, details need to be sent using a recognisable method, e.g. latitude (50°47′.95N) and longitude (1°06′.53W).

Provided that the same horizontal datum is used for the determination of latitude and longitude in both places, it is possible to calculate with accuracy the position of one place relative to the other. However, when places are a long way apart, the same horizontal datum is frequently not used. Thus, although the latitude and longitude of both locations may be 'known', an exact calculation of the bearing and distance between them cannot be made.

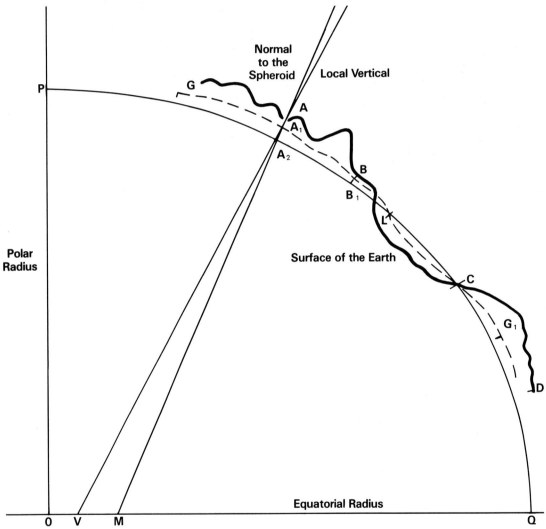

Fig. 3–6. The spheroidal shape of the Earth

The geoid

The basis for the determination of latitude and longitude depends upon the spheroidal shape of the Earth. However, the shape cannot be measured directly although it is possible to measure a section of its surface, e.g. *AB* in Fig. 3–6. This measurement is usually taken along a meridian of longitude.

The positions of *A* and *B* may be determined using instruments such as the theodolite to measure horizontal and vertical angles on the Earth, and the theodolite or the astrolabe to obtain the astronomical position. These instruments must however be levelled before use, and thus require the use of gravity to determine the vertical. But the vertical itself is deflected by the mass of the Earth and this means that the 'horizontal' with reference to which the observation has been made is irregular. In Fig. 3–6, this 'horizontal' is shown by the pecked line GLG_1. This pecked line is known as the *geoid* and may be defined as that surface which corresponds to the Mean Sea Level of the oceans, assuming that it would be possible to take a mean sea level through the Earth's continents. It tends to rise under mountains and dip above ocean basins. The direction of gravity (or local vertical) is always perpendicular to the *geoid*.

Since the *geoid* is not of a regular shape, its surface cannot be defined by a single, simple, algebraic formula. It is not, therefore, used for the mathematical calculations required to determine latitude and longitude because of the complexity involved.

This difficulty is overcome by using a regular but fictional surface, *PLQ* in Fig. 3–6, called the *spheroid* for the calculation. This spheroid is chosen as the closest *fit* to the geoidal section GLG_1.

Calculation of the position

The observer at *A* measures his position by observation of heavenly bodies and adjusts it to mean sea level to fit the *geoid* at A_1. He then very carefully measures the position of *B* on the spheroid by use of his instruments, using chosen values of *OP* and *OQ*. The position of *B* on the geoid, B_1, may now be calculated. Astronomical observations at *B* will show the difference between the two positions, and this difference is a measure of the way the chosen spheroid *PLQ* 'fits' the geoid GLG_1. Usually at least two more places *C* and *D*, etc. are also observed, to check that the chosen spheroid is satisfactory.

Geodetic latitude and longitude

Before these calculations can be used for the determination of latitude and longitude using the selected values of the spheroid, there is one further problem to resolve.

The astronomical observation at *A* (reduced to Mean Sea Level to give the position at A_1) is determined by the direction of the local vertical at A_1, A_1V. Thus, the astronomical (observed) latitude of A_1 is the angle A_1VQ. But as it is intended to use the spheroid *PLQ* for calculating latitude and longitude, the observed latitude must be corrected for the fact that the normal to the spheroid is not A_1V but A_2M and the geodetic (spheroidal) latitude which is the one actually charted is the angle A_2MQ.*

Geodetic (charted) longitude may be determined in the same way, being the angle between the plane of the geodetic meridian at Greenwich and the geodetic meridian of the place. The astronomical (observed) longitude is

---

* The deviation of the vertical, i.e. the difference between the angle A_1VQ and A_2MQ is very small (only a few seconds of arc) in flat countries, and larger in mountainous regions. In extreme cases (e.g. Colombia in South America) it may be as much as 1 minute of arc.

adjusted for any difference between the local vertical at Greenwich and the local vertical at the place, to arrive at the geodetic (charted) longitude.

Once the observed latitude and longitude have been adjusted in this way, the chart may be drawn up for geodetic latitude and longitude using the assumed values of the spheroid.

Very often, to make the calculation simpler, the spheroid and the geoid are assumed to be coincident and parallel at the chosen point known as the origin. There is then no difference between the two verticals. This is not a necessary requirement, however, and geodetic values may be chosen which give the 'best fit' over the largest area, or use the same spheroidal shape as adjacent systems.

A horizontal datum is thus a connected series of survey stations whose positions are defined by a spheroid and by the relationship between the spheroid and a point established as the origin, e.g. the Ordnance Survey of Great Britain (1936) Datum is based on the Airy Spheroid and has its origin at Herstmonceux.

Reference datums and spheroids

Throughout the world, a number of these datums and associated spheroids have been used for charting. In consequence, there are differences to geodetic latitudes and longitudes, albeit small, between different charting systems. Table 3–1 gives some examples of the datums and spheroids used.

Satellite geodesy

Since the 1960s the limitations of the classical methods have been overcome by the use of extremely accurate satellite techniques. Accurate co-ordinates of ground stations and the Earth's gravity field have been determined from Doppler and laser observations to satellites, and the height of the geoid has been measured over sea areas by satellite altimetry.

By combining these data with surface measurements, a worldwide 3-D reference system and a spheroid which best fits the geoid have been defined. It has also been possible to establish the relationships between previously unconnected datums and to convert them to the world datum.

World geodetic systems (WGS)

In the past the differences in the various datums used for charting had very little effect on the day to day navigation of ships, particularly as the errors inherent in astronomical observation were larger than any discrepancy in charted latitude and longitude. However, it became clear in the late 1950s that the increasing range of weapon systems (thousands of miles in some cases) and the requirements for manned space flight necessitated the establishment of an agreed worldwide spheroid which fitted the actual shape of the whole Earth as closely as possible and whose centre coincided with its centre of mass. This came about with the development of the World Geodetic System 1972 (WGS 72) spheroid, details of which are given in Table 3–1. A few metric charts throughout the world are now compiled on this basis.

The US Navy Navigation Satellite System (TRANSIT), which came into being in 1964, is now based on WGS. The increasing world-wide use of this system, accurate to the order of 100 metres, shows up the discrepancies in the various

Table 3–1. Comparison of datums and spheroids

CHARTED AREAS	DATUM	SPHEROID	EQUATORIAL RADIUS a METRES (N MILES)	POLAR RADIUS b METRES (N MILES)	FLATTENING $f = \dfrac{a-b}{a}$	ECCENTRICITY $e = (2f - f^2)^{1/2}$	ECCENTRICITY^2 $e^2 = 2f - f^2$
British Isles	Ordnance Survey of Great Britain (1936) Datum	Airy	6 377 563 (3443.609)	6 356 257 (3432.104)	1/299.325	0.081673374	0.006670540
North-west Europe	European Datum (1950)	International* (1924)	6 378 388 (3444.054)	6 356 912 (3432.458)	1/297	0.08199189	0.006722670
North America	The North American (1927) Datum	Clarke 1866	6 378 206 (3443.956)	6 356 584 (3432.281)	1/294.98	0.08227185	0.006768658
Southern Africa	Arc Datum	Clarke† 1880	6 378 249 (3443.98)	6 356 515 (3432.245)	1/293.465	0.0824834	0.006803511
Worldwide	World Geodetic System 1972	WGS 72	6 378 135 (3443.917)	6 356 751 (3432.371)	1/298.26	0.0818188	0.00694318

* The International (1924) Spheroid is used for the calculations of distances in the *Admiralty Distance Tables* and *Ocean Passages for the World*.

† Meridional parts (*see* Chapter 4) for the Clarke (1880) Spheroid are tabulated in *Norie's Tables*.

datums used for charting. It has thus become necessary to tabulate this discrepancy on any chart not based on WGS in the form of a correction to the latitude and longitude of the position obtained from TRANSIT. This correction is known as the *datum shift* and may be as large as several hundred metres in well surveyed areas. For example, in Southampton Water the datum shift amounts to about 130 metres (145 yards). A further error, amounting to a mile or more in poorly surveyed areas such as parts of the Pacific Ocean, may also arise from errors in the charted geographical position.

A similar problem exists with the Royal Navy's automated Navigational Plotting System, which is also based on WGS.

NAVSTAR GPS is based on the WGS 84 Datum, which uses the GRS (Geodetic Reference System) 80 Spheroid. As far as the navigator is concerned, the differences between WGS 72 and WGS 84 are negligible.

These three systems are described in detail in Volume III of this manual.

CHAPTER 4
Projections and Grids

GENERAL

For the purposes of navigation it is necessary to *project* the features of the Earth's surface on to a chart. A *projection* is a means of representing a spheroidal surface on a plane. It is usually expressed as a mathematical formula for converting geographical co-ordinates on the spheroid to plane co-ordinates on the chart or map. Provided it is suitable a projection may be used to represent any portion of the Earth's surface.

Since it is impossible to fit exactly a plane surface on to a spheroidal one, projections of anything but very small areas will contain some distortion. For example, in Fig. 4–1 it can be seen that three identical circular areas on the Earth's surface are each represented by a quite different size and shape when the outline is projected from a point of origin at the centre of the Earth on to a plane *chart*.

The distortion of a projection must involve some or all of the following properties:

1. Shape.   2. Bearing.   3. Scale.   4. Area.

It is possible to devise a good projection which will eliminate or reduce to negligible proportions some of these distortions while keeping the others within reasonable and thus usable limits. The choice of projection for a chart or map is governed by the requirements of the user. The mariner requires a chart which will not only show the correct shape of the land he is looking at, but also give him his correct position, course and speed when he plots bearings and distances on it. Unfortunately all these requirements *cannot* be met in one single projection, and a compromise must be made by accepting a very close approximation to all three (shape, bearing, distance), or satisfaction of two (usually shape and bearing) at the expense of the third (distance or scale).

The network of lines representing the meridians of longitude and parallels of latitude which derive from any projection is known as a *graticule*.

A *grid* is a reference system of rectangular (Cartesian) co-ordinates obtained when a projection is applied to a particular part, or the whole of the world. Grids are described in detail at the end of this chapter.

Further information on projections, including their mathematical derivations, is given in Appendix 4.

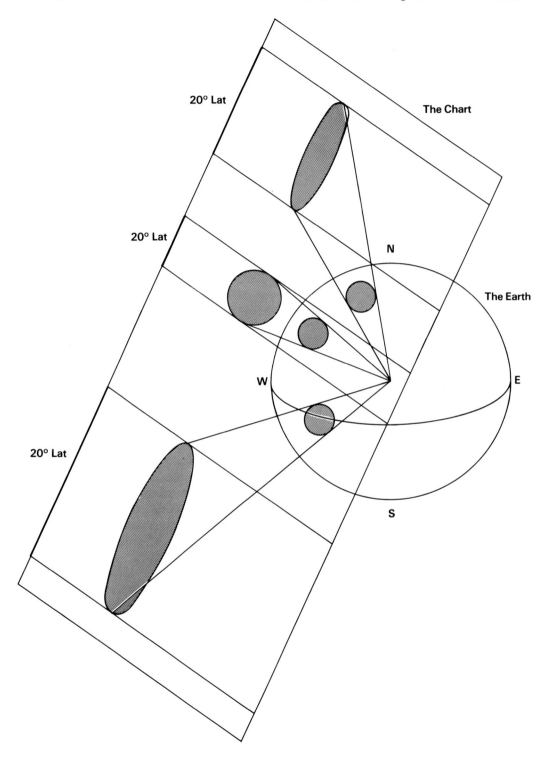

Fig. 4–1.   Distortion on a chart of the Earth's features

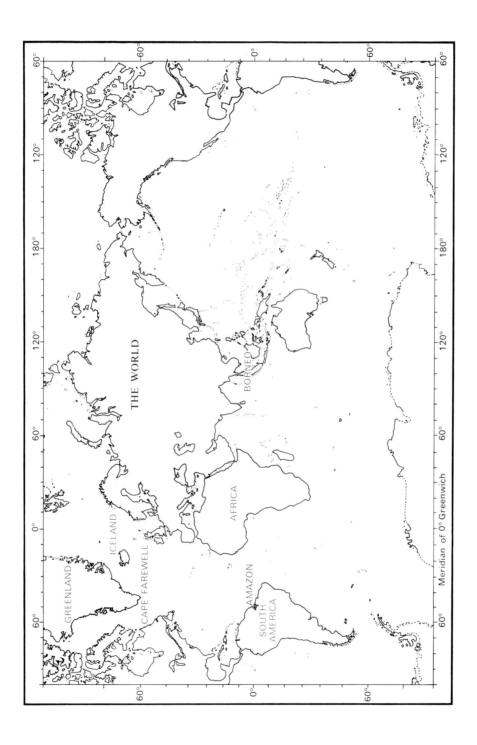

Fig. 4–2. Mercator chart of the world

The 'flat Earth'

Over a limited area (12 mile radius from a point) the Earth may be assumed to be flat for all practical purposes, as the errors introduced by this assumption are *less* than those resulting from the measurement of angles and distances. At a distance of 50 miles from a point, the errors introduced by assuming the Earth is flat are about 1:12,000 for distance (i.e. approximately 8 metres in 50 miles) and 8″ for angles, and increase fairly rapidly beyond this distance. A plan may be constructed on the principle of the assumed flatness of the Earth by transferring measurements made on the spherical surface directly to a sheet of squared paper.

Orthomorphism or conformality

An orthomorphic or conformal projection is a type of chart or map projection on which the shape of the land truly pictures that on the Earth. At any point on that chart or map the scale, whatever it may be, is the same in all directions, and also the parallel of latitude and meridian of longitude at that point are at right angles to each other. *Thus, angles around any point on that chart or map are correctly represented.*

Correctness of shape applies only to small areas. *On the same chart* the scale in one latitude may not be the same as the scale in another latitude, but so long as the scale along the meridian is equal to the scale along the parallel, the immediate neighbourhood of that point is just as correctly shown as the immediate neighbourhood of a point some distance removed. Mercator charts are orthomorphic. On a Mercator chart of the world, for example (Fig. 4–2), the area around Cape Farewell in Greenland is just as correctly shown for shape as is the estuary of the Amazon in South America, although Greenland as a whole 'appears' about the same size as South America whereas it is actually about one-tenth the size. This is because the scale of distance in the Greenland area is quite different from the scale being used to depict South America on the same chart.

The real significance for navigation of this orthomorphic property of charts is as follows. If distortion of shape occurs, then distortion of the bearing scale or compass rose must also occur. A compass rose on a chart which is not orthomorphic will not be circular, nor will its graduation be uniform, and it would be very difficult if not impossible to lay off courses and bearings correctly.

Derivation of projections of a sphere

Consider an imaginary sphere shown in Fig. 4–3. It would be possible to fit plane surfaces around it in a variety of ways, six of which are shown. In (1), (3) and (5) the surfaces touch the sphere along a circle or at a point; in (2), (4) and (6) they have been sunk into the sphere, in (2) and (4) cutting it along two circles and in (6) cutting it along a single circle.

If the detail on the sphere is now projected on to the plane surface from a point on the axis of the cone, cylinder or plane circle, there will be no distortion of scale along the tangential circles or points which are shown in stipple. Elsewhere there is distortion of some sort or another, which will persist when the planes are unwrapped and laid flat.

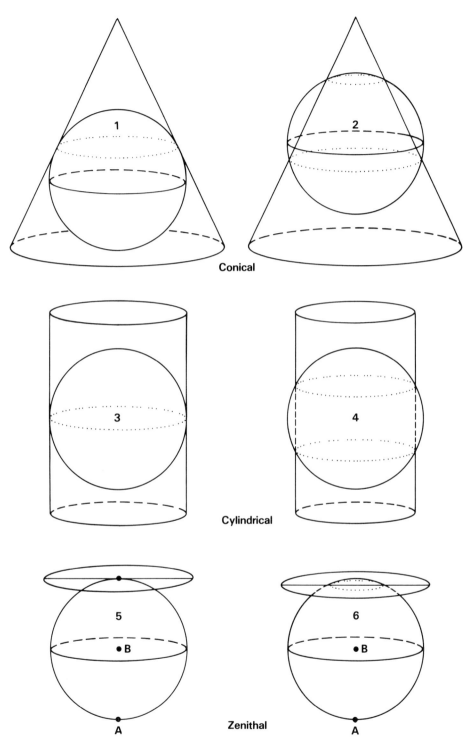

Fig. 4–3.   Projections of a sphere

In (1), (2), (3) and (4) the point from which the projection takes place is usually the centre of the sphere, while with (5) and (6) it may take place from anywhere on the axis at right angles to the plane but usually either from B, the centre of the sphere, or A, the opposite 'pole'. The projections are usually referred to as follows:

1   Conical with one standard parallel.
2   Conical with two standard parallels.
3   Cylindrical with one standard parallel.
4   Cylindrical with two standard parallels.
5 and 6 $\begin{cases} \text{Zenithal projected from } A \text{ — stereographic.} \\ \text{Zenithal projected from } B \text{ — gnomonic.} \end{cases}$

There is no reason except convenience why the cones should occupy the upright position as in Fig. 4–3; they could equally well be inclined at any angle to the vertical.

Projections of the spheroid

None of the projections shown in Fig. 4–3 (except 5 and 6 when projected from A) is orthomorphic for the sphere, and none of them is orthomorphic for the spheroid (the shape of the Earth). To overcome this, a whole family of projections has been devised, analogous to the graphical ones in Fig. 4–3 but all completely mathematical, with their formulae adjusted in such a way as to ensure that some are orthomorphic, some are equal area and so on, as required.

Types of projection in current use both for charts and grids are summarised in Table 4–1 pp. 58–9.

Lambert's conical orthomorphic projection

This projection (Table 4–1, A) is a modification of the conical projection with one or two standard parallels (Fig. 4–3(1) and (2)). The parallels other than the standard parallels appear as circular arcs concentric with the standard parallels, but the distances between them are chosen so that the projection is orthomorphic. To achieve this, the scale along the meridian at any place must be equal to the scale along the parallel at that place. Clearly, the scale along the meridians cannot now be uniform but must be adjusted to the scale along the parallels. The scale is correct only along the standard parallels; if there are two of these, the scale is smaller between them and it becomes increasingly large outside. The extent of latitude covered by the projection is limited so that the scale error does not become unacceptable. Great circles are very nearly represented by straight lines on this projection.

Lambert's projection is suitable for countries with a large extent in longitude but not much in latitude; however, it cannot be used at all in very high latitudes. It has been used a great deal in the past but is being superseded by the Universal Transverse Mercator (UTM) projection.

Mercator's projection

This projection (Table 4–1, B) is described in detail later. It is a special case of the Lambert's conical orthomorphic projection in which the equator is used as the latitude of the origin. It is also special in that the units employed are generally minutes of longitude measured along the equator. Owing to its unique properties the projection is widely used for navigational charts. In this form the actual grid is not shown, although accurate calculations are generally carried out in terms of meridional parts which form the unit of the grid.

Transverse Mercator projection

This projection (Table 4–1, C) is described in detail later. It is made by turning the Mercator projection through 90° so that the equator becomes in effect a central meridian and a chosen geographical meridian becomes the *transverse equator*. The scale error and distortion in shape away from this central meridian or transverse equator are the same as those of the standard Mercator away from the equator. If wide bands of longitude have to be covered, new central meridians must be chosen for new zones. The projection is orthomorphic while the geographical meridians and parallels are curved lines (except the meridian where the cylinder touches the sphere, Fig. 4–3(3) turned through a right angle).

This projection may be used for polar charts and maps although RN polar charts are based on the polar stereographic projection (*see* below).

The transverse Mercator projection has been used for new Admiralty large-scale charts and harbour plans since the mid 1970s instead of the modified polyconic (*see* page 61).

Skew orthomorphic projection

The skew orthomorphic projection (Table 4–1, D) is the general case, of which both the Mercator and transverse Mercator projections are special cases. It is used mainly for land surveys, particularly those of narrow extent, e.g. Malaysia and Malagasy. Instead of a central meridian, a central great circle passing through the axis of the country is used as the transverse equator.

Gnomonic projection

The gnomonic projection (Table 4–1, G) is described in detail later. It is only applied to a sphere which represents the Earth and on it great circles project as straight lines. It is not orthomorphic. It is used for very small scale charts, which enable the navigator easily to obtain great-circle tracks.

Stereographic projection

The point of origin of a stereographic projection (Table 4–1, F) may be anywhere; however, as this projection is only used in polar areas, only a brief description of the Universal Polar Stereographic projection is given.

The meridians and parallels of latitude are projected on to a plane tangential to the pole, the centre of projection being the opposite pole (Fig. 4–3(5)). Meridians appear as straight lines originating from the pole, parallels of latitude as circles radiating outwards from and centred on the pole. The projection is orthomorphic and has less distortion than the polar gnomonic projection previously used for polar charts. Great circles (except meridians) are not projected as straight lines (although in practical terms little accuracy is lost by plotting them as such).

Table 4–1.   Types of projection in use

	PROJECTION	TYPE	ORTHOMORPHIC	GRIDS
A	Lamberts Conical Orthomorphic		Yes	Very many, with one or two Standard Parallels.
B	Mercator		Yes	Not often used. Grids can be made from Navigational Tables.
C	Transverse Mercator		Yes	—
				National Grid of Gt. Britain
				Universal T.M.
				Many others
D	Skew Orthomorphic		Yes	Malaya
				Borneo
E	Inverse (oblique) Mercator	or	Yes	Not often used
F	Stereographic		Yes	Universal Polar Stereographic.
G	Gnomonic		No	Not used
H	Polyconic		No	U.S.C. & G. Polyconic Projection Tables.
I	Cassini		No	Very many, but most being superseded.
J	Flat Earth		No	Local

USED FOR SURVEYING	USED FOR CHARTS	REMARKS
Yes	Yes, but not many	Being superseded by U.T.M. Not suitable for high latitudes, where the modified Lambert conformal is used instead.
Yes, on small scales	Yes	Used for most small scale Admiralty charts.
Yes	Yes	Being introduced for large-scale charts.
Yes	No	Based on Airy's spheroid.
Yes	No	Worldwide between 84°N and 80°S.
Yes	No	
Yes	No	Skew is designed to keep scale errors small, over the area covered by the grids.
No	Yes	Excellent for air charts of Polar areas. A very close relation of the Transverse and Skew Orthomorphic.
Yes	Yes (Polar Charts)	Good for surveys between the Pole and 80°. Not so good for small scale charts.
No	Yes	Used for small scale great-circle charts.
Yes	Yes	The so-called 'gnomonic' of large scale Admiralty plans. Being superseded by the Transverse Mercator.
Yes, but not advised	No	Always transfer to T.M. and back if necessary.
Yes	No	Used for surveying, only in very special circumstances.

This projection is used for polar charts and orthomorphic maps of polar regions. It should be noted that there are now no Admiralty charts on the polar gnomonic projection.

Polyconic projection

The polyconic projection (Table 4–1, H and Fig. 4–4) is another modification of the simple conical projection. The chosen central meridian of the area to be shown is divided correctly for intervals of latitude, but each parallel is constructed as if it were the standard parallel of a simple conical projection. The parallels are arcs of circles, the radii of which steadily increase as the latitude decreases. The meridians, other than the central one, are curved. The central meridian is of course a straight line.

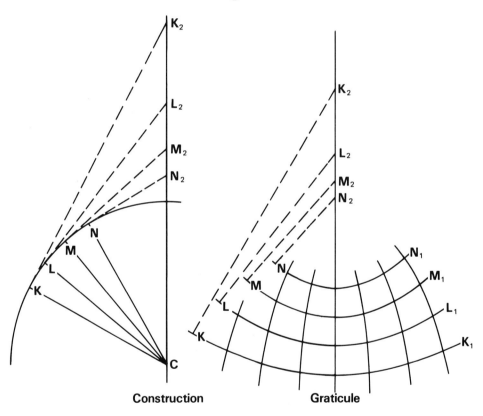

Construction   Graticule

Fig. 4–4.   Polyconic projection

The projection is neither orthomorphic nor equal area, so it is unsuitable for large areas. Its main advantage is that, if small areas are shown on this projection, each area covering the same amount of longitude, the sheets on which the geographical graticules are drawn fit exactly along their northern and southern edges and, for ordinary purposes, along their eastern and western edges, although the join here is a 'rolling fit' as the meridians are curved. It is therefore suitable for topographical maps which, individually covering a small area, combine to cover a large one.

In slightly modified form (in which the meridians project as straight lines) the polyconic projection is used for the 1:1 Million International maps, and for most large-scale Admiralty charts. In this latter form it has often wrongly been referred to as the gnomonic projection, and is indeed so referred to on the large-scale chart itself. As mentioned on page 57, this projection has now been superseded by the transverse Mercator for large-scale charts since the mid-1970s.

MERCATOR PROJECTION/CHART

To the navigator, the most useful chart is one on which he can show the track of his ship by drawing a straight line between his starting point and his destination, and thus measure the steady course he must steer in order to arrive there. The Mercator chart permits him to do this because it is constructed so that:

1. Rhumb lines on the Earth appear as straight lines on the chart.
2. The angles between these rhumb lines are unaltered, as between Earth and chart.

It therefore follows that:

1. The equator, which is a rhumb line as well as a great circle, appears on the chart as a straight line.
2. The parallels of latitude appear as straight lines parallel to the equator.
3. The meridians appear as straight lines perpendicular to the equator.*

The idea of the projection belongs to Gerhard Kremer, a Fleming who adopted the name Mercator. Kremer used the graticule derived from the projection in the world map which he published in 1569. The graticule, however, was inaccurately drawn above the parallels of 40°, and there was no mathematical explanation of it. That was not forthcoming until Wright calculated the positions of the parallels and published the results in his *Errors of Navigation Corrected* thirty years later. The chart came into general use among navigators in about 1630, but the first complete description of it did not arrive until 1645, when Bond published the logarithmic formula.

Principle of the Mercator projection

Earlier in this chapter (page 56) the Mercator projection is referred to as a special case of the Lambert conical orthomorphic projection in which the equator is used as the latitude of the origin ϕ_O. Fig. 4–5 shows what happens when the latitude of the origin is 0°.

RO is a central meridian and is equal in length to $V_O \cot \phi$, where V_O is the radius of curvature at right angles to the meridian at O for the figure of the Earth in use, and ϕ is the latitude of O. As the cotangent of 0° is infinity, R recedes northwards (or southwards) to infinity.

---

* For all practical purposes, a meridian may be considered as a rhumb line on a Mercator projection. The argument that it cannot be one since there is a change of direction of 180° at the pole is academic as the Mercator projection cannot extend as far as the pole.

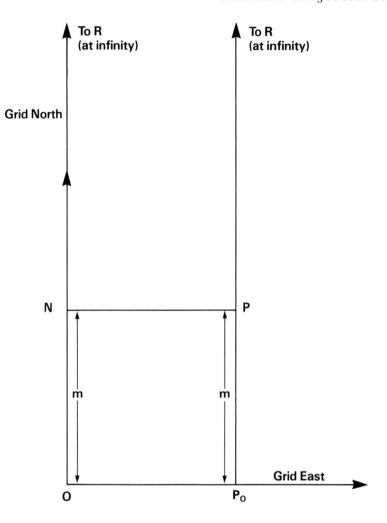

Fig. 4–5.   Mercator projection

The angle between true north and grid north becomes zero for this projection, thus there is no convergence.

OP_O coincides with grid east, all the parallels become straight lines parallel to OP_O and, since there is no convergence, all the meridians are parallel to grid north.

The choice of a minute of longitude measured along the equator (or standard parallel) as the unit of the grid makes this projection very suitable for navigational work.

The characteristics of this projection are governed by two considerations: it is orthomorphic and the constant of the cone is zero.* For this reason it is always known among cartographers as a cylindrical orthomorphic projection, and it is a mathematical, not a perspective, projection.

---

* The quantity $\sin \phi_o$ is known as the Constant of the Cone, and it is of course a constant for any given latitude of the point of origin. When the equator is the point of origin:
$$\sin \phi_o = \sin 0° = 0$$

The orthomorphic property is achieved by spacing the parallels at increasing intervals as they approach the poles; this arrangement, coupled with the fact that the meridians and the parallels on any cylindrical projection where the standard parallel is the equator must be straight lines at right angles, the meridians furthermore being equally spaced, leads to the other property so important to the navigator, namely that rhumb lines also are straight lines. The meridians on a Mercator chart being thus parallel straight lines running north and south, any straight transversal makes a constant angle with them, and there is no distortion of this angle because the orthomorphic property ensures that the correct shape is preserved at all points along the transversal. It is thus the true angle and, since it is constant, the transversal is a rhumb line.

The problem of the Mercator chart is thus the problem of finding the chart length of any parallel from the equator when the orthomorphic property is to be achieved.

Longitude scale on a Mercator chart

Since the meridians of the Mercator graticule are straight lines at right angles to the equator, the longitude scale is the same everywhere and provides the means of comparing chart lengths. Let the scale of any Mercator chart be x millimetres to $1'$ of d.long. Then, since departure $\simeq$ d.long cos lat,* the departure on the chart represented by x millimetres approximates to $1'$ cos lat: i.e. one mile in that particular latitude is represented by x sec lat millimetres on the chart, approximately.

The latitude scale cannot be used because it is continually being streched as the latitude increases, and the distance of any parallel from the equator must be expressed in units of the longitude scale in order that the parallel may be drawn in its correct position on the graticule. The scale of latitude and distance at any part of a Mercator chart is proportional to the secant of the latitude of that part. For this reason, the amount of distortion in any latitude is governed by the secant of that latitude. Greenland, in 70°N, for example, appears as broad as Africa is drawn at the equator, although Africa is three times as broad as Greenland (sec 70° $\simeq$ 3). For a similar reason Borneo, an island on the equator, appears about the same size as Iceland in 65°N, although in *area* Borneo is about five and a half times as large as Iceland.

Graduation of charts and the measurement of distance

Graduation of charts

Mercator charts are graduated along the left- and right-hand edges for latitude and distance, and along the top and bottom for longitude. *The longitude scale is used only for laying down or taking off the longitude of a place, never for measuring a distance.*

Measurement of distances on the chart

The length of the rhumb line between two places is referred to as the distance between them.

---

* This formula is only correct for the sphere. For the spheroid, the precise length of one minute of longitude is given by formula (3.12) (*see* page 45).

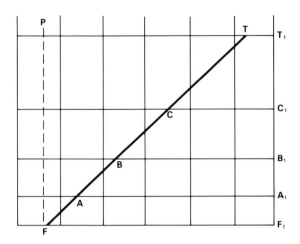

Fig. 4–6.   Measurement of distance

In Fig. 4–6 *FABCT* is a rhumb line as it appears on the chart; *FF₁*, *AA₁*, *BB₁* etc. are parallels of latitude.

The distance *FA* must be measured on the latitude scale between *F₁* and *A₁*, the distance *AB* on the scale between *A₁* and *B₁*, and so on. If *FT* is not large — less than 100′ — no appreciable error is made by measuring it on the scale roughly either side of its middle point.

Meridional parts

Since the latitude and distance scale at any part of a Mercator chart is proportional to the secant of the latitude of that part, this scale continually increases as it recedes from the equator, until at the pole it becomes infinite. (For this reason, the complete polar regions cannot be shown on a Mercator chart.) The latitude scale thus affords no ready means of comparison with the fixed longitude scale. The tangent of the course-angle *PFT*, for example, is not *PT* divided by *FP*, where *PT* is measured on the longitude scale and *FP* on the latitude scale. For that ratio to be valid, *PT* and *FP* must be measured in the same fixed units. The fixed longitude scale provides this unit, which is the length of 1 minute of arc on that scale. This length is called a *meridional part*, and gives rise to the definition:

> ***The meridional parts of any latitude are the number of longitude units in the length of a meridian between the parallel of that latitude and the equator.***

The number of meridional parts for any latitude may be found from formulae **(4.1)** for the sphere (page 65), and **(5.21)** for the spheroid (page 95). They are also tabulated in:

Norie's Nautical Tables (NP 320) (compression ratio 1/293.465)
Burton's Nautical Tables
Table of Meridional Parts based on the International (1924) Spheroid (NP 239)
    (compression ratio 1/297)

If the longitude scale on the Mercator chart is 1 degree or 60 meridional parts to 10 mm, the length of the meridian between the parallel of 45°N and the equator, when measured on the chart, is not 450 mm but 502.3 mm, the length of 3013.58 meridional parts (NP 239). Meridional parts thus involve chart lengths. They are not in any way connected with distance on the Earth's surface, which is expressed in sea or n miles.

To find the meridional parts of any latitude

In Fig. 4–7, the upper half of which represents a part of the Earth's surface, F is a point on the equator, and FT the rhumb line joining it to T. The lower half of the figure shows this same rhumb line as the straight line ft on a Mercator chart.

If TQ is now divided into n small lengths α, so that $(n\alpha)$ is equal to the latitude of T, the arcs of parallels drawn through the points of division are equally spaced and, with the meridians, form a series of small triangles FAX, ABY, . . . If, furthermore, α is so small that these triangles may be considered plane, they are equal in *all* respects, since:

$$FX = AY = \ldots = \alpha$$
$$FXA = AYB = \ldots = \text{one right angle}$$
$$XFA = YAB = \ldots = \text{the course}$$
$$\therefore AX = BY = \ldots$$

and, since these small arcs recede in succession from the equator, the meridians which bound them are spaced successively farther apart. Hence:

$$FQ_1 < Q_1Q_2 < \ldots$$

A comparison of the two halves of the figure should make clear the relation between the small triangles when they are drawn on the Earth and their appearance on the chart. On the Earth they are all equal, but on the chart they are only similar. They increase progressively as they recede from the equator. This increase can be found by considering two similar and corresponding triangles. Thus:

$$\frac{fx}{FX} = \frac{ax}{AX} = \frac{FQ_1}{AX} = \text{sec lat } A$$
$$fx = FX \text{ sec lat } A$$
$$= \alpha \sec \alpha$$

Similarly, by considering the triangles ABY and *aby:*

$$ay = \alpha \sec 2\alpha$$

But qt, the length of the meridian between the parallel through t and the equator, is the sum of all the elements fx, ay . . . kz. That is:

$$qt = \alpha (\sec \alpha + \sec 2\alpha + \sec 3\alpha + \ldots + \sec n\alpha)$$
$$= 7915.7045 \log_{10} \tan \left(45° + \frac{T°}{2}\right) \qquad \ldots \textbf{4.1}$$

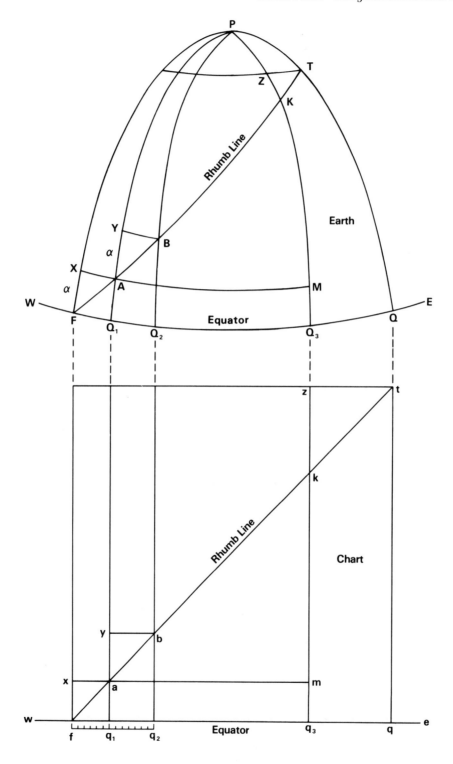

Fig. 4–7.   Meridional parts

This formula (*see* Appendix 3) gives the number of meridional parts in the latitude of *T* for a perfect sphere. In the *Table of Meridional Parts* (NP 239), as previously mentioned (page 64), the meridional parts are given allowing for the spheroidal shape of the Earth; the accurate formula is given in Chapter 5, formula **(5.21)** (page 95) and its proof given in Appendix 5. For example, the number of meridional parts between the parallel of 20° and the equator is 1217.23.

Difference of meridional parts

Where the two positions are both remote from the equator, for example *A* and *K* in Fig. 4–7, their relative position may be determined by the difference between the meridional parts for *K* and the meridional parts for *A*, which gives the number of longitude units in the length of a meridian between the two parallels of latitude through *A* and *K*. This length *mk* is usually referred to as the difference of meridional parts and written as DMP. (*See* the examples given on pages 87 and 95 of this volume for the sphere and the spheroid respectively.)

Property of orthomorphism

Since the scale along a meridian in the neighbourhood of a point in latitude ϕ is stretched by the same amount (sec ϕ) as the scale along the parallel through that point, and the meridians and parallels on the Mercator projection are at right angles, the projection must be orthomorphic. (*See* pages 54 and 62 of this chapter.)

To construct a Mercator chart of the world

Since there is no distortion at the equator, the base on which the chart is built must be the line representing the equator, and convenience governs the length of this line. Suppose it is 720 mm (about 28 in). Then the longitude scale must be:

$$\frac{\text{length of equator in degrees}}{\text{length of base in millimetres}} = \frac{360}{720}$$

that is, $\frac{1}{2}$° of longitude or 30 meridional parts to 1 mm; more conveniently, 5° of longitude or 300 meridional parts to 10 mm. Vertically the scale will be the same, 300 meridional parts to 10 mm.

If it is required to draw the meridians for every 20°, for example, the equatorial line must be divided into eighteen equal parts, 40 mm long. The perpendiculars drawn through the points of division will be the meridians. The one through the left-hand extremity will be the meridian of 180°W, the one through the right-hand extremity the meridian of 180°E.

The *Table of Meridional Parts* (NP 239) gives all the information necessary for deciding the positions of the parallels of latitude. The number of meridional parts between the parallel of 20° and the equator is 1217.23 and, since these are drawn on a scale of 300 meridional parts to 10 mm, the parallels of 20° must be drawn 1217.23 ÷ 30, or 40.57 mm either side of the equatorial line on the chart.

The number of meridional parts between the parallel of 40° and the equator is 2607.82. The parallel of 40° is therefore drawn 2607.82 ÷ 30, or 86.93 mm from the equatorial line.

In the same way the other parallels are drawn, and on the graticule thus formed it is possible to insert the position of any place the latitude and longitude of which are known.

To construct a Mercator chart on a larger scale

In order that small portions of the Earth may be shown in detail, it is necessary to employ a larger scale and construct only the relevant portion of the chart. If it so happens that the equator is not included, the chart lengths between successive parallels of latitude on the chart are found by reducing to millimetres, according to the scale employed, the difference between the corresponding meridional parts.

Suppose, for example, it is required to construct a chart from 142°E to 146°E, and 45°N to 49°N, the scale of the chart being 1° of longitude to 30 mm, or 1′ of longitude to $\frac{30}{60} = 0.5$ mm.

The difference of longitude between limiting meridians is 4° and, since the scale of the chart is 1° of longitude to 30 mm, the line at the bottom of the chart representing the parallel of 45°N is 120 mm long, as shown in Fig. 4–8. The meridians of 142°, 143°, 144°, 145° and 146° will be perpendiculars erected on this line at its two ends and at the points dividing it into four equal parts.

The length in millimetres beween the parallels of 45° to 49° can be deduced from the difference of meridional parts as shown in Table 4–2.

Table 4–2.   Chart lengths between parallels

LATITUDE	MERIDIONAL PARTS (INTERNATIONAL SPHEROID)	DMP	CHART LENGTH BETWEEN PARALLELS (DMP × 0.5)
49°	3364.62		mm
48°	3274.33	90.29	45.14
47°	3185.79	88.54	44.27
46°	3098.90	86.89	43.45
45°	3013.58	85.32	42.66

In order to increase the accuracy with which positions can be plotted, the chart lengths between meridians and between parallels are divided, if necessary, into convenient units: 10′ of longitude between meridians, and 10′ of latitude between parallels. This division is easily effected on the longitude scale because that is fixed. On the latitude scale, however, it can be carried out only with the further aid of the relevant table of meridional parts (see page 64), which is now entered for every 10′ between 45° and 49° instead of every degree.

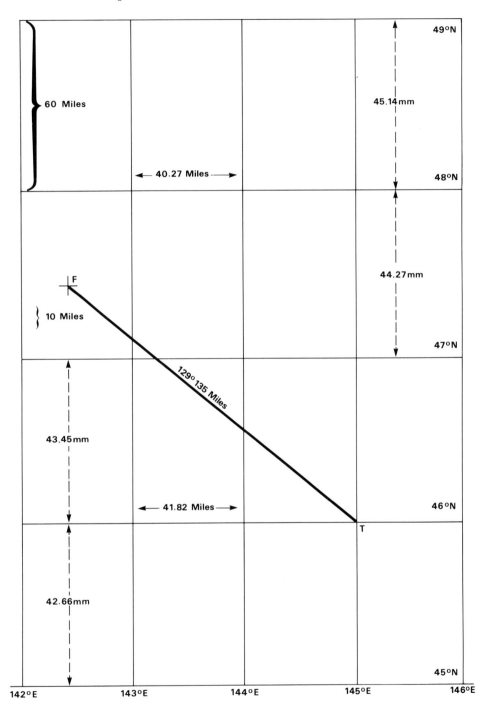

Fig. 4–8.   Constructing a Mercator chart

Fig. 4–8 shows the complete graticule. Each rectangle, whatever its dimensions in millimetres, represents a part of the Earth's surface bounded by meridians 1° apart in longitude and parallels 1° apart in latitude; and, although the chart lengths between these parallels vary from 42.66 mm to 45.14 mm as shown, each length represents a distance of 60 miles on the Earth's surface. The actual distance in miles between the meridians depends on the latitude in which it is measured on the chart, and may be obtained from *Spheroidal Tables* (NP 240), published by the Hydrographer of the Navy, *Norie's Tables*, or formulae **(3.12)** and **(3.9)**.

As already explained, distances between places must be measured on the latitude scale on either side of the places. The distance between *F* and *T*, for example, is measured on the latitude scale between 46° and 48°, and is found to be 135 miles.

Great-circle tracks on a Mercator chart

Since only rhumb lines appear as straight lines on a Mercator chart, great circles will in general appear as curves.

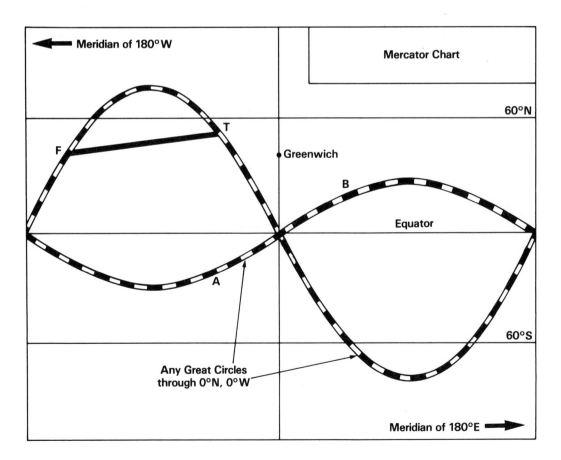

Fig. 4–9.   Great-circle tracks on a Mercator chart

Moreover, since the limiting great circles are the equator, which appears as a horizontal line, and any double meridian, which appears as two separate lines 180° apart and perpendicular to the equator, any other great circle passing through their points of intersection must appear as two curves with vertices towards the poles, as shown in Fig. 4–9. The great circle joining F and T will, therefore, always lie on the polar side of the rhumb line joining them and, when the difference of latitude between F and T is small and the difference of longitude large, it is seen that the difference between the two tracks is considerable. If, however, the two points lie on opposite sides of the equator, as at A and B, then the rhumb line almost coincides with the great circle.

TRANSVERSE MERCATOR PROJECTION/CHART

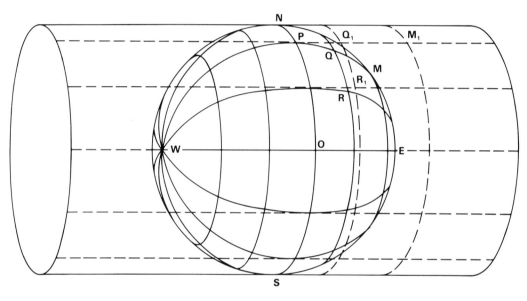

Fig. 4–10.   Transverse Mercator projection (1)

This very important projection, also known as the Gauss conformal projection, is essentially a Mercator projection turned through 90°.

In the transverse Mercator projection a cylinder is chosen touching the Earth along a chosen geographical meridian. This central meridian is then the *transverse equator* of the chart — *NOS* in Fig. 4–10. If a system of great circles is drawn through the places where the axis of the cylinder cuts the surface of the Earth, E and W in Fig. 4–10, then these may be regarded as *transverse meridians*. A system of small circles parallel to *NOS* corresponds to *transverse parallels*.

These systems are transferred to the cylinder in the same way as the meridians and parallels are transferred in the normal Mercator projection; the expansion of the distance between successive small circles is proportional to the secant of their angular distance from the central meridian *NOS*. The small circle QR is projected at Q_1R_1 and the transverse meridian PQM is projected at PQ_1M_1.

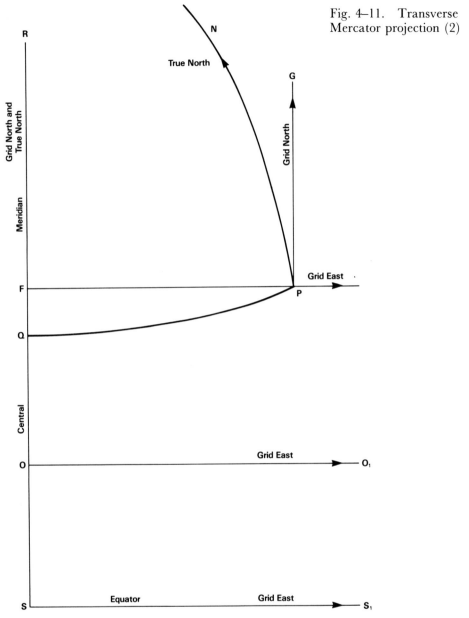

Fig. 4–11.   Transverse
Mercator projection (2)

Fig. 4–11 shows part of a transverse Mercator grid, which has been made by turning the Mercator projection through 90°, where the central meridian is represented by *SOQFR* and is similar to the equator on the Mercator projection. The lines *SS₁*, *OO₁* and *FP* are all great circles (or geodesics) cutting the central meridian at right angles. They are therefore analogous to the meridians on the Mercator projection, and will plot on the transverse Mercator projection as parallel straight lines at right angles to the central meridian.

   Grid north on the projection is defined as the direction *SOQFR*; it is coincident with true north on the central meridian only. Grid east is defined as the directions *SS₁*, *OO₁* or *FP*, all of which are parallel on the projection. It follows that the meridians and parallels (with the exception of the central meridian and the equator) will plot as curves on the projection. *PN* is the meridian through *P,* and *PQ* is the parallel through *P;* the angle *NPQ* is of course 90°. Geodesics on the projection will all plot as curves unless they coincide with the central meridian, or grid east lines. (The grid east lines are not quite geodesics, due to the fact that scale factor changes very slowly with grid northing, but the difference is very small indeed.)

In order to make the projection orthomorphic, the scale in an east–west direction has to be increased, away from the central meridian, to make it everywhere equal to the slowly increasing scale in a north–south direction. Put another way, this means that the east–west distance on the Earth, from the central meridian to a point P, has to be increased slightly before plotting the point by its co-ordinates on the projection, whilst the north–south distance is plotted direct. The analogy with the Mercator projection is exact.

In Fig. 4–11 the point of origin of this particular grid is on the central meridian at *O;* it might equally well be anywhere else along the central meridian. The true point of origin of the projection is always on the central meridian and the equator.

The scale error and distortion in shape away from the central meridian are exactly those of the standard Mercator away from the equator so that, for topographical large-scale map use, when the maximum permissible scale errors are limited to amounts of less than 0.1%, this projection can be used only for a limited extent in longitude. If wide bands of longitude have to be covered, new central meridians must be chosen for new zones.

This projection has now been used since the mid-1970s for new Admiralty large-scale charts instead of the modified polyconic or gnomonic projection (*see* page 61).

GNOMONIC PROJECTION/CHART

In order to assist the navigator in finding the great-circle track between two places, charts are constructed so that any straight line drawn on them shall represent a great circle. These are known as *gnomonic charts,* and they are formed by projecting the Earth's surface from the Earth's centre on to the tangent plane at any convenient point. They are thus a zenithal projection from position *B* (*see* Fig. 4-3(5) on page 55). The angle at the apex of the cone is 180°, whereby the cone becomes a plane, touching the surface of the sphere at the one tangent point. The gnomonic projection is a perspective projection, the meridians and parallels being projected on to the tangent plane from the centre of the sphere. The tangent point is chosen at the centre of the area to be shown on the chart, to minimise distortion.

Since a great circle is formed by the intersection of a plane through the Earth's centre with the Earth's surface, and as one plane will always cut another in a straight line, all great circles will appear on the chart as straight lines. However, the meridians will not be parallel unless the tangent point is on the equator, nor will rhumb lines be straight. Angles are also distorted, except at the tangent point. It is therefore impossible to take courses and distances from a gnomonic chart. The mathematical theory of this chart is explained in Appendix 4.

Fig. 4–12 shows the graticule of a gnomonic chart in which the tangent point is on the equator, and it will be noticed that the graticule is symmetrical about the meridian through this tangent point, which is independent of the longitude. The longitude scale can therefore be adjusted to suit the navigator's convenience. In the figure the tangent point is in longitude 0°.

Chart 5029, the *Great-circle Diagram*, is a graticule of this type.

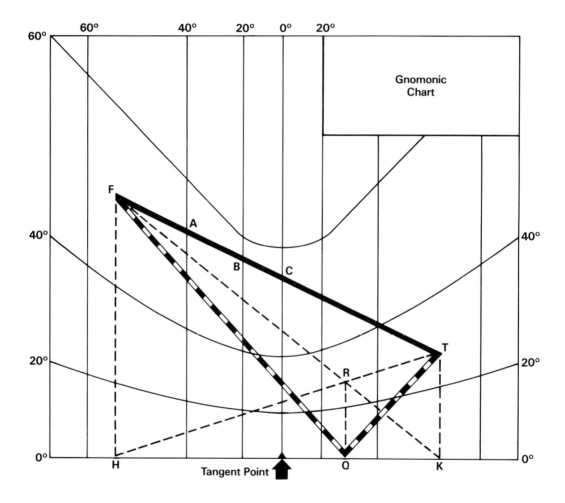

Fig. 4–12.   Gnomonic chart

To transfer a great-circle track to a Mercator chart

The transference of a great-circle track, such as *FT* in Fig. 4–12, from a gnomonic to a Mercator chart, which is the normal navigational chart, is effected by noting the latitude and longitude of convenient points *A, B, C . . .* on the line *FT*, marking these points on the Mercator chart, and joining them by a smooth curve.

When *F* and *T* lie on opposite sides of the equator, *F* being north and *T* south, the same chart can be used because a gnomonic chart of both hemispheres when the tangent point is on the equator must be symmetrical about the equator. The following geometrical construction therefore suffices:

1. Mark the position of *T* as if it were in the northern hemisphere.
2. Join *F* to *K*, the point on the equator which has *T*'s longitude.
3. Join *T* to *H*, the point on the equator which has *F*'s longitude.
4. Drop a perpendicular *RQ* on the equator from *R*, the point where *FK* cuts *TH*.
5. Draw *FQ* and *QT*. Then *FQ* is the great-circle track in the northern hemisphere, and *QT* is the reflection of its continuation south of the equator. Points on *QT* may therefore be treated as if they were in the southern hemisphere.

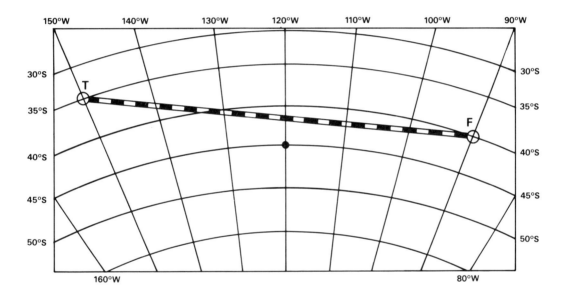

Fig. 4–13.   Gnomonic graticule

In Fig. 4–13, *FT* is the great-circle track between the points 40°S, 90°W, and 35°S, 150°W. As it appears on the gnomonic chart, it tells the navigator little about the course he must steer in order to follow it because angles, other than bearings from the tangent point, are distorted. The track must therefore be transferred to a Mercator chart, a transference that is easily made by noting the latitudes of the points where the great-circle track cuts the meridians. The result is the smooth curve *FT* in Fig. 4–14. The dotted line *FT* shows the rhumb line.

Fig. 4–15 shows three tracks — rhumb-line, great-circle and composite — between two places, for comparison, all on a Mercator chart.

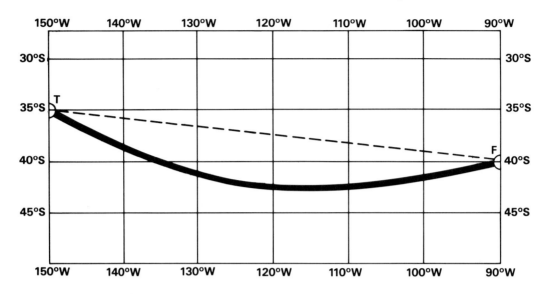

Fig. 4–14.   Great-circle track transferred to a Mercator chart

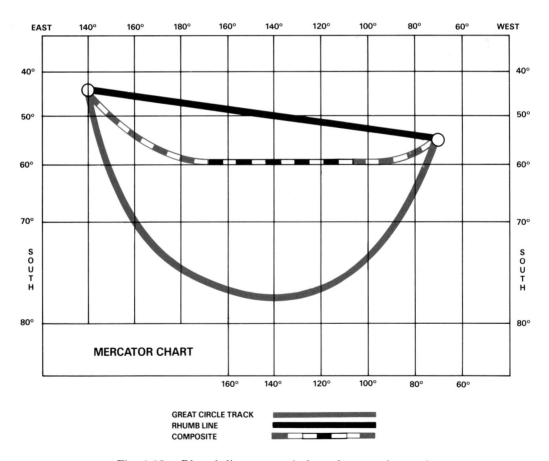

Fig. 4-15.   Rhumb-line, great-circle and composite tracks

Practical use of gnomonic charts

The distortion of the gnomonic graticule, which is a perspective distortion that gives neither the orthormorphic nor the equal area property, makes the graticule quite unsuitable for civil purposes. Its purpose is limited entirely to the use that can be made of the fact that, on it, great circles are represented by straight lines.

GRIDS

A *grid* is a reference system of rectangular (Cartesian) co-ordinates obtained when a projection is applied to a particular part, or the whole, of the world. It will have all the properties of a projection and may have some special ones peculiar to itself. Several grids, all different, may be based on the same projection.

Fig. 4–16 shows a grid on which has been superimposed a geographical graticule. It is simply a large piece of graph paper, specially constructed, and graduated in suitable units north, south, east and west from the point of origin.

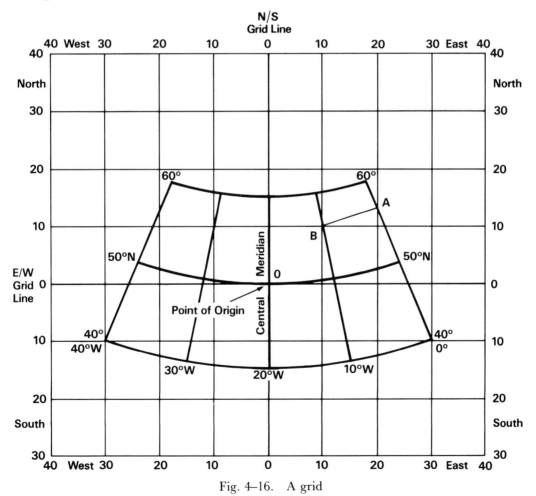

Fig. 4–16. A grid

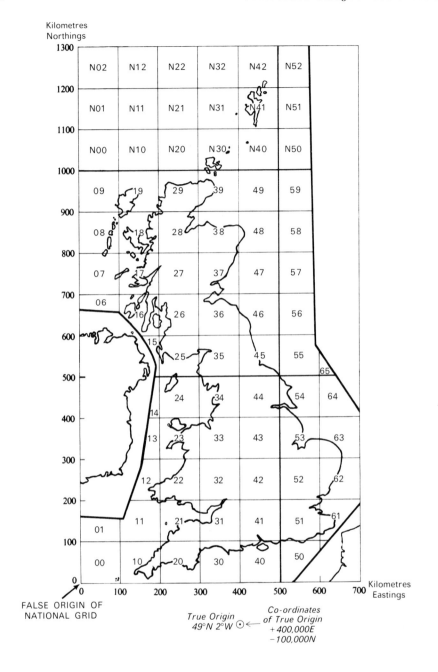

Fig. 4–17. The National Grid of Great Britain

The intersections of the meridians and parallels are converted into quantities known as grid eastings and northings. Eastings refer to the linear distance eastwards from the north–south grid line which passes through the origin. Northings refer to the linear distance northward from the east–west grid line which passes through the origin. Distances west and south of the point of origin are given negative values of eastings and northings respectively.

The northings and eastings are then plotted as individual points on the grid and the points joined by smooth curves to form the geographical graticule. To make this conversion simple, a set of tables will have been constructed, depending on the projection in use.

At the point of origin of the grid, in this case (0,0) or 50°N, 20°W, the scale factor of any projection in all directions is such that there is no distortion at this point. Distortion elsewhere on the grid will depend upon the type of projection in use.

The point of origin does not necessarily have to be numbered (0,0). For example, the point of origin of the Ordnance Survey National Grid of Great Britain is 49°N, 2°W (Fig. 4–17). To ensure that all positions in Great Britain are covered by positive co-ordinates (i.e. above and to the right of the point of origin) this position is given a false easting of +400 000 metres. It is also given a false northing of −100 000 metres to ensure that all points on the mainland of Scotland will have northings less than 1 000 000 metres. This then produces a false origin 100 kilometres north and 400 kilometres west of the true origin. It is from this false origin that all positions on the National Grid are referenced.

Grid convergence

All the north–south grid lines do not point due north, as may be seen from Fig. 4–18, and this has a significance for navigation when using grids (*see* page 81). At any point, the angle between the meridian, as represented on the plane of the projection and grid in use, and the grid north line is known as the *grid convergence C*.* It will vary from place to place, depending on the projection, and can be as much as 180° on certain projections (e.g. polar stereographic). On the Mercator projection, on which most small-scale charts are constructed, the convergence is zero everywhere but grid convergence still exists if the grid is a different projection.

In Fig. 4–18 that part of the grid in Fig. 4–16 containing the points A and B is shown enlarged. AP_1 and BP are the meridians through A and B respectively. It will be noticed that they are both curved. AN_1 and BN both define the direction of grid north.

$$C, \text{ the convergence at } B \quad = \text{ angle } PBN$$
$$C_1, \text{ the convergence at } A \quad = \text{ angle } P_1AN_1$$

---

* The quantity used by mariners to correct a great-circle bearing (or true azimuth) to a Mercatorial or grid bearing which is a straight line on the chart is usually referred to as *half-convergency* and must not be confused with grid convergence. The correction for half-convergency is described in Volume III of this revised edition.

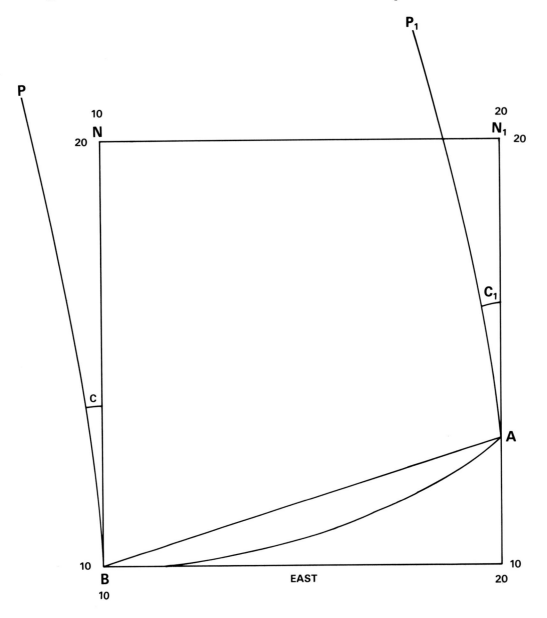

Fig. 4–18.   Grid convergence

Grids constructed on the transverse Mercator projection

There are many grids constructed on the transverse Mercator projection, such as the National Grid of Great Britain (Fig. 4–17), the Universal Transverse Mercator Grid and the Jamaica Grid. Scale on the central meridian of this projection is correct over the entire distance from the North to the South Pole so that it is suitable for world-wide cover using several zones of similar limited longitude extent, and as such is used for US military surveys.

Universal Transverse Mercator (UTM) Grid

If, in Fig. 4-11, *O* is made to coincide with *S*, the figure represents the UTM Grid. *P* is then a point north and east of the point of origin; by inverting the diagram, overturning it, or both, the figure can be made to represent the situation in either hemisphere or on either side of the central meridian.

The UTM Grid covers the whole world from latitude 84°N to 80°S, in zones of longitude 6° wide. These zones are numbered from 1, which covers 180°W to 174°W in an easterly direction, to 60, which covers 174°E to 180°E. Each zone is therefore about 360 miles wide at the equator, 180 miles wide in latitude 60°, and 62 miles wide in latitude 80°. The central meridian of each zone bisects it.

Latitude and longitude may be converted into grid terms and vice versa, using the appropriate formulae and a suitable programmed calculator or mini-computer (*see* Appendix 4).

Transferring grid positions

Sometimes it will be found necessary to transfer a grid (e.g. for bombardment purposes) from a map to a chart. There is a theoretical difficulty in doing this, because the chart and map projections will almost certainly be different. Thus, the lines of the grid may not be parallel to the parallels of latitude nor to the meridians of longitude, and may indeed be curved (*see* Fig. 4–16). Also, the degree of distortion from the central meridian or standard parallel may not be the same for both projections. Moreover, there may be a difference in the geodetic datums (*see* Chapter 3) used for chart and grid.

On a small-scale chart drawn on the Mercator projection, a grid transferred from any of the topographical map projections would be formed by curved lines but, in practice, when a larger scale chart (such as the standard coastal chart) is used and the area covered *small*, the grid may be drawn with straight lines without appreciable loss of accuracy. If, however, the whole of the coastal chart is gridded up, grid positions on the eastern and western edges being joined together by a straight line, appreciable errors can occur. These can be as much as 200 yards in the centre of a 1:75,000 chart and 800 yards in the centre of a 1:150,000 chart. Grid positions of suitable intermediate points across the chart must be identified and the *curved* east–west grid lines drawn accordingly.

Ideally, the transfer of the grid position to the chart and vice versa should be carried out using the appropriate mathematical formulae on a computer, provided the appropriate programs are available and the computer itself is suitable. If such facilities are not available, grid positions may be transferred using rough graphical methods as described below.

A gridded map usually gives the geographical positions of the corners of the map and, if these are plotted on the chart, the grid may be inserted according to scale. This assumes, however, that the determinations of latitude and longitude for map and chart are in agreement. If they are not and this can be seen by inspection, an adjustment must be made before the grid is transferred. On a small-scale Mercator chart, where rapid change of scale occurs away from the equator, the transferred grid will appear as a series of trapeziums of curved sides, but on a larger scale coastal chart, where the scale over the small area to be covered is approximately the same in all directions, the transferred grid will be in the form of squares, (Fig. 4–19).

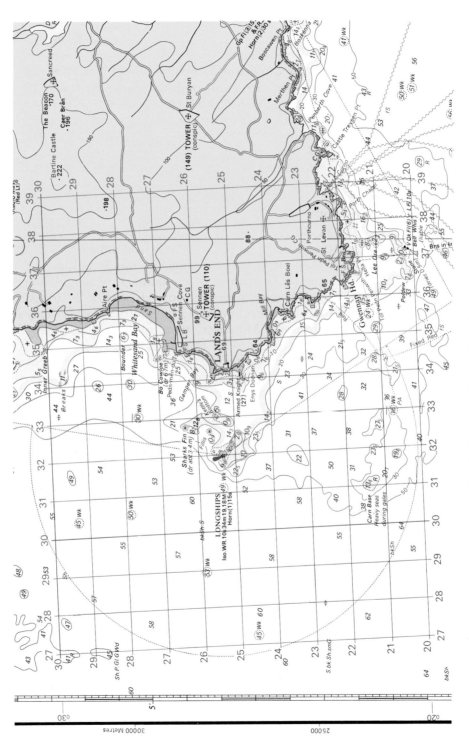

Fig. 4–19.   A grid transferred to a chart

Another method, and probably the most satisfactory graphical method for all practical purposes, is to identify at least two and preferably four (one towards each corner of the area to be gridded) marks common to both chart and map. From these the grid may be constructed taking into account:

1. The difference between true and grid north.
2. The scales of the chart and map.

When the geographical positions of the corners of a gridded map are not given, the geographical position of the origin is normally shown, and from this the grid corners of the map may be calculated.

A map may sometimes have to be used as a chart, as happened for example during the Korean War. Maps, however, do not usually show enough navigational information and may have insufficient sea area.

Provided that the map is orthomorphic, it may be used with the following modifications:

1. A compass rose is cut from a chart and pasted on the map. More than one rose may be needed, as the grid convergence (*see* page 79) may be different on different parts of the map.
2. Distance scales, which must take account of any change in scale away from the central meridian or standard parallel over the area to be used, should be pasted in a convenient position.
3. The sea may have to be extended to seaward with blank chart paper pasted along the edge and navigational information, marks, soundings, etc. transferred.

The most likely projections used for the map are the Lambert conical orthomorphic (*see* page 56) or some form of the transverse Mercator (*see* page 57). The former is steadily being superseded by the latter. In both cases the map is orthomorphic. The other projection still used for topographical maps is the polyconic (*see* page 60) and the mariner may come across this from time to time. Although not orthomorphic, provided the map is of a reasonably large scale (i.e. similar to that for the standard coastal chart or larger), the mariner may treat it as such for all practical purposes without any measurable loss of accuracy.

CHAPTER 5
The Sailings (2)

The sailings were introduced in Chapter 2, which dealt with the parallel, plane, mean and corrected mean latitude, traverse and great-circle sailings. This chapter now deals with the somewhat more complex sailings, which are as follows:

1. Mercator sailing on the sphere.
2. The vertex and the composite track in spherical great-circle sailing.
3. Spheroidal rhumb-line sailing.
4. Spheroidal great-circle sailing.

MERCATOR SAILING ON THE SPHERE

This was introduced in Chapter 2 (page 33). It uses meridional parts, which were described in Chapter 4 (page 64). Meridional parts for the sphere are given by formula **(4.1)**, ϕ being the latitude:

$$\text{meridional parts} = 7915.7045 \log_{10} \tan \left(45° + \frac{\phi°}{2} \right) \qquad \ldots \textbf{(4.1)}$$

To find the course and distance from the meridional parts

Where any point does not lie on the equator, its latitude has its meridional parts. The number of meridional parts in the length of a meridian on a Mercator chart between the parallels of latitude through two points F and T (Fig. 5–1) will therefore be;

1. *F and T on the same side of the equator (Fig. 5–1(a))*

$$\text{mer. parts } T \text{ } minus \text{ mer. parts } F \qquad \ldots \textbf{5.1}$$

2. *F and T on opposite sides of the equator (Fig. 5–1(b))*

$$\text{mer. parts } T \text{ } plus \text{ mer. parts } F \qquad \ldots \textbf{5.2}$$

This length MT is always called the *difference of meridional parts* and written DMP.

From the triangle FTM in Fig. 5–1, it is apparent that:

$$\tan \text{ course} = \frac{FM}{MT} = \frac{\text{d.long(E/W)}}{\text{DMP(N/S)}} \qquad \ldots \textbf{5.3}$$

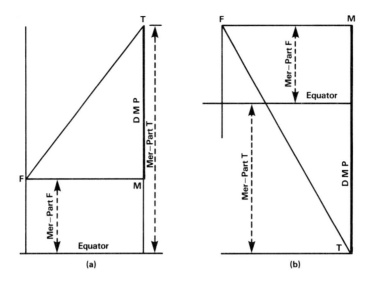

Fig. 5–1.   Difference of meridional parts (DMP)

The angle thus obtained is exact, irrespective of the length of *FT*. That length, as in plane sailing, is obtained from formula **(2.3)**, slightly modified:

$$\text{distance} = \text{d.lat sec course} \qquad \qquad \dots \textbf{5.4}$$

Formula **(5.4)** is quite satisfactory in use for courses approaching 90°, when using a calculator which will register the course to at least 6 decimal places. There is, however, a fundamental weakness in this formula at course angles between 60° and 90° because, as mentioned in Chapter 2, small errors in the course introduce increasingly large errors in the distance. When using tables in these circumstances it is preferable to use the formula:

$$\text{distance} = \text{d.lat} \frac{\text{d.long}}{\text{DMP}} \text{ cosec course} \qquad \qquad \dots \textbf{5.5}$$

$$\text{or} \qquad \text{distance} = \text{dep cosec course} \qquad \qquad \dots \textbf{5.6}$$

Fig. 5–2 shows the relation between the two methods of finding the course. In the meridional parts method the d.lat is stretched into DMP and the d.long remains unchanged; in the departure method, the d.lat remains unchanged and the d.long is compressed into departure. Hence:

$$\frac{\text{d.long}}{\text{DMP}} = \text{tan course} = \frac{\text{dep}}{\text{d.lat}} \qquad \qquad \dots \textbf{5.7}$$

The use of the departure formula, however, involves finding a corrected mean latitude (page 28) if an error in the course is to be avoided. For this reason, the DMP formula is preferred.

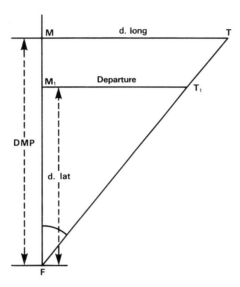

Fig. 5–2.   DMP/d.long/departure/d.lat

EXAMPLE

What is the rhumb-line course and distance by Mercator sailing from F(45°N, 140°E) to T(65°N, 110°W) (the positions given in the example in Chapter 2, page 39)?

$$\text{d.long } 110°\text{E}, \ 6600'\text{E}$$
$$\text{d.lat } \quad 20°\text{N}, \ 1200'\text{N}$$

From formula **(4.1)**:

$$\text{mer. parts } T: \quad 7915.7045 \ \log_{10} \tan \left(45° + \frac{65°}{2} \right) = 5178.81$$

$$\text{mer. parts } F: \quad 7915.7045 \ \log_{10} \tan \left(45° + \frac{45°}{2} \right) = \underline{3029.94}$$

$$\text{DMP}(F \text{ to } T) = 2148.87\text{N}$$

From formula **(5.3)**:

$$\tan \text{course} = \frac{\text{d.long(E)}}{\text{DMP(N)}}$$

$$= \frac{6600}{2148.87}$$

$$= 3.0713817$$

$$\text{course} = \text{N71}°.97\text{E (calculator reading } 71°.965457)$$

$$= 072°$$

From formula **(5.4)**:

$$\text{distance} = \text{d.lat sec course}$$

$$= 1200' \sec 71°.965457 = 3876'.09$$

Using the alternative formula **(5.5)**, the distance is also 3876′.09.

The rhumb-line distance may also be found from formula **(2.7)** using the corrected mean latitude (56°.052499 in this example) but this is always bound to give the same result as using meridional parts directly, as the formula:

$$\sec L = \frac{DMP}{d.lat}$$

may be manipulated into

$$\tan \text{course} = \frac{d.long}{DMP}$$

using formulae **(2.5)** and **(2.4)**.

THE VERTEX AND THE COMPOSITE TRACK IN SPHERICAL GREAT-CIRCLE SAILING

The vertex and the composite track were introduced in Chapter 2 (page 36). The calculations of the vertex and the composite track are given below.

To find the position of the vertex of a great circle

If a series of parallels is drawn, it is clear that one parallel will touch the great circle *FT* at a point *V*, the *vertex* of the great circle, and it is the point on the great circle nearest the pole in the appropriate hemisphere (Fig. 5–3). (*See also* page 36.)

Since the great circle and the parallel touch at *V* and the meridian *PV* cuts the parallel at right angles, it also cuts the great circle at right angles, and the spherical triangles *PFV* and *PTV* are right-angled at *V*.

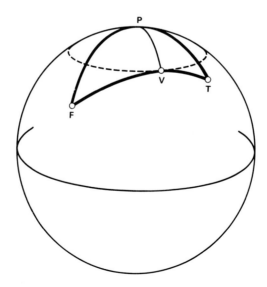

Fig. 5–3.   The vertex

The longitude of the vertex can be found at once from the formula:

$$\tan \text{d.long } VT = \tan \text{lat } F \cot \text{lat } T \operatorname{cosec} \text{d.long } FT$$
$$- \cot \text{d.long } FT \qquad \qquad \ldots 5.8$$

The latitude may be found from:

$$\cot \text{lat } V = \cot \text{lat } F \cos \text{d.long } FV \qquad \qquad \ldots 5.9$$

Otherwise, if the initial course has been found, the position of V can be obtained from Napier's rules (Appendix 2, page 603). Thus:

$$\cos \text{lat } V = \cos \text{lat } F \sin \text{initial course} \qquad \qquad \ldots 5.10$$

$$\tan \text{d.long } FV = \operatorname{cosec} \text{lat } F \cot \text{initial course} \qquad \qquad \ldots 5.11$$

EXAMPLE

Find the position of the vertex in the example given on page 39, F (45°N, 140°E) to T (65°N, 110°W), using the information from the cosine method (page 39).

$$\cos \text{lat vertex} = \cos \text{lat } F \sin \text{initial course}$$
$$= \cos \text{lat } 45° \sin 28°.122305$$
$$\text{lat vertex} = 70°.530896\text{N} = 70°31'.85\text{N}$$
$$\tan \text{d.long } FV = \operatorname{cosec} \text{lat } F \cot \text{initial course}$$
$$= \operatorname{cosec} 45° \cot 28°.122305$$
$$\text{d.long } FV = 69°.297735\text{E} = 69°17'.86\text{E}$$
$$\text{long vertex} = 150°.70227\text{W} = 150°42'.14\text{W}$$

Note: The vertex may not be situated between F and T. There is only one great-circle between F and T, and the point at which it most nearly approaches the pole may be beyond F or T. For example, if the final course angle is less than 90° the vertex lies beyond T.

To plot a great-circle track on a Mercator chart

The simplest method of plotting a great-circle track on a Mercator chart is that by which points are transferred from a gnomonic chart (*see* Chapter 4) but, if a gnomonic chart is not available, the track can be plotted with reference to the vertex.

Consider the position of any point G on the great circle joining F and T, G being fixed by its difference of longitude from V (Fig. 5–4, page 90).

Having found the position of V (formulae **5.10, 5.11**), intermediate positions are obtained from the following formula, where G is any position on the great circle:

$$\cos \text{d.long } VG = \cot \text{lat } V \tan \text{lat } G \qquad \qquad \ldots 5.12$$

or $$\tan \text{lat } G = \tan \text{lat } V \cos \text{d.long } VG \qquad \qquad \ldots 5.13$$

A table of latitudes may now be prepared using suitable intervals of longitude.

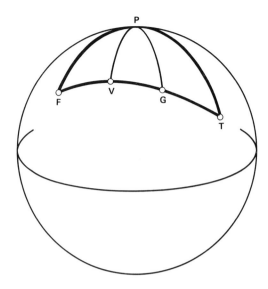

Fig. 5–4.   Plotting a great-circle track on a chart

EXAMPLE

Find the latitudes where the great-circle track in the example given on page 89 cuts the meridians of 150°E, 160°E, 170°E, 180°, 170°W, 160°W, 150°W, 140°W, 130°W, 120°W. (F (45°N, 140°E), T (65°N, 110°W).)

Using formula (**5.13**), Table 5–1 may be prepared.

Table 5–1

	LONGITUDE				
LONG	150°E	160°E	170°E	180°	170°W
VG (D.LONG)	59°.298	49°.298	39°.298	29°.298	19°.298
LAT *G*	55°18′.1	61°32′.3	65°26′.9	67°56′.1	69°28′.0
LONG	160°W	150°W	140°W	130°W	120°W
VG (D.LONG)	9°.298	0°.702	10°.702	20°.702	30°.702
LAT *G*	70°17′.5	70°31′.8	70°12′.8	69°17′.9	67°39′.0

The latitudes and longitudes of *G* may now be plotted on the Mercator chart and joined by means of a series of rhumb lines, which the navigator may now steer.

Alternatively, the following formula may be used to find where a track cuts intermediate meridians. This method avoids the need to find the position of the vertex.

$$\tan \text{lat } G = \frac{\tan \text{lat } F \sin \text{d.long } GT + \tan \text{lat } T \sin \text{d.long } FG}{\sin \text{d.long } FT} \qquad \dots \mathbf{5.14}$$

If, however, a number of intersections are required, it is simpler to find the vertex first, then apply (**5.12**) or (**5.13**).

There is no simple formula for finding where a track cuts parallels of latitude without knowing the position of the vertex.

Calculating the composite track

The reasons for adopting composite sailing were described in Chapter 2.

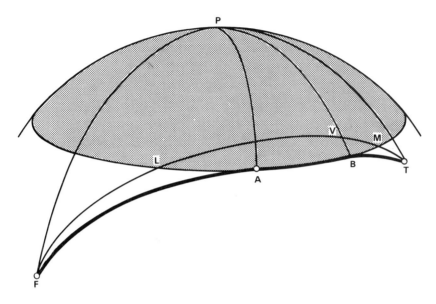

Fig. 5–5.   The composite track

In Fig. 5–5 *LABM* is the limiting parallel; the great circle joining *F* and *T* is *FLVMT*. The composite track is *FABT*, in which *FA* and *BT* are great-circle arcs touching the parallel at *A* and *B*, and *AB* is part of the limiting parallel itself.

The positions of *A* and *B* are quickly found because the course angles at *A* and *B* are right angles. Also, along *AB* the ship is steering a course of 090°/270° and, if the latitude of this limiting parallel is ϕ:

$$AB = \text{d.long } \cos \phi$$

The formulae to be used are those for the spherical right-angled triangle:

$$\cos PF = \cos PA \cos FA$$

i.e. $\qquad \cos FA = \dfrac{\cos PF}{\cos PA}$ $\qquad\qquad$ . . . **5.15**

$$\sin FPA = \dfrac{\sin FA}{\sin PF} \qquad\qquad \text{. . . } \textbf{5.16}$$

Formula (**5.15**) gives the length of the great-circle arc *FA* and formula (**5.16**) the d.long between *F* and *A* by which the position of *A* may be found. *BT* may also be found in a similar manner.

EXAMPLE

Find the distance in the example on page 89, when a limiting latitude of 67°N is applied.
(F (45°N, 140°E), T (65°N, 110°W).)

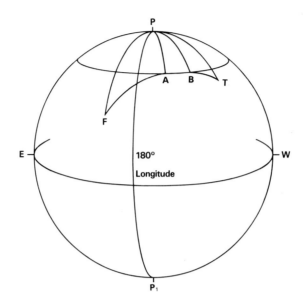

Fig. 5–6.   The great-circle example. *F* and *T* in the Northern Hemisphere

The total distance $= FA + AB + BT$

$$\cos FA = \frac{\cos PF}{\cos PA} = \frac{\cos 45°}{\cos 23°}$$

$$FA = 39°.809911$$

$$= 39°48'.6 \quad = 2388.6 \text{ miles}$$

$$\cos BT = \frac{\cos PT}{\cos PB} = \frac{\cos 25°}{\cos 23°}$$

$$BT = 10°.075896$$

$$= 10°04'.6 \quad = 604.6 \text{ miles}$$

$$\sin FPA = \frac{\sin FA}{\sin PF} = \frac{\sin 39°.809911}{\sin 45°}$$

$$FPA = 64°.882575 = 64°53'E$$

Thus   position of *A* is 67°N, 155°07'W.

$$\sin TPB = \frac{\sin TB}{\sin PT} = \frac{\sin 10°.075896}{\sin 25°}$$

$$TPB = 24°.454656 = 24°27'.3$$

Thus   position of *B* is 67°N, 134°27'.3W.

$$AB = APB \cos 67°$$
$$= [FPT - (FPA + TPB)] \cos 67°$$
$$= 20°.662769 \cos 67°$$
$$= 8°.0735870 = 484.4 \text{ miles}$$

Thus   composite distance $= 2388.6 + 604.6 + 484.4$ miles
$$= 3477.6 \text{ miles}$$

The course from F to A and B to T may be found by the usual methods described earlier.

SPHEROIDAL RHUMB-LINE SAILING

The formulae for plane sailing, corrected mean latitude (Chapter 2) and Mercator sailing (Chapter 5) are accurate for the sphere. If these formulae are used for the spheroid without suitable adjustment, the rhumb-line solution will be inaccurate to some extent, dependent on course, distance and latitude. In the days before computers and accurate navigational aids such as SATNAV, these small inaccuracies (less than about 0.5% at worst) were swept up in those larger errors incidental to the practice of navigation and thus did not matter to the practical navigator. Nowdays, however, they have to be considered.

Various efforts have been made from time to time to resolve this problem. Meridional parts have been used for the spheroid instead of the sphere, but this method is still inaccurate if the eccentricity of the Earth is not also allowed for in formula **(5.4)**, distance = d.lat sec course. Other methods use the corrected

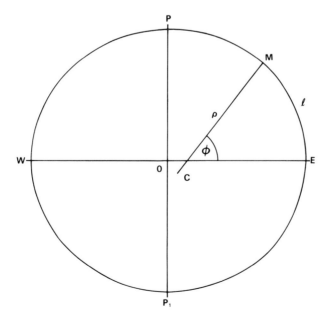

Fig. 5–7.   Length of the meridional arc

mean (middle) latitude derived from meridional parts for the spheroid, but some of these mid.lat correction tables are wrong, erroneous in principle and only valid for small latitude differences.

Provided that the meridional parts *and* the length of the meridional arc between the latitudes of the two places concerned, e.g. *EM* in Fig. 5–7, are computed for the spheroid, an accurate rhumb-line course and distance on any spheroid may be determined.

To find the rhumb-line course and distance

The length of the meridional arc

The length ℓ of the meridional arc *EM* may be found from the formula:

$$\ell = \int_0^\phi \rho d\phi \qquad \qquad \dots \textbf{5.17}$$

where ϕ is the geodetic latitude of the place and ρ the radius of curvature in the meridian. The value of ρ is given in formula **(3.8)** in Chapter 3 (page 44) and thus the precise formula to be integrated becomes:

$$\ell = a\,(1 - e^2) \int_0^\phi \frac{1}{(1 - e^2 \sin^2 \phi)^{3/2}}\, d\phi \qquad \dots \textbf{5.18}$$

ℓ may be determined for any spheroid of known major semi-axis a and eccentricity e (*see* Chapter 3), and expressed, dependent on what unit is used for a, in metres, international nautical miles, etc.

Such a formula is expanded in the form:

$$\int_0^\phi \rho d\phi = a\,(A_0\,\phi - A_2 \sin 2\phi + A_4 \sin 4\phi - A_6 \sin 6\phi + \dots) \dots \textbf{5.19}$$

where ϕ is measured in radians and:

$$A_0 = 1 - \frac{1}{4}e^2 - \frac{3}{64}e^4 - \frac{5}{256}e^6 - \dots$$

$$A_2 = \frac{3}{8}\left(e^2 + \frac{1}{4}e^4 + \frac{15}{128}e^6 + \dots \right)$$

$$A_4 = \frac{15}{256}\left(e^4 + \frac{3}{4}e^6 + \dots \right)$$

$$A_6 = \frac{35}{3072}e^6 + \dots$$

A computer is ideal for this calculation; a program may be devised to carry out the computation to as many terms as the user wishes.

Meridional parts for the spheroid

Meridional parts for the spheroid are tabulated in the following publications:

Table of Meridional Parts based on the International (1924) Spheroid (NP 239), published by the Hydrographer.

Norie's Nautical Tables (NP 320), based on the Clarke (1880) Spheroid.
Burton's Nautical Tables, also based on the Clarke (1880) Spheroid.

Meridional parts m may be evaluated for any spheroid from the formula:

$$m = \frac{10800}{\pi} (1 - e^2) \int_0^\phi \frac{\sec \phi}{1 - e^2 \sin^2 \phi} \, d\phi \qquad \text{... 5.20}$$

$$= \frac{10800}{\pi} \left[\ln \tan\left(\frac{\pi}{4} + \frac{\phi}{2}\right) - e^2 \sin \phi - \frac{1}{3} e^4 \sin^3 \phi \right.$$
$$\left. - \frac{1}{5} e^6 \sin^5 \phi - \dots \right] \qquad \text{... 5.21}$$

where ϕ is measured in radians.
Once again a computer is ideal for this calculation.

Calculation of the rhumb-line course and distance

The rhumb-line course and distance may now be calculated as follows:

$$\tan \text{course} = \frac{\text{d.long}}{m_1 \pm m_2} \qquad \text{... 5.22}$$

where m_1 and m_2 are the meridional parts evaluated from formula (5.21), or extracted from the appropriate tables.

$$\text{distance} = (\ell_1 \pm \ell_2) \sec \text{course} \qquad \text{... 5.23}$$

where ℓ_1 and ℓ_2 are the lengths of the meridional arcs evaluated from formula (5.19).

EXAMPLE

What is the rhumb-line course and distance from F (40°43'N, 74°00'W) to T (55°45'S, 37°37'E) on the International (1924) Spheroid?

$$\text{d.long} = 111°37'E = 6697'E$$

Using formula (5.21) or NP 239:
$$m_1 \ (F) = \quad 2664.031$$
$$m_2 \ (T) = -4028.034$$
$$\text{DMP} = \overline{-6692.065} \text{ (i.e. 6692.065S)}$$

Using formula (5.22):
$$\text{course} = S45°.021E(-45°.021118) = 134°.98$$

Using formulae (5.19) and (5.23):
$$\text{distance} = 8166.09 \text{ n miles}$$

Such a calculation may also be determined reasonably quickly and to a high degree of accuracy using an ordinary pocket calculator and disregarding terms of e^6 ($10^{-7} \times 3.1$) and higher powers.

$$a = 3444.0540 \text{ n mile}$$
$$e^2 = 0.00672267$$
$$\text{lat } F = 0.71063989 \text{ radians}$$
$$T = 0.97302106 \text{ radians}$$

Meridional parts **(5.21)**	F	T
$\text{Log}_e \tan \left(\dfrac{\pi}{4} + \dfrac{\phi}{2} \right)$	0.77932467	1.1772729
$- e^2 \sin \phi$	$- 0.00438532$	$- 0.00555689$
$- \dfrac{1}{3} e^4 \sin^3 \phi$	$\underline{- 0.00000418}$	$\underline{- 0.00000851}$
	0.77493517	1.1717075
m	2664.031	4028.034
$m_1 \pm m_2$	6692.065S	

Meridional arc **(5.19)**

$$\ell = a \left(\phi - \frac{e^2 \phi}{4} - \frac{3e^2}{8} \sin 2\phi - \frac{3e^4}{64} \phi - \frac{3e^4}{32} \sin 2\phi + \frac{15e^4}{256} \sin 4\phi \right)$$

$$\dots 5.24$$

	F	T
ϕ	$+ 0.71063989$	$+ 0.97302106$
$- \dfrac{e^2 \phi}{4}$	$- 0.00119435$	$- 0.00163532$
$- \dfrac{3}{8} e^2 \sin 2\phi$	$- 0.00249287$	$- 0.00234558$
$- \dfrac{3}{64} e^4 \phi$	$- 0.00000151$	$- 0.00000206$
$- \dfrac{3}{32} e^4 \sin 2\phi$	$- 0.00000419$	$- 0.00000394$
$+ \dfrac{15}{256} e^4 \sin 4\phi$	$\underline{+ 0.00000078}$	$\underline{- 0.00000181}$
	0.70694775	0.96903235
ℓ	2434.7662 n mile	3337.3997 n mile
$\ell_1 \pm \ell_2$	5772.1659 n mile	

Using formulae **(5.22)** and **(5.23)**:

$$\text{course} = 134°.978882 \ (135°)$$
$$\text{distance} = 8166.09 \text{ n mile*}$$

---

* If the DMP for the spheroid were to be used with d.lat only, the rhumb-line distance would be 8188′.49 measured in units of minutes of latitude.

SPHEROIDAL GREAT-CIRCLE SAILING*

There are a variety of solutions for computing the shortest distance (the geodesic) and course on the spheroid. Some of these use the geodetic and some the parametric latitude, terms described in Chapter 3. Some of the formulae required are much too complex for general use.

One of the most suitable formulae is the Andoyer-Lambert method using parametric latitude; this is described below. This method has been adopted by the US Naval Oceanographic Office for navigational applications and is also used in the Royal Navy's automated plotting system. The method has a maximum error of 1 metre at 500 miles and 7 metres at 6000 miles, the azimuth (bearing) being correct to within 1 second of arc.

In this method distance and bearing are pre-computed on a sphere of radius equal to the semi-major axis of the spheroid on which the positions are located (*see* Fig. 3–4 on page 44). Corrections are then made to obtain the corresponding spheroidal values.

Calculation of the initial course and distance

In this calculation latitude N, longitude E, and d.long E are given a positive ($+$) value, while latitude S, longitude W, and d.long W are given a negative ($-$) value.

The latitudes are reduced to parametric form to compensate for the flattening of the Earth using formula (3.7):

$$\tan \beta = \frac{b}{a} \tan \phi$$

where β is the parametric and ϕ the geodetic latitude, and a and b are the equatorial and polar radii.

The azimuth from the departure point F to the arrival point T may be found from the formula:

$$\tan az = \frac{\sin d.long}{\cos \beta_1 \tan \beta_2 - \sin \beta_1 \cos d.long} \qquad \ldots 5.25$$

where β_1 and β_2 are the parametric latitudes of F and T.

The spherical distance σ is now computed using formula (2.9):

$$\cos \sigma = \sin \beta_1 \sin \beta_2 + \cos \beta_1 \cos \beta_2 \cos d.long$$

and converted into radians.

The spheroidal corrections M, N, U, V are now calculated as follows:

$$M = (\sin \beta_1 + \sin \beta_2)^2$$
$$N = (\sin \beta_1 - \sin \beta_2)^2$$
$$U = \frac{\sigma - \sin \sigma}{1 + \cos \sigma}$$

---

* Strictly speaking, the title should be spheroidal geodesic sailing but the term 'great-circle' has been used in preference as it is more familiar.

$$V = \frac{\sigma + \sin \sigma}{1 - \cos \sigma}$$

$$\text{geodesic distance} = \sigma - \frac{f}{4}(MU + NV) \text{ in radians}$$

$$= a \left[\sigma - \frac{f}{4}(MU + NV) \right] \text{n miles} \qquad \ldots \textbf{5.26}$$

where a is the equatorial radius measured in international nautical miles and f the flattening coefficient for the spheroid in use (*see* Chapter 3).

EXAMPLE

What is the geodesic course and distance from F (40°43′N, 74°00′W) to T (55°45′S, 37°37′E) on the International (1924) Spheroid?

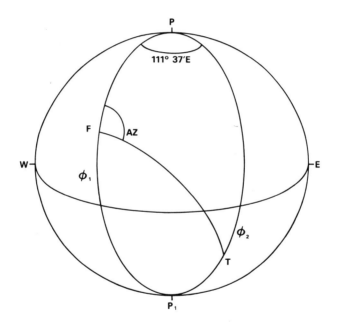

Fig. 5–8.   Geodesic course and distance

On the International Spheroid:

$$a = 3444.0540 \text{ n mile}$$
$$b = 3432.4579 \text{ n mile}$$
$$f = 1/297$$
$$\text{d.long} = +111°.61667$$

$$\phi_1 = +40°.71667 \qquad\qquad \phi_2 = -55°.75$$

$$\tan \beta_1 = \frac{b}{a} \tan \phi_1 \qquad\qquad \tan \beta_2 = \frac{b}{a} \tan \phi_2$$

$$\beta_1 = +40°.621149 \qquad\qquad \beta_2 = -55°.660048$$

From formula **(5.25)**:

$$\tan az = \frac{\sin 111°.61667}{(\cos 40°.621149 \tan -55°.660048) - (\sin 40°.621149 \cos 111°.61667)}$$

$$az = 133°.140011 \text{ or } 313°.140011$$

which by inspection must be the former.

Initial course = 133°.14

From formula **(2.9)**:

$$\cos \sigma = (\sin 40°.621149 \sin -55°.660048)$$
$$+ (\cos 40°.621149 \cos -55°.660048 \cos 111°.61667)$$
$$\sigma = 134°.05233 = 2.3396545 \text{ radians}$$
$$M = (\sin 40°.621149 + \sin -55°.660048)^2 = 0.03050287$$
$$N = (\sin 40°.621149 - \sin -55°.660048)^2 = 2.1808189$$
$$U = \frac{2.3396545 - \sin 134°.05233}{1 + \cos 134°.05233} = 5.3200842$$
$$V = \frac{2.3396545 + \sin 134°.05233}{1 - \cos 134°.05233} = 1.8040066$$

$$\text{geodesic distance} = \sigma - \frac{f}{4}(MU + NV) \text{ radians}$$
$$= 2.3396545 - 0.00344822 = 2.3362063 \text{ radians}$$
$$= 3444.0540 \times 2.3362063 \text{ n miles} = 8046.02 \text{ n miles}$$

A comparison of distances

Table 5–2 gives a comparison of distances when evaluated by different methods, using the positions in the example on page 95, also when T is in the Northern Hemisphere.

Table 5–2. Comparison of distances

POSITION	SPHERE			INTERNATIONAL (1924) SPHEROID (WGS 72 IN BRACKETS)		
	MERIDIONAL PARTS	RHUMB-LINE DISTANCE	GREAT-CIRCLE DISTANCE	MERIDIONAL PARTS	COMPUTED RHUMB-LINE DISTANCE	COMPUTED GREAT-CIRCLE DISTANCE
F 40°43′N 74°00′W	2679.12			2644.031 (2644.094)		
T 55°45′S 37°37′E	−4047.17	8167′.67	8048′.08	−4028.034 (−4028.114)	8166.09 (8165.83)	8046.03 (8045.78)
T 55°45′N 37°37′E	4047.17	4506′.74	4052′.35	4028.034 (4028.114)	4522.75 (4522.54)	4066.54 (4066.35)

Note: Distances on the spheroid are in international nautical miles.
　　　Distances on the sphere are in units of minutes of latitude.

CHAPTER 6
Charts and Chart Outfits

This chapter includes: general remarks on charts; navigational charts; the arrangement of charts; other types of charts and diagrams; upkeep of chart outfits; navigational warnings; correction of charts and publications; hydrographic reports; and production of the Admiralty chart. Reference is also made to some associated navigational publications including the *Admiralty Sailing Directions*, *Admiralty List of Lights and Fog Signals* and *Admiralty List of Radio Signals*.

British Admiralty charts are produced by the Hydrographic Department of the Ministry of Defence (Navy). This department was formed in 1795 because, it was said, more HM Ships were being lost on uncharted or badly charted shoals than were being sunk by enemy action.

Lead and line was the only means of obtaining soundings until the echo sounder came into general use in about 1935, although the hand lead continued for inshore work into the 1950s. A sounding with lead and line covered only the few centimetres actually struck by the lead and objects less than a metre away from each cast remained undetected. Echo sounders only examine a narrow strip immediately under the hull of the ship, and even on a large-scale harbour chart these strips can be as much as 60 metres apart. It only became possible to detect shoals and wrecks lying between sounding lines in about 1973, with the advent of sidescan sonar — a form of towed sonar equipment which enables the survey ship to 'look sideways' and thus search, and record, depths of bottom features between the sounding lines.

Although this equipment is now employed extensively by the Hydrographer, the large majority of charts in use are still based on older surveying data. Ships can still find that in every part of the world there are areas which were surveyed using the hand lead only.

Up to the early 1960s, the survey service did not examine in detail any object likely to be deeper than 66 feet (20 metres). Deep-draught ships need to exercise care within the 200 metre depth contour, even in well recognised shipping lanes, because of this problem.

It is still quite possible to find uncharted rocks, shoals and wrecks anywhere in the world. Within recent years, rocky pinnacles rising to within 30 feet of the surface have been found in well used waters such as the approaches to Holyhead in Wales and Auckland in New Zealand. Walter Shoals, with 18 metres over them and surrounded by great ocean depths, lying on the route from the Cape of Good Hope to the Sunda Strait, were not discovered until 1962. It is estimated that there are some 20,000 wrecks or underwater obstructions in British coastal waters alone, but the exact position or the depth of water over many of them is unknown.

It follows, therefore, that no chart is infallible. Every chart is liable to be incomplete, either through imperfections in the surveys on which it is based, or through subsequent alterations to the topography and sea-bed.

Ideally, all charts should include information concerning the origin, date, scale and limits of the various surveys. Around the British Isles, a special chart (Q6090) shows the dates of the surveyed areas on the Continental Shelf.

GENERAL REMARKS ON CHARTS

Charting policy

British charting policy is to chart all waters, ports and harbours in UK home waters and certain Commonwealth and other areas on a scale sufficient for safe navigation. Elsewhere overseas, Admiralty charts are schemed to enable ships to cross the oceans and proceed along the coasts of the world to reach the approaches to major ports using the most appropriate scale. In general, smaller foreign ports are only charted on a scale adequate for ships under pilotage although a number of major ports (e.g. New York) are charted on larger scales.

In some overseas areas, charts (particularly the large-scale ones) of other national Hydrographic Offices, whose addresses are given in the *Catalogue of Admiralty Charts and Other Hydrographic Publications*, may be required. British merchant ships are legally required to carry an adequate outfit of charts and in certain places, for particular purposes, this may require that charts produced by other nations should be held on board.

Description and coverage

There are about 3400 British Admiralty navigational charts covering the whole world. In addition, over 600 of these charts are available with overprinted lattices for use with electronic navigation systems (*see* page 104). In areas where the United Kingdom is, or until recently has been, the responsible hydrographic authority — i.e. home waters, some Commonwealth countries, British colonies, and certain areas like the Persian Gulf, Red Sea and parts of the eastern Mediterranean — the Admiralty charts afford detailed cover of all waters, ports and harbours. In other areas, charts are compiled mainly from information given on published foreign charts, and the Admiralty versions are designed to provide charts for ocean passage and landfall, and approach and entry to the major ports, usually under pilotage.

The Admiralty chart series contains charts on many different scales ranging from route planning charts on the smaller scales through medium scale coasting charts to very large scale harbour plans.

In recent years, a new-style chart has been designed to meet the needs of modern navigation, to take advantage of present-day cartographic techniques including automation, and to facilitate updating procedures. At the same time, the units of charted depth are being converted from fathoms and feet to metres.

Metrication

The first Admiralty chart showing the depth of water in metres instead of fathoms and feet was published in 1968 and, if the present rate is maintained, the conversion of all Admiralty charts should be completed by the year 2000.

Metric charts are added to the series of navigational charts in three ways. First, there is the traditional way, a new chart being published to meet a fresh requirement or because the extent of newly acquired information is such as to make replacement preferable to correction. Secondly, metric charts are acquired through bilateral or international arrangements, for example adoption into the British Admiralty series of Australian and New Zealand charts. The third way is 'active metrication' through following a policy of block metrication region by region. Resources are devoted exclusively to the chosen area irrespective of the degree of outdatedness of the existing charts. The first such area to be covered in this way was home waters between 1972 and 1980 and it has been followed by, for example, Europe and the Far East.

A criticism made of the earlier metric charts was that the process of reducing the amount of detail shown, not only for clarity but also to speed up the change-over process, had gone too far, and so the amount of detail in inshore waters and in the topography has been increased. Other changes since 1979 have been:

1. The introduction of the transverse Mercator projection for large-scale charts instead of the modified polyconic ('gnomonic') projection.
2. The graduation for latitude and longitude of most harbour plans, however small their size or inextensive their cover; this should facilitate chart correction.
3. The introduction of a graduated central meridian on certain Mercator charts of NW Europe including the British Isles. This is particularly welcome in small craft where lack of space necessitates the folding of the chart in use, thereby denying the chart user the linear scales in the east and west borders.

Geographical datum

The completely recompiled metric chart permits the adoption of a generally accepted basis for the determination of latitude and longitude, either a regional one such as the European Datum or an international one such as that based on the World Geodetic System 1972 (WGS 72) (*see* page 48).

The increased use of satellite navigation systems (the US Navy Navigation Satellite System (TRANSIT) is based on WGS) has shown the wide discrepancies in horizontal datums in use on charts. These discrepancies have arisen from astronomical fixes used for early surveys, the accuracy of which may have been affected by local gravitational anomalies. There are two main reasons for this. First, the geographical position in which a given point on the earth is charted will usually have been computed on a local geographical datum. The reference spheroid of this local datum will have been chosen to give the 'best fit' to the Earth's surface in the limited area concerned, whereas the reference spheroid of WGS is chosen to give the 'best fit' to the whole surface of the Earth. This causes a discrepancy known as the *datum shift*, which is usually of the order of a few hundred metres. Secondly, the survey from which the chart was compiled may itself have contained errors in geographical positions. Such errors, though negligible for modern surveys, may amount to 1 mile or more in poorly charted areas such as parts of the Pacific Ocean. The systematic acquisition and publication of datum shift information on Admiralty charts is now being undertaken by the Hydrographic Department.

International charts

The 1967 conference of the International Hydrographic Organisation (IHO) set up a six-nation Commission to determine an agreed set of specifications for a series of small-scale International (INT) charts with a view to sharing the production of these charts among a number of member states. The intention was that any member state of the IHO could reprint any or all of these International charts, making modifications as necessary to conform with its own national chart series. Two separate world-wide schemes have been agreed for use in route planning and ocean navigation: a 1:10 million series comprising 19 sheets and a 1:3.5 million series comprising 60 sheets. Sixteen member states participate in their production. It is expected that all the charts in these two series will have been completed and incorporated into the Admiralty series by the mid-1980s.

International charts are now also being published on larger scales including medium- and large-scale charts, priority being given to large-scale INT charts for ports. A regional charting group has already devised a scheme of INT charts for the North Sea and the north-east Atlantic between Greenland, North Cape and Ushant. Further regional charting groups are being established to extend schemes of medium- and large-scale INT charts across the world, for example in the Mediterranean and in the Straits of Malacca and Singapore.

INT charts follow the new internationally agreed chart specification of the IHO. This specification differs little from that used for the standard Admiralty chart.

INT charts are treated as part of the national series of charts, having a national chart number as well as an INT number. They should be ordered, corrected, etc. in exactly the same way as any other national chart, using the appropriate national chart number.

Latticed charts

Many nautical charts are available with coloured overprints showing the position-fixing lines of various radio navigation systems. By far the most commonly used of these is the Racal–Decca Navigator, and latticed versions of appropriate medium- and small-scale charts in the area of system coverage are available. Omega Navigation System lattices for the 10.2 kHz basic frequency are available on many small-scale ocean charts throughout the world. Charts with Loran-C overprints are available for the coasts of USA and Canada and for those areas of the North Atlantic within the ground wave coverage of the system. The lattices for these systems are overprinted on the standard navigational charts. They can therefore always be corrected for ordinary navigational changes. The colours are carefully controlled in printing so that the charts may be used in a dual role, for navigation both with and without electronic aids.

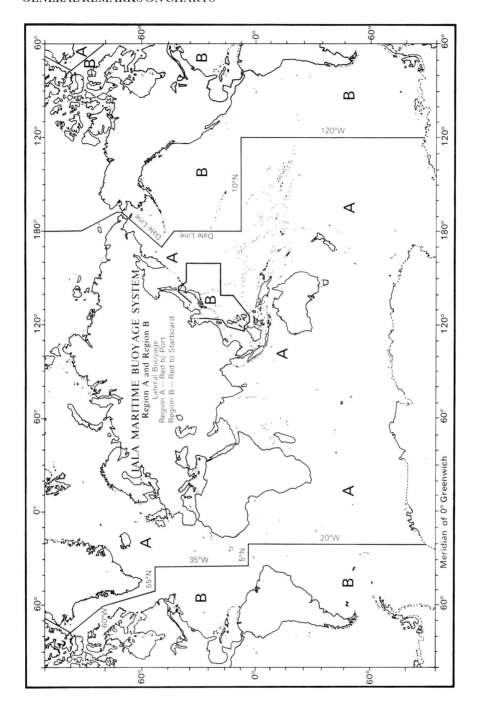

Fig. 6-1.   The IALA Maritime Buoyage System regions

IALA Maritime Buoyage System

Details of the IALA system of buoyage are given in Chapter 10; but the system is introduced here because of the implications for charts and charting policy. Two systems were originally envisaged, System A (Red to Port) and System B (Red to Starboard). These two systems have been merged into one single *IALA Maritime Buoyage System* which, when applied to Region A and Region B (Fig. 6–1), differs only in the use of red and green in lateral marks. In Region A, lateral marks are red on the port hand, and in Region B, red on the starboard hand, related to the conventional direction of buoyage. Full harmonisation to eliminate this difference was not attainable due to long-standing differences in practice. Shapes of lateral marks are the same in the two regions; can to port, conical to starboard.

Within both regions, use is made of the full range of cardinal and other marks established for System A. Some minor features, appropriate in both regions, have been added to the existing System A range, the most significant being the provision of a modified lateral mark for indicating the preferred route where a channel divides.

The standardisation of the buoyage system in Region A should have been largely completed by about 1985 and in Region B some time after 1987.

NAVIGATIONAL CHARTS

Charts drawn on the Mercator projection

As discussed in Chapter 2, a line on the Earth's surface which cuts all the meridians and parallels at the same angle is called a *rhumb line*. If two places on the Earth's surface are joined by a rhumb line and the ship steers along that line, the direction of the ship's head will remain the same throughout the passage. This direction is determined by the angle from the meridian to the rhumb line, measured clockwise from 0° to 360°, and is called the *course*. The rhumb line itself is often spoken of as the course. On the Earth's surface, a continuous rhumb line will in general spiral towards the pole. To the navigator, the most useful chart is one on which he can show the track of his ship by drawing a straight line between his starting-point and his destination, and then measure the steady course he must steer in order to arrive there. The Mercator chart permits him to do this (*see* page 61) and the main properties are set out here for ease of reference:

1. Rhumb lines on the Earth appear as straight lines on the chart.
2. The angles between these rhumb lines are unaltered, as between Earth and chart.
3. The equator, which is a rhumb line as well as a great circle, appears on the chart as a straight line.
4. The parallels of latitude (which are both small circles and rhumb lines) appear as straight lines parallel to the equator.
5. The meridians (which are rhumb lines as well as great circles) appear as straight lines at right angles to the equator.
6. A straight line joining two points does not represent the shortest distance between them, unless it happens to be a great circle as well. A great circle

which is not a meridian or the equator will appear as a curve (Fig. 6–2).

7. The chart is orthomorphic, that is, at any point on it the scale is the same in all directions and angles are preserved; hence, the chart correctly represents the shape of charted features in any small area.

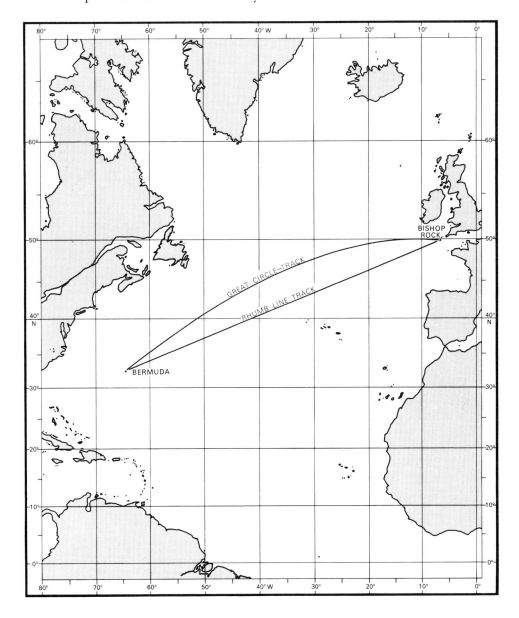

Fig. 6–2.   Mercator projection of the North Atlantic Ocean

Scale on a Mercator chart

Since the equator is shown on a Mercator chart as a straight line of definite length, and the meridians appear as straight lines perpendicular to it, the longitude scale throughout the chart is determined by the horizontal distance between the meridians. This distance remains constant in all latitudes represented on Mercator's projection. On the Earth, however, the meridians converge (Fig. 6–3(a)) and therefore land masses on a Mercator chart (Fig. 6–2) will be increasingly distorted in an east–west direction proportional to their distance from the equator, until at the poles their sizes would be infinite.

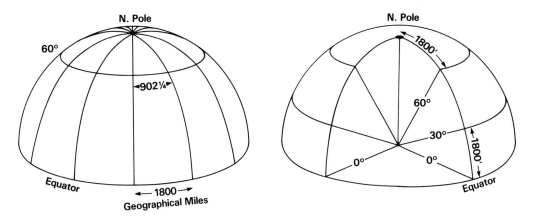

Fig. 6–3(a)   Converging of
the meridians

Fig. 6–3(b)   Spacing of
the parallels of latitude

In order to preserve the correct shape or orthomorphic property, therefore, the parallels of latitude, which are equally spaced on the Earth's surface (Fig. 6–3(b)), must be increasingly spaced towards the poles on the Mercator chart (Fig. 6–2) until at the poles the latitude scale is infinite.

This distortion, explained in Chapter 4, is governed by the secant of the latitude. Thus, on a Mercator chart of the world (Fig. 6–1) Greenland appears as broad as Africa at the equator, although the latter is three times wider. This becomes apparent once the distance is measured at the latitude scale in the vicinity of the two areas.

The Mercator projection is used for all Admiralty charts having a natural scale* smaller than 1:50,000 — a scale, that is, of less than $1\frac{1}{2}$ inches to 1 mile. The latitude scale is displayed down both sides of the chart margin and, on some charts, along a central meridian as well.

Because the parallels of latitude have to be increasingly spaced towards the poles, the representation of distance on the Mercator chart varies with latitude. As explained in Chapter 4, distances should always be measured, using the latitude scale, at the latitude of the place concerned. The longitude scale must not be used for measuring distances on the Mercator chart.

Charts drawn on the gnomonic projection

A full description of this projection is given in Chapter 4.

The chart drawn on a flat surface is conceived as touching the Earth at one point, usually the central point of the chart, known as the *tangent point*.

---

* The natural scale is the ratio of a length measured on the chart to the corresponding length measured on the Earth's surface.

Lines are drawn from the centre of the Earth, through points on the Earth's surface, until they reach the flat surface of the chart. Hence:

1. Great circles appear as straight lines on the chart, and rhumb lines appear curved.
2. Meridians are straight lines converging to the poles.
3. Parallels of latitude are curves.
4. The farther a point on the chart is away from the tangent point, the greater will be the distortion.

This projection is used for great-circle sailing charts (*see* page 123). On many Admiralty charts of scale 1:50,000 and larger, the term 'gnomonic' has been quoted to describe the projection on which they are constructed although in fact a modified form of polyconic projection has been used. The use of the term gnomonic (through strictly incorrect) indicates that, on the chart, lines of sight and other great circles are represented by straight lines. Thus, for all practical purposes, straight lines can be used to plot all bearing and direction lines. Modern charts of this scale are drawn on the transverse Mercator projection.

Charts drawn on the transverse Mercator projection

This projection is essentially a Mercator projection turned through 90°; it is described in detail in Chapter 4. Since the late 1970s it has been used for new Admiralty charts of natural scale 1:50,000 and larger.

The projection is orthomorphic but the geographical meridians and parallels are curved lines, except the meridian at which the cylinder touches the sphere. Because of the large scale, these lines will appear as straight lines to the user and, for all practical purposes, straight lines can be used to plot all bearings and direction lines on the chart.

Harbour plans

Most harbour plans are graduated for latitude and longitude, which facilitates chart correcting. Linear scales of feet, metres and cables (1 cable = 0.1 sea mile, *see* page 7) are given on all plans.

An example of a modern harbour plan is given in Fig. 6–4.

Constructing a scale of longitude on a plan

On older plans, the scale of longitude may not be given. This may be found from the following construction.

From the zero on the scale of latitude draw a line making an angle with it equal to the latitude of the plan — for example 45°, as shown in Fig. 6–5.

From each division on the scale of latitude draw a perpendicular to this line. The intersections of these perpendiculars with the line mark the scale of longitude.

The plotting chart

The navigator wishing to work out his position, after manoeuvring in a limited area out of sight of land, normally determines his position by reference to the automatic plotting table, transferring his 'run' at regular intervals to the chart. If such a table is not available to him, he has to work out his position by laying off courses and distances on a plan of his own making, called a *plotting chart*. On

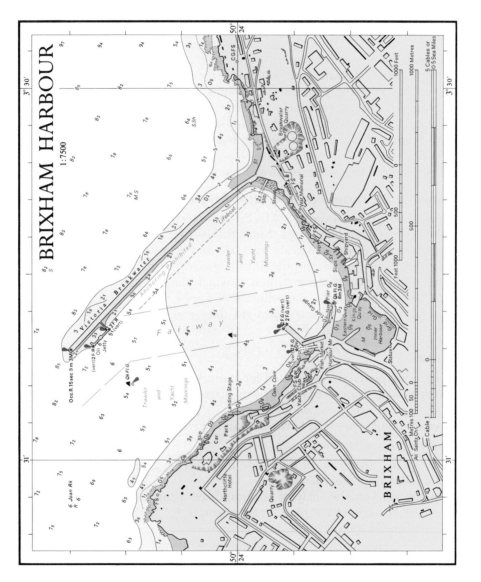

Fig. 6–4.   A harbour plan — Brixham — depths and heights in metres

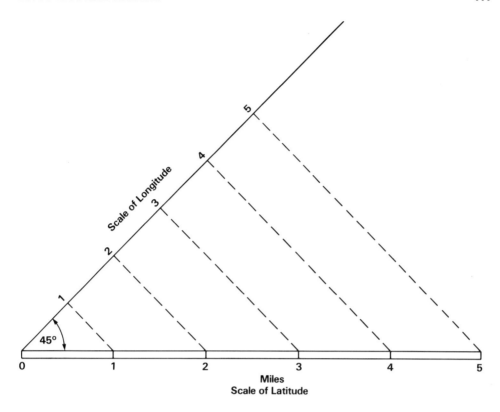

Fig. 6–5.   Constructing a scale of longitude

this, a convenient meridian and parallel of latitude are taken as axes, and the scale for latitude and distance assumed to be constant anywhere on the plotting chart. He may draw up a scale of longitude if he so desires, as set out above, or he may use formula **(2.5)** slightly modified:

$$\text{d.long} = \text{departure sec (mean latitude)}$$

Fig. 6–6 shows the track of a ship as it would appear on a plotting chart (turning circles being disregarded) if the ship steams 6′ on a course 075°, a distance and course indicated by OA; 4′ on a course 340° (AB); and $3\tfrac{1}{2}'$ on a course 210° (BC). The position of C is then fixed in relation to O by its d.lat and departure.

$$\text{d.lat } (CX) = 2'.3\text{N}$$
$$\text{dep } (CY) = 2'.7\text{E}$$

If the position of O is 43°N, 15°W, the latitude of C is:

lat O	43°00′.0N
d.lat	2′.3N
lat C	43°02′.3N

By calculation (2′.7 sec 43°) d.long is seen to be 3′.7 E. The longitude of *C* is:

$$\begin{aligned}
\text{long } O \quad &15°00'.0\text{W} \\
\text{d.long} \quad &\underline{3'.7\text{E}} \\
\text{long } C \quad &14°56'.3\text{W}
\end{aligned}$$

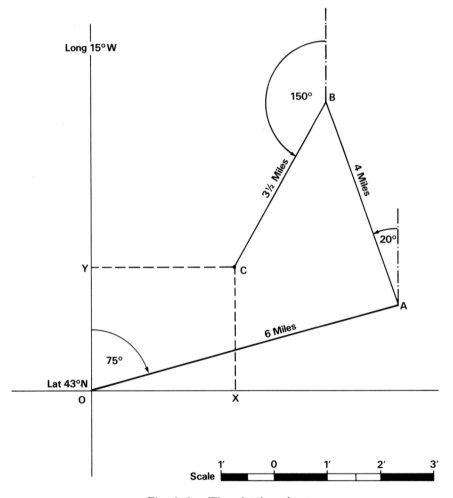

Fig. 6–6.   The plotting chart

Distortion of the printed chart

Charts are liable to slight distortion at various stages in the process of reproduction but the effect is seldom sufficient to affect navigation. Any distortion may be observed by checking the dimensions (*see* page 114). If there is distortion, bearings of objects, however accurate, may not plot correctly, particularly if those objects are at a distance as displayed on the chart. The larger the scale of the chart, the less becomes the effect of distortion.

Information shown on charts

Number of the chart. This is shown outside the bottom right-hand and top left-hand corners of the chart, and in the thumb-label on the reverse of the chart.

Title of the chart. This is shown in the most convenient place so that no essential navigational information is obscured by it, and in the thumb-label on the reverse of the chart.

Survey data. This will either be given under the title of the chart, thus:

> 'Torbay and the plans of Torquay Harbour and Brixham Harbour from Admiralty surveys of 1950 with subsequent corrections. Soundings in upright figures are taken from older surveys. Teignmouth Harbour from an Admiralty survey of 1962. The topography is taken chiefly from the Ordnance Survey.'   *or*

A source data diagram (Fig. 6–7) will be published on the chart. These diagrams indicate the source, date and scale of the survey in each part of the chart.

Satellite derived positions. The datum shift (*see* page 103) is published on many charts adjacent to the title, indicating the amount by which a position obtained from a satellite navigation system should be moved to agree with the chart.

Date of publication. This is shown outside the bottom border of the chart in the middle, thus:

Published at Taunton, 14th November 1980

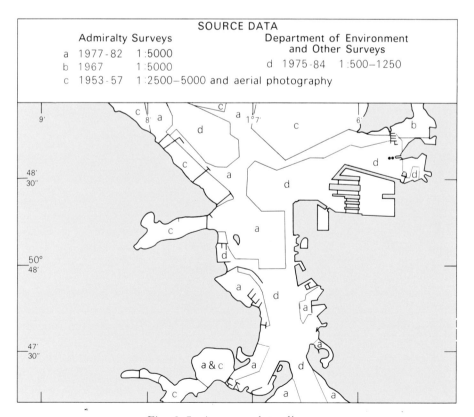

Fig. 6–7. A source data diagram

New Edition. When a chart is completely or partly revised, a New Edition is published, the date being shown to the right of the date of publication, thus:

New Edition 23rd February 1979

Large Correction. Until 1972 charts were revised by either New Editions or Large Corrections; the former term was used when the chart was revised throughout, and the latter when only a portion of the chart was revised. Since 1972 the term New Edition has been used for all revisions of the chart but, where a Large Correction has been made to a chart, the notation will remain on the chart until its next revision.

The date on which a Large Correction was made appears to the right of the date of publication under the date of the New Edition (if any), thus:

Large Correction 10th Feb., 1969

Small Corrections. These give essential information for navigation published in Admiralty Notices to Mariners, or information of secondary importance which is added to the chart plates by Bracketed Correction as opportunity affords.

Admiralty Notices to Mariners from which charts have been corrected are indicated by the year and number of the Notice in the Small Corrections outside the bottom left-hand corner of the chart, thus:

Small Corrections 1980 — *1556*

Admiralty charts corrected for Australian or New Zealand Notices to Mariners have the number of the Notice, prefixed AUS or NZ, entered in sequence in the list of small corrections.

Bracketed Corrections. Until 1986, bracketed corrections were used to give information of use to the mariner but not essential for navigation. This was done by an unpromulgated correction to the plate at a routine printing of the chart; thus, any mariner replacing his copy before the next New Edition got the benefit of the information concerned.

A Bracketed Correction is shown outside the bottom left-hand corner of the chart, thus:

Small Corrections 1980 — [*15.7*]

This indicates that on 15th July 1980 the chart plate received a minor correction.

Date of printing. This is shown by the date in the thumb-label on the reverse of the chart, thus:

Printed November 1980

Identification of chart plates. The type of printing plate used for the black detail of the chart, with its year of preparation, together with the month and year of preparation of the black and magenta printing plates, is indicated outside the bottom right-hand corner of the chart.

Chart dimensions. The figures in parentheses shown outside the lower right-hand border of the chart, thus: (630.0 × 980.0 mm) or (38.43 × 25.49) express the dimensions in millimetres or inches of the plates from which the chart is printed. The dimensions are those of the inner border of the chart (neat lines) and exclude the chart borders. In the case of charts on the gnomonic projection, dimensions are quoted for the north and south borders, and on the transverse Mercator projection for all four borders.

Corner co-ordinates. Co-ordinates expressing the latitude and longitude of the limits of Admiralty charts published after 1972 are shown at the upper right and lower left corners of the chart. Charts corrected by New Edition after 1972 also display corner co-ordinates.

Scale of the chart. The natural scale is shown beneath the title. A scale of kilometres is shown in the side margins of certain charts of scale larger than 1:100,000 to facilitate the plotting of ranges from radar displays graduated in this way.

Abbreviations and symbols. Standard abbreviations and symbols used on Admiralty charts are shown in Chart Booklet 5011 which in RN ships is supplied with Chart Folio 317/318, *Miscellaneous Charts, Diagrams and Tables.* An extract from this Chart Booklet is reproduced in Fig. 6–8 (pages 116–17).

Wreck symbols. Examples of wreck symbols are shown in Fig. 6–8. The criteria used to determine what depths are dangerous to shipping have changed since 1960 from 8 fathoms (48 feet) in 1960 to 28 metres in 1982. The wreck symbol is *not* necessarily updated when the chart is revised and a 'dangerous wreck' alludes to the depth criteria in force in the area at the time of survey, which can be determined from the source data diagram (*see* page 113).

Depths. The unit in use for depths is stated in bold lettering below the title of the chart. It is also shown, in magenta, outside the bottom right and top left-hand corners of metric charts.

On all charts, the position of a sounding is the centre of the space occupied by the sounding figure(s). On metric charts, soundings are generally shown in metres and decimetres in depths of less than 21 metres; elsewhere in whole metres only. Where navigation of deep-draught vessels is a factor and where the survey data are sufficiently precise, soundings between 21 and 31 metres may be expressed in metres and half-metres.

On fathom charts, soundings are generally shown in fathoms and feet in depths of less than 11 fathoms, and in fathoms elsewhere. In areas used by deep-draught vessels where the depth data are sufficiently precise, charts show depths between 11 and 15 fathoms in fathoms and feet. Some older charts show fractional parts of fathoms in shallow areas and a few older charts express all soundings in feet.

Depths on charts are given below *chart datum.* On metric charts for which the UK Hydrographic Department is the charting authority, chart datum is a level as close as possible to Lowest Astronomical Tide (LAT), the lowest predictable tide under average meteorological conditions. On earlier charts and those based on foreign charts, chart datums are low water levels which range from Mean Low Water to lowest possible low water in tidal waters; in non-tidal waters, such as the Baltic, chart datum is usually Mean Sea Level. A brief description of the level of chart datum is given under the title of metric charts.

Large- and medium-scale charts contain a panel giving the heights above chart datum of either Mean High and Low Water Springs and Neaps, or Mean Higher and Lower High and Low Water, whichever is appropriate.

Depth contours. On charts, all soundings less than and equal to certain depths are enclosed by appropriate metre or fathom lines, as in Fig. 6–9 (page 118).

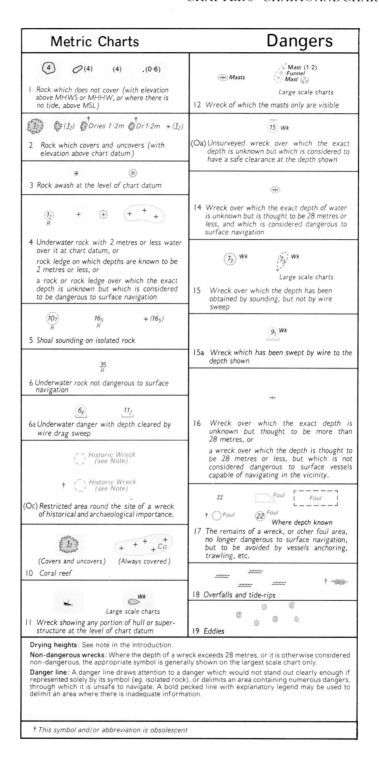

Fig. 6–8.   Extract from Admiralty Chart 5011

Fathoms Charts	Dangers
1 Rock which does not cover (with elevation in feet above M.H.W.S. or M.H.H.W., or where there is no tide, above M.S.L.)	⊞ Masts — Mast (4), Funnel, Mast (7) — Large scale charts 12 Wreck of which the masts only are visible
2 Rock which covers and uncovers (with elevation in feet above chart datum) — Dries 4ft	8 Wk (Oa) Unsurveyed wreck over which the exact depth is unknown but which is considered to have a safe clearance at the depth shown
3 Rock awash at the level of chart datum	14 Wreck over which the exact depth of water is unknown but is thought to be 15 fathoms or less, and which is considered dangerous to surface navigation
4 Underwater rock with 6 feet or less water over it at chart datum, or rock ledge on which depths are known to be 6 feet or less, or a rock or rock ledge over which the exact depth is unknown but which is considered to be dangerous to surface navigation	4 Wk 4 Wk — Large scale charts 15 Wreck over which the depth has been obtained by sounding, but not by wire sweep
5 Shoal sounding on isolated rock	5 Wk 15a Wreck which has been swept by wire to the depth shown
6 Underwater rock not dangerous to surface navigation	┿
6a Underwater danger with depth cleared by wire drag sweep	16 Wreck over which the exact depth is unknown but thought to be more than 15 fathoms, or a wreck over which the depth is thought to be 15 fathoms or less, but which is not considered dangerous to surface vessels capable of navigating in the vicinity
Historic Wreck (see Note) † Historic Wreck (see Note) (Oc) Restricted area round the site of a wreck of historical and archaeological importance.	# Foul † Foul 12 Foul Where depth known 17 The remains of a wreck, or other foul area, no longer dangerous to surface navigation, but to be avoided by vessels anchoring, trawling, etc.
(Covers and uncovers) (Always covered) Co 10 Coral reef	18 Overfalls and tide-rips
Wk — Large scale charts 11 Wreck showing any portion of hull or super-structure at the level of chart datum	19 Eddies

Drying heights: See note in the Introduction

Wrecks: The limiting depth at which a wreck is categorised "dangerous" was changed from 8 to 10 fathoms in 1960, to 11 fathoms in 1963 and 15 fathoms in 1968. Where the depth of a wreck exceeds the relevant limit (depending on the publication date of the chart) or it is otherwise considered non-dangerous, the appropriate symbol is generally shown on the largest scale chart only.

Danger line: A danger line draws attention to a danger which would not stand out clearly enough if represented solely by its symbol (eg. isolated rock), or delimits an area containing numerous dangers, through which it is unsafe to navigate. A bold pecked line with explanatory legend may be used to delimit an area where there is inadequate information.

† This symbol and/or abbreviation is obsolescent

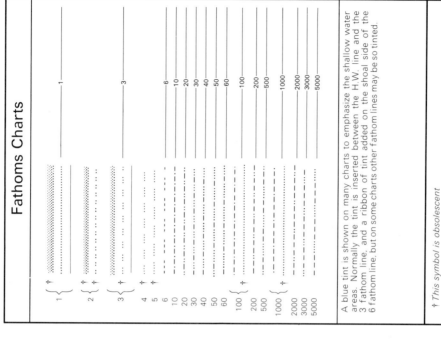

Fig. 6–9.   Depth contours on Admiralty charts

Heights. All heights except those shown by underlined figures (*see* Drying heights) are given in metres or feet above a stated vertical datum, usually Mean High Water Springs, or Mean Higher High Water or, in places where there is no tide, Mean Sea Level. In most instances, the position of the height is that of the dot alongside the figure, thus: **·135**. Heights which are displaced from the feature (e.g. a small islet) to which they refer, or which qualify the description of a feature (e.g. a chimney) are placed in parentheses.

Drying heights. Underlined figures on rocks and banks which uncover (*see* Fig. 6–8) give the drying heights above chart datum in metres and decimetres or in feet, as appropriate.

Tidal stream information

1. All information about tidal streams, whether in tables, or in notes giving the times of slack water and the rate of the tidal streams, is given in some convenient place on the chart and referred to by a special symbol — e.g. ◇ — at the position for which the information is given.
2. This information may be shown by means of tidal stream arrows on certain charts when insufficient data for constructing tables are available.

Colours used on charts

A variety of colours is now used on Admiralty charts, as in Fig. 6–10 (page 120). Shallow water areas are distinguished by a flat blue tint between the coastline and an appropriate depth contour; the tint includes all isolated patches within this depth range. In addition, a ribbon of blue tint is commonly employed to emphasise the limit of water of slightly greater depth. Drying (intertidal) areas are shown in a green tint on metric charts. Magenta is used for the emphasis of certain details, notably lights and radio aids and, nowadays, to distinguish numerous features superimposed on the basic hydrography.

To describe a particular copy of a chart

When describing a particular copy of a chart, state in the following order:

1. The number of the chart.
2. Title.
3. Date of publication.
4. Date of the last New Edition.
5. Date of the last Large Correction (if applicable).
6. Number (or date) of the last Small Correction.

Distinguishing a well surveyed chart

Source data diagrams (*see* page 113) are the key to how well the area shown on the chart has been surveyed, bearing in mind the opening remarks in this chapter on lines of soundings and wrecks (pages 101 to 102). If such information is not available, then bear in mind the following points:

1. The survey should be reasonably modern (*see* date given in title notes).
2. Soundings should be close together, regular, with no blank spaces.
3. Depth and height contour lines should be continuous, not broken.
4. Topographical detail should be good.

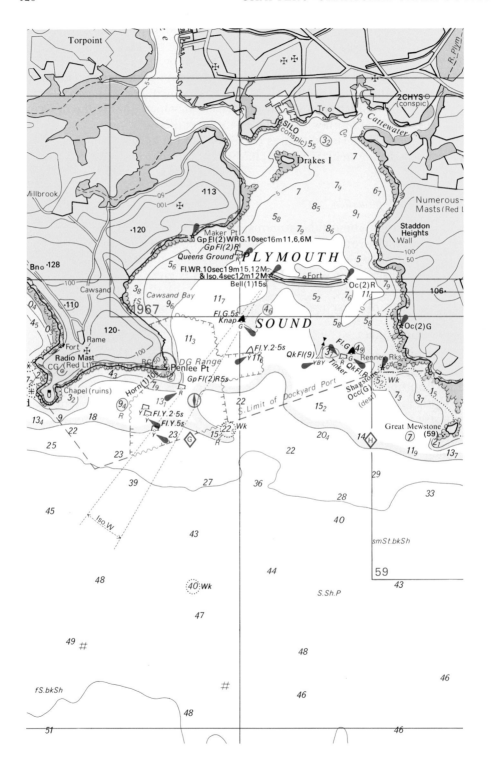

Fig. 6–10.   Colours used on Admiralty charts

5. All the coastline should be completed, with no pecked portions indicating lack of information.

The reliability of charts

As mentioned previously, no chart is infallible; every chart is liable to be incomplete in some way or another. Charts based on lead–line surveys are particularly fallible; a single lead–line sounding, which surveyed at best a few centimetres on the sea-bed, may be reflected by a figure occupying several hectares of ground depending on the scale of the chart. Any such chart being used for pilotage would have to be treated with the greatest suspicion.

The degree of reliance to be placed on a chart must depend upon the character and completeness of the original survey material and on the completeness of reports of subsequent changes. Apart from any suspicious inconsistencies, e.g. errors in geographical position (latitude and longitude), matters which must be taken into account are the scale of the chart, its soundings in relation to the dates of the surveys or authorities from which it has been compiled and examination of the chart itself. Even these considerations can only suggest the degree of reliance to be placed on the chart. The chart must never be taken for granted.

Hints on using charts

Each Admiralty chart, or series of charts, is designed for a particular purpose. Large-scale charts are intended for entering harbours or anchorages or for navigating close to potential hazards. Medium-scale charts are intended for coastal navigation, while small-scale charts are intended for offshore navigation. *Always use the largest scale chart appropriate to the purpose.*

For passage along a coast, use the continuous series of medium-scale charts provided for that purpose. Transfer to the larger scale chart where this more clearly depicts potential hazards close to the intended route.

There is usually no need to transfer for short distances to a larger scale chart intended for entering an adjacent port or anchorage. Although the larger scale chart depicts information in more detail, the next smaller scale shows all the dangers, traffic separation scheme, navigational aids, etc. that are appropriate to the purpose for which the smaller scale chart is designed.

Remember that the sea-bed is likely to correspond to the adjacent land features, even when the chart gives no hint of irregularities of the bottom. Thus, off an area where sharp hillocks and rocky, off-lying islands abound, the sea-bed is likely to be equally uneven and old surveys must be even more suspect than off a coast where the visible land is flat and regular. There are also likely to be uncharted dangers on or near the rim of a saucer-like plateau surrounding a coral group.

THE ARRANGEMENT OF CHARTS

The chart folio

Ships may be supplied either with individual charts or with charts made up into folios. These folios are issued in numbered geographical sets, the charts in each folio being arranged as far as possible in numerical order, and contained in a buckram cover.

Lists of folios are given in the *Hydrographic Supplies Handbook* (NP 133) and in the *Catalogue of Admiralty Charts and other Hydrographic Publications* (NP 131), and their approximate limits are shown on an index chart in those publications.

On the outside cover of each folio is:

1. A folio label, H119, showing the folio number, the dates of issue, the correction state, and the names of ships, etc. to which it was issued. H82 label is used for Fleet folios.
2. A folio list showing the numbers and titles of the charts contained in the folio, the navigational publication (NP) numbers and titles of the appropriate volumes of *Admiralty Sailing Directions* and of the *Admiralty List of Lights and Fog Signals* and, sometimes, any other appropriate publication.

Duplicate folio lists are supplied and kept together in a buckram envelope.

A small label, known as the thumb-label, is printed on the back of each chart. The thumb-label shows the number, title and printing date of the chart, and provides space for notation of the folio number.

The scheme of chart folios

Navigational chart folios are divided into two categories:

1. Standard folios which together provide cover for the whole world. Each folio contains all the navigational charts published for the area concerned. Where Racal–Decca charts have been published, these are supplied in place of the non-latticed chart, unless there is a request to the contrary.
2. Local and special folios provide for local services in the vicinity of dockyard ports and for particular requirements not readily met by standard folios. The folio numbers (all in the 300 series) or their geographical limits are not related to the standard folios.

    Special folios contain Loran, Omega, Routeing charts, etc.

The *Hydrographic Supplies Handbook* (NP 133)

This handbook contains information for Navigating Officers and others regarding the supply and correction of Admiralty charts (except classified charts) and navigational publications.

The *Chart Correction Log and Folio Index* (NP 133A, 133B)

This contains:

1. A preface listing the contents and instructions for use.
2. A folio check list.
3. Sheets for logging new charts and New Editions as promulgated in Notices to Mariners.
4. As Part I: a folio correction sheet for each navigational folio held, showing charts in numerical order, and with space for logging Notices to Mariners.
5. As Part II: a numerical index of all Admiralty (navigational, 5000 series, Loran and Fleet), Australian and New Zealand charts (in BA folios) and US Loran and Omega charts showing the folios in which they are contained.

The *Catalogue of Admiralty Charts and Other Hydrographic Publications* (NP 131)

This catalogue, published annually, is supplied to all warships down to and including coastal survey vessels. It contains details of all the navigational charts published by the Hydrographer of the Navy including adopted Australian, New Zealand and International charts, grouped in numerical sequence under different geographical areas. All navigational publications used *(Sailing Directions, Lists of Lights,* astronomical, radio, tidal material and so on)* are included as are all other charts and diagrams (Decca, Omega, Loran-C, Routeing and so on). The catalogue also lists Admiralty Chart Agents who are required to supply RN ships with any items ordered in an emergency.

Classified charts

Certain charts normally classified Restricted, including all Fleet charts, are contained in folios numbered in the 700 series. Other classified charts may be contained in the miscellaneous folios (*see* page 126).

The folio and serial numbers of charts classified Confidential and above and the copy numbers of any similarly classified hydrographic department publications held on charge, should be recorded on CB Form R held by the Navigating Officer.

A *Catalogue of Classified and Other Charts and Hydrographic Publications* (NP 111) is issued to all frigates and above. These charts and publications are not normally available for sale.

OTHER TYPES OF CHARTS AND DIAGRAMS

Astronomical charts and diagrams

A very small number of azimuth diagrams and star charts are produced for use in astro-navigation.

Co-tidal charts

Five of these are available, three of waters around the UK and two of other areas where tidal conditions are of particular significance. Instructions for their use are printed on each one. (*See* Chapter 11.)

Gnomonic charts

Small-scale ocean charts (one covering each of the major ocean areas) are available on the gnomonic projection. These charts are in outline only and are intended for use in plotting ocean courses. A great-circle course between two points is represented on them by a straight line. This course can be easily transferred to a navigational chart, on the Mercator projection, by plotting the latitude and longitude of the ends of sections of convenient length. Special versions of these charts are also available, overprinted with curves showing the true bearings, from all parts of the chart, of certain well used destinations, such as Bishop Rock, Panama, and Gibraltar.

Magnetic charts

There are twelve magnetic charts, six of which show the magnetic variation and the annual rates of change in variation. Of these one is a world chart, four cover the main ocean areas and the sixth covers the north and south polar areas. The polar sheet is on the polar stereographic projection, and all the others are on the Mercator projection. These charts are renewed every five years. The other six charts show other magnetic elements, e.g. inclination or dip (I); they are renewed every ten years.

Routeing charts

Routeing charts include the following data:
1. Limits of load line zones (load line rules).
2. Routes and distances between ports.
3. Ocean currents ⎫
4. Wind roses   ⎬   data supplied by the Meteorological Office.
5. Ice limits   ⎭
6. Air, dew point, and sea temperatures, barometric pressure, and the incidence of fog, gales and storms.

In this series there are five regional sheets on the Mercator projection, covering the North Atlantic, South Atlantic, Indian, North Pacific and South Pacific Oceans. Each of these sheets is published in a separate version for each month of the year, there being 60 sheets in all. They are corrected by Notices to Mariners and occasional New Editions.

Passage planning charts

A guide chart (BA 5500) has been published by the Hydrographer of the Navy, bringing together in text and diagrams much information necessary for those planning to navigate the English Channel and the Dover strait.

Ships' boats' charts

These charts are issued for use in ships' boats as a survival kit for mariners in case of shipwreck. For many years they were printed on tough linen, but they are now printed on a water-resistant plastic.

There are six charts, all on the Mercator projection, covering the North and South Atlantic, the North and South Pacific, and the Indian Ocean. For the Indian Ocean only, there are separate versions for the periods May to October and November to April. Each chart is folded into a waterproof wallet complete with simple plotting tools.

The charts carry a simplified outline of the surrounding land masses and details of winds, ocean currents, ice and magnetic variations, as well as compass roses. On the backs are printed full notes on their use including information about plotting a position and laying a course by simple graphical means. Information is also given on the management of boats, and on the effects of winds, weather and currents.

The charts are corrected by New Editions at intervals of between ten and fifteen years, though it is planned to reduce this period. They are not corrected by Notices to Mariners and make no claim to be ordinary navigational charts, being purely for use in an emergency.

Instructional charts and diagrams

Some of the sheets of the navigational chart series, covering a selection of the navigable waters of the world, are reproduced and printed on thin, tough paper for instructional purposes. A few diagrams used in navigation are also included in the series. These items are not kept corrected and are sold on the condition that they are not to be used for navigation.

Details of instructional charts are given in the *Catalogue of Admiralty Charts* (NP 131) (*see* page 123). More than 30 charts are available on various scales, including the 1:75,000 and 1:150,000 intricate or congested coastal waters scale. Some of the charts are printed with the Racal–Decca Navigator overlay; an increasing number are metric charts.

Ocean sounding charts

The Hydrographic Department maintains a series of ocean sounding charts, covering the world's oceans. Their content is limited to observations made seaward of the outer edge of the Continental Shelf. True depths are shown on the charts, all observed soundings having been corrected for the variable velocity of sound in water. Most of the sheets are now in metric units.

Ocean sounding charts are used extensively for the compilation of small-scale navigational charts, such as the International charts published by various Hydrographic Offices under the auspices of the IHO. Other users of ocean sounding charts include cable-laying ships, deep-sea drilling operators, geophysicists and oceanographers.

Further details of the numbers and limits of the ocean sounding charts are given in the *Catalogue of Admiralty Charts* (NP 131). Arrangements for obtaining copies are also described in the catalogue.

Practice and exercise area (PEXA) charts

PEXA (Q series) charts show the maritime areas off the coast of the United Kingdom which are in use, or available for use, by the Ministry of Defence for firing practice and exercises. There are six sheets at a scale of 1:500,000. They are a development of the firing danger area charts first produced during World War II, when practice areas become so numerous that it was no longer practicable to show them on navigational charts.

Two broad categories of information are displayed:

1. Danger, prohibited and restricted areas which extend above ground/sea level (i.e. airspace reservations).
2. Similar exercise areas in which the activities are at surface and sub-surface levels.

In addition, the charts show the authority (Navy, Army, Air Force, MOD Procurement Executive, etc.) controlling each area.

The charts are compiled from several sources, including the *UK Air Pilot*, Air Notices, aeronautical information circulars, and RAF flight information publications. Correction is by Notices to Mariners and New Editions.

These charts are in addition to those issued to RN ships and are in the 300 series of folios (*see* page 122).

Meteorological working charts

The Hydrographic Department publishes about 40 meteorological working charts in all, comprising surface working charts (*see* below), upper air working charts, charts for use with radio facsimile transmissions and radial charts for pilot balloon observations.

Surface working charts

There are about 30 of these charts, of varying sizes and scales, which cover the world, except for the Arctic regions north of western Canada and eastern Asia, and the Antarctic regions south and east of Australasia. There is a large degree of overlap between them, and some areas, such as UK home waters, feature on a number of sheets at different scales. The largest area covered by any one chart embraces half of the Northern Hemisphere. A large selection of meteorological observation stations are marked on the charts in their appropriate locations.

Miscellaneous folios

Chart Folio 317 (or 318, abridged set) is supplied to HM Ships. This contains a quantity of miscellaneous charts, diagrams and tables for general use, ranging from the Weir's azimuth diagram to foreign fishing rights and concessions within the fishery limits of the United Kingdom.

Other miscellaneous items such as Folio 320, *Plotting Diagrams* are also supplied to HM Ships.

UPKEEP OF CHART OUTFITS

Full information is given in the *Hydrographic Supplies Handbook* (NP 133). This is regularly amended and should therefore be taken as the authority on the upkeep of chart outfits.

First supply

The Hydrographic Department at Taunton holds and maintains the main stock of all charts, navigational and meteorological publications and Admiralty Notices to Mariners. It also arranges for the supply through Chart Depots of this material.

Correspondence on matters of supply should be addressed to: The Ships Section, Hydrographic Department, Ministry of Defence, Taunton, Somerset, TA1 2DN.

The requirements of HM Ships on commissioning are normally met by a local Admiralty Chart Depot which is in the charge of a Chart Supply Officer. There are three of these, one each at Plymouth, Portsmouth and Rosyth.

It is the Commanding Officer's responsibility to ensure that adequate charts are held on board for the service on which the ship may be employed, and that these are ordered in good time. The Ships Section, Hydrographic Department normally arranges the first supply of chart and publication outfits without demand.

State of correction upon supply

Charts supplied in navigational and Fleet folios are corrected for Permanent Notices only. Corrections will have been made up to the Notice to Mariners number shown on the folio correction sheets in NP 133B, the folio labels and on the copy of the supply note H62 which accompanies the outfit.

The charts will therefore need to be corrected in pencil from Temporary (T) and Preliminary (P) Notices in force, a list of which is published in Notices to Mariners at the end of each month. To enable this to be done, the following are supplied with the outfit:

1. The *Annual Summary of Admiralty Notices to Mariners* in force on 1st January of the year in question, which gives full details of all (T) and (P) Notices in force at that time.
2. A set of Weekly Editions of Notices to Mariners from No. 1 of the current year, which includes full details of all (T) and (P) Notices published since the first of the year.

Charts should also be corrected in pencil for radio navigational warnings in force. A complete reprint of all radio navigational warnings in force at the beginning of the year is published in Weekly Edition No. 1 of Notices to Mariners. NAVAREA I warnings in force, together with full details of the latest warnings, are published weekly in Notices to Mariners. Selected important warnings from other NAVAREAS are reproduced on a weekly basis, while the numbers of those in force are listed once a month usually in the last Weekly Edition of the month.

When a chart has been cancelled by a new chart or New Edition which is not available when the outfit is issued, the obsolescent chart is included in the appropriate folio after being corrected as far as possible and is stamped with the following cautionary note:

> 'CAUTION. This chart will shortly be replaced by a new chart or New Edition and in the meantime is to be used with caution for navigational purposes.'

Admiralty Sailing Directions are issued with the latest supplement, where appropriate. Each volume of the *Admiralty List of Radio Signals* is issued from Chart Depots with a recapitulatory supplement containing corrections which have arisen whilst the publication has been in print, together with sets of further corrections promulgated to date in Section VI of Notices to Mariners. Each volume of the *Admiralty List of Lights* is issued with subsequent corrections published in Section V of Notices to Mariners. All these publications should be checked against the list of current hydrographic publications published quarterly in Section II of Weekly Notices to Mariners at the end of March, June, September and December.

If a *List of Radio Signals* is supplied for use by radio operators, a second copy of the supplement to each volume and a set of separate Sections VI of the Weekly Edition of Notices to Mariners are supplied for the radio operators to correct their list up to date.

Corrections to *Sailing Directions* are published in Section IV of the Weekly Edition of Notices to Mariners. A summary of corrections in force is published at the end of each month and in the *Annual Summary*.

Action on receipt of the chart outfit

1. Check the folios against the Supply Note H62.
2. Check the associated publications against NP 133, and against the latest quarterly list of current hydrographic publications.
3. Check the charts in each folio against the folio list.
4. Check the charts' labels to ensure no chart is incorrectly labelled.
5. Check classified publications against NP 111.
6. Sign and return the duplicate copy of Supply Note H62 to the issuing Chart Depot.
7. Insert, in pencil, the folio number on thumb-labels.
8. Record relevant details of charts and publications classified Confidential and above on CB Form R.
9. Correct charts for any permanent notices published since the number shown on the Supply Note H62.
10. Correct charts for (T) and (P) Notices, and radio navigational warnings, starting with the folios in use. It saves unnecessary work if (T) and (P) Notices and radio navigational warnings for other areas are left to the time when the ship will be operating there.
11. Correct the publications, in particular *Sailing Directions, List of Lights, List of Radio Signals*.

Action on receipt of a newly published chart or a New Edition

The first intimation that a new chart or a New Edition of an existing chart has been published will be a Notice to Mariners at the beginning of Section II of the Weekly Notices. The action to be taken at this time is as follows:

1. Make a notation in the *Chart Correction Log and Folio Index* (NP 133A, 133B) on the sheet for logging new charts and New Editions.
2. Amend the *Catalogue of Admiralty Charts* (NP 131) and the relevant *Sailing Directions* (new charts only).
3. Note any Notices to Mariners affecting the chart between publication date and date of receipt.

Action will normally be taken by the Ships Section, Hydrographic Department (*see* page 126), to issue without demand new charts and New Editions to ships as required; nevertheless, it is the Commanding Officer's responsibility to ensure that new charts or New Editions necessary for service are held on board.

On receipt of the new chart or New Edition, take the following action:

New chart

1. Note the arrival in the *Chart Correction Log and Folio Index*.
2. Note the arrival on the folio and spare folio lists.
3. Correct for any outstanding Notices to Mariners, (T) and (P) Notices and radio warnings.

New Edition

1. Change the New Edition for the old one in the folio concerned.
2. Note the arrival in the *Chart Correction Log and Folio Index*.

3. Correct for any outstanding Notices to Mariners, (T) and (P) Notices and radio warnings.
4. Cancel the old chart.

Action on transfer of chart folios

Transfers of chart folios, navigational publications, etc. between officers, ships or establishments or to a Chart Depot should be notified immediately on Form H11, (Transfer and Receipt Certificate, in book form, for chart folios, etc.), copies of which are included in the Small Envelope containing H forms (NP 129). Prompt reporting of transfers is essential so that Notices to Mariners can be diverted without delay.

As all necessary replenishments, etc. are supplied for their maintenance, chart folios and navigational publications are considered to be up to date and available for transfer at any time to other ships or establishments.

Subsequent upkeep of chart outfits

After the first supply of a chart outfit from a Chart Depot, maintenance items, as set out below, are issued automatically direct from the Hydrographic Department, Taunton. Discrepancies should be reported to the Ships Section, Hydrographic Department (*see* page 126).

1. *Notices to Mariners, Weekly Edition.* Their regular receipt may be checked by noting whether they are in sequence. HM Ships also receive Fleet Notices to Mariners, Weekly Edition.
2. *Charts.* New charts, New Editions and, occasionally, corrected reprint copies, are supplied when published and the receipt of such charts to which a ship is entitled should be checked from the weekly list included in Section II of Weekly Notices to Mariners, or from detail recorded in the *Chart Correction Log and Folio Index* (NP 133A, 133B, *see* page 122). Details of Confidential Fleet charts issued to HM Ships should be checked against Fleet Notices and CB Form R in a similar manner.
3. *Publications.* New editions of *Sailing Directions*, supplements to *Sailing Directions*, *Lists of Lights*, *Lists of Radio Signals* and their supplements, *Tide Tables*, etc. are supplied when published and the receipt of such publications to which a ship is entitled should be checked from the quarterly list in Section II of Notices to Mariners.
4. Replacements for worn or damaged charts and publications, or any additional charts required, for example for blind navigation, are issued on demand.

Demands for charts on form H262C and for publications on form H262B (held in the Small Envelope, NP 129) should normally be sent in duplicate to the Ships Section, Hydrographic Department, (*see* page 126) or in triplicate to the Admiralty Chart Depot if the requirement is urgent. Items should be listed in numerical sequence. The reason for demand should be stated in full in such instances on the appropriate demand form. Requests for charts and publications should be signed by the Navigating Officer.

Disposal of chart outfits

When a ship is to pay off and recommission immediately, charts and publications should be retained on board. If the ship is proceeding to a different station or is to go on different service, arrangements will be made and notified by the Hydrographic Department regarding the adjustment of the chart outfit.

On reducing to reserve, the charts should be returned to the nearest Chart Depot. Instructions regarding publications will be notified by the Hydrographic Department.

If undergoing long refit or extensive repairs, charts and publications should be returned to the nearest Chart Depot.

If undergoing short refit, publications should be retained on board, and charts returned to the nearest Chart Depot. If recommissioning on a different station or for different service, instructions should be requested from the Hydrographic Department.

Chronometers and watches

Chronometers and watches, etc., which were formerly issued by and returned to the Chart Depots, are now dealt with as valuable and attractive stores in the Naval store account. Demands and returns should be made to the appropriate Principal Supply and Transport Officer (Naval) (PSTO(N)).

NAVIGATIONAL WARNINGS

Two main systems are used to provide the mariner with the latest navigational information. These are Admiralty Notices to Mariners, and, for more urgent information, radio navigational warnings. A third system, Local Notices, may be used by commercial or Naval Harbourmasters for their local port area. Around the United Kingdom, HM Coastguard also operates a Local Warning Service covering the gap between the limits of one port or harbour and the next.

Admiralty Notices to Mariners

Admiralty Notices to Mariners, containing important information for the mariner and enabling him to keep his charts and books corrected for the latest information, are issued daily to Admiralty Chart Depots and certain Admiralty Chart Agents by the Hydrographic Department, and are published in Weekly Editions for issue to ships.

Since Australian and New Zealand Notices are now the sole authority for correcting all Admiralty, Australian and New Zealand charts of Australian and New Zealand waters, such Notices as are relevant are included in the Weekly Notices. But Temporary and Preliminary Australian and New Zealand Notices are not usually republished: they can be obtained from Australian and New Zealand Chart Agents.

Notices, and the Weekly Editions containing such Notices, are each numbered consecutively, commencing at the beginning of each year.

Temporary and Preliminary Notices are identified by the addition of (T) and (P) respectively after their consecutive numbers. An asterisk preceding the number of a Notice indicates that the Notice is one based on original information, as opposed to one that republishes information from another country.

Notices can be consulted in the ports listed in the relevant Notice in *Annual Summary of Admiralty Notices to Mariners*. The Weekly Notices can be obtained gratis from Admiralty Chart Agents and Depots (*see* the relevant Notice in the same *Summary*), and from British Mercantile Marine Offices and Custom Houses, or they can be despatched regularly by surface or air mail from Admiralty Chart Agents.

Weekly Editions

Each Weekly Edition consists of the following sections:

     I Index.
    II Admiralty Notices to Mariners.
  III Navigational warnings.
  IV Corrections to the *Admiralty Sailing Directions*.
   V Corrections to the *Admiralty List of Lights and Fog Signals*.
  VI Corrections to the *Admiralty List of Radio Signals* and the Notices in the *Annual Summary of Admiralty Notices to Mariners* relating to those volumes (3, 3A, 3B — Official Messages to British Merchant Ships).

Each Weekly Edition is bound by staples to enable Temporary and Preliminary Notices and Sections III to VI to be detached for filing, or to facilitate the correction of books. Section VI can be obtained separately.

In addition to the Notices for the correction of charts, the following information is regularly contained in Weekly Editions.

New charts and publications

New charts and New Editions of charts published during the week, and any charts withdrawn, are listed in a Notice near the beginning of Section II. This Notice also mentions other charts affected by these changes, and gives notice of forthcoming publications and withdrawals.

The publishing of new editions of volumes of the *Sailing Directions* or their supplements, *List of Lights*, *List of Radio Signals*, *Tide Tables* and other publications, are announced in Notices immediately following the above Notice.

In the Weekly Editions at the end of March, June, September and December, a Notice at the beginning of Section II gives the dates of the latest editions of the various volumes of the *Sailing Directions*, *List of Lights*, *List of Radio Signals*, certain other miscellaneous publications, and any supplements affecting them. The Notice also indicates which books and supplements are under revision and in the press.

Temporary and Preliminary Notices

Temporary (T) and Preliminary (P) Notices are found at the end of Section II. Once a month, usually in the last Weekly Edition of the month, all Temporary and Preliminary Notices in force are listed in a Notice near the end of Section II. All (T) and (P) Notices in force at the end of the year are reprinted in *Annual Summary of Admiralty Notices to Mariners*.

Notices affecting Sailing Directions

Corrections to *Sailing Directions* which cannot await the next supplement are promulgated in Section IV of the Weekly Notices.

Navigational warnings

Long-range navigational warnings issued during the week are reprinted in Section III. These reprints quote only the most appropriate chart, though others may be affected by the message.

All such warnings in force on 1st January are reprinted in Section III of Weekly Edition No. 1 of each year.

Admiralty List of Lights

The volumes of the *Admiralty List of Lights* are corrected by Section V, which includes any relevant alterations mentioned in Section II.

Admiralty List of Radio Signals (ALRS)

The volumes of the *Admiralty List of Radio Signals*, and the Notices in the *Annual Summary of Admiralty Notices to Mariners* relating to those volumes, are corrected by Section VI, which also includes any relevant alterations mentioned in Section II.

Cumulative List of Admiralty Notices to Mariners (NP 234)

A *Cumulative List of Admiralty Notices to Mariners* was introduced in January 1986 and is issued at intervals of approximately six months. It records the date of issue of the current edition of each chart and of subsequent relevant Notices to Mariners issued during the previous two years.

Annual Summary of Admiralty Notices to Mariners

The first few Notices of each year are included in the *Annual Summary*, published on 1st January of each year, and not in Weekly Edition No. 1. Most of these important Notices are Annual Notices which deal with the same subject each year.

The *Annual Summary* also contains all Admiralty Temporary and Preliminary Notices and a reprint of corrections affecting *Sailing Directions* only, as well as any Australian and New Zealand Temporary and Preliminary Notices which have been republished, and which are in force at the end of the preceding year. It is obtainable in the same way as Weekly Notices.

Fleet Notices to Mariners

When required, Fleet Notices to Mariners are published in Weekly Editions to promulgate information or details of corrections affecting classified charts or publications. Each issue is allocated the number corresponding to its week of publication; in appropriate cases, the number of those weeks in which no issue was made is quoted so that it is possible to check that all published editions have been received.

Small Craft Editions of Notices to Mariners

Covering an area in NW Europe from the Elbe to the Gironde including the British Isles, this quarterly edition was introduced in December 1978. An improved service to yachtsmen results from careful selection of Notices, which are reprinted in full, together with relevant block insertions. For ease of reference they are divided into eight geographical areas and are well indexed.

Distribution of Notices to HM Ships

Every HM Ship holding a chart outfit is supplied with the Weekly Edition. HM Ships holding Fleet folios are supplied with the classified edition of Fleet Notices.

Supply is started automatically from the Hydrographic Department on notification of the issue of the chart outfit to the ship concerned and is continued until the outfit is returned.

Radio navigational warnings

Radio navigational warnings are designed to give the mariner early information of important incidents which may constitute a danger to navigation, such as particulars of recent dangerous wrecks, shoal depths, casualties or alterations to major navigational aids, salvage and survey operations in congested waters, movements of oil drilling rigs, extensive maritime exercises, significant malfunctioning of radio-navigation aids, etc.

There are three types of radio navigational warnings: coastal, local and long-range. Coastal and long-range warnings are primarily for international shipping and local warnings are for vessels operating inshore.

Coastal radio warnings

Coastal radio navigational warnings for all parts of the world are broadcast from the country of origin. Particulars are given in Volume 5 of the *Admiralty List of Radio Signals (ALRS)* , where times, frequencies and other relevant information may be found. This publication is corrected by Section VI of the Weekly Notices to Mariners.

For waters around the British Isles, coastal radio navigational warnings of a temporary nature are broadcast from British Telecom coast radio stations by WT and RT (*see ALRS*, Volume 5 and the *Annual Summary of Admiralty Notices to Mariners*). Warnings originated by the Ministry of Defence (Navy) are numbered sequentially in the WZ series. Other warnings are unnumbered.

The information is primarily to assist the mariner in coastal navigation and between ports as far as the port outer limits. Information of a less essential nature and matters within a harbour entrance, which may form the subject of a Notice to Mariners or local harbour warning, might not be broadcast.

Local radio warnings

Local radio warnings, usually referred to as *local radio navigational warnings* and primarily affecting vessels in inshore waters, are normally issued by Port and Harbour Authorities within their respective limits. Around the United Kingdom, the inshore gap between the limits of one port or harbour and the next is covered by a Local Warning Service operated by HM Coastguard.

Local Naval port radio warnings

HM Naval bases issue their own numbered series of *local port navigational warning signals* containing important navigational information for the port area.

Long-range radio warnings

Details of the procedure adopted by various countries for the dissemination of long-range radio warnings are given in *ALRS*, Volume 5.

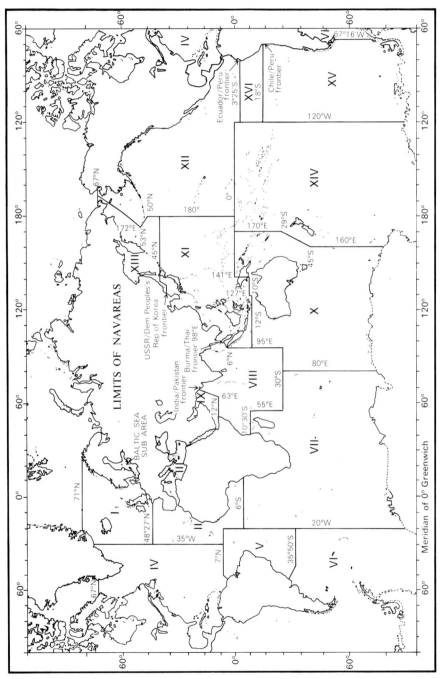

Fig. 6–11.   The World-wide Navigational Warning Service areas

The World-wide Navigational Warning Service

The World-wide Navigational Warning Service of long-range radio navigational warnings, which became fully operational in April 1980, comprises 16 geographical sea areas termed NAVAREAS identified by Roman numerals (Fig. 6–11).

The authority charged with collating and issuing warnings to cover the whole of an area is known as an *area co-ordinator*. The limits, area co-ordinator and transmitting stations of each NAVAREA are given in *ALRS*, Volume 5. Details are also to be found in the *Annual Summary of Admiralty Notices to Mariners*.

NAVAREA I is co-ordinated by the United Kingdom. The text of the week's warnings together with a numerical list of those in force is included in Section III of the Weekly Notices to Mariners. This list includes warnings cancelled when superseded by a Notice to Mariners.

A Navigational Information Telex Service (NAVTEX) is available in NAVAREA I. This service provides shipping with the latest urgent information on navigation, weather warnings and initial distress messages, by means of an automatic direct print-out from a dedicated NAVTEX receiver. This service is also available outside NAVAREA I; full details may be found in *ALRS*, Volume 5.

Long-range warnings issued by the United States

In addition to NAVAREA IV and NAVAREA XII warnings, the United States issues HYDROLANT and HYDROPAC warnings for the remainder of the Atlantic and Pacific/Indian Ocean areas respectively.

Details are given in *ALRS*, Volume 5 and in the *Annual Summary of Admiralty Notices to Mariners*.

Correction of charts for long-range radio warnings

The correction of charts for radio navigational warnings and the frequency of publication in Notices to Mariners is covered on page 127.

Local Notices to Mariners

Local Notices to Mariners are issued by commercial and Naval Harbourmasters and contain navigational information for the local port area. Each Notice has a local serial number. HM Ships are required to keep Local Notices for their base port and any other dockyard that they are likely to visit regularly.

Local Notices are not supplied automatically, except in a ship's base port, and application for them should be made to the local Harbourmaster.

Lists of Local Notices in force are issued from time to time.

CORRECTION OF CHARTS AND PUBLICATIONS

Navigational warnings and chart and publication corrections are brought to the mariner's notice by a number of different methods depending on their urgency and importance; the following methods are available, all of which have been discussed earlier in this chapter.

Annual Notices to Mariners.   Fleet Notices to Mariners.
Weekly Notices to Mariners.   Local Notices to Mariners.
Radio navigational warnings—long-range, coastal and local.

Correction and warning system

The following items are required to run a satisfactory correction and warning system.

1. *Chart Correction Log and Folio Index* (NP 133A, 133B).
2. Temporary and Preliminary Notices Log Book.
3. Local Notices File divided into areas with totes.
4. Long-range Radio Navigational Warning Log divided into the 16 NAVAREAS, HYDROLANTS and HYDROPACS, with totes and Log Book.
5. Coastal and Local Radio Navigational Warning Log (WZs, etc.) divided into areas with totes.
6. Local (Naval) Port Navigational Warning Log divided into areas with totes.
7. Wall chart to record radio navigational warning signals.
8. Fleet Notices to Mariners File with totes (HM Ships only).

Tracings for chart correction

Tracings to facilitate the correction of chart outfits are supplied automatically to certain HM Ships and Royal Fleet Auxiliaries carrying large chart outfits. They are used extensively by all Admiralty Chart Depots and Admiralty Chart Agents who sell corrected charts.

When tracings are supplied, they are provided for all permanent navigational chart corrections promulgated in the Weekly Edition of Admiralty Notices to Mariners, except when a block correction only applies. Each tracing is a pictorial presentation of the printed notice and contains in addition the following details:

The chart number.
The Notice to Mariners number for the current correction.
The previous correction.
The standard folios in which the chart is contained.

Copies of these tracings are reprinted by the British Nautical Instrument Trade Association and may be purchased through most Admiralty Chart Agents. The text of the printed Notice must invariably be consulted when using tracings.

Hints on correcting charts

Chart corrections, except those from Temporary or Preliminary Notices, should be neatly made in waterproof violet ink on the charts affected. (The recognised abbreviations shown on Chart 5011 should be used.) Notation of the year (if not already shown) and number of the Notices inserted should be made, also in waterproof violet ink, in the bottom left-hand corner of the chart. Always check that the previous Notice has been inserted — its number is given in brackets against the number of the chart at the bottom of the Notice.

Erasures should never be made but the details should, when necessary, be crossed through in waterproof violet ink.

If several charts are affected by one Notice, the largest scale chart should be corrected first. Correct the chart folios in use first.

Whenever possible, writing should be inserted clear of the water unless the relevant objects are on the water, and care should be taken not to obliterate any information already on the chart. Unless cautionary, tidal or other such notes are inserted, they should be written in a convenient but conspicuous place, preferably near the title where they will not interfere with other details.

Generally speaking, the amount of information which should be inserted on a chart should be in accordance with that already shown. The insertion of excessive detail not only clutters the chart, but can lead to errors. The amount of detail inserted from each Notice on each of the charts affected should be reduced as the scale of the chart decreases.

Detail is inserted on charts in accordance with the following principles, depending upon the purpose of each chart, its scale and complexity. These principles have been defined for the guidance of the mariner hand-correcting his charts without overlay correction tracings, which make due allowance for the reduction of detail.

On large-scale charts, the full details of all lights, light-buoys and fog signals are inserted, together with the year dates of obstructions, reported shoals, swept areas, dredged channels and depths on bars in shifting channels.

On coastal charts, full details of only the principal lights and fog signals, and those lights, fog signals, light-vessels, lanbys and light-buoys that are likely to be used for navigation on the chart, are inserted.

The usual order for omitting detail from light descriptions as the scales of charts decrease is:

1. Elevation.   2. Period.   3. Range.

Details should be retained if a shortened description would result in ambiguity between adjacent aids.

On coastal charts, navigational aids in harbours and other inner waters are not usually shown. If the use of a larger scale chart is essential (e.g. for navigation close inshore or for anchoring), details are given of those aids which must be identified before changing to it, even though short-range navigational aids and minor sea-bed obstructions are usually omitted.

However, it sometimes happens that a small-scale chart is the largest scale on which a new harbour can be shown, in which case it might be appropriate to insert on it full details of certain aids, such as a landfall buoy.

On ocean charts, normally only those lights which have a range of 15 miles or over are inserted and then only their light-stars and magenta flares.

Radio aids are inserted only on the charts in which they may be found useful. Radiobeacons are therefore omitted from large-scale charts where their use would be inappropriate. Similarly, on small-scale or ocean charts only the long-range radiobeacons are charted.

On metric charts, and certain fathom charts which have had recent New Editions, the limits of larger scale charts are shown in magenta.

Admiralty Notices to Mariners are occasionally accompanied by reproductions of portions of charts (known as 'blocks') for pasting on the chart. When correcting charts from blocks the following points should be borne in mind:

1. A block may indicate not only the insertion of new information, but also the omission of matter previously shown. The text of the Notice should invariably be read carefully.
2. Owing to distortion the blocks do not always fit the charts exactly. Care

should therefore be taken when pasting a block on to a chart that the more important navigational corrections fit as closely as possible. This can best be assured by fitting the block while it is dry and making two or three pencil ticks round the edges for use as fitting marks. Paste should then be applied to the chart and not to the block to avoid distortion of the latter.

Corrections from Temporary or Preliminary Notices to Mariners should be inserted on the charts in pencil. The year and number of each Notice should be shown against it, e.g. NM 625/1981 (T), and also outside the bottom left-hand corner of the chart, in pencil, below the Small Corrections notations. Temporary corrections should be rubbed out when the Notice cancelling them is received, and Preliminary corrections should be replaced by the final information when the Notice is received reporting that the changes have been made. Similar action should be taken with radio navigational warnings and Local Notices.

Charts stocked by the Hydrographic Department, Admiralty Chart Agents and Admiralty Chart Depots are not corrected for Temporary or Preliminary Notices and, when charts are received from one of these sources, they should be corrected in pencil as necessary from the copies of such Notices already held, or from those supplied with the charts.

Corrections from information received from authorities other than the Hydrographic Department may be noted, in pencil, on the charts affected, but no charted danger should be expunged without the authority of the Hydrographer of the Navy.

Certain Admiralty Chart Agents provide a chart correcting service which enables charts to be brought up to date, either from Notices to Mariners, or by replacement if charts have been superseded by New Editions or new charts.

Hints on correcting publications

Corrections are not made to publications stocked by the Hydrographic Department or Admiralty Chart Depots (except to folio correction sheets NP 133B at Depots).

Arrangements for the supply of corrections for *Admiralty Sailing Directions*, *Admiralty List of Lights and Fog Signals*, and *Admiralty List of Radio Signals* have already been referred to in this chapter.

It is recommended that pages of *Sailing Directions* be annotated in pencil, giving a reference to the relevant corrections promulgated in Section IV of the Weekly Edition of Admiralty Notices to Mariners. It may be helpful to record brief details (Weekly Edition number, title of the correction, page number of the *Sailing Directions*) on a tote kept inside the front cover of the relevant *Sailing Directions*.

Sections V and VI of the Weekly Notices contain corrections to the *List of Lights and Fog Signals* and the *List of Radio Signals* respectively. The amendments from these two sections should be cut out and stuck into the appropriate volume, ensuring that the amendment is in the correct numerical position. The left-hand edge only should be stuck down so that information underneath may still be read. Manuscript amendments are sometimes required as well; these should be inserted in ink in the appropriate volume.

HYDROGRAPHIC REPORTS

Since the intervals between published surveys may be long, it is essential that hydrographic notes are rendered whenever necessary by ships, Harbourmasters and so on, to ensure that the charts issued by the Hydrographer are kept up to date.

Forms

Hydrographic notes are rendered on Forms H102 and H102A. Completed examples may be found in *The Mariner's Handbook* (NP 100) and may be obtained gratis from the Hydrographic Department, Ministry of Defence, Taunton, Somerset TA1 2DN, or from Admiralty Chart Depots and principal Chart Agents. Smaller copies of these forms, issued at the end of each month in the Weekly Notices to Mariners, may also be used. These forms are issued to HM Ships with the chart outfit as part of the Small Envelope containing hydrographic forms (NP 129). Instructions for HM Ships on their use are given in *The Mariner's Handbook* and in Volume IV of this manual.

General remarks

Every opportunity should be taken to obtain information which may be of value to the Hydrographic Department for the correction of charts and other publications.

Ships can also be of great assistance in planning re-surveys by reporting on the adequacy or otherwise of existing charts and plans and the need for re-surveys or new surveys in the light of new development and possible future strategy. In this connection, the views and requirements of Harbour Authorities and pilots are of great assistance. A short letter giving the reasons for surveys or re-surveys or for the proposed withdrawal of an obsolete chart or plan, the authority and if possible a priority 1, 2 or 3 (bearing in mind that each Harbour Authority considers his own area of paramount importance) is all that is required.

The Captain of a ship employed on special service, such as an experimental cruise, or on a visit to an unfrequented place, is to forward a hydrographic report with his Report of Proceedings. This should contain all matters which may be of interest to the Hydrographer and which have not been included in a report on Form H102/102A. A copy is to be sent direct to the Hydrographer.

Officers rendering hydrographic notes should be guided by the following points in addition to those in Volume IV of this manual, *The Mariner's Handbook* and on the forms themselves:

1. If a new danger is reported, its position should be accurately plotted on the chart and two tracings of the portion of the chart in question should be made. One copy should be forwarded to the Commander-in-Chief or Senior Officer and the other direct to the Hydrographer at Taunton.

   Similarly, any error detected on a chart or any improvement being suggested should be plotted on the chart and tracings made and transmitted as above.

In all cases, as much of the adjacent coastline should be included as will enable the tracing to be laid accurately over the chart affected, marking also the true meridian line, the number of the chart, the date of the last New Edition or the date of publication, whichever is the later, and the most recent Small Correction.

Tracings should always be accompanied by a hydrographic note.

2. The Admiralty charts and navigational publications should be compared constantly with the conditions found actually to exist.

3. Information, to be of value, must be as precise and up to date as possible. However, ships should not hesitate to forward information unavoidably obtained to a lower degree of accuracy, provided that full details of the method by which it has been obtained are given. The date of the information should invariably be given.

4. The amount of useful information which can be supplied will generally be greatest when ships visit unfrequented places. Confirmation of matter already appearing in the *Admiralty Sailing Directions* is very acceptable. The volume and page of the *Sailing Directions* affected must always be given, not only when some correction is made to a passage in the book, but also when information is entirely new and cannot be placed under any heading appearing on the relevant page.

5. The number of the largest scale chart affected should always be quoted. When any chart is specifically mentioned in the report, the date of the last New Edition or Large Correction is to be stated, together with the date or number of the last Small Correction, as shown on the copy used.

6. True course and bearings are invariably to be given, measured in degrees (clockwise) from 000° to 360°.

7. When photographs, sketches, tracings, etc. are sent in, they should be included as enclosures. (*See also* Sketches and photographs, page 145).

8. Reports should be forwarded on separate sheets and arranged so that the subject-matter proper to each of the numbered sections can be used separately.

9. When information is supplied which leads to the correction of an Admiralty chart or plan of a place in foreign waters for which a recognised hydrographic authority exists, credit will not be given, in the title of that chart or plan, to the ship or officer supplying the information, because reference to the national authority concerned is always made before chart action is taken.

10. Since the value of the material supplied will depend principally on the extent to which it can be used for the improvement of hydrographic publications, officers should take care that all objects quoted, when fixing positions or for other purpose of reference, can be identified on the chart without any risk of ambiguity.

11. When dredging operations or building work — such as that on breakwaters, wharves, docks and reclamations — are described, a clear distinction should be made between work completed, work in progress, and work projected. An approximate date for the completion of unfinished or projected work is valuable.

Information for charts and *Admiralty Sailing Directions*

Newly discovered dangers

The position and extent of any shoal or danger discovered, especially of one upon which a vessel has struck or grounded, should be determined, if practicable, by five horizontal sextant angles between well selected objects; and a careful true bearing to one of these objects should be given. The least depth should be obtained whenever possible and, if there is shoal water, the nature of the bottom.

Reports of shoal soundings, uncharted dangers and navigational aids which are out of order should, if urgent, also be made by radio to the nearest coast radio station. The draught of modern tankers is such that any uncharted depth of less than 30 metres may be of sufficient importance to justify a radio message.

Soundings

When soundings are recorded, the methods of sounding are always to be stated, as well as the dates and times and the tidal reductions used.

Soundings are to be reduced to the level of the datum of the Admiralty chart or, when this is not known, to a level below which the tide will seldom fall. Details of the datum used must be given. Soundings may also have to be corrected for the velocity of sound in water: *see* the remarks on echo sounders in the revised Volume III of this manual and *The Mariner's Handbook* (NP 100). Corrections to true depth may be found from the *Echo Sounding Correction Tables* (NP 139).

In order that the Hydrographer can make use of echo-traces forwarded from ships, the following points should be noted:

1. Mark the trace each time a fix is obtained either by means of a fix marker, if one is provided, or by annotating the record.
2. Number the fix and note the time.
3. Insert the recorded depth of all peak soundings.
4. On completion of soundings using a 'wet paper' echo sounder, and before rolling up the paper, draw in the bottom trace and transmission line and dry the paper, preferably in a dim light. This will ensure that, when the trace fades, the record will remain clear.
5. Mark conspicuously all changes of phase.
6. Insert the make and type of echo sounding machine and:
   'Transmission correctly set at x metres.'
   'Add (subtract) y metres increased (decreased) draught.'
   'Speed set to suit 1500 m/sec sounding velocity.'
   Also, mark the graduations of the depth scale at convenient intervals.
7. It is recommended that an indelible pencil or ball-point pen should be used for all writing on the echo sounding trace. All writing or marking should be kept well clear of the bottom trace.

When depths are found that are at variance with charted depths, the value of the report will be much enhanced by continuing to run the echo sounder until reasonable, or even approximate, agreement with the chart is reached, as this will enable shoal depths which are false to be identified.

When reports of shoals are received in the Hydrographic Department, they are carefully considered in the light of accompanying or other evidence before any action is taken to amend the charts. In the past, much time and effort has been wasted by surveying ships searching for non-existent shoals. When unexpected shoal soundings are obtained in waters where the charted depth gives no indication, even though discoloured water may be seen, the only certain method of confirming their existence is by taking a cast of the lead. It has often been found that an apparent shoal sounding in relatively deep water has been the result of a double echo.

Shoals

If an unexpected shoal is encountered, every endeavour should be made to run back over the same ground, provided the ship is not endangered, to get a further sounding with, if possible, an accurate fix of its position. If further time can be spared, several lines of soundings running across the shoal area and recorded by the methods described above would make a very useful report, especially if the least depth on the shoal is obtained and the limits of the shoal area defined.

Discoloured water

The legend 'discoloured water' appears on many charts, particularly those of the Pacific Ocean where shoals rise with alarming abruptness from great depths. Most of these legends remain on the charts from the last century, when very few deep-sea soundings were available and less was known of the causes of discoloured water. Only a few of the reports of discoloured water have proved on examination to be caused by shoals; the remainder have been caused by such things as plankton, cloud reflections, etc.

Today, such reports can be compared with the accumulated information for the area concerned, a more thorough assessment made and, as a result the legend 'discoloured water' is now seldom inserted on charts.

Discoloured water should be approached as closely as possible, in order to ascertain whether or not the discolouration is due to shoaling, whilst having due regard to the safety of the ship. If there is good reason to suppose that the discolouration is due to shoal water, a hydrographic note should be rendered to the Hydrographer of the Navy accompanied by an echo sounder trace and any other supporting evidence. Reports of discolouration due to other causes should be forwarded to the Meteorological Office, London Road, Bracknell, Berks.

Port information

When opportunity occurs, Admiralty publications should be checked for inaccuracies, out of date information and omissions. Port regulations, pilotage, berthing and cargo handling, provisions and water and other facilities are frequently subject to change, and it is often only by reports from visitors that charts and publications can be kept up to date for such information. The value of such reports is enhanced if they can be accompanied by the local Port Handbook.

When reference is made to piers or wharves, the depths at the outer end and alongside are the most important items of information that can be given (although all dimensions are useful).

The length and bearing of any extension should be given in such a way that they can be plotted with as great a precision as the scale of the chart permits. The position of any new lights on the extension should be stated exactly, and the removal or continuance of any lights charted on the pier or breakwater before extension should be mentioned.

Where dredged channels exist, the date of the last dredging and the depth obtained should be noted.

A Port Officer sometimes has a large-scale manuscript plan of the harbour and approaches, which is merely his own enlargement of the plan published by the government. The value of such a plan can, however, be judged only by the comparison with the Admiralty chart and a copy should, if possible, be forwarded to the Hydrographer for evaluation. It is important to note whether the datums for heights and sounding, the scale and the true north are given, and then to check them — or to supply them if not given.

Lights

When reporting on lights, the simplest way to ensure a full report is to follow the columns in the *Admiralty List of Lights and Fog Signals,* giving the information required under each heading; some details may have to be omitted for lack of data whilst others might be amplified, at the discretion of the observer. Characteristics should be checked with a stopwatch.

The numbers assigned to lights in the *List of Lights,* prefixed by the volume letter, e.g. G0153.4, are the international numbers adopted in accordance with the resolutions of the International Hydrographic Organisation. These letter–figure combinations should be quoted whenever lights are referred to.

Buoys

Buoys should be checked against the details given on the latest large-scale chart. Where possible, the position of a buoy should be checked by range and bearing or other suitable method and details forwarded as described below.

Beacons and marks

For new marks, the position should be fixed by 'shooting up' from seaward, verified where possible from the responsible authorities in the area, who should be quoted in the report.

Conspicuous objects

Reports on conspicuous objects are required frequently since objects which were once conspicuous might later be obscured by trees, other more conspicuous buildings, etc. The positions of conspicuous objects can sometimes be obtained from local authorities, but more frequently must be fixed from seaward as stated above.

Wrecks

Stranded wrecks showing any portion of the hull or superstructure at the level of chart datum should be fixed by the best available method and details recorded. The measured or estimated maximum height of a wreck above water, or the amount which it dries, should be noted together with the date and time of observation (for tidal correction purposes). The direction of heading and the extremities of large wrecks should be fixed if the scale of the chart is sufficiently large.

Submerged wrecks can usually only be located by vessels fitted with the necessary searching equipment.

Channels and passages

When reports are made on a discrepancy in the charting of a channel, or a passage between islands, and when information is supplied about one shore only of a strait, or about some island in such water, every effort should be made to obtain a connection by angle or bearing between the two shores. The absence of such a connection may have been the original cause of the discrepancy reported, and may cause serious difficulty in making proper use of the information supplied.

Positions

Observations of positions of little-known places are always welcomed, especially if the reporting officer has reason to question the charted position. Full details of observations should be given, in order that their value may be assessed. When practicable, the position should be linked with some existing triangulation or known position. Care should always be taken to dispel uncertainty about the existence, extent and precise position of reported dangers and doubtful islands, and to obtain the least depth where appropriate. Careful examination of such objects is of the greatest importance, both in the general interests of navigation and for the maintenance of the reputation of the Admiralty charts for accuracy and completeness of information.

Whenever a search or examination is made, the state of the weather and light should be described fully if they are likely to have had any influence on the result.

It cannot be emphasised too strongly that, in general, the only effective method of obtaining evidence about the existence of reported dangers is to take positive soundings in the vicinity and, if possible, to obtain specimens of the bottom.

Tidal streams

Observations of tidal streams should be obtained whenever possible. If only a general description can be given, care must be taken to avoid any ambiguity that might arise from the use of the terms 'flood' and 'ebb' streams. It is generally preferable to give the direction of the stream, e.g. 'east-going' or 'west-going'. The time of the change of stream should always be referred to high water; for instance, 'the north-going stream begins two hours after high water'. When the time of local high water is not known, the turn of the stream should be referred to high water at the nearest port for which predictions are given in the *Admiralty Tide Tables*.

Ocean currents

Much useful knowledge of ocean currents can be obtained by ships on passage. Form H568 (Sea Surface Current Observations) is designed for the collection of such information and is obtainable gratis from the Hydrographic Department or from the principal Chart Agents. This form is issued to HM Ships as part of the Small Envelope (NP 129).

Instructions for rendering the form, which are carried on it, call mainly for a record of courses and distances run through the water, together with accurate observations of the wind to enable this component of the ship's drift to be eliminated in analysis, and sea surface temperature readings to enable the observed current to be related to different water masses.

Though primarily intended for reporting unexpected currents, the form can be usefully maintained on a routine basis for all passages outside coastal waters to give valuable information of predicted currents.

Magnetic variation

In many parts of the world, precise information for the plotting of isogonic curves on charts is still inadequate. Observations for variations made at sea, preferably using Form H488 (Records of Observation for Variation), are valuable, particularly where the isogonic curves are close together or change quickly, or where there are local magnetic anomalies. These forms are issued to HM Ships as part of NP 129.

Reports should be forwarded to the Hydrographic Department.

Information concerning radio services

Reports should be made of any irregularities in radio signals that have not already been announced. Any other information that may be useful for the *Admiralty List of Radio Signals* should be forwarded.

If radiobeacons are observed to have characteristics differing from those given in *ALRS*, as amended by the latest Notice to Mariners, an attempt should be made to ascertain locally whether these alterations are permanent.

Similarly, any changes observed in the time or type of transmission of weather bulletins and storm warnings, navigational aids, warnings or time signals, should be verified locally, and confirmation sought that these alterations are permanent.

Zone time

Information should be supplied concerning the time kept locally, if it differs from that given in the most recently published *ALRS* (Volume 5), or *The Nautical Almanac* (NP 314).

Sketches and photographs

Sketches and photographs form a very valuable adjunct to the *Admiralty Sailing Directions*, and every opportunity should be taken of adding to them. The existing views in the *Sailing Directions*, or on charts, should be examined for possible improvements — for example the addition of a conspicuous object.

Sketches and photographs of navigational interest may be divided broadly into three classes.

1. General views of a coast or anchorage, showing the principal charted features. These enable the mariner, when making land or approaching the anchorage, to identify these features more readily than can be done from a written description.
2. Views of leading marks or anchoring marks.
3. Sketches or photographs of special objects that cannot easily be described in words.

In the case of (1) and sometimes in the case of (2) also, a photograph will have to be taken from a considerable distance, and will usually give poor results unless enlarged or taken with a telephoto lens. Even when enlarged, the photograph will usually require treatment in order to emphasise the desired conspicuous features. This can be done satisfactorily only by the man on the spot, either when he is in a similar position on a subsequent occasion, or by his referring to an outline sketch made at the time the photograph was taken. Alternatively, a photograph may be used for the purpose of improving or correcting a sketch.

If an outline sketch is made in order to supplement a photograph, the names or descriptions of the conspicuous objects shown on it can conveniently be inserted against them, and it can then be attached to the photograph. The vertical scale on outline views should be $1\frac{1}{2}$ times or twice as large as the horizontal — i.e. the heights of objects should be exaggerated somewhat; but this should be done with discretion, especially if there are any objects, such as islets, in the foreground.

When no outline sketch has been made, the names can be inserted on the photograph itself but, when this is done, a second print without names should be attached.

Always state, in the report and on the photograph or sketch itself, the exact position from which the photograph was taken or the sketch made, the date and time.

Sketches and photographs fowarded with a view to reproduction should never be gummed or pasted to the pages of a report, but should be placed in an envelope which should be attached securely to the report.

NAVIGATIONAL FORMS

Contents of the Small Envelope (NP 129)

One of these is supplied with the chart outfit and contains various quantities of the forms listed in Table 6–1.

Form H62 (*see* page 128) is used by the Hydrographic Department or the Admiralty Chart Depot for the issue and receipt of chart folios and publications.

THE PRODUCTION OF THE ADMIRALTY CHART

Data for use in the compilation of Admiralty charts are received from many sources. The permanent archives of the Hydrographic Department at Taunton

Table 6–1.   Forms contained in the Small Envelope

NUMBER	TITLE	REMARKS
H11	Transfer and Receipt Certificate, in book form, for chart folios etc.	Used for chart and map folios and navigational publications. *See* Upkeep of chart outfits (in this chapter), page 129.
H102	Hydrographic note	*See* Hydrographic reports (in this chapter), pages 139 to 146).
H102A	Hydrographic note for port information	
H262B	Demand Form for publications (pads)	*See* Upkeep of chart outfits (in this chapter), page 129.
H262C	Demand Form for charts (pads)	
H488	Record of Observation for Variation	*See* page 145.
H493	Record of Observations of Magnetic Declination (variation)	
H568	Observation of Sea Surface Currents	*See* page 145.
—	Tracing paper	For use with hydrographic notes, etc.

hold over half a million documents, and modern surveying techniques have resulted in a 10% increase in the annual rate of data acquisition, thereby giving rise to a considerable problem in maintaining the published charts up to date. Surveys are continually being carried out by the ships of the Royal Navy Hydrographic Service, which operates in various parts of the world. Similar work is carried out by foreign hydrographic authorities. Close international co-operation between the member nations (50 in 1981) of the International Hydrographic Organisation ensures a free exchange of data including copies of surveys, foreign charts, and Notices to Mariners. In addition, the Hydrographic Department at Taunton receives surveys from ships, Harbour Authorities and commercial companies, hydrographic reports from Naval and mercantile vessels, land maps, air photographs and many other relevant documents from a great variety of sources throughout the world.

When a decision is made to produce a new chart — perhaps because an extensive hydrographic re-survey has been carried out, or because a port development project, including new terminals and dredged approach channels, has been completed — a period of approximately 18 months will pass before the chart is ready for publication. A scheme is prepared indicating the scale at which the chart will be constructed, its geographical limits, and the general layout of the information it will contain. The source material is obtained from the archives or is sought from other authorities who may also have supplementary data. Specifications are written for the compilation draughtsman, who selects the required detail and assembles it in accordance with approved policies governing the display of information on Admiralty charts. After the draft of the chart has been fully edited and verified, reproduction processes take over and transform the compilation, the approved draft, into a printed image. Automated cartography, and photographic and mechanical techniques, are employed where possible, but successful chart making still depends primarily on the skill of the compiler and the reproduction craftsman.

Reproduction methods

In the past, charts were always engraved on copperplate, printed copies being taken directly off the plate. This was a slow process which involved dampening the paper to obtain the best impression. Thus, there was consequent shrinking of the chart as the paper dried out. Such instability in paper size was unacceptable when the use of colours was introduced into chart making. This created the need for the exact registration of each colour plate during the printing process, and led to the replacement of direct copperplate printing by lithographic reproduction. The earliest lithographic printing used the surface of a flat polished stone; this was subsequently replaced by a zinc plate and then by aluminium. For some time, copperplate continued in use as the base or master plate, the image being transferred to the printing plate by either a transfer or a photographic process. Media other than copper were subsequently used as master plates; one such was an aluminium sheet spray-coated with white enamel. This type of surface was ideal for drawing by hand and the resulting image was directly photographed and photo-printed on the printing plate and also on a fresh enamel as a permanent record. Correction of such a base was easier and quicker than with copper.

The residual use of copperplate bases finally ceased in 1981, having been overtaken by the plastics revolution of the 1970s, the increasing application of modern scribing methods, photo-typesetting and computer-assisted cartography. Enamel coated aluminium plates are still used as the master plates for some Admiralty charts. The charts themselves are printed using the off-set process (the image is transferred from the plate to a rubber cylinder, then to paper), on a rotary printing press which will print up to four colours in succession as the paper is threaded automatically through the machine. Additional detail in other colours can be overprinted by repeating this process.

Since the metrication of the Admiralty charts began in 1967, the standard method of chart production has been on plastic, using automated techniques. A brief summary of the production process is set out below.

1. A computer is programmed to produce the necessary tapes for an automatic plotter to scribe on a specially prepared film negative the graduated border, meridians and parallels, to the required projection, scale and limits.

2. Using an image from this negative, the new chart compilation is prepared on a sheet of plastic. After rigorous checking of all details, the compilation is put through a series of photographic processes using both negative and positive film to produce an image of printing quality. During these processes, certain details are scribed by hand — coastline, contours, roads, towns, etc; other standard details — compass roses, soundings, symbols, etc. — are added, together with all the type matter particular to that chart. These type requirements are photo-set on a thin film which is then cut and patched in position.

3. The production of an increasing number of new charts is partly automated. The detail of the compilation is digitised and the tape output from the digitiser processed by the computer, which controls the automatic plotter to plot all the digitised details. The resulting film positive has the type matter patched to it and the chart then continues in the same production stream as those produced entirely by hand.

4. Once the chart has been proofed, checked throughout in detail and up-dated as necessary, the final production negatives are prepared. These negatives are then contact printed to sensitised aluminium printing plates, one for each of the colours to be used. Standard metric charts are printed on a four-colour off-set rotary printing press.

Plate correction

Limited corrections and additions can be made to the printing plates prior to printing, either at the proof stage of new charts and New Editions or, subsequently, when amendments announced in Notices to Mariners have to be inserted. However, this process has certain technical limitations and, on average, after 5 or 6 printings, a plate will have to be replaced. Thus, in the case of many popular charts, reprinted 3 or 4 times each year, new printing plates are required every $1\frac{1}{2}$ to 2 years.

CHAPTER 7
Publications

Publications used by the Navigating Officer are divided into two categories:

1. Publications supplied by the Hydrographer (the NP series).
2. Textbooks, reference books, handbooks and forms obtained from the CB Officer or the Supply Department (CBs, BRs, and 'S' series forms).

PUBLICATIONS SUPPLIED BY THE HYDROGRAPHER

Sets of navigational publications

Navigational publications (NPs) are made up into sets, details of which are given in the *Hydrographic Supplies Handbook* (NP 133), already mentioned in the previous chapter. All major war vessels are supplied with a complete set of NPs. Ocean-going Royal Fleet Auxiliaries and chartered merchant ships are supplied with an abridged set; mine countermeasures vessels, tugs and other small craft employed in home waters are supplied with a Home Local Service set; similar ships employed abroad with a Foreign Local Service set. In addition, the appropriate *Admiralty Sailing Directions* (*Pilots*) and *Admiralty List of Lights and Fog Signals* are issued automatically with each chart folio, as indicated at the bottom of the folio list.

State of correction upon supply

Navigational publications are not corrected on supply, but the latest supplements, summaries of Notices, etc. are automatically included with the set (*see* Chapter 6, page 127).

Meteorological publications

A list of these publications together with the scale of issue is given in the *Oceanographic and Meteorological Supplies Handbook*, W1 (NP 452).

The handbook *Meteorology for Mariners* (NP 407) is issued to all HM Ships and ocean-going RFAs except some smaller warships. This publication covers:

The meteorological element.
Climatology.
Weather systems.
Weather forecasting.
Ocean surface currents.
Ice and exchange of energy between sea and atmosphere.

The *Naval Oceanographic and Meteorological Service Handbook*, W11 (NP 510) is issued to all major HM warships. It includes chapters on:

> Meteorological and oceanographic equipment and stores including instructions for the precision aneroid barometer.
> Publications and charts.
> Reports and returns.

Aviation publications

Details of air charts, air chart folios, plotting sheets and reference chart folios and their scale of issue are given in the *Catalogue of Admiralty Air Charts* (NP 110). Issue is limited to larger warships, Royal Fleet Auxiliaries and Front Line Squadrons. The catalogue and a set of Air Notices are supplied to these ships with the initial chart outfit, after which Air Notices are supplied automatically when published.

Navigational publications

Books published by the Hydrographic Department are listed in the *Catalogue of Admiralty Charts and Other Hydrographic Publications* (NP 131) and the *Hydrographic Supplies Handbook* (NP 133). They fall into the following subject groups:

> Sailing directions.
> Lights and fog signals.
> Radio signals.
> Tides and tidal streams.
> Astronomical observations.
> Catalogues.
> Hydrographic practice and symbols.
> Nautical almanacs.
> Oceanography.
> Admiralty marine science publications.
> Miscellaneous.

Brief details of the more commonly used publications are given below. Details of publications concerning charts are given in Chapter 6.

Admiralty Sailing Directions (NP 1 to 72)

Admiralty Sailing Directions, also called *Pilots*, were first regularly published in 1829 after some agitation by the Fleet for officially published books to complement Admiralty charts. During the nineteenth century, the volumes gradually grew in size and in numbers from fairly small publications of 'Hydrographical Notices' of surveyors' reports on areas surveyed, to some 70 volumes by the end of the century. This growth corresponded with the expansion of the chart series, which by this time covered virtually all the navigable waters of the world except for the polar regions. Present-day titles and the area covered by each volume are shown in NP 131 and NP 133.

Each volume of the *Sailing Directions* contains descriptions of the coast and off-lying features, notes on tidal streams and currents, directions for navigation in intricate waters, and other relevant information about the channels and harbours. In addition, each book includes information about navigational hazards, buoyage systems used in the area covered, pilotage, regulations, general notes on the countries within the area, port facilities, and a general summary of seasonal current, ice and climatic conditions with direct access to the sea except Great Lakes of Canada and USA. The indices of the various volumes provide a fairly comprehensive gazetteer of coastal names.

Uses and users

The *Sailing Directions* should be read in conjunction with the appropriate Admiralty charts quoted in the text. They are intended to aid the mariner in navigation at sea and are for all classes of vessel, from sea-going small craft up to the largest super-tankers. The books are also convenient works of reference for shore-based maritime authorities, in connection with planning and for general information.

Sources of information

Sailing Directions were originally compiled from first-hand reports and descriptions of the coast, mainly from British ships. In foreign waters where British ships had not navigated, foreign charts and publications were used. Subsequently, the books have been kept up to date on a regular basis from the latest editions of charts, maps, foreign sailing directions and other publications, and also from reports of surveys, reports from ships, and notices to mariners issued by other countries and maritime authorities.

Each volume is completely revised at intervals of from 12 to 15 years. In the intervening period, each is kept up to date by supplements issued at regular intervals of $1\frac{1}{2}$ to 2 years. Each new supplement is cumulative and incorporates all previous corrections. A number of corrections to *Sailing Directions* are also issued in the Weekly Editions of Admiralty Notices to Mariners. Notices in force affecting *Sailing Directions* are listed in the last Weekly Edition of each month. (*See* Chapter 6, page 138 for advice on correcting *Sailing Directions*.)

When a supplement to a volume has been issued, a copy of the supplement accompanies that volume on first supply of the chart outfit. Each supplement should be kept intact, and should invariably be consulted when using the volume to which it refers.

Of the vast amount of information needed to keep charts up to date, only the most important items can be used to correct the charts by Notices to Mariners. Less important information, though it may not reach the chart until its next major correction, is nevertheless included in *Sailing Directions* or their supplements, if appropriate.

Editions of *Sailing Directions* published after the end of 1972 use metric instead of Imperial units when describing depths, heights and distances on land. Where the large-scale chart quoted in *Sailing Directions* is still in fathoms and feet, depths and dimensions printed on the chart are given in *Sailing Directions* in brackets so that chart and *Sailing Directions* can be more easily compared.

Views for Sailing Directions (NP 140)

This publication contains guidance and requirements for taking photographs for *Sailing Directions*.

The Mariner's Handbook (NP 100)

This book contains information of general interest to the mariner and is complementary to the *Sailing Directions*. The contents include: general remarks on charts and publications; notes on orthography and terms used; use of charts and navigational aids, observing and reporting; notes on offshore hazards and restrictions to navigation; tides, currents, characteristics of the sea, magnetic anomalies and sea-bed sound waves; basic meteorology and navigation in ice; a selection of conversion tables.

The *Handbook* is reviewed and updated regularly by the Hydrographic Department. It is corrected by supplements and by new editions at intervals of about 5 years.

Ocean Passages for the World (NP 136)

This book is intended for planning an ocean passage. It gives recommended routes and distances between the principal ports of the world, with details of winds, weather, currents and ice hazards that may be encountered. It links the various volumes of the *Sailing Directions*. Much useful information is included which will not be found in the *Sailing Directions* since the latter are concerned mainly with coastal waters.

The book is corrected periodically by supplements, in the same way, but less frequently, as the *Sailing Directions*. It is accompanied by diagrams showing the main ocean routes for power vessels and sailing ships, world charts of climate and ocean currents, and by Diagram D6083 *(Load line rules, zones, areas and seasonal periods)* relating to The Merchant Shipping (Load Line) Rule, 1968. If required, separate copies of these diagrams are obtainable from Admiralty Chart Agents.

Admiralty Distance Tables (NP 350(1), (2), (3))

The *Admiralty Distance Tables* give the shortest navigable distance in international nautical miles between focal points and chief ports of the world. This distance may differ from the distance in sea miles by up to $\frac{1}{2}$% at the equator or at the poles. These routes are not necessarily the quickest and most suitable route for a particular passage, as other routes may offer more favourable currents or better conditions of sea, swell or weather. Remarks on the various routes will be found in *Ocean Passages for the World* or in the *Admiralty Sailing Directions* while Routeing charts show the principal commonly used routes.

Most routes are available for ships drawing 10 m; where this depth is not available, as may be the case where there are off-lying shoals or in the harbour approach, the deepest recommended channel has been used.

Volume 1 covers the North and South Atlantic Oceans, the Arctic Ocean, Baltic Sea, North-west Europe, Mediterranean Sea, Black Sea, Caribbean and the Gulf of Mexico. Volume 2 covers the Indian Ocean, and part of the Southern Ocean from South Africa to New Zealand, Red Sea, Persian Gulf and the Eastern Archipelago. Volume 3 covers the Pacific Ocean.

Full instructions for use are given in the Introduction to the *Distance Tables*.

Use of the Distance Tables

To find the distance from Devonport to Gibraltar

Locate the nearest terminal points by referring to the appropriate chartlets.

Devonport — Plymouth sound: Part I   North-west Europe
Gibraltar   — Europa Point: Part II   Atlantic Ocean

As these two places are in adjacent tables, find a suitable place common to both tables, in this case Ushant (Île d'Ouessent).

Table 1c, North-west Europe, Channel:
Plymouth Sound – Ushant (10′W)   123

Table 2a, Atlantic Ocean, NE Atlantic:
Ushant–Europa Point (6′S)   929

Distance from Plymouth Sound to 6 miles south
of Europa Point passing 10 miles west of Ushant (*n miles*)   1052

If places are in non-adjacent areas, Part IV, the Link Tables, may be used provided the places concerned are marked by an asterisk in the tables.

Admiralty List of Lights and Fog Signals (NP 74 to 84)

The *Admiralty List of Lights and Fog Signals* is published in eleven volumes giving a worldwide tabulation of all lighthouses and lights of navigational significance. Also listed are lightships, lit floating marks 8 metres and over in height, and fog signals; but *not* buoys of a height of less than 8 metres.

The areas covered by each volume are:

Volume A (NP 74)   British Isles and north coast of France.
Volume B (NP 75)   Southern and eastern sides of North Sea.
Volume C (NP 76)   Baltic Sea.
Volume D (NP 77)   Eastern side of Atlantic Ocean.
Volume E (NP 78)   Mediterranean, Black and Red Seas.
Volume F (NP 79)   Arabian Sea, Bay of Bengal and North Pacific Ocean.
Volume G (NP 80)   Western side of South Atlantic Ocean and East Pacific Ocean.
Volume H (NP 81)   Northern and eastern coasts of Canada.
Volume J (NP 82)   Western side of North Atlantic Ocean.
Volume K (NP 83)   Indian and Pacific Oceans, south of the equator.
Volume L (NP 84)   Norwegian and Greenland Seas and the Arctic Ocean.

For each light the following details are given. (For further information, *see* Chapter 10.)

1. Number, used for index purposes.
2. Name and descriptive position, e.g. Longships. Highest rock off Land's End.
3. Approximate latitude and longitude.
4. Characteristics. Intensity may be shown when nominal range is not used.
5. Elevation of the light in metres above Mean High Water Springs level.

6. Range of visibility in sea miles.
7. Description of the structure on which the light is situated and the height of the structure above the ground in metres.
8. Phases, sectors, arcs of visibility, periods of illumination, important temporary information, and other relevant remarks — also any minor associated lights which do not merit separate numbering.

In addition, each volume contains tables for the calculation of the geographical and luminous ranges of lights; definitions of, and general remarks on, the characteristics of lights and fog signals; and a list of foreign language equivalents of the abbreviations used in light descriptions. In some volumes, special comments are found on problems peculiar to the areas covered by them. Items covered include off-shore oil rigs, light vessels and distress signals.

While the main details of important lights are also shown on Admiralty charts, item (1) above is not shown on charts, (2), (7) and (8) are sometimes not shown, and other details are progressively omitted from charts as the scale decreases. Complete information about lights and the minor and temporary amendments which are made to them (see below) can therefore only be obtained from the *List of Lights* volumes.

Sources of information

The volumes of the *List of Lights* are compiled from information received from the following sources:

1. Lighting authorities in home waters (Trinity House, Northern Lighthouse Board, Commissioners of Irish Lights), Harbourmasters and Port Authorities.
2. Foreign lights lists and notices to mariners.
3. Ships' reports and hydrographic surveys.
4. Foreign charts.

On receipt of information about important changes to lights which affect the safety of navigation, a Notice to Mariners is issued for the correction (or temporary correction) of charts. Each week these Notices, together with temporary alterations and many other minor changes to lights, are included in Section V of the Weekly Edition of Notices to Mariners. They are arranged in numerical order and are intended for cutting out and pasting into the printed books. Changes to lights shown on charts are made by Notices in Section II of the Weekly Editions, which are usually published later than the corresponding information in Section V, as chart-correcting Notices take longer to produce. **The List of Lights should therefore invariably be consulted whenever details of a light are required.**

A new edition of each volume of the *List of Lights* is published at intervals of about 18 months, the previous edition being thereby cancelled. The Weekly Notices announcing the publication of a volume will contain all corrections in Section V received between the date of going to press and the date of issue. From the latter date, correction by Section V of the Weekly Notices is resumed. The requisite up-dating corrections are readily available through Chart Agents.

Admiralty List of Radio Signals

The *Admiralty List of Radio Signals* (*ALRS*) consists of six volumes of text and four booklets of diagrams.

Volume 1: Coast Radio Stations (2 parts)

This volume contains particulars of coast radio stations, including call signs, hours of service, transmitting and receiving frequencies, and the times of traffic lists. Stations are listed in geographical sequence.

Other sections of this volume give information on: medical advice by radio; arrangements for quarantine reports, pollution reports, and locust reports; the INMARSAT Maritime Satellite Service; regulations for the use of radio in territorial waters; distress, search and rescue procedures; the AMVER ship rescue organisation; a brief extract from the international radio regulations.

Part 1 (NP 281(1)) covers Europe, Africa and Asia (excluding the Philippines and Indonesia).

Part 2 (NP 281(2)) covers the Philippines, Indonesia, Australasia, the Americas, Greenland and Iceland.

Volume 2: Radio Navigational Aids

Volume 2 (NP 282) contains particulars of radiobeacons including aero radio-beacons in coastal regions; radio direction-finding stations; coast radio stations providing a QTG service (the transmission of signals on request for use with ships' DF); calibration stations (stations giving special transmissions for the calibration of ships' DF); radar beacons (racons and ramarks).

Volume 2a: Diagrams relating to Radiobeacons

Volume 2a (NP 282a) contains diagrams showing the location of radiobeacons throughout the world (marine radiobeacons in black, coastal aero radio-beacons in red), also a diagram for obtaining the half-convergency correction for DF bearings.

Volume 3: Radio Weather Services

Volume 3 (NP 283) contains particulars of radio weather services and related information, including certain meteorological codes provided for the use of shipping. Frequencies and times of transmission of storm warnings and other weather messages, including the transmission of facsimile maps, are also given. Details of ships' weather reports are also given in this volume.

Volume 3a: Diagrams relating to Weather Reporting and Forecast Areas

Volume 3a (NP 283a) shows the regions, zones and coast radio stations for the collection and dissemination of ships' weather reports, also the limits of forecast areas covered by radio weather transmissions.

Volume 4: Meteorological Observation Stations

Volume 4 (NP 284) comprises a list of world-wide meteorological observation stations giving the number, location and elevation of each station and serving as a key to meteorological working charts on which selected station numbers appear.

Volume 5: Radio Time Signals: Radio Navigational Warnings: Position-fixing Systems

Volume 5 (NP 285) contains particulars of: standard (legal) times, including the dates between which daylight-saving time is observed in certain countries; radio time signals, including details of co-ordinated Universal Time (UTC), and a list of stations providing radio time signals giving the frequencies and times of transmission and the system employed by each station; radio navigational warnings including details of the world-wide navigational (NAVAREA) Warning Service (*see* page 135); national practices; ice reports; reports of transmission failure in position-fixing systems; a list of stations transmitting radio navigational warnings giving the frequencies, times of transmission and area covered by each station; electronic position-fixing systems (Decca, Consol, Loran-A, Loran-C, Omega, Differential Omega, and satellite navigation).

Volume 5a: Diagrams relating to Radio Communications and Position-fixing Systems

Volume 5a (NP 285a) comprises diagrams for radio communications and electronic position-fixing systems. Radio communication diagrams include details of: international radio watchkeeping periods; standard time zone chart of the world; the format of radio time signals; the limits of NAVAREAS, HYDROPAC and HYDROLANT areas; details of the transmissions of navigational warnings by RT in the Baltic and North-west Europe. Electronic position-fixing system diagrams show the fixing accuracy and coverage of the various systems (except Consol) in use throughout the world.

Volume 6: Port Operations, Pilot Services and Traffic Management (2 parts)

Volume 6 contains particulars of: stations working in the Port Operations and Information Services; services to assist vessels requiring pilots; services concerned with traffic management. Details of various ship movement report systems such as MAREP (English Channel) are also given in this volume. Further information is contained in Volume III of this *Manual of Navigation*.

Part 1 (NP 286(1)) covers NW Europe and the Mediterranean.

Part 2 (NP 286(2)) covers Africa and Asia (excluding Mediterranean coasts), Australasia, Americas, Greenland and Iceland.

Volume 6a: Diagrams relating to Port Operations, Pilot Services and Traffic Management

Diagrams (NP 286a) accompanying traffic management systems described in Volume 6, Parts 1 and 2, are provided.

Sources of information

The information contained in *ALRS* is taken from the relevant international publications (of the International Telecommunication Union and the World Meteorological Organisation) and from radio lists, sailing directions, and notices to mariners published by other national Hydrographic Offices. Information is also obtained through enquiries to operating authorities and administrations.

A few items, of major importance to the safety or convenience of shipping, are issued in the series of long-range radio navigational warnings. These items, together with others of lesser urgency, are also included in Section VI of the Weekly Notices to Mariners.

New editions of these volumes are published annually, except for Volume 4, which is revised every 3 years.

Tide and tidal stream publications

Tide and tidal stream publications are dealt with in detail in Chapter 11.

Admiralty Tide Tables

Admiralty Tide Tables (ATT) are published in three volumes annually as follows:

    Volume 1   European waters (including Mediterranean Sea).
    Volume 2   Atlantic and Indian Oceans.
    Volume 3   Pacific Ocean and adjacent seas.

Volumes 2 and 3 (*Admiralty Tide Tables and Tidal Stream Tables*) contain, in addition to tidal predictions, a number of predictions of tidal streams. Harmonic constants for some tidal streams are also published in all three volumes.

Each volume is divided into three parts. Part I gives daily predictions of the times and heights of high and low water for a selected number of *standard ports*. Part II gives time and height differences for prediction of high and low water at a much larger number of *secondary ports*. Part III gives the harmonic constants for use with the Simplified Harmonic Method of Tidal Prediction for those ports, where they are known. Details showing how this method can be used on any programmable calculator or computer are published in the Introduction to each volume of *ATT*.

The tables for the secondary ports vary considerably in completeness and accuracy. In general, where full information is given, it can be assumed that predictions will satisfy the normal demands of navigation; where information is incomplete, it is prudent to regard it as approximate only.

Outside the British Isles, it is the general principle to publish only a selection of the standard port predictions from foreign tide tables and these should be consulted where necessary. Foreign tide tables are obtained from the appropriate national Hydrographic Office, and usually from national agencies at the larger ports. A note of those places for which daily predictions are given in foreign tide tables is included in Part II of all three volumes.

Admiralty Tide Tables are corrected annually by Notice to Mariners No. 1 contained in *Annual Summary of Admiralty Notices to Mariners*.

Other tidal publications

A list of Admiralty tidal publications is given at the end of *Admiralty Tide Tables*. These include tidal stream atlases covering the whole of the British Isles and selected areas elsewhere, miscellaneous tidal charts, forms for predicting tides and instructional handbooks on tidal subjects. In addition, HM Ships are supplied with *Home Dockyard Ports—Tides and Tidal Streams* (NP 167). The information in this publication is supplementary to that given in *ATT*, tidal stream atlases and *Admiralty Sailing Directions*.

Astronomical publications

Sight Reduction Tables for Marine Navigation (NP 401)

>   *Sight Reduction Tables for Marine Navigation* are published in six volumes, each covering a band of 15° of latitude. They contain the data necessary for the solution of sights of heavenly bodies. Values of altitude and azimuth are tabulated for all combinations of latitude, local hour angle and declination at intervals of 1 degree. The calculated altitude and azimuth of the heavenly body being observed is extracted from the tables and compared with the true altitude to obtain a position line.

>   The explanation of the tables includes instructions on how to solve great-circle problems.

Sight Reduction Tables for Air Navigation

>   The *Sight Reduction Tables for Air Navigation* (AP 3270) consist of three volumes (NP 303(1) to (3)) of tables of altitude and azimuth designed for the rapid reduction of astronomical sights. Volume 1 contains the tables for selected stars for all latitudes and a new edition is issued about every 5 years. Volume 2 (latitudes 0° to 39°) and Volume 3 (latitudes 40° to 89°) contain tables for integral degrees of declination providing for sights of the sun, moon and planets; these tables are permanent. The tables are published by the United States as Pub. No 249, *Sight Reduction Tables for Air Navigation*. The United Kingdom edition (published by HMSO) is a reproduction of the US publication with an Introduction conforming to RAF usage.

The Nautical Almanac (NP 314)

>   *The Nautical Almanac* is compiled jointly by HM Nautical Almanac Office, Royal Greenwich Observatory, and the Nautical Almanac Office, United States Naval Observatory, and published annually by HMSO. It is issued by the Hydrographic Department to HM Ships and RFAs, and is available to merchant ships through most Admiralty Chart Agents. It tabulates all the data for the year required for the practice of astronomical navigation at sea.

Star Finder and Identifier (NP 323)

>   The *Star Finder and Identifier* consists of a star chart on which are printed the navigational stars and on which the positions of planets and other stars may also be plotted. The elevation and true bearing of a star at any time can be obtained by inspection, using a superimposed transparent grid.

Miscellaneous publications

Norie's Nautical Tables (NP 320)

>   *Norie's Tables* consist of a set of navigational and mathematical tables which include:

>>   Meridional parts.
>>   Logarithms.
>>   Log of trigonometrical functions and natural functions of angles.
>>   Haversines.

A B and C azimuth tables.
Bearing amplitudes and corrections.
Ex-meridian tables I to IV.
Dip of sea horizon.
Refraction.
Sun, star and moon total corrections.
Radar range.
Distance by vertical angle.
Distance of the sea horizon.
Ports of the world.

Norie's Tables are issued without demand to HM Ships by the Hydrographer and are available to merchant ships through most Admiralty Chart Agents.

The Decca Navigator Mark 21 Operating Instructions (NP 315)

This publication contains information on the Decca Mark 21 receiver (QM 14) fitted in HM Ships.

The Decca Navigator Marine Data Sheets (NP 316)

This publication contains general information on the Decca system including the accuracy of Decca fixing; data sheets for individual chains showing the areas covered, the accuracy of position fixing within the chain, fixed error corrections for the individual patterns. It is issued to ships direct from the Racal–Decca Navigator Co., although amendments are issued by the Hydrographer.

Publications on other radio aids (satellite navigation, Loran-C, Omega, etc.) are usually issued to HM Ships as technical books of reference (BRs) (*see* page 163).

OTHER BOOKS OF INTEREST TO THE NAVIGATING OFFICER

In addition to the five volumes of the *Admiralty Manual of Navigation*, there are a number of BRs issued through the Supply Department of interest to the Navigating Officer. Some of these are on sale to the public.

The Queen's Regulations for the Royal Navy (QRRN, BR 31)

Regulations laid down in *QRRN* and in Volume IV of this manual include the following subjects which are of concern to the Navigating Officer:

The authority of the Officer of the Watch.
Special Duties Officers, Seamen specialists — Certificates of Competence, Watchkeeping and Ocean Navigating Certificates.
Officers, general — Bridge Watchkeeping Certificates.
Officers, general — Ocean Navigation Certificates.
Regulations for the conduct of courts martial — evidence on navigational matters.
Speed of ships.
Instructions to Captains.
Instructions to officers — Officers of the Watch.

Navigation — instructions to Navigating Officers; collisions and groundings; definitions of terms to be used at sea.
Classification of speed and power.

Admiralty Manual of Seamanship, Volumes I to IV (BR 67(1) to (4))

Volume I is the basic book of seamanship for officers and men joining the Royal Navy. Volume II contains more technical detail and is a general textbook and reference book for ratings seeking advancement and for junior officers. Volume III is intended mainly for officers. It covers such essential seamanship knowledge as the handling of ships and also information on a variety of subjects that could be classed as advanced seamanship, such as aid to ships in distress. The following chapters in Volume III are of particular interest to the Navigating Officer:

Chapter 6   Towing at sea.
9   Officer of the Watch in harbour.
11   Officer of the Watch at sea.
12   Propulsion and steering of ships.
13–16   Handling ships in narrow waters; in company; in heavy weather; while replenishing at sea.

Volume IV amplifies information in Volumes I to III for RN purposes only and is not available to the public.

Rules for the Arrangement of Structures and Fittings in the Vicinity of Magnetic Compasses and Chronometers (BR 100)

This book sets out the rules for the siting of equipment in the vicinity of magnetic compasses and chronometers. It tabulates the minimum distance at which magnetic material that is part of the ship's structure, electrical equipment, and so on, should be sited from the compass. It also grades the position for the magnetic compass dependent on its function; for example, a standard compass providing the primary means of navigation is a Grade I compass while an Emergency Compass fitted for the purpose of conning or steering the ship after action damage or breakdown is a Grade IV compass.
This publication is not available to the public.

Collisions and Groundings (and Other Accidents) (BR 134)

This book contains cases of groundings, collisions, berthing incidents and other accidents affecting the safety of men and ships. There is a narrative of each incident, followed by comments and a summary of the lessons to be learned from it.
This publication is required reading for all officers in HM Ships. It is not available to the public.

A Seaman's Guide to the Rule of the Road (BR 453)

This is a programmed book designed to teach Royal Navy and Merchant Navy personnel sufficient theoretical knowledge of the Regulations for Preventing Collision at Sea to meet the needs of the Officer of the Watch.

Tactical publications

Certain tactical publications are of interest to the RN Navigating Officer, covering such matters as:

> Formations, manoeuvres, sea manners and customs.
> Evasive steering — zigzag plans.
> Search and Rescue.
> Replenishment at Sea.
> Nuclear Fallout Forecasting and Warning Organisation.

These books are not on sale to the public. Certain tactical publications may be issued to selected British merchant ships in times of war or other emergencies.

Classified books

Certain books classified Confidential or higher are of interest to the RN Navigating Officer. These books cover such matters as:

> Particulars of Royal Fleet Auxiliaries.
> Operational endurance data.
> Fleet data.
> Maritime Law and claimed territorial seas.
> Fleet Operating Orders.

Technical publications

There are a number of technical BRs covering the whole range of navigational equipments available to the RN Navigating Officer. These cover such items as echo sounders, radio aids to navigation (satellite navigation, Loran-C, Omega, Decca, etc.), bottom logs, compasses and automated navigation systems.

'S' FORMS OF INTEREST TO THE NAVIGATING OFFICER

There are a number of 'S' forms, supplied from PSTO(N), HM Naval Base, Portsmouth, and demanded through the ship's supply department, which are of interest to the Navigating Officer. These are summarised in Table 7–1 (p.164) and brief details of individual forms follow.

Report of Collision or Grounding (S232)

The procedure for reporting collisions or groundings in HM Ships is laid down in *QRRN*. The initial signalled report is to be followed without delay by a written report on Form S232. Whether or not legal claims or proceedings are anticipated, the form is to be rendered as follows:

Original to be completed and forwarded by the Captain direct to the Treasury Solicitor, Central Buildings, Matthew Parker Street, London SW1.

Copies to be forwarded to the Administrative Authority for transmission, through Commander-in-Chief Fleet to the Ministry of Defence (Naval Law Division), and the Area Flag Officer.

Table 7–1.   'S' forms of interest to the Navigating Officer

NUMBER	TITLE
S232	Report of Collision or Grounding
S322	Ship's Log
S322A	Cover for current Ship's Log
S374A	Record of Observations for Deviation
S376	Manoeuvering Form (pads)
S387	Table of Deviations
S425(4)	Inspection Report — Navigation
S428(6)	Inspection Report (Submarines) — Navigation and AIO
S529	Mership and Fish Vessel Sighting Report
S548A	Navigating Officer's Note Book
S553	Order Book (used for Captain's Night Orders)
S580	Record Book for Wheel and Engine Orders
S1176	Fishing Vessel Log
S1301	Report on Damage to Fishing Gear (Attended or Unattended) Alleged to have been Caused by HM Ships, etc.
S1372	Order of the Court and Report of Navigation Direction Officers at Trial on Navigational Charge
S1750–1775	Degaussing Forms
S2040	Ship Activity Return
S2624	Formex 110 — Wheelhouse Record
S2677	Navigational Data Book
S3020A/B/C	Turning, Starting and Stopping Trials
S3034	Navigational Record Book

The Ship's Log (S322)

'The Navigating Officer, or other such officer or senior rating to whom the Captain has approved he should delegate this duty, is to have charge of the Ship's Log, Form S322, and is to present it weekly for the Captain's signature . . .' (BR 45(4)). Instructions for compiling the Ship's Log are laid down in Volume IV of this manual and in the front of the Log Book itself. A complete account of the ship's movements is kept in the Ship's Log or in the Navigational Record Book (S3034) by noting navigational information in sufficient detail for *the track of the ship at any time to be reconstructed accurately.*

A specimen log illustrating sea and harbour usage is in Fig. 7–1 (pp.166–7).

Record of Observations for Deviation (S374A) and Table of Deviations (S387)

Form S374A is supplied for the purpose of keeping a record of the deviation of all the magnetic compasses installed in one of HM Ships. Anything likely to affect the compass which has occurred since the previous occasion of rendering the form (such as alterations in the ship's structure or armament), or anything likely to affect the accuracy of the swing which is being recorded (such as the nearness of other ships, or the rapidity of the swing) should be noted in the 'Remarks' space of the form.

Form S387 is an abridged version of this form and is intended to be kept on the bridge if necessary and in the vicinity of the compass concerned.

Full details on the use of these forms are given in Volume III of this manual.

Manoeuvring Forms (S376)

These forms are supplied in pads. Each form consists of a spider's web of 254 mm (10 inch) diameter suitable for plotting the positions of ships in company; it also gives various scales, and a tote to record such things as the stations of ships in company, the base course, the zigzag plan, flying course, PIM (position and intended movement) and so on. It is a very useful form for calculating courses and speeds for changing station, particularly when on a tactical screen, or for precise manoeuvres such as taking station from ahead.

Navigating Officer's Note Book (S548A)

The Navigating Officer is to *'keep a Navigating Officer's note book (S548A) containing full and sufficient pilotage information to enable him to conduct the navigation of the ship in safety along predetermined tracks in pilotage waters'* (BR 45(4)). He should also use this Note Book for all his navigational planning including ocean and coastal navigation as well as pilotage and anchorages. Instructions for using the Note Book are given in Chapters 12 and 13.

Captain's Night Order Book (S553)

It has long been the custom for the Captain of HM Ships to keep a Night Order Book in which he puts instructions for the Officers of the Watch and Principal Warfare Officers of the night watches. He also gives information about the special circumstances of the night, states when he wishes to be called and also usually draws attention to his Standing Orders on calling. Instructions for calling the Captain are pasted inside the front cover. The Night Order Book is an essential link between the Captain and his OOWs and PWOs, who should initial it on taking over their watch. It is also used in harbour to implement instructions from the Captain for particular circumstances; for example, weather precautions, getting under way. (*See also* Chapter 19 of this volume.)

Record Book for Wheel and Engine Orders (S580)

Volume IV of this manual states that: *'A Bridge record is kept of wheel and engine orders given whenever the ship is operating close to danger'* (land, other ships, etc.). *'Should automatic recording equipment not be available, the Record Book for Wheel and Engine Orders (S580) should be used for this purpose.'*

Fishing Vessel Log (S1176); Report on Damage to Fishing Gear (S1301)

The Fishing Vessel Log is used to record passing through or near a fishing fleet; if possible, the names and distinguishing numbers of the fishing vessels are to be entered. In the event that damage to gear may have been caused by an HM Ship, the circumstances are to be recorded in the Log. These details may subsequently be needed if it becomes necessary for a Fishery Officer to render a report on Form S1301, Report on Damage to Fishing Gear (Attended or Unattended) Alleged to have been Caused by HM Ships, etc.

The Fishing Vessel Log provides a useful table of port distinguishing letters displayed by fishing vessels.

HMS *Nonsuch*

DATE

Day of week: *Friday*
Day of month: *13th*
Month: *November*
Year: 19 *8 1*
Zone Time kept at Noon: *ZERO*

Time	Log reading	Mean revs. per minute	Est. dist. run through water	Course: True	'A' gyro	'B' gyro	Aux. comp.	Variation in use	Barometer reading in millibars	Wind: Direction	Speed	Sea state	Visibility
0100													
0200													
0300	1265.3	70.3	6.4	133°	133°		143°	6½°W					
0400	1280.5	142	15.0	230°	230°		237°	6½°N	1009.4	230°	9	2	98
0500	1292.1	110.2	11.5	260°	260°		267°	6½°W					91
0600	1305.4	124.9	13.3	260°	260°		267°	6½°W					97
0700	1320.5	142	15.0	260°	260°		267°	6½°W					
0800	1331.9	107.6	11.2	Var	Var		Var	7°W	1005.7	220°	10	2	98
0900	1349.1	114.1	12.0	Var	Var		Var	7°W					
1000	1357.3	121.9	13.0	329°	329°		336°	7°W					
1100	—	58.3	5.6	Var	Var		Var	7°W					
1200									1004.7	215°	10	2	98
1300													
1400													
1500													
1600									1003	210°	15	3	97
1700													
1800									1002.3	210°	15	3	97
1900													
2000									1002	210°	15	3	87
2100													
2200													
2300													
2400									10015	200°	16	4	96

Notice for power:

1026 4 hrs

Fuel remaining at:

(time) 0800
(amount) 220 t

Draught:

Time	Forward	Aft
0230	3.96m	5.03m
1026	3.96m	4.88m

NBCD State:

Time	State
0200	3Y
0245	3X
0430	3Y
0515	3X
0730	3Y
0800	1ZA
0915	3Y
1030	3X

Berth, or anchor bearings:

S. Railway Jetty

1026 {
A Head 178½°
House 329° (Canopus)
Weymouth 253°
B'water Hd

Ship's position:

0400 { Lat. 50° 35'.2 N
Long. 0° 08'.2 W

1200 { Lat. / Long.

2000 { Lat. / Long.

Estimated distance run (midnight to midnight):

103.0 miles

Fig. 7–1. The Ship's Log

FROM: PORTSMOUTH	DAILY SUMMARY, and Leave granted:
TO: WEYMOUTH	Proceeded from Portsmouth to Weymouth for ASW exercise.
and/or AT: WEYMOUTH	Leave to Port Watch and 1st Starboard 1600-0730 Normal W/K leave CPO & PO 1600-0800

REMARKS		Initials of QM	Initials of OOW or OOD
0145 Port watch employed preparing for sea 0200 Guard boat hailed 0215 SSD closed up - singled up 0230 Cast off - courses and speeds for leaving harbour 0235 Hasler Lake clearing lights φ 217½° - Gyro correct 0252 a/co 133° sp 15kn. 0400 0320 a/co 230°	0238½ No.4 buoy L Std 0.4c (Horse Sand Fort 110° 0252 (No Mans Land Fort 190° (Spit Sand Fort 343° 0315 0342 Nat Tr. 133°2'.4		(AA)
0411 a/co 260° 0420 Spoke SS QUEEN ELIZABETH 2 0430 Entered Fog - speed 8 kn - started siren, placed lookouts 0515 Fog lifted - speed 15 kn 0710 Sonar Control Room and Ops Room closed up 0725 S/M OBELISK dived 50°27'N, 02°15'W 0800 0730 Started ASW exercise, co. & sp. as requisite	0402 (St Catherines Light 216½° (Ventnor Pier 287° (Shanklin Pier 353° 0530 (50°29'N (Decca) (01° 33'.3 W 0615 Anvil Point 324° 8'.0 0755 Portland Bill Lt 302°4'.8		D.E.F.
0800 Both watches employed cleaning ship 0900 Exercised action stations. 0915 secured. 0920 ASW exercise completed, course 270° sp 15 kn. 0933 S/M OBELISK surfaced 160° 1000 yards. 0935 a/co 020°, 0955 a/co 319° 1015 Sp. 12 kn. 1019 Courses and speeds as required for anchoring in 1026 Came to Starboard anchor in 13m, 4½ shackles Weymouth Bay 1200 on waterline.			(AA)
1315 Both watches of hands employed washing ship's side, painting mast 1415 H.M.S. Corley anchored in S 11 1500 Lieutenant A.P. Quain RN joined from HMS NEPTUNE 1600			P.F.T.
1730 H.M.S. CARLEY sailed 1800			
2000			C.R.W.
2100 Rounds correct			
2400			P.F.T.

Order of the Court and Report of Navigation Direction Officers at Trial on Navigational Charge (S1372)

In the event of a court-martial arising from the loss, stranding, hazarding, etc. of an HM Ship, the court will direct one or more Navigating or other competent officers to work up the ship's position from the time when her position was last accurately ascertained and render a report on this form. A copy or tracing of the chart by which the ship was navigated is also delivered to the court.

Navigational Data Book (S2677)

In order to maintain a complete record of the performance of an HM Ship under all conditions of wind and weather from one commission to the next, the Navigating Officer is to keep the Navigational Data Book (BR 45(4)). This book should contain details of items listed at the start of each section of the book. These items are reproduced here as follows:

Section 1. Dimensions and Tonnage

All details of length, breadth, height and draught, including the amounts by which any fittings protrude below the keel.

Heights of eye (six foot man) for the various decks from which sights may be taken.

Distance from bridge pelorus, emergency conning position (ECP) pelorus and navigational radar aerial to stem and stern.

Distances at which buoys are in transit with the base of the jackstaff, etc. (shadow diagram).

Standard and full load displacement: net, gross and Danube Rule (for Suez Canal) tonnages.

Tracing of end elevation (from astern) of ship's stern, showing proud propellers.

Tonnes per centimetre immersion (TPC).

Visibility diagram (carriers and similar ships).

Section 2. Anchors and Cables

Details of size, age, weight, capacity and all tests and ranging of anchors, cable and cable-holders.

Diagram showing the position of each shackle within its cable (a series of these diagrams after each ranging will assist in maintaining an even rate of wear).

Speed of weighing anchor in minutes per shackle.

Section 3. Engines

Make and power.

Economical speed range.

Maximum revolutions ahead and astern and standard revolutions for Slow Ahead and Slow Astern.

Drill for disconnecting and connecting engines and shafts (if applicable).

Drills for operating variable-pitch propellers (if applicable).

Drills for blowing soot.

Working-up rates and any special limitations.

Section 4. Revolution Tables and Full Power Trials

Table and/or graph of engine revolutions/speeds after various periods out of dock.

Tables and/or graphs of speeds available (Table 7–2) and optimum revolutions for different combinations of engines connected (if applicable).

All available information on engine revolutions for speeds when various shafts are stopped or trailed.

Brief details of each Full Power Trial: date, position, depth, water temperature, power developed and speed through the water.

Details of speed lost/gained by using stabilisers in varying weather conditions (if applicable).

Table 7–2. Revolutions for specific speeds (BR 45(4))

CLASSIFICATION	PERCENTAGE OF FULL POWER	APPROX. PERCENTAGE OF FULL SPEED	REVS
At full speed (authorised full power)	100	100	
With all despatch (maximum continuous sea-going power)	85	96.5	
With despatch	60	87	
With all convenient despatch	40	77	
With moderate despatch (unless below economical speed)	15	62.5	
At economical speed	As determined by trial for fuel economy and for optimum gas turbine life		

Section 5. Fuel Oil Capacity and Consumption Data

Total theoretical quantity of fuel that can be carried and total practical quantity of fuel oil normally embarked.

Details of any quantity of fuel oil that cannot be used (due to design of tanks or other reason).

Graphs of consumption (in tonnes/hour)/speed, in both temperate and tropical waters.

Graph of range/speed allowing for 20% usable fuel remaining.

Section 6. Turning Trials

Report of Turning Trials (S3020A/B/C) from which should be prepared:

> Table and/or graph for taking station from the bow and templates for use on the radar display.
> Losing ground diagram.
> Amount of wheel for altering course, including tactical diameter at selected speeds for various rudder angles.
> Time taken to turn at rest.

Starting and stopping data, including working rules for gain/loss in speed in yards per knot.

Section 7. Shiphandling Characteristics

Standard distance at which to reduce speed, stop and go astern when approaching an anchorage, buoy or alongside berth.

Recommended positions for handling the ship during different evolutions.

Recommended revolutions to be used when manoeuvring, including limitations while turning at rest, going astern or on one boiler.

Limitations on shiphandling and blind pilotage caused by compass repeater and radar blind arcs.

Effect of wind at various speeds ahead and astern.

Amount of leeway for various directions of relative wind.

Steerage way at various speeds ahead and astern.

Record of tricky berthing, with solution to each problem.

Towing speeds attained (and revolutions required) when towing different classes of ships, and amount of cable veered with depth of water.

Man Overboard — diagrams to show shiphandling action for various directions of relative wind, including the Williamson turn.

General observations from experience.

PIM table (carriers only).

Turning-into-wind graph (carriers only).

Section 8. Berthing Information

All special features of the ship with regard to berthing, e.g. catamarans for berthing a carrier port side to, proud propellers, minimum length of catamarans as dictated by frame spacing.

Recommended brow lengths.

Section 9. Replenishment

Diagram of ship's replenishment positions (on same scale as ATP 16 for RFAs).

Recommended method for approaching the close-aboard position.

Distance usually maintained for various rigs.

Abnormalities of interaction, particularly in shallow water, and notes of experience gained.

Section 10. Conning Positions

Bridge — large-scale diagram of layout, with explanatory notes.

Other conning positions — a brief description of all communications, chart tables and compasses available at these positions.

Section 11. Navigational Communications

Full details of intercommunication system, voice pipes and telephones (with simple diagrams).

Section 12. Steering and Stabilising Equipment

Full details of steering arrangements and equipment.

Orders for steering gear breakdowns.

Drill for operating active rudders (if fitted).

Brief description of stabilisers (if fitted), including position and amount they protrude, and drills for operating.

Section 13. Compasses

MAGNETIC COMPASSES — DETAILS OF THOSE FITTED.

Record of swings for adjustment of compasses (Form S374A): all swings done by the compass directorate should be kept, plus the last two swings for each similar latitude.

Details of special communications and other requirements during compass adjustment.

Details of abnormal performance, with description of remedies taken.

GYRO-COMPASSES — DETAILS OF THOSE FITTED.

Details of abnormal performance, with description of remedies taken.

REPEATERS — WHERE FITTED.

Drills for changing over in the event of compass failure, including AIO.

Section 14. Echo Sounder

Details of fitting.

Record of calibration (*see* Handbooks).

Section 15. Bottom Log and Plotting Tables

Details of fitting.

Record of measured mile runs and other log calibrations, with table of errors for the log and plotting tables on each occasion.

Section 16. Degaussing Equipment and Ranging

Details of fitting, including diagram showing layout of compass corrector-coil resistances.

Record of occasions on which ship is ranged, wiped and depermed.

Chart of the most recent DG ranging (DG Chart No. 1).

Reference: The *Manual of Degaussing* (BR 825).

Section 17. Navigation Lights

Pattern numbers and location of all mains and battery-operated lights, with location of all switches (simple diagram useful).

Details of dimmer settings for Close A/S Action, etc. (if applicable).

Section 18. Radio Aids

Details of all equipment fitted (including navigational radars), with comments on failures, irregular performance and interference experienced. Comments on accuracies achieved.

Blind pilotage organisation.

Section 19. Special Sea Dutymen

Full details of all personnel, with their positions and tasks. (Details of all fixing teams for entering and leaving harbour should be entered here.)

List of reports to be made to the Bridge when Special Sea Dutymen close up.

Section 20. Ship's Narrative

Steaming table (to show following details):

Year	Month	Distance steamed	Hours underway	Total distance steamed this commission	Total hours underway this commission

Brief narrative of the ship's employment:

EXAMPLE

Year	From	Details	To	Remarks
1986	20 Feb	GIBRALTAR	3 Mar	CinC Fleet embarked 24–28 February.
	3 Mar	Exercise ATLANTEX	12 Mar	Convoy exercise with USN.
	12 Mar	PORT EVERGLADES	18 Mar	Navy Days 15 & 16 Mar.

Note: Information gained during visits to foreign ports or on passage which would be of general interest to all ships (not just to the next commission) should be reported as:

1. Amendments to the Station Guide Book   *or*
2. Hydrographic notes   *or*
3. Amendments to Port Information Sheets, etc.

Each passage should be analysed and lessons to be learnt recorded, e.g.

Tidal streams, currents or weather different from that expected.
Whether time in hand allowed for at the planning stage was adequate or not.

Turning, Starting and Stopping Trials (S3020A/B/C)

These forms are used to record details of the ship's turning, starting and stopping characteristics and the necessary detail is then transcribed into the Turning Trials section in the Navigational Data Book (*see* page 169). Guidance on carrying out these trials is given in Volume IV of this manual and in BR 67(3), *Admiralty Manual of Seamanship*, Volume III.

Navigational Record Book (S3034)

The Navigational Record Book is an official record complementary to the Ship's Log, designed for use on the Bridge and for recording at first hand. The Officer of the Watch is to ensure that a complete account of the ship's movements is kept in the Ship's Log or in the Navigational Record Book by noting navigational information in sufficient detail for the track of the ship to be reconstructed accurately.

It is the responsibility of the Navigating Officer to arrange for the necessary records to be kept to allow this accurate reconstruction.

CHAPTER 8
Chartwork

SYMBOLS USED IN CHARTWORK

Chartwork must be clearly intelligible to all who practise it: thus, standard symbols should be used for all forms of chartwork, including both the planning and passage phases, blind as well as visual.

Positions and position lines

Fig. 8–1 sets out the standard symbols used in the Royal Navy to display positions and position lines.

Arrowheads on position lines (Fig. 8–1)

A position line obtained from a bearing of a terrestrial object, visually or by means of a navigational aid (e.g. DF bearing), is distinguished by a *single* arrow at the *outer* end.

A position line obtained from an astronomical observation or from the range of a terrestrial object is distinguished by a *single* arrow at *both* ends.

A position line that is *transferred* (*see* Chapter 9) is distinguished by a *double* arrow at the outer end for a terrestrial object and at both ends for an astronomical observation.

Positions (Fig. 8–1)

The *fix* is shown on the chart as a dot surrounded by a circle, with the time alongside, and the position lines, if appropriate, passing through the position of the fix. A suffix may be added to the fix to indicate it has been obtained by a method other than by visual bearings.

The *Dead Reckoning* (DR) position is shown on the chart as a small line across the course being steered, with the time alongside. A small cross may be used to originate the DR if a fix or Estimated Position is not available.

The *Estimated Position* (EP) is shown on the chart as a dot surrounded by a small triangle, with the time alongside, the estimated track of the ship over the ground (the *ground track*) passing through the dot.

The *Position Probability Area* (PPA, *see* page 181) may be shown on the chart as an ellipse with a major and a minor axis.

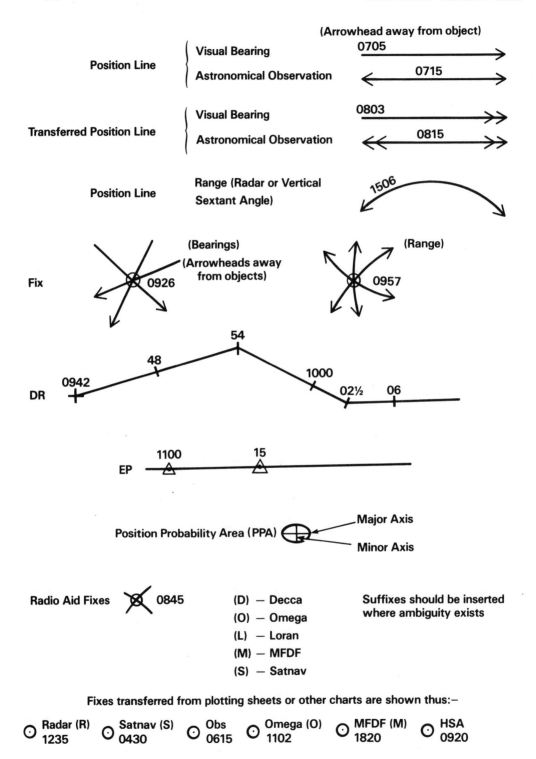

Fig. 8–1.   Positions and position lines — symbols in use in the Royal Navy

DEFINING AND PLOTTING A POSITION

Plotting a position

A position may be expressed by its latitude and longitude, or as a range and bearing from a specific object. It may be plotted on the chart using a parallel rule, dividers, and the scale of latitude and longitude appropriate to the chart itself. The detailed techniques of plotting are given in BR 454, *Notes on Navigation*, which is available on sale to the general public.

Transferring a position

When transferring a position from one chart to another, it is best to use bearing and distance from a distinguishing feature common to both charts, such as a point of land or light. This should then be checked by latitude and longitude to ensure no error has occurred (*see* page 195).

Position by observation

The position line

The navigator finds his position using landmarks, heavenly bodies or radio aids and, from his observations, obtains what are known as *position lines*.

A position line is any line, drawn on the chart, on which the ship's position is known to lie. It may be straight or curved. The methods of obtaining a position line are described in the next chapter.

The simplest form of position line is the line of bearing obtained from a terrestrial object of known position.

Suppose, for example, that a lighthouse (*L* in Fig. 8–2) is seen to bear 065° at 1030. A line drawn in the direction 065° passing through *L* is the position line. In chartwork, it is only necessary to draw the position line in the vicinity of the ship's position, the arrowhead being placed at the *outer* end. This arrowhead indicates the direction in which the observer must lie *from* the observed object.

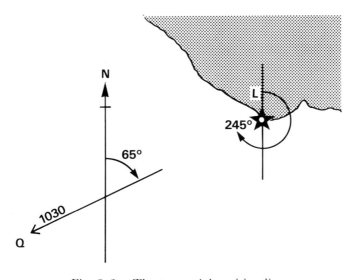

Fig. 8–2.   The terrestrial position line

The fix

If two or more position lines can be obtained at the same moment, the position of the ship must be at their point of intersection. The position thus obtained is known as a *fix*. The position lines, as discussed in Chapter 9, may be obtained from a variety of sources: visual bearings, horizontal sextant angles, radio navigation aids, radar, astronomical observations and so on, and the fix is usually given a suffix (D), (O), (L), (M), (S), Obs, HSA, etc. to indicate it has been obtained by a method other than by visual bearings or radar ranges (Fig. 8–1). Position lines obtained from different sources may often be combined for the purposes of fixing the ship.

The observed position

It is desirable to distinguish between the position obtained by observation of terrestrial objects and that obtained by observations of heavenly bodies. For this reason, the position decided by the point of intersection of two position lines derived from astronomical observations, or derived from a number of such position lines, is known as an *observed position* and is marked 'Obs' (Fig. 8–1).

CALCULATING THE POSITION

When it is not possible to obtain the ship's actual position by fixing, a position may be worked up based upon the most recent fix.

Dead Reckoning (DR)

Dead Reckoning is the expression used to describe that position obtained from the *true course steered* by the ship and her *speed through the water*, and from *no other factors*.

The DR position* is thus only approximate for, while the speed through the water will allow for the amount by which the ship's speed is reduced or increased by wind and sea, there is no allowance for leeway, tidal stream, current, or surface drift.

True course steered through the water may be obtained from the plotting table or course recorder if either is available. If not it can only be determined by the Officer of the Watch by very close observation of the course being steered.

Speed through the water may be obtained from the log, provided the latter is reliable and the error known and allowed for. If the log is unreliable or not available, then the average engine revolutions over the hour must be used. These revolutions may be converted into speed through the water having regard to:

1. The graph† of engine revolutions/speed (power percentage/speed for

* In practice, the term Dead Reckoning is occasionally used to describe the Estimated Position. Such a practice is incorrect and should be avoided.
† Many merchant ships have the data provided in the form of a revolution/speed/percentage slip table usually ranging between 0% and 15%. Experience will be the best guide in establishing what is the apparent percentage slip for various situations; this will vary according to the draught, trim, state of the ship's underwater hull and so on. It should be possible to establish the various slips with a considerable degree of accuracy during the first eighteen months of service. The percentage slip to be used should be based upon recent ship performance in similar conditions; for example, a ship operating in tropical waters will usually suffer much greater fouling than in colder waters.

controllable-pitch-propeller-driven ships) for time out of dock, as obtained from the Navigational Data Book (page 169).

2. The wind and sea reducing or increasing the ship's speed through the water. Such data should be recorded in the Navigational Data Book and subsequently analysed, so that a quick and accurate assessment of this effect may be made in any given situation. It is rare for a stern sea to increase ship's speed by any appreciable amount because yawing, which usually accompanies this situation, tends to reduce ship's speed through the water. A head wind and sea, however, will invariably reduce the speed of a ship. In full gale conditions, the reduction can be as much as 50% even in large ships.

Estimated Position (EP)

This position is the most accurate that the navigator can obtain by calculation and estimation only. It is derived from the DR position adjusted for the estimated effects of leeway, tidal stream, current and surface drift. The EP must always remain an approximate position, because these four variable factors are difficult to determine exactly, although experience goes a long way to resolving them. It is essential for the navigator to estimate the effects as accurately as possible; each is now described.

Leeway

Leeway is the effect of wind in moving a vessel bodily to leeward at right angles to the course steered. The effect of wind in reducing or increasing the ship's speed through the water has already been described under Dead Reckoning.

The effect of wind varies with every type of ship. The navigator should collect as much information as possible concerning the effects of the force and direction* of the wind on the behaviour of his own ship and record such data in the Navigational Data Book.

Leeway depends upon a number of factors:

1. Own ship speed: the higher the speed, the less the leeway.
2. Wind speed: the higher the component of wind speed at right angles to the course, the greater the leeway.
3. Longitudinal area: the greater the ratio of fore and aft area above the waterline to that below, the greater the leeway.
4. The depth of water: the shallower the depth of water in relation to the draught, the less the leeway.

Leeway is thus a complex relationship and, whilst attempts have been made to quantify it in mathematical terms, it is probably best for the navigator to rely on his own experience and on the data in the Navigational Data Book.

As a rough guide, in modern warships, which have a high ratio of longitudinal area above the waterline to that below, one would normally expect leeway to vary between about $\frac{1}{4}$ knot in a 10 knot beam wind at 10 knots speed, and up to 3 knots in a 30 knot beam wind while lying stopped, as shown in Table 8–1. Exact leeway will vary with ship class.

---

* The system of naming the direction of the wind is exactly the opposite to that of naming tidal streams and currents. A northerly wind, for example, blows *from* the north, while a northerly or north-going current sets *to* the north.

Table 8–1.   An approximate guide to leeway in HM Ships

BEAM WIND SPEED / SHIP SPEED	10 KNOTS	30 KNOTS
	LEEWAY	
Stopped	1 knot	3 knots
10 knots	$\frac{1}{4}$ knot	$\frac{3}{4}$ knot
20 knots	Less than 0.1 knot	$\frac{1}{4}$ knot

In ships not fitted with an automatic pilot, an inexperienced or careless helmsman is likely to steer a course two or three degrees off that ordered, usually to windward as most ships tend to 'fly' into the wind. This may compensate for the effect of leeway, and may be gauged by comparing the course ordered with that registered on the plotting table or the course recorder, or by close observation over a period of time. This 'boring to windward' is particularly noticeable in light craft running with the wind and sea on the quarter.

As HM Ships are frequently proceeding at a whole range of different speeds, it is usual to quantify leeway in terms of a *leeway vector* (e.g. 120° $\frac{1}{2}$ knot). In merchant ships, which normally proceed at a set service speed, leeway is normally quantified in terms of *leeway angle* — the angular difference between the ship's course and her track through the water (*water track*).

Tidal streams

A tidal stream is the periodical horizontal movement of the sea surface caused by the tide-raising forces of the sun and moon.

Information concerning tidal streams is given on Admiralty charts, in the *Admiralty Sailing Directions*, in tidal stream publications and in special tidal stream atlases. The various methods of estimating the direction and strength of the stream are described in Chapter 11.*

Tidal stream data must always be used with caution, particularly at springs and around the calculated time of change-over from ebb to flood and vice-versa. It will often be found that the tidal stream experienced is different from that calculated.

Currents

A current is the non-tidal horizontal movement of the sea due mainly to meteorological, oceanographical or topographical causes. In some areas this movement may be nearly constant in rate and direction (e.g. the Gulf Stream)

* The direction of a current or tidal stream is always given as the direction in which the water is moving. If, for example, it is said to set 150° 2 knots, a ship that experiences such a stream for 3 hours will be set 6 miles in a direction 150°.

while in others it may vary seasonally or fluctuate with changes in meteorological conditions (e.g. the Arabian Sea).

Information concerning currents is given on Admiralty charts, in the *Sailing Directions*, on the Routeing charts, in *Ocean Passages for the World* (NP 136), in *The Mariner's Handbook* (NP 100), in *Meteorology for Mariners* (NP 407), in current atlases such as the *Straits of Gibraltar: Surface and Sub-surface Water Movements* (NP 629), and Volume II of this manual.

The main cause of most surface currents in the open sea is the direct action of the wind on the surface of the sea. A current formed in this way is known as a *drift current*, and a clear correlation exists between the directions of the prevailing drift currents and the prevailing winds.

Surface drift

Sometimes, however, there may be no recorded data on wind currents, or the wind itself may be in a contrary direction to that normally prevailing. It may therefore become necessary to make an estimate for *surface drift* which may or may not, depending on the circumstances met with at the time, be in addition to that already made for currents.

Surface drift can only be estimated from experience and with a knowledge of the meteorological conditions in the area through which the ship is steaming.

The matter is a complex one and studied more fully in Volume II, but some guidelines are set out here.

The maximum *rate* of surface drift approximates to $\frac{1}{40}$ of the wind speed. However, the strength of the surface drift depends on how long the wind has been blowing and upon the fetch* of the wind. The build-up of surface drift in response to wind is slow and a steady state takes some time to become established. With light winds the slight current resulting may take only about 6 hours to develop, but with strong winds about 48 hours is needed for the current to reach its full speed. Hurricane force winds may give rise to a current in excess of 2 knots, but it is rare for such winds to persist for more than a few hours without a change in direction. The piling up of water caused by a storm near a coastline may lead to particularly strong currents parallel to that coast.

The effect of the rotation of the Earth (Coriolis force) is to deflect water movement to the right in the Northern Hemisphere and to the left in the Southern Hemisphere. This produces a *direction* of the surface flow inclined at some 20° to 45° to the *right* of the wind direction in the Northern Hemisphere and to the *left* in the Southern Hemisphere.

If, for example, the wind has been blowing steadily from the north-east at 20 knots for several days, the *rate* and *direction* of the surface drift in the Northern Hemisphere may be expected to be of the order of $\frac{1}{2}$ knot in a direction between 245° and 270°.

Plotting the track

Plotting the Estimated Position (EP) from a known position is carried out in two steps (Fig. 8–3).

---

* *Fetch* is the extent of open water over which the wind has been blowing before it reaches the observer.

1. Plot the course steered and the speed through the water, thus arriving at the Dead Reckoning (DR) position.
2. Plot on from the Dead Reckoning position the effect of:
   (*a*) leeway;
   (*b*) tidal stream;
   (*c*) current;
   (*d*) surface drift;
   thus arriving at the Estimated Position (EP).

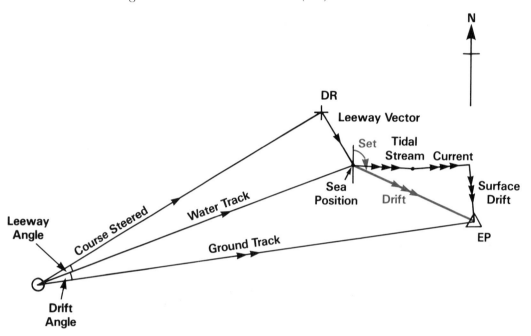

Fig. 8–3.   Plotting the Estimated Position (EP)

Fig. 8–3 also displays the navigational terms used. Those that have not already been described are defined in Table 8–2. In the figure the effects of leeway, tidal stream, current and surface drift have been purposely exaggerated for the sake of clarity.

Arrowheads on tracks (Fig. 8–3)

A *single arrow* denotes course steered, water track, leeway vector.
A *double arrow* denotes ship's ground track.
A *treble arrow* denotes tidal stream, current, surface drift and drift.

Quantification of set and drift

Set and *drift* result from the combined effects of tidal stream, current and surface drift. They are quantified in terms of direction and distance, e.g. 103° 3.5 miles. Drift may also be given a *rate* measured in knots; e.g. if the time over which the drift of 3'.5 has been determined is 2 hours, the rate would be 1.75 knots. Thus, set and drift would be defined as *set* 103°, *drift* 3'.5, *rate* 1.75 knots.

Table 8-2

TERM	DEFINITION
Track	The path followed or to be followed, between one position and another. This path may be that over the ground (ground track) or through the water (water track). When radar plotting (Chapter 17), this path may also be a relative track or a true track.
Track angle	The direction of a track.
Track made good	The mean ground track actually achieved over a given period.
Set	The resultant direction towards which current, tidal stream and surface drift flow.
Drift	The distance covered in a given time due solely to the movement of current, tidal stream and surface drift.
Drift angle	The angular difference between the ground track and water track.
Sea position	The point at the termination of the water track.

Position Probability Area (PPA)

The Position Probability Area (PPA) is the area derived from a combination of appropriate position lines obtained from available navigational aids (including log and compass), after applying the relevant statistical error correction to each position line in turn. It may be shown on the chart in the form of an ellipse with a major and a minor axis (Fig. 8-1). Within the PPA, the Navigating Officer determines his *Most Probable Position* (MPP) which, dependent on the quality of the input, he should treat as a fix, an EP or a DR.

Allowing for wind, tidal stream, current and surface drift

Most of the examples which follow are given for tidal stream only; the same method of solution applies to problems associated with leeway, current or surface drift.

To shape a course to steer allowing for a tidal stream

When the navigator knows the direction of the place he wishes to reach and the direction and strength of the tidal stream he will experience on passage, he must then find the course to steer.

EXAMPLE

What course must a ship steer, when steaming at 12 knots, to make good a track 090° if it is estimated that the tidal stream is setting 040° at 3 knots?

Lay off the course to be made good (AB in Fig. 8-4). From A lay off the direction of the tidal stream AC. Along AC mark off the distance the tidal stream runs in any convenient interval on a chosen scale. In Fig. 8-4 a 1 hour interval* has been allowed: thus, AD will be 3 miles.

* The dimensions of the triangle used are to a large extent controlled by the scale of the chart. On a large-scale chart a ½ hour interval may suffice, while on a smaller scale it may be necessary to use a 2 or even a 3 hour interval.

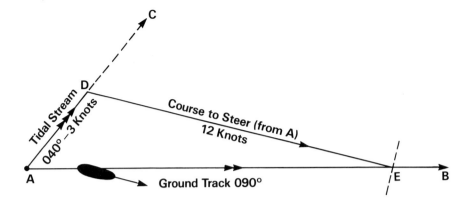

Fig. 8–4.   To shape a course allowing for tidal stream (drawing not to scale)

With centre D and radius equal to the distance the ship runs in the same interval (12 miles), and on the same scale, cut AB at E. Then DE (101°) is the course to steer.

AE (13.7 miles) is the distance made good in an 090° direction in 1 hour.

To reach a position at a definite time, allowing for a tidal stream

EXAMPLE

What course must a ship steer, and at what speed must she steam, to proceed from A to a position B in 1½ hours, allowing for a tidal stream setting 150° at 3 knots?

Join AB, as shown in Fig. 8–5. This determines the course and distance to be made good in 1½ hours: 090° 15 miles; thus, the speed to be made good is 10 knots. Mark a position D along AB using a convenient time interval depending on the scale of the chart, say 1 hour: in this case AD will be 10 miles.

From A lay off AC using the direction and rate of the tidal stream for the same interval: 150° 3 miles. Join CD. CD will give the course (073°) to steer and the speed (8.9 knots) at which to proceed.

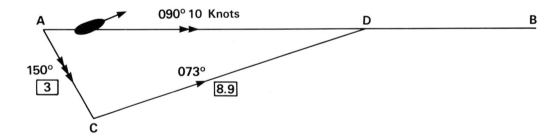

Fig. 8–5.   To reach a position at a definite time, allowing for a tidal stream

To clear a point by a given distance and find the time when an object will be abeam, allowing for a tidal stream

EXAMPLE

> *A ship at A (Fig. 8–6) steers so as to clear a lighthouse L by 2 miles, allowing for a tidal stream setting 345°. When will the lighthouse L be abeam?*

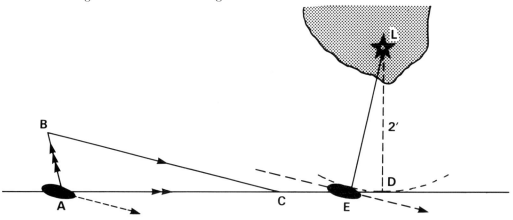

Fig. 8–6.   To clear a point by a given distance

From *L* draw the arc of a circle, radius 2′. From the ship's present position draw a tangent to the arc. This is the course to be made good, *AD*.

Find the course to steer *BC* by the method explained above. The light is abeam when it bears 90° from the course steered, that is to say, when the ship is at *E* and not when she is in position *D* (the point at which she passes closest to the lighthouse). The time elapsed will be the time taken to cover the distance *AE* at a speed represented by *AC*, the speed made good.

To find the direction and rate of the tidal stream experienced between two fixes

EXAMPLE

> *A ship is at A at 0100, as shown in Fig. 8–7, and steering 110° at 10 knots. At 0300 she fixes herself at B. What is the direction and rate of the tidal stream from 0100 to 0300?*

Plot the ship's course 110° for a distance of 20′ from *A*. The difference between the Dead Reckoning position *C* and the observed position *B* at 0300 gives the direction of the tidal stream *CB* (025°) and the distance it has displaced the ship in 2 hours (7.6 miles). From these data the tidal stream may be calculated as setting 025° at 3.8 knots.

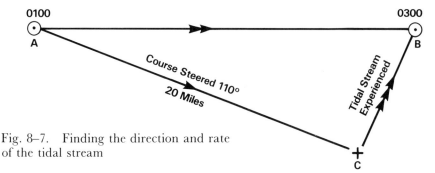

Fig. 8–7.   Finding the direction and rate of the tidal stream

To determine the Estimated Position (EP) allowing for leeway, tidal stream, current and surface drift*

EXAMPLE

> *The ship's position is fixed at 0700, course and speed ordered are 090°, revolutions for 15 knots. At the end of 1 hour, course steered as recorded by the plotting table is 090½°, speed through the water as recorded by the log, allowing for the error in the instrument, is 14.7 knots. Estimated tidal stream (tidal stream tables) is 295° 1.5 knots. Estimated current (current charts) is 060° 0.75 knots.*
>
> *The wind has been blowing steadily in the area from the south at about 20 knots over the past 2–3 days. Leeway as deduced from the data in the Navigational Data Book is ¾ knot. Plot the Estimated Position after 1 hour, and deduce the estimated course and speed made good, and the set and drift from the combined effects of tidal stream, current and surface drift. The ship is in the Northern Hemisphere. From a study of the area and the data available it is estimated that surface drift will be in addition to the predicted current.*

The leeway vector will be at right angles to the course steered; thus, in this case it will be 000½° ¾ knot. (The leeway angle is 3°.) Estimated surface drift will be 020° to 045° ½ knot; allow for 030°.

Plot the DR position *B* at 0800 from the course steered 090½° at the speed through the water 14.7 knots—*AB* in Fig. 8–8 (lay the parallel ruler through 091° and 270° on the compass rose to achieve 090½°).

Plot the leeway, *BC*, 000½° 0.75 knot (parallel ruler through 000°/181° on the compass rose).

Plot the tidal stream *CD*, 295° 1.5 knots.

Plot the current *DE*, 060° 0.75 knot.

Plot the surface drift *EF*, 030° 0.5 knot.

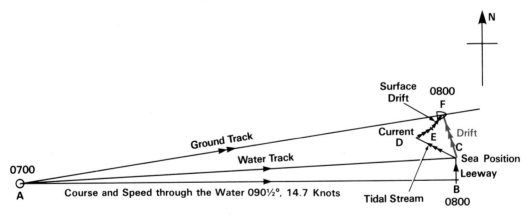

Fig. 8–8.   Determining the Estimated Position

F is the Estimated Position at 0800, *AF* is the estimated ground track (course and speed made good over the ground) and *CF* is the estimated set and drift.

The estimated course and speed made good is 082° 14.4 knots; the set and drift are estimated to be 343° 1.5 miles, rate 1.5 knots.

* The example shows the resolution of all four factors, although frequently only one or two at a time will be met with in practice.

Allowing for the turning circle

When a group of warships is manoeuvring, alterations of course are frequently so numerous, and the distance run on each course so short, that the curves described by the ship while making the various turns form a large proportion of the plot, and it is therefore essential that allowances should be made for the turning circle and the loss of speed while turning, if the reckoning is to be accurate.

At any time during manoeuvres, it may be necessary for the ship to shape a course for a particular position, so it is essential that the reckoning should be kept in such a way that her position at any moment may be plotted on the chart with the least possible delay.

When the ships form part of a group within easy visual touch of the Guide, and are unlikely to be detached during the manoeuvres it is advisable that they should also plot the Guide's track, for the following reasons:

1. The Guide's less frequent alterations of course and steadier speeds reduce the chance of errors.
2. The times recorded in the signal log give a valuable check on the times taken for the plot.
3. If the ship is detached unexpectedly, a range and bearing of the Guide should at once give the ship's position.
4. The alterations of course can often be plotted before it is necessary for the Navigating Officer to devote his attention solely to the handling of his own ship.

When HM Ships are engaged in manoeuvres or exercises, it is usual to establish the DR by obtaining the course steered and distance run through the water from the plotting table at regular intervals, adjusting for gyro and log errors as appropriate. If, however, the plotting table is not available, the turning circles will have to be plotted on the chart or plotting sheet by hand.

The turning circle must always be allowed for in pilotage waters (Chapter 13), also in coastal waters (Chapter 12), where the turning circle of the ship and the scale of the chart are such that the turning circle forms a measurable part of the estimated track. Further offshore, when the scale of the chart is small, and if the alterations of course are few, it may be possible to disregard the turning circle, whilst remaining within the bounds of the required accuracy.

Before the various methods of allowing for the turning circle are considered, it is necessary to define the terms which are used, and these are illustrated in Figs 8–9 and 8–10 (pp.186, 187).

The *advance* is the distance that the compass platform of a ship has advanced in the direction of the original course on completion of a turn (the steadying point). It is measured from the point where the wheel was put over.

$$AD = \text{the advance}$$

The *transfer* is the distance that the compass platform of a ship is transferred in a direction at right angles to the original course.

$$DB = \text{the transfer}$$

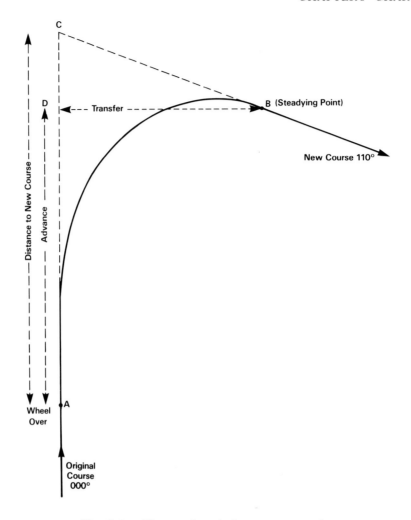

Fig. 8–9.   The turning circle — terms used

The *distance to new course* is the distance from the position of the compass platform when the wheel was put over to the point of intersection of the original course produced and the new course laid back.

$$AC = \text{ the distance to new course}$$

The perpendicular distance between the ship's original course and her position when she has turned 180°, is called the *tactical diameter*.*

$$BD = \text{ the tactical diameter}$$

The *final diameter* is the diameter of the approximately circular path which a ship describes if the wheel is kept over.

$$EF = \text{ the approximate final diameter}$$

* Tactical diameter will vary with both speed and rudder angle.

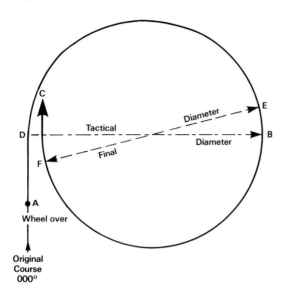

Fig. 8–10.   Tactical and final diameter

The *length of the arc* is the distance from point to point along the path actually described by the ship when turning.

All the above data for a ship can be obtained from Turning Trials (*see* Volume IV of this manual and BR 67(3), *Admiralty Manual of Seamanship*, Volume III for details).

Either the advance and transfer method or the distance to new course method should be used when plotting the track by hand (Fig. 8–11). In coastal and pilotage waters, an allowance for the tidal stream may also have to be made and this is discussed in later chapters.

Method 1. Advance and transfer

In Fig. 8–11, a ship is steering a course 000°. If the wheel is put over to alter course to 120° when in position *A* (at 0900), she will follow the curve *AEB* and will be steady on her new course 120° at the point *B*.

With data obtained from the Turning Trials, the point *B* can be plotted and the time taken to travel from *A* to *B* along the arc can be found.

During the turn from *A* to *B*, the ship will lose speed so that, when steady on the new course, she will be moving at less than her original speed. It will not be correct, therefore, to continue plotting from the point *B*, unless some allowance is made for this loss of speed.

The additional distance which must be travelled at the original speed to regain each knot of speed lost may be between 15 and 60 yards in an HM Ship. Such data are normally recorded in the Navigational Data Book and known as the *speed factor*.

Suppose that a warship (in Fig. 8–11), with an original speed of 15 knots and a speed factor of 60 yards per knot, loses 3 knots on the turn. She will then be moving at 12 knots when she steadies on the new course at *B*, and will have to regain 3 knots. This can be allowed for by making her cover an additional 3×60 = 180 yards, at 15 knots; i.e. she may be plotted on *at 15 knots* from a position

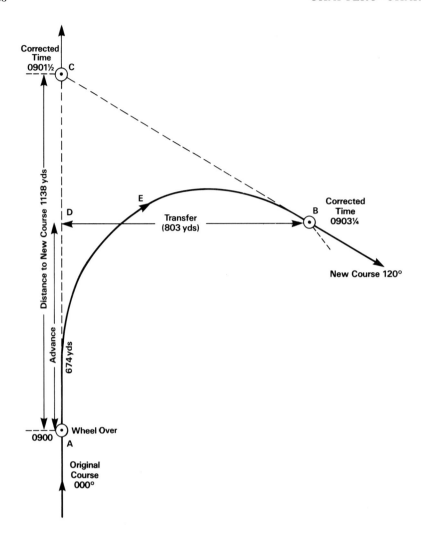

Fig. 8–11.   Plotting a turn

180 yards 300° from B. Her position on the plot will then be correct when she has
regained her speed of 15 knots.

To obviate the additional plotting, a *time correction* is provided which takes this
additional distance into consideration. It consists of the time taken to turn plus
the time taken to cover the additional distance at the original speed, and should
be added to the time of 'wheel over' to give a time of arrival at *B* which will
enable the ship to be plotted on from *B* at her original speed.

All subsequent positions can now be laid off along the new course and
worked from the point *B*, the time interval being calculated from the corrected
time.

A table may be constructed from the turning data to give the advance and
transfer and time correction for any alteration of course, for different speeds
and rudder angles.

Table 8–3 is an example of such a table, constructed for a warship steaming at 15 knots, using 20° of rudder.

Table 8–3. Advance and transfer

AMOUNT OF ALTERATION	ADVANCE	TRANSFER	TIME CORRECTION	
degrees	yards	yards	min	s
20	332	26	0	42
40	516	110	1	12
60	640	233	1	41
80	719	415	2	12
100	735	612	2	42
120	674	803	3	12
140	546	964	3	41
160	366	1064	4	09
180	175	1107	4	38

If this table is used, point B may be plotted from A using an advance of 674 yards and a transfer of 803 yards, and a corrected time of arrival at B of 0903¼ (odd seconds being ignored).

Method 2. Distance to new course

If this method is used for the turn shown in Fig. 8–11, the ship plots her new course from the point C, where the new course laid back cuts the original course produced, although in fact she puts her wheel over at A, as before, and steadies on the new course at B.

If the time taken to travel the distance CB at the original speed is subtracted from the time correction previously described, then the time of arrival at the imaginary point C is obtained. This calculation is incorporated in another time correction, which is again added to the time of 'wheel over' so that the ship in this case may be plotted on from C at her original speed although it is clear that the ship does not in fact pass through the point C at all.

Table 8–4 is an example of a 'distance to new course' table constructed for the same warship, speed 15 knots, using 20° of rudder.

Table 8–4. Distance to new course

ALTERATION OF COURSE	DISTANCE TO NEW COURSE	TIME CORRECTION	
degrees	yards	min	s
20	261	0	33
40	385	0	52
60	505	1	09
80	646	1	22
100	843	1	28
120	1138	1	22

If this table is used, the point C in Fig. 8–11 is plotted 1138 yards along the original course 000°, and the time of arrival at this imaginary point is 0901½ (odd seconds being ignored).

This method involves only two simple corrections:

1. A distance to be plotted along the original course.
2. A time correction to be added at the time of 'wheel over' in order to obtain the corrected time at the point C.

Its disadvantage is that it cannot be used for alterations of course over 120° or so, because beyond this point the distance to new course becomes excessive.

Correction for change of speed

The gain or loss of distance when speed is altered while on a straight course must also be allowed for when plotting by hand. The actual correction for any ship is found during acceleration and deceleration trials and recorded in the Navigational Data Book (*see* Volume IV of this manual and BR 67(3), *Admiralty Manual of Seamanship*, Volume III).

CHARTWORK PLANNING

At the planning stage, the following symbols should be used for chartwork (Fig. 8–12). Blind pilotage symbols are to be found in Chapter 14.

(*a*) *Planned track*. Draw the planned track boldly, writing the course along the track with the course to steer in brackets alongside and the speed in a box, north orientated, underneath. The figures for course and speed should be sufficiently far away from the track to permit the necessary chartwork.

(*b*) *Tidal stream*. Indicate the expected tidal stream, showing the direction by a three-headed arrow, the strength in a box, and the time at which it is effective. This symbol can also be used for ocean currents and surface drift although the following symbol is often used instead: ⌇⌇⌇⟹

$$\boxed{0.3}$$

(*c*) *Dangers*. Emphasise dangers near the track by outlining them boldly in pencil (or coloured ink if the chart is to be used often). In pilotage waters, the safe depth sounding line should be drawn in to show the limits of the navigable channel. Remember that this will vary with the height of the tide.

(*d*) *Clearing bearings* (*see* Chapter 13). Draw in clearing bearings boldly, using solid arrowheads pointing towards the object. NLT . . . (not less than . . .) or NMT . . . (not more than . . .) should be written along the arrow line. A clearing bearing should be drawn sufficiently clear of the danger so that the ship is still safe even if the bridge is on the bearing line but turning away from danger. Allow for the bridge being on the line with the stem or stern on the dangerous side of it, whichever is the greater distance.

(*e*) *Distance to run*. Indicate the distance to run to the destination, rendezvous, etc. Numbers should be upright.

(*f*) *Planned position and time*. Indicate the time it is intended to be at particular positions at regular intervals, using 'bubbles' close to but clear of the track.

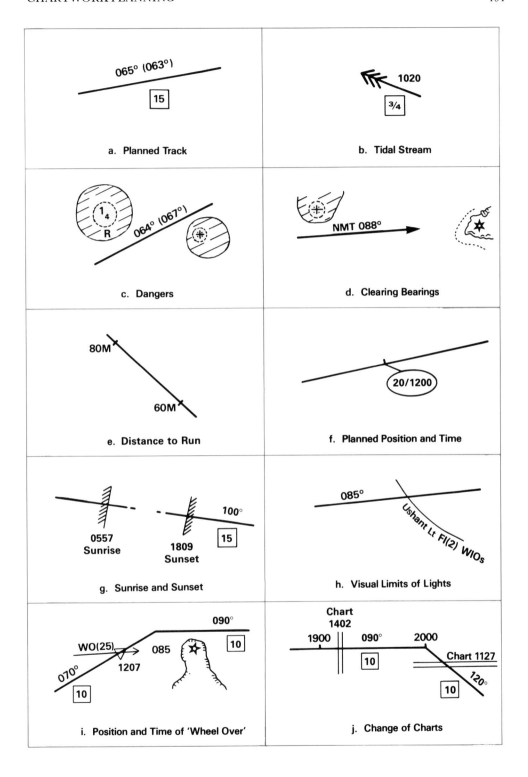

Fig. 8–12. Chartwork planning symbols

It is suggested that ocean passages be marked every 12 hours (0001 and 1200 or 0600 and 1800), coastal passages more frequently, every 2 or 4 hours.

(g) *Sunrise and sunset.* Indicate the times of sunrise and sunset at the expected positions of the ship at those times.

(h) *Visual limits of lights.* Indicate the arcs of the visual limits of lights that may be raised or dipped—the rising/dipping range.

(i) *Position and time of 'wheel over'.* Show position and planned time of 'wheel over' for alterations of course. The amount of wheel can be stipulated if this differs from standard.

(j) *Change of chart.* The positions of changes of chart should be indicated by double parallel lines, either vertical or horizontal.

CHARTWORK ON PASSAGE

Fixing

The various methods of fixing the ship are described in Chapter 9. The visual fix is the foundation of all coastal navigation, once a sound plan has been made. Fixes are vital, yet their observation and plotting takes the eye of the Navigating Officer or Officer of the Watch away from other vital tasks of lookout.

Plotting the ship's position

The DR from the last fix must always be maintained for some distance ahead of the ship and an EP must be derived from all available information of tidal stream, current, etc. As soon as a new fix is obtained, the fix position must be compared with the DR and EP to ensure that there has been no mistake in identifying features ashore, and also to obtain an estimate of the strength and direction of any stream or current since the last fix. It is particularly important to generate a DR or EP after an alteration of course.

Use of a DR may be acceptable when wind, tidal stream and current are negligible but, when these are significant, the EP *must* be generated. This should happen in any case once an appropriate course has been determined, to make good a track allowing for these factors.

Frequency of fixing

Frequency of fixing should depend on the distance from navigational hazards and the time the ship would take to run into danger before the next fix. This depends mainly on the ship's speed. For example, at passage speeds, say 10 to 15 knots, a fix every 10 to 15 minutes on a 1:75,000 coastal chart gives a position every 2 to 3 inches on that chart; this is normally sufficient. At higher speeds or on a larger scale chart, the time interval will need to be much less and may require a fixing team.

It is recommended that fixes should be taken at times coinciding with DR or EP times on the chart. This practice will make immediately apparent the effects of leeway, tidal stream, etc. and whether or not the effects experienced are the same as those expected.

A 6 minute interval between fixes is convenient for converting distance to speed made good because the multiplier is 10; e.g. 1.35 miles in 6 minutes equals 1.35 × 10 or 13.5 knots.

Useful fixing intervals for easy conversion of distance to speed are shown in the following table. The multipliers are all whole numbers.

Interval (minutes)	3	4	5	6	10	12	15	20
Multiplier	20	15	12	10	6	5	4	3

For example, if the distance run in 4 minutes is $0'.82$, the speed made good is $15 \times 0'.82 = 12.3$ knots.

At speeds of about 15 knots, a useful rule of thumb is to fix every 20 minutes (5 miles approx.) when navigating offshore on the 1:150,000 coastal chart; every 10 minutes ($2\frac{1}{2}$ miles approx.) when coasting closer inshore on the larger 1:75,000 chart; and every 4 minutes (1 mile approx.) when approaching a port using a 1:20,000 chart. On entering the pilotage stage of the passage, a different fixing technique is required and this is described in Chapter 13.

Speed

The speed ordered (rung on) is normally shown in a box north orientated alongside the track. It should be remembered that the speed made good along the water track (sea speed) or along the ground track (ground speed) is not usually shown against the track worked up on the chart. Ground speed may be deduced from the distance run between successive fixes, or it may be estimated from the expected effects on the speed ordered of wind, sea, tidal stream, current and surface drift. Actual or estimated ground speed should always be used when projecting the EP ahead. Ground speed is liable to fluctuate when any sea is running, also when the strength or direction of the tidal stream is changing.

Time taken to fix

The time taken to note the bearings and the time, plot the fix on the chart, check the DR and lay off further DR, verify time to 'wheel over' (if applicable) and return to lookout, should not be more than 2 minutes. A practised navigator should be able to complete the task within 60 seconds. If it is essential to reduce the fixing time further, an assistant or a team should be used. Using an assistant, the time can be reduced to less than 30 seconds.

Keeping the record

A complete record, showing navigational information in sufficient detail for the track of the ship at any time to be reconstructed accurately, is to be kept in the Navigational Record Book (S3034). An example is given in Fig. 8–13. The following symbols may be employed:

←————	left-hand edge (of land, etc.)
————→	right-hand edge (of land, etc.)
⊥ Port (5c)	abeam to port (5 cables)
⊥ Stbd ($1'.2$)	abeam to starboard (1.2 miles)

Further information on the record is given in Chapter 12.

DATE	15th June		WATCH FORENOON	OOW AGD
TIME	**CO**	**SP**	**REMARKS**	
0900	090	15	Fidra Ø Bass Lt. 089½° (091½°T)	
			Elie Ness Lt. 047°G +2°	
			← E WEMYSS 344°G +2°	
			GYRO 2° LOW	
0903	089G			
	091T		North Carr Lt. 335°G +2°	
0915			Balcombe Tr. 279°G +2°	
			Fidra 243°G +2°	
0927	103C		GYRO FAILURE Total Error Correction	
	090T		13°W	
			Bell Rock 328°C −13°	
0930			Pint Stoop 294°C −13°	
			Fife Ness 237°C −13°	
0937		18		

Fig. 8–13.   The Navigational Record Book

Establishing the track

A fix must always be taken immediately after altering course and a further fix taken shortly after (*see* page 192). From them the following conclusions may be drawn:

1. Whether the ship is on track or not.
2. The course and speed being made good, and hence the effect of wind, tidal stream and current.

From this information the following questions arise:

1. Is the actual track the same as that intended and is it safe?
2. Should the course be adjusted now to regain the intended track?
3. Can the divergence (if any) from the intended track be accepted until the next alteration of course?
4. When is the next alteration of course?

Time of arrival

During the final stages of a passage, show the exact times at which it is intended to pass through regular positions so that speed may be quickly adjusted to achieve the correct time of arrival (Fig. 8–14).

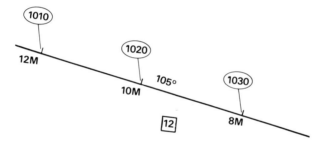

Fig. 8–14.   Time of arrival

Plan when to change from regular chart fixing to 'Note Book' pilotage (i.e. to keeping on a predetermined track).

General points on chartwork

1. Always show the time of the next alteration of course as a four-figure time at the appropriate position on the ship's track. This should be done as early as possible.
2. Transfer positions from one chart to another by bearing and distance from a point common to both charts, and check by latitude and longitude. This is most necessary as a check against mistakes, as the graduations on the two charts may differ. However, it must be remembered that the charts may be based on different geographic datums, and small differences in position between the two transfer methods may arise.
3. Always obtain a fix as soon as possible after the ship's position has been transferred from one chart to another.

4. Always use the nearest compass rose, because:
   (*a*) There will be less effect of distortion, and the correct variation will be used.
   (*b*) An error will be avoided if the chart used is drawn on the modified polyconic (gnomonic) projection.
5. Remember the changes of variation printed on each compass rose.
6. Keep only one chart on the chart table, to avoid the error of measuring distances off the scale of a chart underneath the one in use.
7. Make certain whether the units denoting soundings on the chart are fathoms, feet or metres.
8. When measuring distance by the latitude scale, measure as far as possible the same amount on each side of the mean latitude of the track being measured.
9. The surface of the chart can best be preserved—and plotting will be most clear—if a 2B pencil and a soft rubber are used. In wet or hot and humid weather, it is a good plan to place a towel along the front of the chart table when working on the charts, and to remove dripping headgear.

SUMMARY

The necessity for developing the DR and the EP has been emphasised in this chapter. Despite the world-wide availability of a whole range of sophisticated and accurate navigational aids, it is nevertheless true that a high proportion of groundings still result from a failure to work up a proper DR/EP. An accurate DR/EP over which the Navigating Officer has taken care will often prevent a potentially dangerous grounding situation from developing in the first place.

CHAPTER 9
Fixing the Ship

Fixing the ship was introduced in Chapter 8 in connection with chartwork. This chapter sets out the methods of fixing the ship by the use of position lines obtained mainly by visual observation of terrestrial objects. It is worth remembering, however, that a visual bearing of a terrestrial object may sometimes be combined with a position line from some other navigational source to produce a fix; for example, the echo sounder, radar, or a radio aid. For this reason, position lines from these sources will be covered to a greater or lesser extent, although how they are obtained is dealt with in detail elsewhere in this manual. Radar is covered in Chapter 15 of this volume, and the echo sounder and radio fixing aids in Volume III.

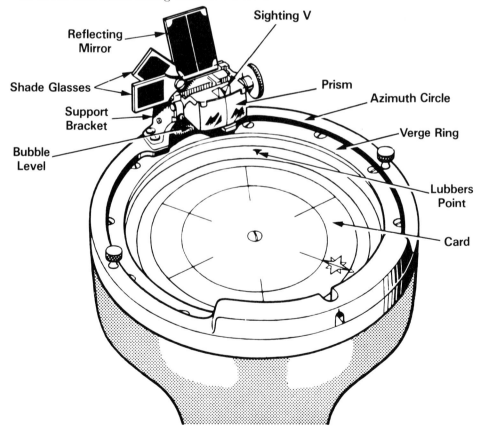

Fig. 9–1.   Azimuth circle

Taking bearings

The azimuth circle shown in Fig. 9–1 is designed so that the accurate alignment of the circle itself is not essential, and therefore a foresight is not fitted. The optical principles on which the instrument is designed are such that, provided the object is seen through the V, the correct bearing can be read, whether or not the circle itself is aligned to point at the object. A line is engraved on the face of the prism to facilitate the reading of the bearing. An example of a bearing being taken of a chimney is given in Fig. 9–2. It is not absolutely essential for the azimuth circle and repeater to be horizontal when the bearing of a surface object is being taken, and a slight skew will not affect the reading. In both cases in Fig. 9–2, the bearing of the chimney is 355°.

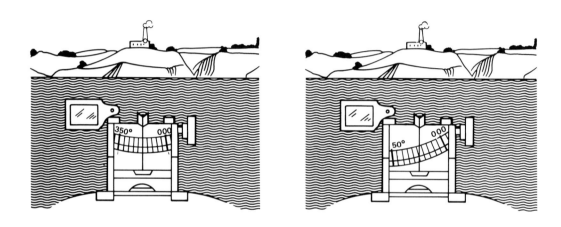

Fig. 9–2.   Taking a bearing

To take a bearing of an object at high altitude, the reflection of the object in the reflector should be sighted through the V sight, and the circle trained until the reflection is on the engraved line on the reflector. The bearing is then read on the engraved line on the prism. During this operation, care should be taken to keep the circle horizontal by means of the bubble level.

It is sometimes difficult to read off the bearing of a terrestrial object when observing into strong sunlight. Usually a judicious manipulation of the sighting prism and the reflecting mirror will overcome this problem.

METHODS OF OBTAINING A POSITION LINE

A position line may be obtained from:

1. A compass bearing.
2. A relative bearing.

3. A transit.
4. A horizontal angle.
5. A vertical sextant angle of an object of known height.
6. A range by distance meter when the height of the object is known.
7. A range by rangefinder.
8. A rising or dipping range.
9. Soundings.
10. A radio fixing aid.
11. A radar range.
12. An astronomical observation.
13. A sonar range.

Compass bearing

When the compass bearing of an object is taken, the position line thus obtained is called a *line of bearing* (*see* page 175).

When a bearing of the edge of an object is taken, it is usual to distinguish the right-hand edge with the symbol ———▶| and the left-hand edge with the symbol |◀———. A vertical edge gives the best bearing. Allowance must be made for the height of tide when taking the bearing of a sloping edge of land, as the charted edge is the high water line (Mean Sea Level in areas where there are no tides).

Details of taking bearings by radar are given in Chapter 15.

Relative bearing

A line of bearing may be obtained by noting the direction of an object relative to the direction of the ship's head.

If the lighthouse shown in Fig. 9–3 is observed to be 60° on the starboard bow (Green 60° or 060° Relative) when the ship is steering 030°, the true bearing of the lighthouse is 090°, which may be drawn on the chart.

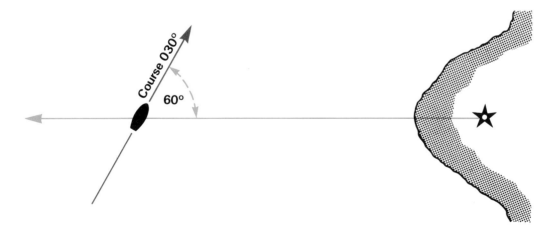

Fig. 9–3. Position line by relative bearing

Transit

If an observer sees two objects in line, then he must be somewhere on the line which joins them, as shown in Fig. 9–4. Ideally, the distance between the observer and the nearer object should be less than three times the distance between the objects in transit. The transit is then sufficiently 'sensitive' for the movement of one object relative to the other to be immediately apparent. It can of course be used at greater distances. It is also most useful for checking the error of the compass (*see* page 219).

The symbol ϕ is used for a transit. The symbol $\neq$ is used by the Hydrographer to designate transits on Admiralty charts, and shown in Chart Booklet 5011, *Symbols and Abbreviations used on Admiralty Charts*.

Fig. 9–4.   Position line by transit

Horizontal angle

Since all angles subtended by a chord in the same segment of a circle are equal, it follows that, if the observer measures by sextant or by compass the horizontal angle between two objects, he must lie somewhere on the arc of a circle which passes through them and which contains the angle observed.

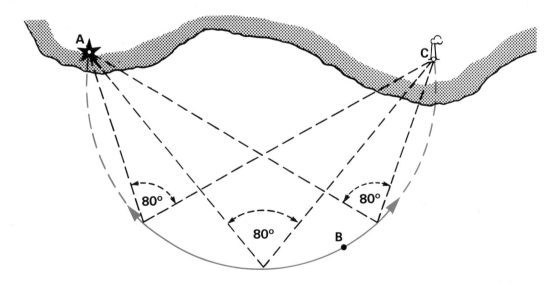

Fig. 9–5.   Position line by horizontal angle

In Fig. 9–5, the angle between the lighthouse A and the chimney C has been measured by sextant and found to be 80°. The ship's position must therefore lie on the arc of the circle ABC along which the angle between A and C is always 80°.

Horizontal sextant angles are dealt with more fully later in this chapter (page 224).

Vertical sextant angle of an object of known height

If the angle subtended at the observer's eye by a vertical object of known height is measured, the solution of a right-angled triangle will give the observer's distance from the base of the object. The position line will then be the circumference of a circle which has this distance as its radius (Fig. 9–6). A vertical sextant angle may be used as a 'danger angle', as may be a horizontal sextant angle, to clear a danger (*see* Chapter 12).

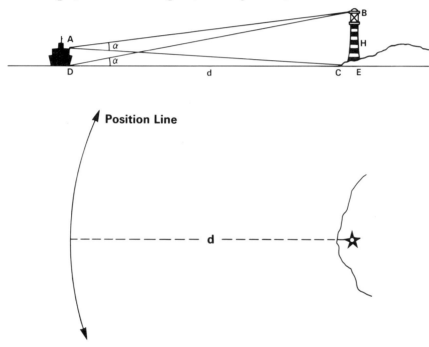

Fig. 9–6. Position line by vertical sextant angle

Whole of the object above the horizon

In Fig. 9–6, DE is the required distance, AD is the height of the observer, BE is the height of the object, while CE is the distance from the shoreline to the point below the object. The observer measures the angle BAC. The required angle is BDE but, provided that DC is greater than BE and BE greater than CE, no appreciable error* is introduced if BAC is used instead.

---

* If the point observed is vertically over the shore horizon, and DE is greater than BE, the error in position will be less than the height of eye AD. If the point is not vertically over the shore horizon as in Fig. 9–6, provided DC is greater than BE and BE greater than the horizontal distance CE, the error in position is less than 3 times the height of eye AD.

The distance DE may be expressed as follows:

$$DE = BE \cot BAC \qquad \qquad \ldots \textbf{9.1}$$

The charted height is given above the level of MHWS or MHHW (*see* page 119) and so this must be adjusted for the height of tide. If no such allowance is made, the calculated distance will be less than the actual distance.

It should be remembered that the charted height of a lighthouse is taken from the centre of the lens and not the top of the structure.

Norie's Nautical Tables solve the triangle for ranges between 1 cable and 7 miles and heights between 7 metres (23 feet) and 600 metres (1969 feet).

EXAMPLE

A vertical sextant angle of a lighthouse, charted height above MHWS 40 metres, is 0°46'.2. The height of tide is calculated as being 2.12 metres below MHWS. The Index Error of the sextant is +1'.2. What is the range of the light?

observed angle	0°46'.2	
index error	+1'.2	
corrected angle	0°47'.4	(0°.79)
charted height	40 metres	
	+ 2.12	
corrected height	42.12m (0'.02274 n miles)	
range	= corrected height × cot corrected angle	... **(9.1)**
	= 0.02274 cot 0°.79	
	= 1.65 n miles	

Norie's Tables give a distance of 1.65 n miles.

Base of the object observed below the observer's horizon

It is sometimes useful to be able to obtain a position line from an object such as a distant mountain peak, where the base is below the observer's horizon. The method of obtaining a position line in such circumstances is set out in Appendix 6.

Long-range position lines obtained in this way are of little value if refraction different from normal (*see* Volume II of this manual) is suspected. Abnormal refraction is likely to be present when the temperatures of the water and air differ considerably.

Range by distance meter when the height of the object is known

This method is based on the principle of the vertical sextant angle.

The various types of distance meter supplied to HM Ships are described in Volume III of this manual. They are useful because no calculation is needed, the range being obtained by a direct reading.

Range by rangefinder

The rangefinder is described in Volume III. This method is useful for finding the distance of a single light at night, or the distance of an object unsuitable for a vertical sextant angle.

Rising or dipping range

This method is useful at night for finding the distance of a light when it first appears above or dips below the horizon.

The theoretical distance of the sea horizon for a height of h metres is $1.92\sqrt{h}$ sea miles, but the effect of normal atmospheric refraction is to increase this by about 8%. Thus, the distance of the sea horizon may be found from the formula:

$$\text{distance} = 2.08\sqrt{h} \text{ sea miles} \qquad \qquad \ldots 9.2$$

where h is measured in metres, or

$$\text{distance} = 1.15\sqrt{h} \text{ sea miles} \qquad \qquad \ldots 9.3$$

where h is measured in feet.

The distance of the ship from the horizon and the light beyond the horizon can both be found by this method. These ranges added together give the distance of the ship from the light. The distances may also be found from *Norie's Tables* or the Geographical Range Table in the *Admiralty List of Lights and Fog Signals* (*see* Chapter 10). As these tables make different allowances for refraction,* the distances obtained will be different. Such ranges must be treated with caution (*see* Chapter 10).

EXAMPLE

A shore light 40 metres above the water is observed from the bridge to dip below the horizon. Height of eye is 12 metres. What is the range of the light?

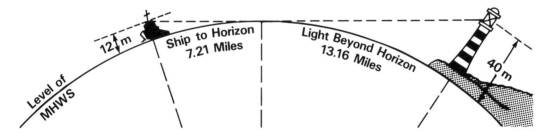

Fig. 9–7.   Position line from a dipping range

From formula **(9.2)**, the following ranges are obtained:

range of horizon for height of eye of 12 metres	7.21 sea miles
range of horizon for height of eye of 40 metres	13.16 sea miles
range of light	20.37 sea miles

The range given in the Geographical Range Table in the *List of Lights* is 19.9 sea miles. Thus, the range at which the light dips is approximately 20 miles.

---

* *Norie's Tables* use the formula: distance of the sea horizon $d = 2.095\sqrt{h}$, where h is the height in metres. The *List of Lights* uses the formula: $d = 2.03\sqrt{h}$, where h is the height in metres, or $d = 1.12\sqrt{h}$, where h is the height in feet.

When abnormal refraction exists (page 202), this method of obtaining a range is inaccurate.

As the height of a light is given above MHWS or MHHW (page 119), a correction to the height should be made for the height of tide.

Soundings

Soundings are frequently of value in establishing a position line. In areas where a particular depth contour on the chart is sharply defined and reasonably straight, or in approaches to the land where there is a steady decrease in depth, a position line may be obtained. Good examples of this are in the south-western approaches to the British Isles, where the depth decreases rapidly from 2000 to 200 metres in a distance of some 10 to 20 miles, or in the southern approaches to Beachy Head, where the depth shoals from 50 to 30 metres in about $1\frac{1}{2}$ miles. In the latter case, it will be necessary to allow for the height of tide, and to ensure that the echo sounder (*see* Volume III) is reading accurately.

Radio fixing aids

Position lines from radio fixing aids may be in the form of a bearing, for example MFDF, or in the form of a hyperbolic position line, for example Decca or Omega. Full details of radio fixing aids are given in Volume III.

Radar range

Radar may be used to obtain a position line in the form of a circular arc at both short and long ranges off the land. Full details are given in Chapter 15.

Astronomical observation

Position lines may be obtained from the observation of heavenly bodies—the sun, moon, stars and planets. Although the position line is circular, to all intents and purposes it may be treated as a straight line, except in the case of very high altitudes. Full details of astronomical observations are given in Volume II.

Sonar range

Provided that the ship is fitted with sonar equipment, it is possible to obtain a range of an underwater object such as a rock which can be used for navigational purposes as a position line in the form of a circular arc. It is, however, often impossible to determine precisely from which part of the sea-bed the range is being obtained.

THE TRANSFERRED POSITION LINE

Suppose, as shown in Fig. 9–8, that a lighthouse bears 034° from the ship at 1600 and that the ship is steaming 090° at 8 knots. What information is available about the ship's position at 1630? There is no tidal stream or wind.

Draw a line *ACE* in a 214° direction from the light. This is the position line at 1600. The position at 1600 is unknown, although the ship must be on the position line *ACE*. Assume the ship is at *A*, *C* and *E* in turn and project *AB, CD*,

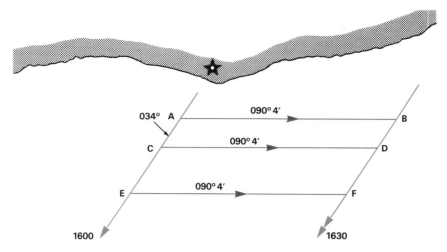

Fig. 9–8. The transferred position line

EF, respectively in a direction equivalent to a 30 minute run, in this case 090°
4 miles. Join *BDF*.

The ship must be on the line *BDF* at 1630. *BDF* is known as the *transferred
position line* and is parallel to the original. It is distinguished by a double
arrowhead at the outer end.

If the ship is set by tidal stream during the run, the point through which to
draw the position line must be determined in two steps, as shown in Fig. 9–9.

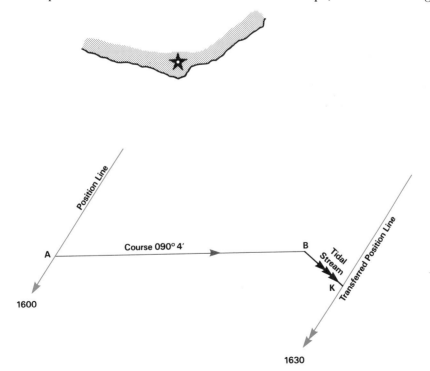

Fig. 9–9. The transferred position line, allowing for tidal stream

1. Lay off, from any point on the original position line, the course and distance (*AB*) steamed by the ship in the interval.
2. From *B* lay off *BK*, which is the direction and distance the ship is estimated to have been set, in the interval, by the tidal stream. The position line is now transferred through *K*.

The use of a single transferred position line

When two position lines cannot be obtained, a single one may often be of use in clearing some danger or making a harbour. For example, suppose that the course to be steered up a narrow and ill-defined harbour is 080°, as in Fig. 9–10.

The ship, steaming 180°, observes the time at which the lighthouse *L* bears 080°. The time taken to run to the 'wheel over' point *B* (*see* page 185) is calculated, allowing for wind and stream, and at the end of this time the ship alters course to 080°. It is clear that, no matter where the ship was on the original position line *AL*, she will turn on to the transferred position line *CK*, which will lead her into harbour, provided that the run between *A* and *B* has been calculated accurately.

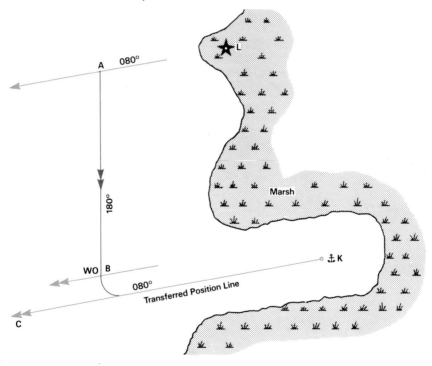

Fig. 9–10.   The use of a single transferred position line

FIXING THE SHIP

A fix is the position obtained by the intersection, at a suitable angle, of two or more position lines from terrestrial objects. Unless the position lines are obtained at practically the same time, one or more of them must be transferred, as described later.

The most common methods of obtaining a fix are as follows:

1. Cross bearings.
2. A bearing and a range.
3. A bearing and a sounding.
4. A bearing and a horizontal angle from which a range may be calculated.
5. A transit and an angle.
6. Two bearings of a single object, with a time interval between observations (running fix).
7. A line of soundings.
8. Two or more ranges.
9. Radio fixing aids (described in Volume III).
10. Astronomical observations (described in Volume II).

Fixing using horizontal sextant angles and bearing lattices is described later in this chapter (page 224).

Fixing by cross bearings

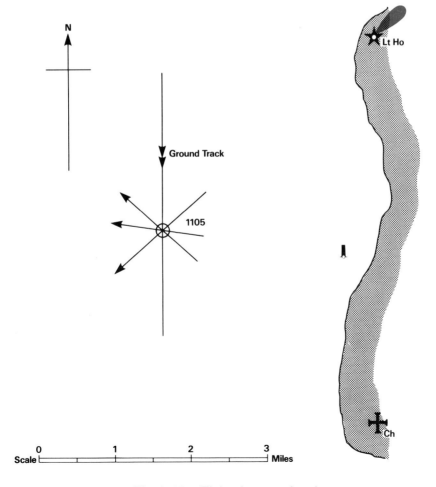

Fig. 9–11.   Fixing by cross bearings

When bearings are obtained from two different objects at the same time, the ship's position must be at the point of intersection of the two lines of bearing.

For example, in Fig. 9–11, assuming that the lighthouse bore 049° and at the same time the church bore 132°, the point of intersection of these two bearings is the ship's position.

To avoid error, a third bearing (called a *check bearing*) should always be taken at the same time and should pass through the point of intersection of the other two bearings. In Fig. 9–11, a check bearing of the beacon was 099°.

The cocked hat

When three bearings are taken from a moving ship, the resulting position lines may not meet in a point but are more likely to form a triangle known as a *cocked hat*. This is illustrated in Fig. 9–12.

Three bearings are taken from a ship steaming 180° at 20 knots. The beacon bore 057° at $1059\frac{1}{2}$, the chimney 127° at $1059\frac{3}{4}$ and the ⟶◄ rock 084° at 1100. If the three position lines are plotted without any consideration being given to the course and distance being steamed between $1059\frac{1}{2}$ and 1100, a cocked hat will be formed; its size depends on the time taken to fix, the course and speed of the ship and scale of the chart. If, however, the position lines for the beacon and the chimney are transferred the correct amount for the distance steamed (180° 0'.17 for the beacon and 180° 0'.08 for the chimney), the cocked hat disappears and the ship's position is found at X at 1100.

The cause of a cocked hat may be any of the following:

1. Time interval between observations.
2. Error in identifying the object.
3. Error in plotting the lines of bearing.
4. Inaccuracy of observation resulting from the limitations of the compass.
5. Inaccuracy of the survey or the chart.
6. Compass error unknown or incorrectly applied.

If the cocked hat is large, the work should be revised to eliminate (1), (2) and (3). Error (1) may be eliminated by reducing the time interval or by applying the 'run', as in Fig. 9–12.

Error (4) should never be greater than $\frac{1}{4}$° with modern compass repeaters and may generally be disregarded.

Error (5) may be judged as described in Chapter 6.

Methods of eliminating error (6) are described later in this chapter (page 219).

A more detailed treatment of errors in lines of bearing is given in Appendix 7.

Fixing by a bearing and a range

A visual bearing may be combined with a range to obtain a fix. Examples of position lines from ranges have already been given in this chapter.

Fixing by a bearing and a sounding

On approaching the land, a position may be obtained in places where the depth

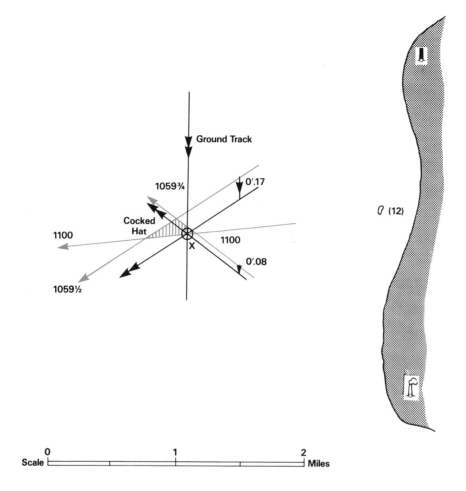

Fig. 9–12.   The cocked hat

is changing steadily, by observing a visual bearing and a sounding simultaneously. Before plotting the sounding position line, an allowance must be made for the height of the tide and also the draught of the ship if the echo sounder is set to read depths below the keel and not the waterline.

The fix will not be reliable unless the depth contours are clearly defined and crossed as nearly as possible at right angles.

This type of fix is illustrated in Fig. 9–13 (page 210).

At 1000 St Anthony's Head bears $342\frac{1}{2}°$ at the same time as a depth below the keel of 47 metres is recorded on the echo sounder. Draught is 6.1 metres, height of tide 3.1 metres. The sounding position line is drawn along the 50 metre depth contour $(47 + 6.1 - 3.1 = 50 \text{ m})$ and where it intersects with the bearing of $342\frac{1}{2}°$ is the position at 1000.

Fixing by a bearing and a horizontal angle from which a range may be calculated

This method is useful when the ship is passing a small island, the compass bearings of the two edges giving too small an angle of cut, and a ranging aid

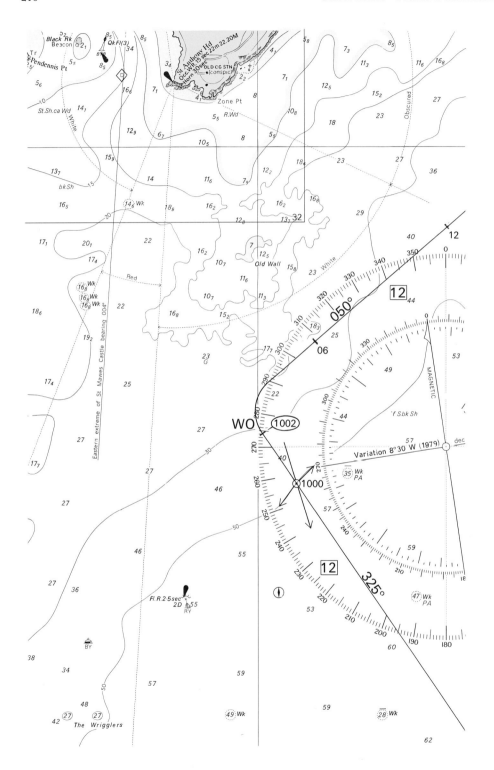

Fig. 9–13.   Fixing by a bearing and a sounding

such as radar or rangefinder is not available. In such a case, observe the bearing of one edge and take a horizontal sextant angle between the edges. From the width of the island as measured on the chart, the range of the ship may be calculated.

EXAMPLE

The sextant angle between the extremes of an island 0.7 miles wide (Fig. 9–14) was found to be 7°, and at the same time the left-hand edge bore 085°.

To find the distance of the ship from the island, let R miles equal the distance. Then, since arc = radius × the angle in radians:

$$\frac{R}{0.7} = \frac{360}{2\pi \times 7}$$

$$\therefore R = 5.73 \text{ miles}$$

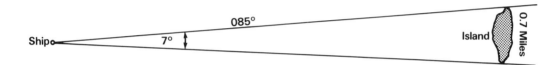

Fig. 9–14.   Fixing by a bearing and a horizontal angle

Fixing by a transit and an angle

A transit is observed at the same time as a horizontal sextant angle is taken between the nearer object of the transit and a third object. The position is the intersection of the transit and the arc of the circle obtained from the horizontal sextant angle (*see* Fig. 9–5).

Such a position has the advantage that no compass is required when using this method.

Fixing by two bearings of a single object, with a time interval between observations (running fix)

If two position lines are obtained at different times, the position of the ship can be found by transferring the first position line to the time of taking the bearing for the second position line, as described on page 204. The point of intersection of the second position line and the transferred position line is the ship's position at the time of the second observation.

*Method 1. To obtain a fix from two position lines obtained at different times, when the tidal stream is known**

EXAMPLE

(See Fig. 9–15.) A ship is steering 090° at 8 knots. The tidal stream is estimated as setting 135° at 3 knots.

At 1600 a lighthouse bore 034°. At 1630 the same lighthouse bore 318°. Find the position of the ship at 1630.

A is any point on the first position line.

AB is the course and distance run by the ship in 30 minutes.

BC is the amount of tidal stream experienced in 30 minutes.

The point where the first position line, transferred and drawn through C, cuts the second position line is the ship's position at 1630, D.

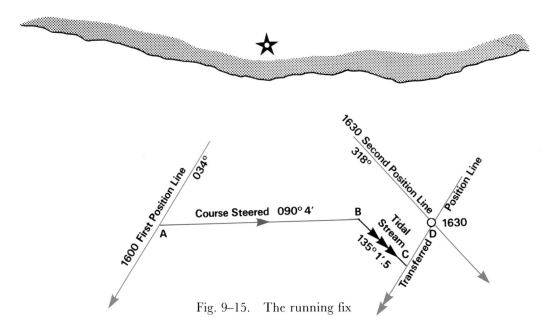

Fig. 9–15.   The running fix

Method 2. To obtain a fix from two position lines obtained at different times, when the tidal stream is unknown but a previous fix has recently been obtained[†]

EXAMPLE

(See Fig. 9–16.) At 1700 a ship was fixed at A, and was steering 180°. At 1800 observed bearing of R was 090°. At 1836 observed bearing of R was 053°. Required: the fix at 1836 and the stream experienced from 1700 to 1836.

Draw AE, the course steered, cutting the first position line in B. On the line AE insert C such that BC is 36 minutes run *at the speed given by AB*. Transfer the

---

* The accuracy of this fix will depend on the accuracy of the estimated run between bearings, and it is therefore essential to make due allowance for the wind and stream experienced by the ship during this interval.

† This method should only be used over a period, or in an area, in which it is certain that the strength and direction of the stream remain constant. Otherwise the fix will be inaccurate.

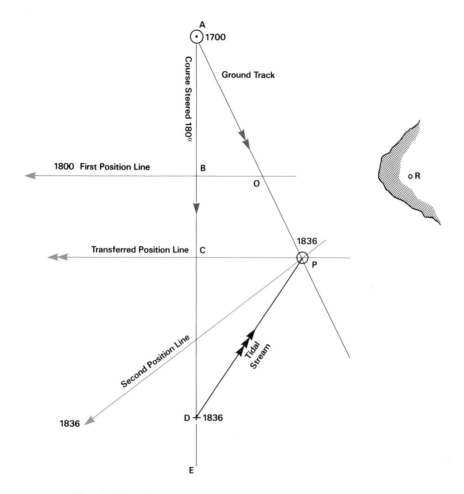

Fig. 9–16. The running fix with unknown tidal stream

first position line through C. The point P, where this cuts the second position line, is then the fix at 1836. AP is the course and distance made good between 1700 and 1836.

To obtain the tidal stream, plot D, the DR at 1836, along AE at the speed of the ship through the water. Join this to P; then DP is the direction and set of the stream between 1700 and 1836.

Proof. Since the triangles ABO and ACP are similar, $AO/OP = AB/BC$. AO and OP represent the speeds made good in 1 hour and 36 minutes respectively. The line AE could have been drawn in any direction which cuts the two position lines and, provided the proportion $AB:BC$ remained the same, the transferred position line would always cut the second one at P. The tidal stream cannot, however, be found unless AE is plotted as described above.

Method 3. Doubling the angle on the bow: the four-point bearing

This special type of running fix may be plotted as a conventional running fix but using a quicker method as follows:

The angle between the ship's head and the bearing of an object is measured;

Fig. 9–17.   Doubling the angle on the bow

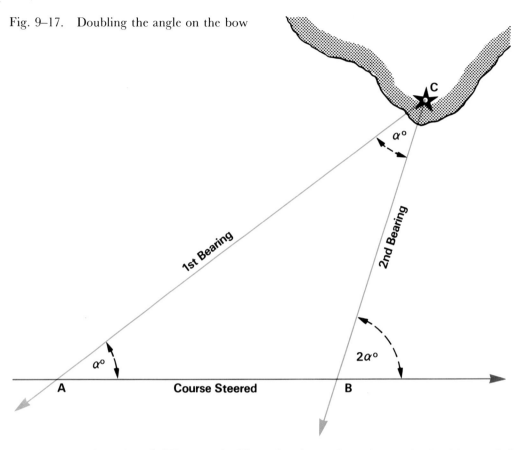

suppose it to be $\alpha°$ (Fig. 9–17). Note the time when the angle doubles to $2\alpha°$. The distance from the light CB is equal to the distance run between the two bearings AB, since ABC is an isosceles triangle.

If the angle $\alpha°$ is equal to 45°, the distance run AB is equal to the beam distance when the relative bearing has doubled to 90°. This method of fixing the ship when the object is abeam is known as the *four-point bearing*.

Doubling the angle on the bow will not give an accurate position if there is any leeway, tidal stream, current or surface drift across the course. In that event, the observation should be plotted as a running fix.

The general theory of doubling the angle on the bow in a current or tidal stream is set out in Appendix 7.

Method 4. Estimating the distance at which a ship will pass abeam of an object

The four-point bearing suffers from the disadvantage that the distance an object will pass abeam is not known until the object is abeam. Certain pairs of angles shown on the table will give this distance.

Table 9–1

ϕ	θ
$26\frac{1}{2}°$	45°
30°	$53\frac{3}{4}°$
35°	67°
40°	79°

Provided that the difference between the cotangents of the two measured angles is 1, the distance run between the two angles equals the distance at which the object will pass abeam. This is illustrated in Fig. 9–18.

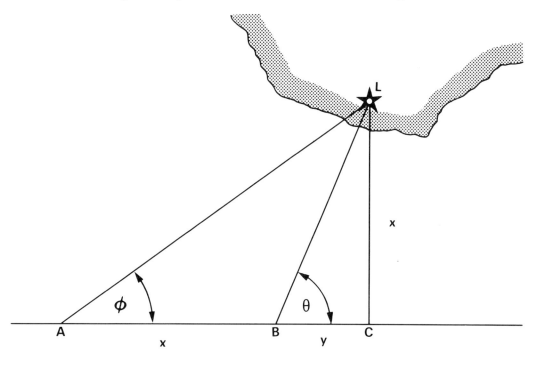

Fig. 9–18.   To estimate the distance at which a ship will pass abeam of an object

$$\cot \theta \ = \frac{y}{x}$$

$$\cot \phi \ = \frac{x + y}{x}$$

$$\cot \phi - \cot \theta \ = \frac{x + y}{x} - \frac{y}{x}$$

$$\cot \phi - \cot \theta \ = 1 \qquad\qquad\qquad \ldots \mathbf{9.5}$$

A great number of pairs of angles will satisfy this requirement, although the limitations of the equipment in use will frequently prevent one or other bearing being measured to the degree of accuracy required, and in any case it is undesirable to use this procedure when the object is too fine on the bow as the change in angle required is very small. Once again, leeway, tidal stream, etc. across the course will prevent an accurate fix being obtained.

The first pair of angles, $26\frac{1}{2}°$ and $45°$ is useful, as the distance run between the two observations, AB, not only equals the abeam distance CL, but also equals the distance to go until the object is abeam, BC.

A further method of estimating the distance that an object will pass abeam, but not involving a running fix, is given on page 327.

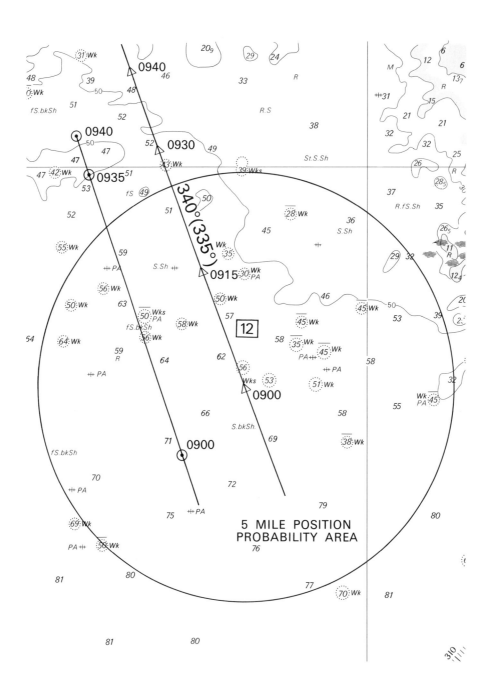

Fig. 9–19.   Finding the position by a line of soundings

Fixing by a line of soundings

When there are no objects suitable for observation, it is sometimes possible to obtain a position from soundings. Although this method does not strictly conform to the definition of a fix as previously given, in that it does not involve the intersection of two or more position lines, a positive indication of the ship's position can be obtained as follows.

Sound at regular intervals, noting the depth. Correct the soundings for the height of tide, also for draught if measured below the keel. On a piece of tracing paper draw in a meridian of longitude and a parallel of latitude. Lay off the ship's estimated ground track at the scale of the chart in use. Along this track plot the reduced soundings at the scale of the chart in use. Place the tracing paper on the chart in the vicinity of the ship's Estimated Position and, using the meridian and the parallel as a guide in keeping it approximately straight, move it about until the soundings on the tracing paper coincide with those on the chart.

The frequency at which soundings should be taken depends on the speed of the ship and the spacing and nature of the soundings on the chart.

The procedure is illustrated in Figs. 9–19 and 9–20.

Caution: The approximate position found from a line of soundings should always be used with caution, because it is often possible to fit a line of soundings in several positions on a chart.

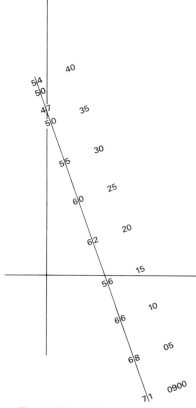

Fig. 9–20. A line of soundings

EXAMPLE

At 0900 a ship is in the estimated position shown in Fig. 9–19, believed to be accurate within 5 miles. She is on a course of 335° 12 knots. Tidal stream is estimated to be setting 080° 1 knot, and her estimated course and speed made good are 340° 11.7 knots. The following soundings, corrected for the height of tide are obtained:

0900	71 m	0930	55 m
0905	68 m	0935	50 m
0910	66 m	0936½	47 m
0915	56 m	0939	50 m
0920	62 m	0940	54 m
0925	60 m		

Determine the position at 0940.

The soundings are plotted (Fig. 9–20) on a sheet of tracing paper along the estimated ground track, 340° 11.7 knots at the scale of the chart. A meridian of longitude and a parallel of latitude are also plotted to help keep the line of soundings lined up to the track.

From a study of the chart concerned, of which Fig. 9–19 is an extract, it is immediately evident from the initial sounding at 0900 that the ship is either further back along the track (2′) or is some distance off to the south-east (3′), or south-west to west (2′ to 4′). The soundings at 0905 and 0910 eliminate the possibility that the ship is to the east of track. The soundings at 0915 onward indicate that the ship may be on track but some 2¼ to 2½ miles astern of the estimated position. The 0915 sounding indicates that the ship is passing over or close to a wreck or other obstruction on the sea-bed. However, the possibility that the ship may be on track but astern or some 4′ to the west is eliminated by the soundings between 0935 and 0940, which clearly indicate the ship is passing over the bank 2½ miles long by ¾ miles wide lying to the west of the 0930 estimated position. The tracing may now be matched to the charted soundings and the positions at 0900, 0935 and 0940 plotted, showing that the ship is some 2 miles to the west and 1 mile astern of the estimated position.

This example shows that it may take some time to establish a position from a line of soundings with a reasonable degree of confidence.

Fixing by two or more ranges

This usually becomes necessary when visual bearings are not available. The intersection of the range arcs fixes the ship's position. This is the normal method of fixing using radar and is described in detail in Chapter 15.

Radio fixing aids

Full details on fixes obtained from radio fixing aids are given in Volume III. General comments on the use of radio fixing aids for coastal navigation may be found in Chapter 12.

It should also be appreciated that it is quite possible to determine the position separately by a radio aid and by visual means, yet find a significant (more than 100 metres) difference in the latitude and longitude in each case. This discrepancy may arise from the use of different geographical datums for the different fixing sources, or it may arise from unknown errors in the radio aid itself. So the navigator may have to adjust his radio aid fix to the visual one. Such information may be available on the chart in the form of a *datum shift*. If not, the discrepancy can be largely eliminated by comparing the radio aid position line or fix with an accurate visual fix, adjusting the former to tie in with the latter.

ERROR IN THE COMPASS AND ELIMINATING THE COCKED HAT

If it seems certain that the cocked hat is caused by compass error alone, then the error must be determined and a correction applied to the plotted bearing.

In the first instance, check that any known error has been correctly applied. A gyro error *high* must be *subtracted* from, and a gyro error *low added* to, the gyro bearing (*see* Chapter 1). Variation and deviation *westerly* must be *subtracted* from, and variation and deviation *easterly added* to, the magnetic compass bearing (*see* Chapter 1). The *deviation* to be applied must be for the *compass course* and not the compass bearing — this is a frequent cause of error in the plotted bearings using a magnetic compass.

The error in the gyro compass and the deviation in the magnetic compass may be checked by any of the following methods:

1. *By a transit.* The compass bearing of two charted objects is observed when they are in line (*see* page 200) and the true or magnetic bearing obtained from the chart. The difference between them will be the gyro error or deviation of the gyro or magnetic compass respectively. For example:

charted transit	079°
gyro compass bearing	081°
gyro error	2° high
charted transit (magnetic)	123°
magnetic compass bearing	120°
deviation (CADET)	3° east (Error East Compass Least)

2. *By azimuth of a heavenly body.* The error of the compass may be found by comparing the observed bearing of a heavenly body with that calculated. Details of the procedure are given on *Weir's azimuth diagram* (to be found in the Miscellaneous Chart Folio 317, *see* page 126) and in *Norie's Tables* (ABC Tables or Amplitudes and Corrections), and also covered in the revised edition Volume II of this manual. The Amplitudes Table (and Corrections) for the rising and setting heavenly body is the most accurate procedure of the three. The HP-41CV calculator, outfit PDQ, may also be used to calculate the true bearing of a heavenly body using the Sight Reduction Table (SRT) sub-routine.

3. *By bearing of a distant object.* The ship may be fixed by horizontal angles, or may be in a known geographical position, e.g. South Railway Jetty, Portsmouth Dockyard. An observed compass bearing of a distant object* may then be compared with the bearing taken from the chart and the error deduced.
4. *By reciprocal bearings with another ship of known compass error.*
5. *By reduction of the cocked hat.* If it seems certain that the cocked hat is due to compass error alone, and none of the above four methods is available to resolve it, then the cocked hat may be reduced and the error found, as follows.

   Assume the error has a definite sign (+) or (−) and is the same for each bearing.[†] Although the actual bearings may be incorrect, the true angles between the objects are known. Two angles may be obtained from three objects. These angles may then be set on a *station pointer* or drawn on a *Douglas protractor* (both instruments are described in Volume III) and the position found by rotating the instrument until the arms or lines go through the charted position of each object. The bearing of the furthest object may then be taken from the chart and compared with the observed bearing, the difference being the error in the compass. The following example illustrates the procedure.

EXAMPLE

The following gyro bearings are taken:

	Beacon Pt	$342\frac{1}{2}°$
	Bolt Tail	$048°$
	Bolt Head	$094°$

What is the gyro error?

The three bearings are plotted (Fig. 9–21) and a cocked hat is obtained. The three bearings are drawn on the matt side of the Douglas protractor (Fig. 9–22, page 222), or the angles between the bearings, $65\frac{1}{2}°$ and $46°$, are set on the station pointer.

The protractor is placed on the chart, matt side down, and rotated until all three lines are in contact with the charted objects. The position *A* may then be pricked through on to the chart. A similar procedure is followed with the station pointer.

If a station pointer or a Douglas protractor is not available, then a sheet of tracing paper should be used instead (*see* page 225). Alternatively, each bearing should be rotated in the same direction, the amount of rotation varying directly with the estimated distance, until all three bearings pass through a point (*see* Fig. 9–21).

* $\frac{1}{2}°$ subtends 100 yards at 6 miles. Provided that one's position is known accurately to within 50 yards, it should be possible to determine the error to the nearest $\frac{1}{2}°$, using an object 6 miles away.

[†] The circumstances in which the errors in the three bearings may be separate and unequal are discussed in Appendix 7.

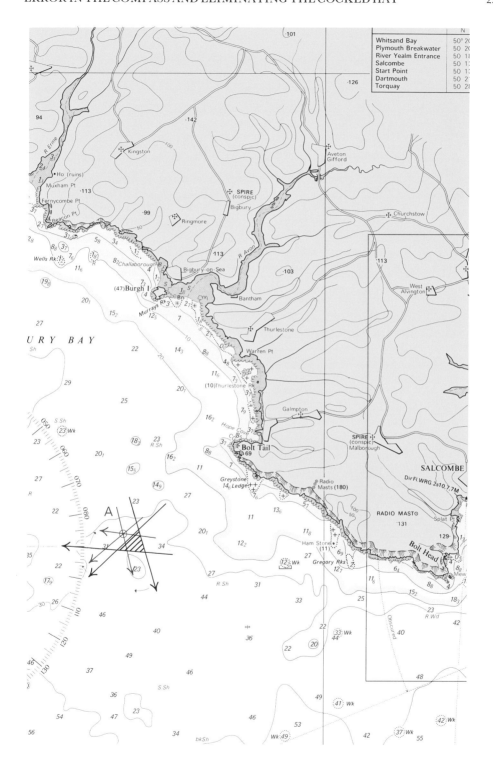

Fig. 9–21. Reduction of the cocked hat

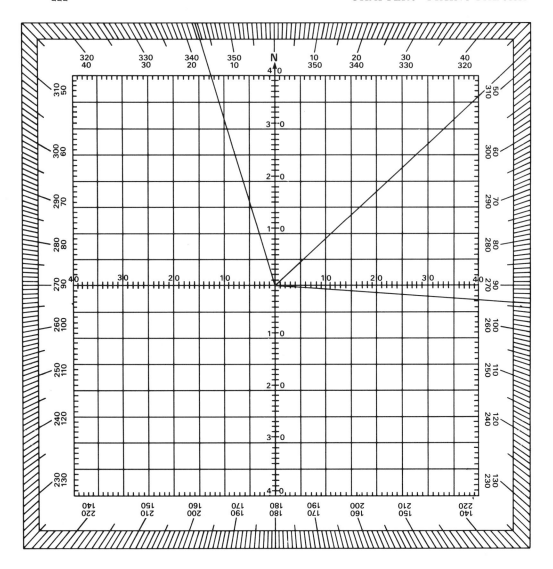

Fig. 9–22. Douglas protractor

The true bearing of the furthest object is obtained from A and compared with the observed bearing, e.g.

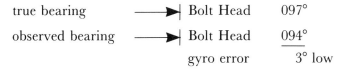

	Bolt Head	097°
true bearing ⟶	Bolt Head	097°
observed bearing ⟶	Bolt Head	094°
	gyro error	3° low

Revised bearings of $345\frac{1}{2}°$ and 051° are plotted from Beacon Point and Bolt Tail respectively to confirm the error.

This example illustrates the danger of assuming that the position of the ship must be somewhere inside the cocked hat. This may frequently not be so, and an assumption on these lines could well place the ship in danger. In Fig. 9–21, the correct position and the centre of the cocked hat are $\frac{1}{4}$ mile apart.

If, however, the cocked hat is very small, then it should normally be safe to assume the ship is in the centre. If, on the other hand, the cocked hat is large yet it seems clear that the error is not due to any of the causes set out on page 208, then almost certainly the fix should be disregarded, and either another fix obtained, or reliance placed upon the EP. If the ship is in the vicinity of danger, it may well be necessary to stop the ship and obtain an accurate position.

If a cocked hat results from an inaccuracy of the survey or the chart as may be the case, for example, in a channel where the charted sides do not correlate, the position should be taken as that corner of the cocked hat which puts the ship closest to danger, dependent upon her subsequent movements. This is illustrated in Fig. 9–23. If, for example, the ship is intending to steer to the northward, the position should be taken as X. If she intends rounding the rocks to the southward, her position should be taken as Y, so that she has sufficient advance before altering course. As a further precaution, the course chosen from Y should be safe to clear the rocks had she actually been at Z.

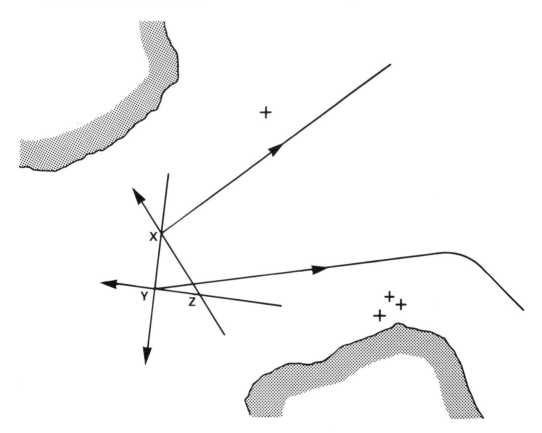

Fig. 9–23. Setting a safe course from a cocked hat fix

In practice, where it is known that such inaccuracies exist, a sensible precaution is to fix using one side of the channel only. If, in Fig. 9–23, the ship is intending to steer to the northward, then marks on the north side of the channel should be chosen, and if steering to the southward, marks on the south side. A cocked hat should not normally be created by accurate bearings in these conditions. It is also a reasonable supposition that the position of the off-lying rocks will probably be tied in with the survey of that particular piece of coastline.

HORIZONTAL SEXTANT ANGLES (HSA) AND VISUAL BEARING LATTICES

It sometimes becomes necessary to navigate to a higher degree of accuracy than that obtainable from normal fixing, while at the same time plotting the fix quickly and maintaining an accurate record of the ship's movements. Examples of the occasions when this may be necessary are mine countermeasures operations, pilotage operations and the anchoring of ships in company.

Two visual methods are available for this type of fixing—horizontal sextant angles and bearing lattices. Radar and radio aids may also be used, and the use of these is described in Volume III.

Fixing by horizontal sextant angles

This method fixes the ship's position by the intersection of two or more position lines; these are found by observing with a sextant the horizontal angles subtended by three or more objects. The method is extremely useful for fixing the ship accurately when moored or at anchor, and for fixing the ship accurately at sea when two trained observers are available.

The advantages of the HSA fix are:

1. It is more accurate than a compass fix, because a sextant can be read more accurately than a compass.
2. It is independent of compass errors.
3. The angles can be taken from any part of the ship.

   The disadvantages are:

1. It can take longer than fixing by compass bearings.
2. Three suitable objects are essential.
3. If the objects are incorrectly charted or incorrectly identified, the fix will be false and the error may not be apparent. For this reason, when a poorly surveyed chart is used, the ship's position should normally be fixed by compass bearings, because inaccuracies in the charted positions of objects will become apparent when lines of bearing drawn on the chart from each object do not meet at a point.

   Errors in HSA fixes are discussed in Appendix 7.

Horizontal sextant angles

A, B and C (Fig. 9–24) are three objects on shore approximately in the same horizontal plane as the observer, and the angles between A and B, B and C are measured. The ship must lie on the arc AOB containing the observed angle between A and B, and on the arc COB containing the observed angle between B

and C. The arcs intersect at B and O; thus, O is the ship's position, as the ship clearly cannot be at B.

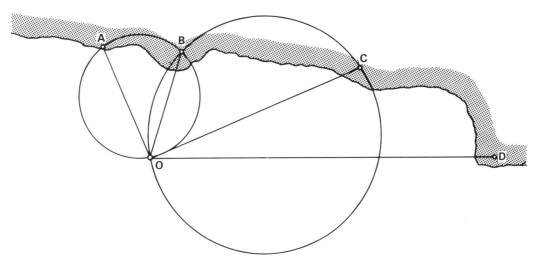

Fig. 9–24.   Fixing by two horizontal sextant angles

To plot the fix, the angles between A and B and between B and C are drawn on a Douglas protractor or set on a station pointer as described on page 220. The instrument is then placed over the chart so that OA, OB and OC pass through the charted positions of A, B, and C. O is then the ship's position.

To guard against incorrect identification, a check angle may be taken between the centre object and a fourth object (D in Fig. 9–24). When a station pointer is used, the fourth angle may be plotted after the fix has been obtained — by holding the instrument steady and moving the appropriate leg to the check angle. This leg should then pass through the fourth object.

The fix shown in Fig. 9–24 would be recorded as follows:

$$A \ 39°12' \ B \ 50°47' \ C$$
$$B \ 73°49' \ D$$

If a station pointer or Douglas protractor is not available, a piece of tracing paper will suffice. The measured angles are drawn from any point on the sheet of tracing paper. The paper is then placed on the chart and rotated until all the lines are in contact with the charted objects. The position may then be pricked through the tracing paper on to the chart.

Strength of the HSA fix

The strength or weakness of an HSA fix may be assessed by the angle of cut between the position circles — the closer to 90°, the better the fix. A major disadvantage of plotting the fix by station pointer or Douglas protractor or tracing paper is that none of these methods shows the position circles.

The position circles may be drawn on the chart using a simple geometrical construction and the angle of cut assessed as shown in Fig. 9–25.

A fix is recorded as follows:

$$A \ 34°15' \ B \ 51°16' \ C$$

The perpendicular bisectors to AB and BC are drawn — HF and KG respectively. The centres O_1 and O_2 of the two relevant position circles through AB and BC may be found as follows (*see* formula **A6.2**):

$$DO_1 = x_1 = \frac{\frac{1}{2}d}{\tan 34°.25} = 37.45 \text{ mm}$$

$$EO_2 = x_2 = \frac{\frac{1}{2}e}{\tan 51°.2667} = 30.48 \text{ mm}$$

where d is the distance on the chart between A and B and e the distance between B and C.

The two position circles, radii AO_1 and BO_2, may now be plotted and the fix at L established.

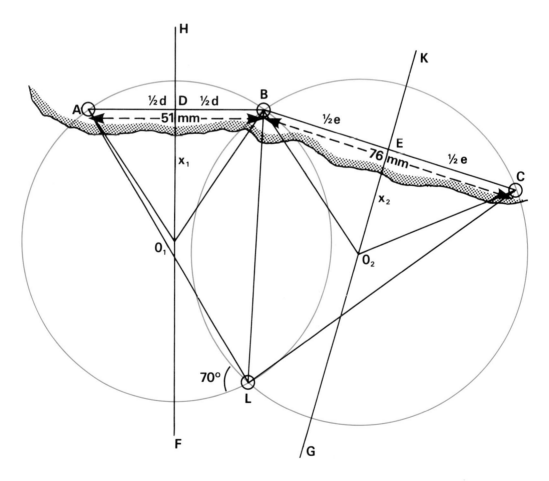

Fig. 9–25. Plotting the HSA fix

The angle of cut between the two position circles is immediately apparent and the closer this is to 90°, the stronger the fix. The angle of cut should if possible never be less than 30°. In Fig. 9–25, the angle of cut at L is about 70°.

If the two angles are small, say about 20° and 30°, the weakness of the fix may be overcome to a greater extent by plotting a third position circle through the two outer marks. (This would be a circle through A, L, C, in Fig. 9–25.)

Choosing objects

Objects should be chosen so that at least one of the following conditions applies:

1. Objects are either all on or near the same straight line, and the centre object is nearest the observer (Fig. 9–26).
2. The centre object is nearer the ship than the line joining the other two (Fig. 9–27, p.228).
3. The ship is inside the triangle formed by the objects or on the outer edge (Fig. 9–28, p.228).
4. At least one of the angles observed changes rapidly as the ship alters position.

The sum of the two angles should be more than 50°. Better results will be obtained if neither angle is less than 30°.

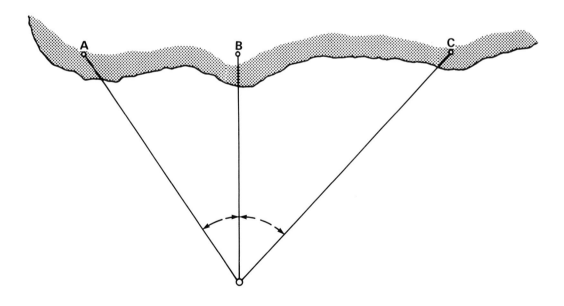

Fig. 9–26.   Suitable objects for a station pointer fix (1)

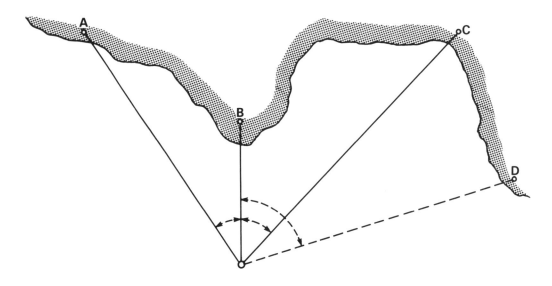

Fig. 9–27.   Suitable objects for a station pointer fix (2)

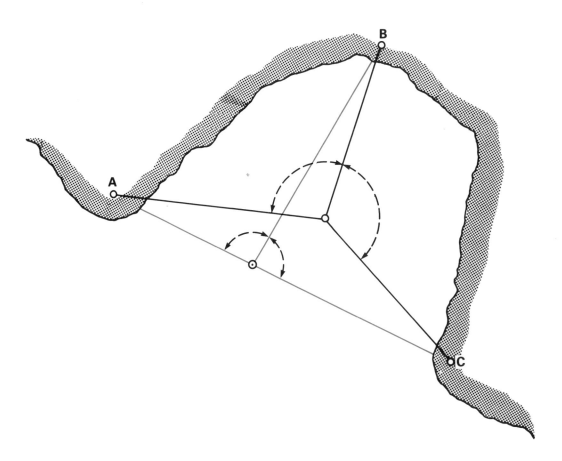

Fig. 9–28.   Suitable objects for a station pointer fix (3)

When not to fix using horizontal angles

If the ship and the objects observed are all on the arc of the same circle (Fig. 9–29), the two position circles become one and the two angles will cut at any point on the arc. A horizontal angle fix is impossible in these circumstances. In Fig. 9–29, the beacon should have been chosen and not the chimney.

It should also be noted that, if such a fix is attempted using bearings *and there is an unknown error in the compass*, this error will not be revealed by plotting. The angles between the objects will be correct but the plotted bearings will always meet at a point on the arc of the circle. The plotted position will differ from the actual position dependent on the amount of the unknown error.

Never fix the ship by horizontal angles or bearings when the ship and the objects observed are all on the arc of the same circle.

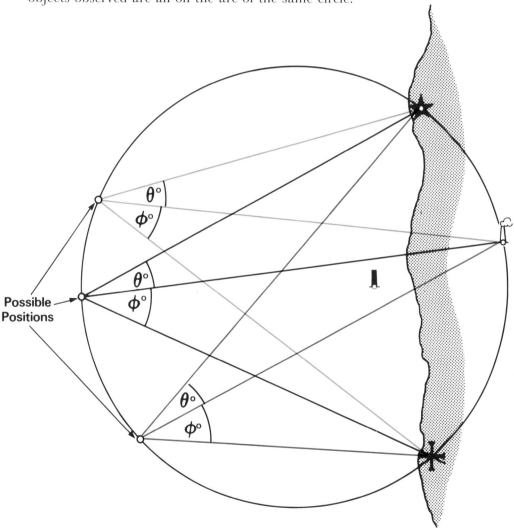

Fig. 9–29.   When not to fix by HSA or bearings

Rapid plotting without instruments

To enable fixes obtained from HSAs to be plotted rapidly without instruments, a lattice of HSA curves (Fig. 9–30) may be constructed on the chart. Sets of curves are plotted from each of two pairs of marks and, if the angle between each pair is observed simultaneously, the fix may be plotted immediately at the intersection of the two curves.

The construction of the HSA lattice is given in Appendix 6.

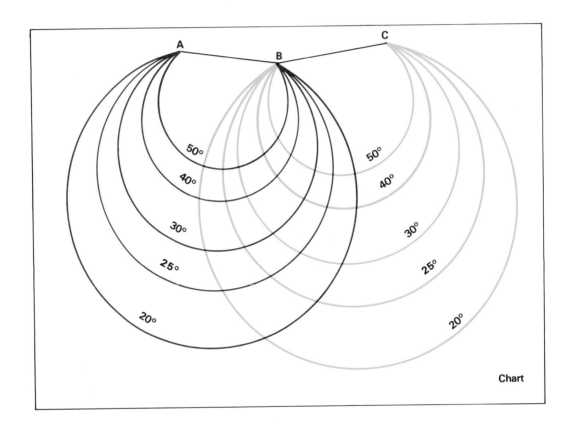

Fig. 9–30.   Lattice of HSA curves

Bearing lattices

The bearing lattice is illustrated in Fig. 9–31. An interlocking lattice of bearing lines from two visual conspicuous objects suitably placed to give an acute angle of cut as close as possible to 60° to 90° (a minimum angle of cut of 30° is acceptable) is drawn on the chart to be used. In Fig. 9–31, the acute angle of cut varies between 55° and 90°. Depending on the distance of the objects and the scale of the chart, lines may be drawn 1° to 5° apart. In Fig. 9–31, the lines are drawn 5° apart, while two 'boxes' are illustrated at 1° apart.

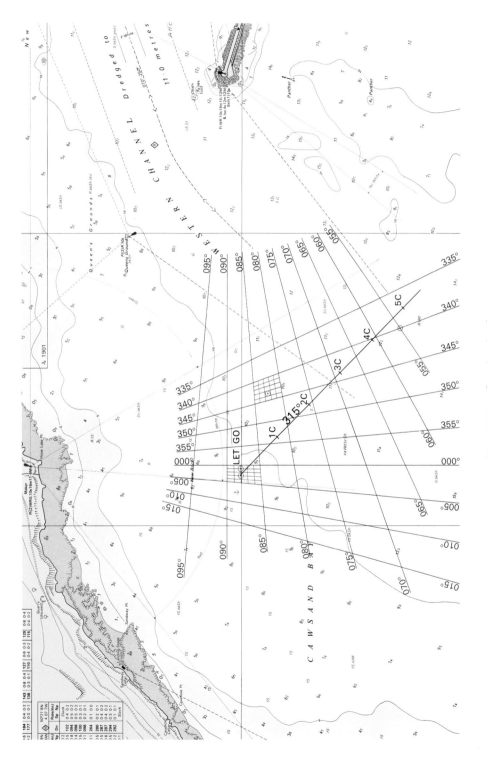

Fig. 9-31. Bearing lattice

If the intended track is then drawn on the chart, in this case 315° towards an anchorage in Cawsand Bay, a simultaneous reading and plotting of the two bearings will give the ship's position immediately and thus the distance off track. For example, if the two bearings are 340° and 055°, it will be seen at once that the ship is some 50 yards off track to port. The intersection of two bearings 343½° and 082½° shows that the ship is 160 yards to starboard of track. If the two bearings at the time of anchoring are 001° and 088°, the ship is slightly to starboard of track by about 30 yards.

To ensure as accurate a track as possible, it is essential that the error of the gyro-compass is checked and allowed for. It is as well to remember that the error does not necessarily remain constant (*see* Volume III) and so it is important to check the compass on each leg of the run.

THE SELECTION OF MARKS FOR FIXING

Choosing objects

Chosen marks should be at least 30° apart in bearing. Ideally, when three objects are observed, they should be 60° apart, two objects, 90°.

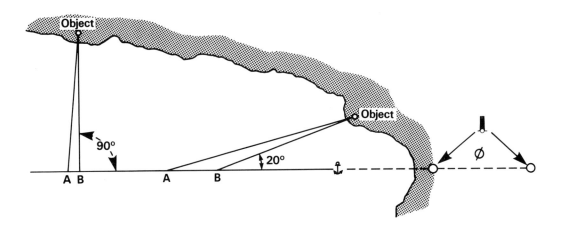

Fig. 9–32.   Effect of a 5° error at various angles of cut

Fig. 9–32 illustrates the difference in position caused by an error of 5° with two cuts of 90° and 20°, *A* being the correct and *B* the incorrect position.

The closer the object, the less will be the difference in position resulting from any error in the bearing.

The chosen marks should not be on the circumference of the same circle as the ship, because any unknown error in the compass will not be revealed when the bearings are plotted (*see* Fig. 9–29).

Marks should also be charted, identifiable, visible from the same repeater if possible, and ahead of the ship rather than astern. When navigating in channels, marks should be selected from one side only to avoid any possible discrepancy arising from a different geographical datum, etc.

Fixing procedure*

1. Look at the chart and select likely marks.
2. Check from the present position (DR or EP) the bearings of the objects to be used.
3. Look out from the bridge and find the marks. It may be necessary to look along the expected bearing with the binoculars if the object is difficult to see. Have at least three marks available; it is no use taking the bearing of one and then having to cast about to find the others.
4. Write down the names of the objects in the Note Book.
5. Observe the bearings as quickly as possible, those ahead and astern first, those for objects whose bearing is changing most rapidly last.[†] Ideally, the time of the last bearing, which is the time of the fix, should coincide with a DR/EP time on the chart (*see* page 191). Subsequent chartwork is simplified.
6. Note the bearings and the time in the Note Book (*see* Fig. 8–13).
7. Plot the fix using the correct symbols (*see* Chapter 8) and the time. If using the magnetic compass, remember that the deviation to be applied is that for the ship's head at the time of observation.
8. Check the DR/EP, verify tidal stream, etc., lay off further DR/EP. Assess the expected bearings of marks for the next fix.
9. Verify time to 'wheel over' (if applicable).
10. Return to lookout.

This procedure should not take the practised navigator more than 1 minute (*see* page 193).

If the fix does not fit, it must not be fudged. It needs to be reworked to eliminate errors (*see* page 208) or retaken. If there is doubt about the ship's position and one is in the vicinity of danger, it may well be a wise precaution to stop the ship. This may prevent a grounding.

The fix shows where the ship was, and the chartwork is not complete until the DR/EP has been laid off from it. The present DR/EP must always be on the chart, also the predicted track at least as far ahead as the time of the next intended fix and the next 'wheel over' if within a reasonable time, say 15 to 20 minutes. (*See also* the section in Chapter 8 on chartwork on passage).

Short cuts to fixing

With experience the navigator will develop short cuts to fixing. Examples of these are as follows, but it should be emphasised that these are not recommended for beginners.

1. The fastest changing bearing will be observed at the exact intended time for the fix: the other bearings will be observed just before or just after this time.
2. The last two digits only of each bearing will be noted, all three bearings being written in the Note Book after the last has been taken.
3. Immediate corrective action, if necessary, will be taken on plotting the fix; the DR/EP will then be generated, and finally the Note Book completed.

---

* Fixing procedure using an assistant is described in Chapter 13.
† A slightly different procedure is desirable when anchoring (*see* Chapter 13).

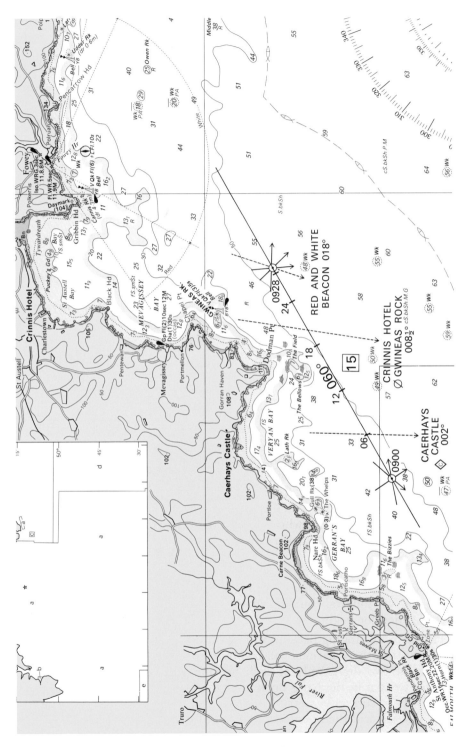

Fig. 9-33. 'Shooting up' shore objects

'Shooting up'

The navigator must always think ahead as to the next suitable object to use for fixing, when navigating along the coast. The procedure to identify suitable marks is known as 'shooting up'. There are several methods available.

1. *DR/EP*
   (*a*) Check from the DR/EP the bearing of a suitable object selected from the chart.
   (*b*) Look along the bearing at the appropriate time, and identify the object. This is illustrated in Fig. 9–33. A fix is obtained at 0900, course 060° speed 15 knots. It is required to identify Caerhays Castle. From the DR position at 0906, Caerhays Castle should bear 002° and just be visible east of the 50 m contour line.

2. *Transits*
   (*a*) Check from the chart the bearing of the chosen object when it comes into transit with a known one.
   (*b*) When the known object is on this bearing, the chosen object should be seen to be in transit (assuming the error in the compass is known).
   In Fig. 9–33, Crinnis Hotel $\frac{3}{4}$ mile ENE of Charlestown Harbour may be identified by its transit with Gwineas Rock, $008\frac{1}{2}°$ just before 0920.

3. *Bearings*
   (*a*) Take the bearings of three known objects and at the same time observe the bearing of a fourth object requiring identification.
   (*b*) Plot the fix.
   (*c*) From the fix plot the fourth bearing and identify the object.
   In Fig. 9–33:

		Dodman Point	$271\frac{1}{2}°$
0928	◄──	Gwineas Rock	318°
		Crinnis Hotel	355°

At the same time, a large red and white beacon bore 018°. This may be identified by plotting 018° from the fix and is seen to be the conspicuous daymark on Gribbin Head.

Identification of uncharted objects

It sometimes happens that a shore object or buoy is visible from the ship but is not shown on the chart. Its position may be determined by bearings or transits in a similar manner to that already described. Fig. 9–34 illustrates the determination of the position of an uncharted buoy, first by bearings, secondly by transits.

Once a shore object has been identified and plotted in this manner, it may be used for fixing the ship.

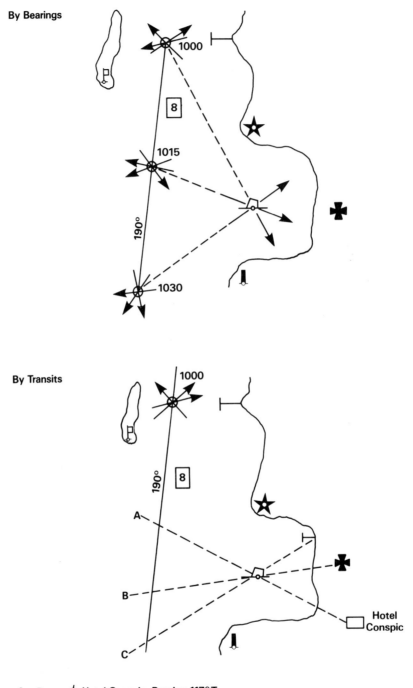

A. Buoy ⏀ Hotel Conspic. Bearing 117° T
B. Buoy ⏀ Church Bearing 083° T
C. Buoy ⏀ Jetty Bearing 061° T

Fig. 9–34.   The identification and plotting of uncharted objects

CHAPTER 10
Visual and Audible Aids to Navigation

This chapter deals in detail with four aids to navigation: lights, buoys and beacons, and fog signals, introduced earlier in Chapters 6 and 7.

LIGHTS

Details of lights may be found as follows:

1. On Admiralty charts, where they are distinguished by a light star and a magenta flare. The greatest detail will usually be found on the largest scale charts; the amount of detail reduces as the scale of the chart decreases, as explained in Chapter 6.
2. In the *Admiralty List of Lights and Fog Signals* (NP 74 to 84), where additional information not given on charts is included.
3. In the *Admiralty Sailing Directions* (NP 1 to 72), where only the height and a description of the light structure is usually to be found.

Characteristics of lights

In order to be correctly identified, a light must maintain a consistent character and exhibit a distinctive appearance. This appearance is called the *character* or *characteristic* of the light. The principal characteristics are usually the sequence of light and darkness and, in some cases, the colour of the light. The colour of a light may be: Blue (Bu);* Green (G); Red (R); White (W); Violet (Vi); Yellow or Orange (Y).* The letters in brackets are the recognised international abbreviations printed on charts and in the *List of Lights and Fog Signals*. The symbol (W) is sometimes omitted from the description on the chart.

Classes of lights

Lights may be divided into three classes, *fixed*, *rhythmic* and *alternating*. *Fixed* lights are those exhibited without interruption. *Rhythmic* lights are those showing a sequence of intervals of light and dark, the whole sequence being repeated at regular intervals. The time taken to complete one sequence is called the *period* of the light. Each element of the sequence (e.g. a flash, an eclipse) is called a *phase*. The characteristic of a rhythmic light may be flashing, quick flashing, isophase or occulting (*see* Table 10–1, pages 238–241) according

(*Text cont. on page 242*)

* Abbreviations for blue and orange lights which may still be found on some older Admiralty charts are Bl and Or respectively.

Table 10–1.   Characteristics of lights

Class of Light	Character	General Description	Abbreviation	Illustration
A – FIXED	Fixed	A light showing continuously and steadily.	F W	
B – RHYTHMIC		A rhythmic light is a light showing intermittently with a regular periodicity. The rhythmic character of a light is the regular periodic rhythm presented by the light.		
1 – Occulting and Group occulting		A light in which the total duration of light in a period is longer than the total duration of darkness and the intervals of darkness (eclipses) are usually of equal duration.		
	(a) Occulting	An occulting light in which an eclipse is regularly repeated.	Oc W	
	(b) Group occulting	An occulting light in which a group of eclipses, specified in number, is regularly repeated. The total duration of light in each period may be equal to the total duration of darkness.	Oc(2)W	
	(c) Composite Group occulting	A light similar to a group-occulting light except that successive groups in a period have different numbers of eclipses. The total duration of light in each period may be equal to the total duration of darkness.	Oc(3 + 4)W	
2 – Isophase	Isophase	A light in which all the durations of light and darkness are clearly equal.	Iso W	
3 – Flashing and Group Flashing	Flashing	A light in which the total duration of light in a period is shorter than the total duration of darkness and the appearances of light (flashes) are usually of equal duration.		

Class of Light	Character	General Description	Abbreviation	Illustration
B – Rhythmic – *(cont'd)*				
	(a) Flashing	A flashing light in which a flash is regularly repeated (at a rate of less than 50 flashes per minute).	Fl W	(Period)
	(b) Long flashing	A single-flashing light in which an appearance of light of not less than 2s duration (long flash) is regularly repeated.	LFl W	Period
	(c) Group flashing	A flashing light in which a group of flashes, specified in number, is regularly repeated.	Fl(3)W	Period
	(d) Composite Group flashing	A light similar to a group-flashing light except that successive groups in a period have different numbers of flashes.	Fl(3 + 2)W	Period
4 – Quick lights		A light in which flashes are repeated at a rate of not less than 50 flashes per minute but less than 80 flashes per minute.		
	(a) Quick	A quick light in which a flash is regularly repeated.	Q W	
	(b) Group quick	A quick light in which a specified group is regularly repeated.	Q(9)W	Period
		See note on page 241	Q(6) + LFl W	Period
	(c) Interrupted quick	A quick light in which the sequence of flashes is interrupted by regular repeated eclipses of constant and long duration.	IQ W	Period
5 – Very quick lights		A light in which flashes are repeated at a rate of not less than 80 flashes per minute but less than 160 flashes per minute.		
	(a) Very quick	A very quick light in which a flash is regularly repeated.	VQ W	

Table 10–1 (cont.)

Class of Light	Character	General Description	Abbreviation	Illustration
B – Rhythmic – (cont'd)	(b) Group very quick	A very quick light in which a specified group of flashes is regularly repeated.	VQ(3)W	
	(c) Interrupted very quick	A very quick light in which the sequence of flashes is interrupted by regularly repeated eclipses of constant and long duration.	IVQ W	
6 – Ultra quick lights		A light in which flashes are repeated at a rate of not less than 160 flashes per minute.		
	(a) Ultra quick	An ultra quick light in which a flash is regularly repeated.	UQ W	
	(b) Interrupted ultra quick	An ultra quick light in which the sequence of flashes is interrupted by eclipses of long duration.	IUQ W	
7 – Morse Code	Morse Code	A light in which appearances of light of two clearly different durations are grouped to represent a character or characters in the Morse Code.	Mo(K)W Mo(AR)W Mo(4)W	
8 – Fixed and Flashing		A light in which a fixed light is combined with a flashing light of higher luminous intensity.		
	(a) Fixed and Flashing	A fixed light varied, at regular intervals, by a single flash of higher luminous intensity.	FFl W	
	(b) Fixed and group flashing	A fixed light varied, at regular intervals, by a group of two or more flashes of higher luminous intensity.	FFl(2)W	

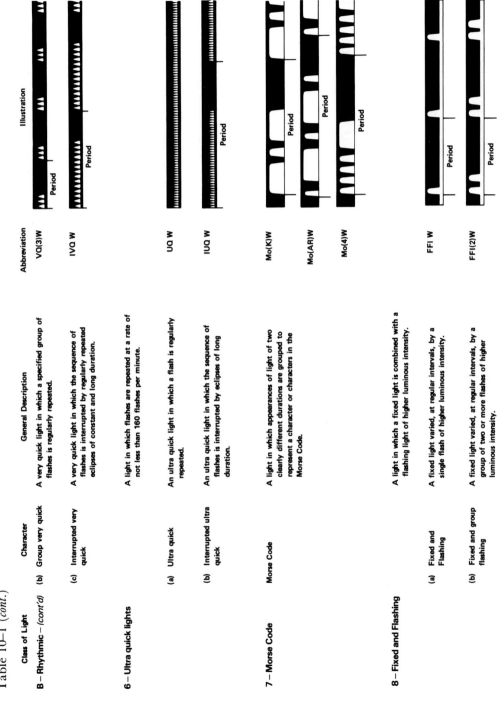

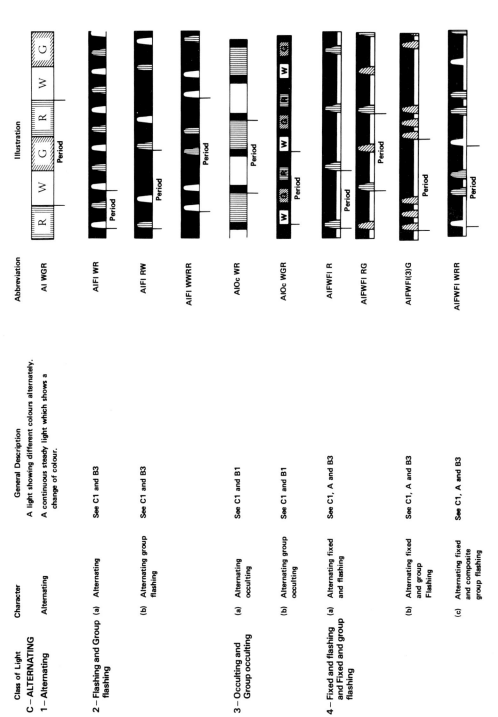

Class of Light	Character		General Description	Abbreviation	Illustration
C – ALTERNATING			A light showing different colours alternately.		
1 – Alternating	Alternating		A continuous steady light which shows a change of colour.	Al WGR	
2 – Flashing and Group flashing	(a)	Alternating flashing	See C1 and B3	AlFl WR	
	(b)	Alternating group flashing	See C1 and B3	AlFl RW	
			See C1 and B3	AlFl WWRR	
3 – Occulting and Group occulting	(a)	Alternating occulting	See C1 and B1	AlOc WR	
	(b)	Alternating group occulting	See C1 and B1	AlOc WGR	
4 – Fixed and flashing and Fixed and group flashing	(a)	Alternating fixed and flashing	See C1, A and B3	AlFWFl R	
			See C1, A and B3	AlFWFl RG	
	(b)	Alternating fixed and group Flashing	See C1, A and B3	AlFWFl(3)G	
	(c)	Alternating fixed and composite group flashing	See C1, A and B3	AlFWFl WRR	

NOTE: The group flashing light (6) + LFl W is an exceptional light character reserved for use in IALA Buoyage System to indicate a South Cardinal mark

to the relative duration of light and darkness. At short distances in clear weather, flashing lights may show a faint continuous light. *Alternating* lights are rhythmic lights showing different colours during each sequence. The period of an alternating light is the time taken to exhibit the complete sequence including the change of colour.

The table, which the reader should study closely, gives details of the various lights and includes a representation of the characteristics of different types of light. It also shows the abbreviations to be found on modern charts.

Admiralty List of Lights and Fog Signals (NP 74 to 84)

A summary of the information available in the *Admiralty List of Lights and Fog Signals* was given in Chapter 7. The full description of a light is tabulated in the *List of Lights* in eight columns:

Column 1 (number). The number assigned to the light, and prefixed by the *List* volume letter, is the International Number and should be quoted when the light is referred to.

Column 2 (name and position). The place, e.g. FALMOUTH HARBOUR, is printed in capitals. Those lights with a range of 15 miles and over are printed in **bold type.** Light-vessels are printed in *ITALIC CAPITALS*, all other floating lights* in *italics*. The letter in brackets after the name indicates the authority responsible for maintaining the light; e.g. in Volume A, (T) is Trinity House, London, (N) the Northern Lighthouse Board, (I) the Commissioners of Irish Lights, and so on.

Column 3 (latitude and longitude). The latitude and longitude given for the light are approximate.

Column 4 (characteristics and intensity). Lights with differing intensities may appear to change their character at different distances because a part of the character may not be visible. Lights exhibiting a very short flash may not be visible at the maximum range calculated from the luminous range diagram (*see* page 248). The intensity of lights may also be given in this column in some volumes; if so, the candle power in candelas is given in italics. Intensities are not listed for lights in countries where nominal range (*see* below) is used. The duration of light and darkness is subject to some degree of fluctuation caused by slight variations in the working speed of the apparatus. The duration of a flash may also appear to be less than normal when seen from a great distance, and haze has the same apparent effect.

Column 5 (elevation in metres). The elevation of the light is the vertical distance between the focal plane of the light and the level of Mean High Water Springs or Mean Higher High Water, whichever is given in *Admiralty Tide Tables* (*see* Chapter 11) or, where there is no tide, above Mean Sea Level.

Column 6 (nominal range, luminous range). The range of visibility is dealt with in detail below. A rhythmic light produced by a rotating apparatus may be detected by its *loom* at ranges greater than that calculated. *Loom* is the diffused glow observed from a light below the horizon caused by atmospheric scattering. It is possible on occasion to obtain a satisfactory bearing from the loom.

---

* Details of light-buoys, etc. of an elevation of less than 8 metres are occasionally included in the *List of Lights*.

Column 7 (structure and height in metres). The height is normally measured from the top of the structure to the ground although this may be different for some areas as shown in the volumes. Where the colour divisions of the structure are horizontal, the term *bands* is used, where vertical, *stripes* and, where the marking is in the form of a spiral, *diagonal stripes*. The shape of top marks is often shown diagrammatically, e.g. 'Orange ∇ on white structure', 'Red and white ◇ on white mast'.

Column 8 (Remarks). *Phase* is normally expressed to tenths of a second and printed in *italics*.

The limits of sectors and arcs of visibility and the alignment of direction lights and leading lights are given *as seen by an observer from seaward*. All bearings refer to the true compass and are measured clockwise from 000° to 359°.

Sometimes a light shows the same colour over separate sectors but with a different intensity. The ranges corresponding to the different intensities will be listed in column 6, while details of the less intense or unintensified sector will be listed in column 8. The different intensity values may also be shown.

Fig. 10–1 (page 244) shows a chart extract giving details of Saint Anthony Head Light. The relevant *List of Lights* (Volume A) contains the following information:

Column 1	0062
Column 2	**Saint Anthony Head**
	(T)
Column 3	50 08.4
	5 00.9
Column 4	OcWR 15s
	Horn 30s
Column 5	22
Column 6	**W22**
	W20
	R20
Column 7	White 8-sided tower
	19
Column 8	*ec 3.7.* W295° − 004° (69°), R004° − 022° (18°) over Manacle rocks, W (unintens) 022° − 100° (78°), W100° − 172° (72°). Fog Det Lt LF1 W 5 min (*fl 5s*) 18 m. 16 M. Vis 148.2° − 151.3° (2.5°). Shown throughout 24 hours.
	bl 3

Saint Anthony Head Light is occulting with a period of 15 seconds, showing a white or red light over different sectors (column 4). The period consists of two elements (phases): 3.7 seconds darkness (*ec*—eclipse 3.7, column 8) and 15 − 3.7 = 11.3 seconds light. The light changes its colour in various sectors as set out in column 8. These sectors are also shown on the chart. The ranges of the light are given in column 6: 22 and 20 miles for the white sectors, 20 miles for the red sector. The unintensified white sector where the range is 20 miles is detailed in column 8 and is also shown on the chart.

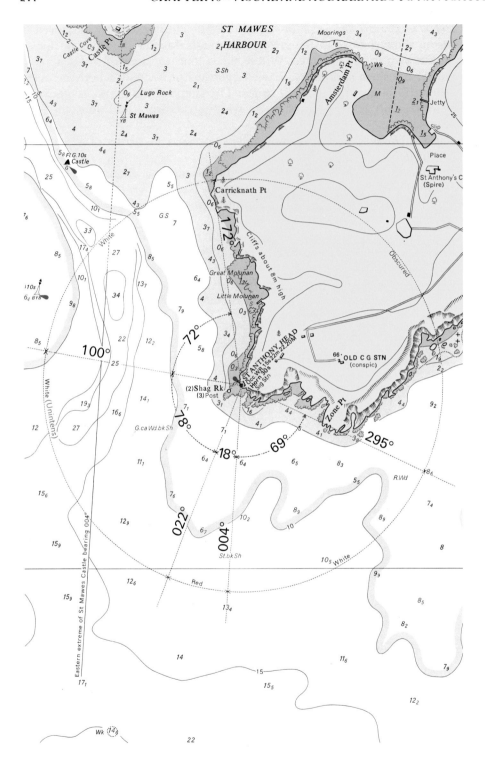

Fig. 10–1.   Saint Anthony Head Light including the light sectors

Details of the fog detector lights (*see* below) are given in column 8 and those of the fog signal (*see* page 266) are given in columns 5 and 8.

The elevation of the light is 22 m above Mean High Water Springs (column 5) and the light is displayed from a white eight-sided tower 19 m high (column 7).

Minor lights

Column 8 in the *List of Lights* also gives details of minor lights. These have special uses; some are shown in Fig. 10–2.

1. *Sector lights*. These are lights presenting different appearances, either of colour or character, over various parts of the horizon.

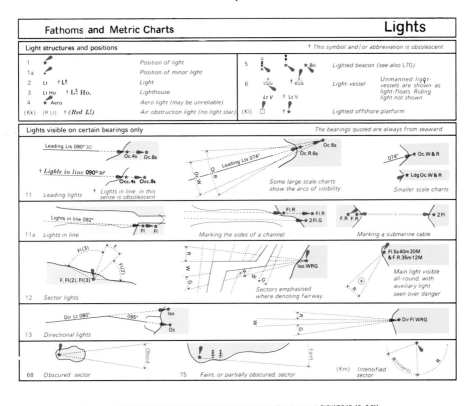

Fig. 10–2.   Light symbols on fathoms and metric charts

2. *Leading lights*. Two or more lights are positioned so as to form a leading line (*see* Chapter 13). Lights described as 'Lts in line' are particular cases intended to mark limits of areas, alignment of submarine cables, etc.

3. *Directional light*. This is a light showing over a very narrow sector, forming a single leading light. This sector may be flanked by sectors of greatly reduced intensity, or by sectors of different colours or character. Directional lights are also used to mark the limits of areas, etc. in the same way as Lts in line. Some directional lights have a moiré effect. These show the observer if he is on the centre line, or the alteration of course to regain the track.

4. *Vertical lights*. These are two or more lights disposed vertically (or horizontally, or in a geometric shape) to give a character or appearance different from normal (single) lights.

5. *Fog detector lights*. The purpose of fog detector lights is to detect fog automatically and to switch on fog signals. Visibility range at the station may be automatically transmitted to a data centre for broadcast to mariners. Fog detector lights may be fitted to the structure of a light station or may be positioned some distance from the light. There are a variety of types in use, some only visible over a narrow arc, some exhibiting a powerful *bluish white* flash; others may sweep back and forth and can therefore be mistaken for signals. Fog detector lights operate by day and night.

6. *Emergency lights*. Emergency lights are automatically actuated by a failure of the main light and are usually of lesser intensity. They may well have a standard character for the country concerned. Some countries (e.g. Canada) have installed them.

Range of lights

There are two criteria for determining the maximum range at which a light can be seen. First, the light must be above the horizon. This depends on:

1. The elevation of the light.
2. The curvature of the Earth.
3. The height of eye of the observer.

Secondly, the light must be powerful enough to be seen at this range. This depends on:

1. The power (intensity) of the light.
2. The prevailing visibility.

Various terms are used to describe the range of a light and these are set out below.

Geographical range

*Geographical range** is the maximum distance at which a light can reach an observer as determined by the height of the observer, the height of the structure and the curvature of the Earth. Geographical range is tabulated in the *List of Lights* and an extract is shown in Table 10-2.

* Until 1972, the geographical range of a light for an observer's height of 5 m or 15 ft was inserted on charts unless luminous range was less, in which case the latter was inserted. New Editions of charts published since 31st March 1972 show luminous or nominal range.

Table 10–2.   Geographical Range Table

Elevation in ft	m	Height of Eye of Observer in feet/metres												
ft		3	7	10	13	16	20	23	26	30	33	39	46	52
	m	1	2	3	4	5	6	7	8	9	10	12	14	16
		Range in Sea Miles												
0	0	2·0	2·9	3·5	4·1	4·5	5·0	5·4	5·7	6·1	6·4	7·0	7·6	8·1
3	1	4·1	4·9	5·5	6·1	6·6	7·0	7·4	7·8	8·1	8·5	9·1	9·6	10·2
7	2	4·9	5·7	6·4	6·9	7·4	7·8	8·2	8·6	9·0	9·3	9·9	10·5	11·0
10	3	5·5	6·4	7·0	7·6	8·1	8·5	8·9	9·3	9·6	9·9	10·6	11·1	11·6
13	4	6·1	6·9	7·6	8·1	8·6	9·0	9·4	9·8	10·2	10·5	11·1	11·7	12·2
16	5	6·6	7·4	8·1	8·6	9·1	9·5	9·9	10·3	10·6	11·0	11·6	12·1	12·7
20	6	7·0	7·8	8·5	9·0	9·5	9·9	10·3	10·7	11·1	11·4	12·0	12·6	13·1
23	7	7·4	8·2	8·9	9·4	9·9	10·3	10·7	11·1	11·5	11·8	12·4	13·0	13·5
26	8	7·8	8·6	9·3	9·8	10·3	10·7	11·1	11·5	11·8	12·2	12·8	13·3	13·9
30	9	8·1	9·0	9·6	10·2	10·6	11·1	11·5	11·8	12·2	12·5	13·1	13·7	14·2
33	10	8·5	9·3	9·9	10·5	11·0	11·4	11·8	12·2	12·5	12·8	13·5	14·0	14·5
36	11	8·8	9·6	10·3	10·8	11·3	11·7	12·1	12·5	12·8	13·2	13·8	14·3	14·9
39	12	9·1	9·9	10·6	11·1	11·6	12·0	12·4	12·8	13·1	13·5	14·1	14·6	15·2
43	13	9·4	10·2	10·8	11·4	11·9	12·3	12·7	13·1	13·4	13·7	14·4	14·9	15·4
46	14	9·6	10·5	11·1	11·7	12·1	12·6	13·0	13·3	13·7	14·0	14·6	15·2	15·7
49	15	9·9	10·7	11·4	11·9	12·4	12·8	13·2	13·6	14·0	14·3	14·9	15·5	16·0
52	16	10·2	11·0	11·6	12·2	12·7	13·1	13·5	13·9	14·2	14·5	15·2	15·7	16·2
56	17	10·4	11·2	11·9	12·4	12·9	13·3	13·7	14·1	14·5	14·8	15·4	16·0	16·5
59	18	10·6	11·5	12·1	12·7	13·2	13·6	14·0	14·4	14·7	15·0	15·7	16·2	16·7
62	19	10·9	11·7	12·4	12·9	13·4	13·8	14·2	14·6	14·9	15·3	15·9	16·5	17·0
66	20	11·1	12·0	12·6	13·1	13·6	14·1	14·5	14·8	15·2	15·5	16·1	16·7	17·2
72	22	11·6	12·4	13·0	13·6	14·1	14·5	14·9	15·3	15·6	15·9	16·6	17·1	17·7
79	24	12·0	12·8	13·5	14·0	14·5	14·9	15·3	15·7	16·0	16·4	17·0	17·6	18·1
85	26	12·4	13·2	13·9	14·4	14·9	15·3	15·7	16·1	16·4	16·8	17·4	18·0	18·5
92	28	12·8	13·6	14·3	14·8	15·3	15·7	16·1	16·5	16·8	17·2	17·8	18·3	18·9
98	30	13·2	14·0	14·6	15·2	15·7	16·1	16·5	16·9	17·2	17·5	18·2	18·7	19·2
115	35	14·0	14·9	15·5	16·1	16·6	17·0	17·4	17·8	18·1	18·4	19·1	19·6	20·1
131	40	14·9	15·7	16·4	16·9	17·4	17·8	18·2	18·6	18·9	19·3	19·9	20·4	21·0
148	45	15·7	16·5	17·1	17·7	18·2	18·6	19·0	19·4	19·7	20·0	20·7	21·2	21·7
164	50	16·4	17·2	17·9	18·4	18·9	19·3	19·7	20·1	20·5	20·8	21·4	22·0	22·5
180	55	17·1	17·9	18·6	19·1	19·6	20·0	20·4	20·8	21·2	21·5	22·1	22·7	23·2
197	60	17·8	18·6	19·3	19·8	20·3	20·7	21·1	21·5	21·8	22·2	22·8	23·3	23·9
213	65	18·4	19·2	19·9	20·4	20·9	21·4	21·7	22·1	22·5	22·8	23·4	24·0	24·5
230	70	19·0	19·9	20·5	21·1	21·5	22·0	22·4	22·7	23·1	23·4	24·0	24·6	25·1
246	75	19·6	20·5	21·1	21·7	22·1	22·6	23·0	23·3	23·7	24·0	24·6	25·2	25·7
262	80	20·2	21·0	21·7	22·2	22·7	23·1	23·5	23·9	24·3	24·6	25·2	25·8	26·3
279	85	20·8	21·6	22·2	22·8	23·3	23·7	24·1	24·5	24·8	25·1	25·8	26·3	26·9
295	90	21·3	22·1	22·8	23·3	23·8	24·2	24·6	25·0	25·4	25·7	26·3	26·9	27·4
312	95	21·8	22·7	23·3	23·9	24·3	24·8	25·2	25·5	25·9	26·2	26·8	27·4	27·9
328	100	22·3	23·2	23·8	24·4	24·9	25·3	25·7	26·1	26·4	26·7	27·3	27·9	28·4

Luminous range

The *luminous range* is the maximum distance at which a light can be seen, determined only by the intensity of the light and the visibility at the time. Luminous range takes no account of elevation, observer's height of eye or the curvature of the Earth. A luminous range diagram is to be found in the *List of Lights* (Fig. 10–3, p.248).

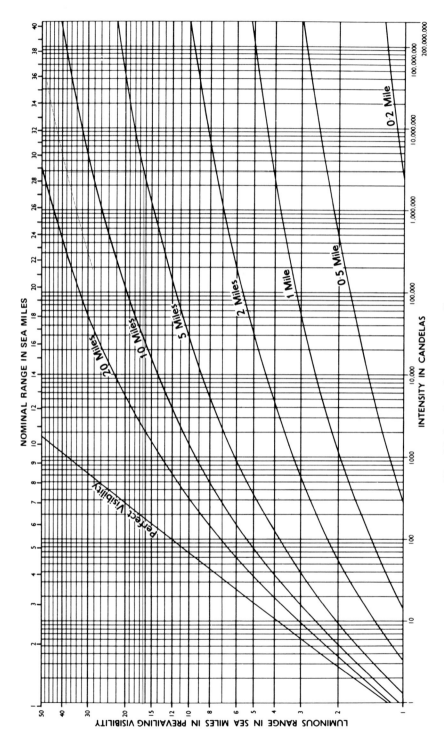

Fig. 10–3. Luminous range diagram

Nominal range

Nominal range is normally the luminous range for a meteorological visibility of 10 miles, and is the one most frequently used for the range of lights shown in the *List of Lights* and on Admiralty charts. The relationship between candle power (candelas) and nominal range may be seen from Fig. 10–3. For example, a light with a candle power of 1 million candelas has a nominal range of just under 26 miles, while a light with a candle power of only 1000 candelas has a nominal range of just over 9 miles.

Range displayed in the *List of Lights*

The type of range used for the light is given in the 'Special Remarks' section of the appropriate volume. As a rule, the ranges given in column 6 of the tables are nominal ranges (e.g. the British Isles) but there may be exceptions (e.g. Cuba) where the range given is luminous range and, in these cases, the intensity of the light in candelas will usually be displayed in column 4. Countries using luminous range generally use a meteorological visibility of 20 miles for determining the range of the light in column 6, and not 10 miles as is the usual practice for nominal ranges.

Determining the maximum range of a light

The range at which a light will be seen by the observer will be either the *geographical* or the *luminous* range, *whichever is the less*. It is necessary to work out each range.

EXAMPLE 1

Height of eye 12 metres, estimated visibility 15 miles; disregarding height of tide, at what range should the Lizard Light (A0060) be sighted? The elevation of the light is 70 metres (column 5). Nominal range (column 6) is 29 miles.

Geographical range. This can be read off directly from the Geographical Range Table for a height of light 70 metres and height of eye 12 metres. Geographical range* is 24'.0.

Luminous range. Enter the luminous range diagram (Fig. 10–3) from the top border for 29 miles nominal range and determine where the vertical line from this point cuts the visibility range curve for 15 miles (which must be interpolated between the 20 mile and 10 mile visibility curves). From this second point move horizontally to the left-hand border and read off the luminous range. In this case, luminous range is 38 miles.

This means that, although the intensity of the light and the visibility would give a range of 38 miles, because of the height of the eye the light must be well below the horizon at this range and therefore cannot be seen by the observer. The loom of the light may of course be visible.

The range at which the light itself will be sighted is therefore the lesser of the geographical and luminous ranges, 24'.0.

---

* The Geographical Range Table in the *List of Lights* is based upon a particular allowance for refraction (*see* Chapter 9, page 203).

EXAMPLE 2

Given the same situation as in Example 1 but with the visibility now down to 5 miles, at what range should the light be sighted?

As before, geographical range is 24′.0.

Luminous range. Follow the same procedure as in Example 1, but this time drop vertically to the point where the 29 mile nominal range cuts the 5 mile visibility curve and read across to the left-hand border, where the luminous range may be found, in this case 16′.5.

This time, although the light will be above the horizon at a range of 24 miles, because of the 5 mile visibility, the intensity of the light is such that it should be seen at 16′.5.

Once again the range at which the light will be sighted is the lesser of the two, 16′.5.

It will be noted from these two examples that lights may be sighted at a range in excess of the estimated meteorological visibility, dependent on the light's intensity.

Luminous range, intensity given in the List of Lights

When the range given in column 6 of the *List of Lights* is *luminous* rather than nominal, the range diagram should be entered from the *bottom border* for the intensity (column 4 of the *List*) followed by the same procedure as before.

EXAMPLE 3

Height of eye 10 metres, estimated visibility 5 miles. Disregarding height of tide, at what range should Punta Gobernadora Light (J4836) be sighted? Height of the light is 33 metres, luminous range (column 6) 46 miles, intensity (column 4) 3 million candelas.

Geographical range is 18′.0.

Luminous range. The luminous range diagram (Fig. 10–3) is entered from the bottom border for 3 million candelas, vertically up to the 5 mile visibility curve, then horizontally to the left-hand border, where the luminous range may be found, 16′.4.

The range at which the light should be sighted is again the lesser of the two, 16′.4.

Luminous range, intensity not given in the List of Lights

If the candle power or intensity of the light is not listed, the range may be found as follows.

Enter the diagram (Fig. 10–3) at the left-hand border with the luminous range given in column 6 of the *List of Lights*, move horizontally to the right until the 20 mile visibility curve (*see* page 249) is reached, then vertically up or down until the actual visibility curve is met, then read back across to the left-hand column, where the range at which the light may be seen in the prevailing visibility may be obtained. Either this or the geographical range, whichever is the less, will be the expected sighting range.

Light-vessels, lanbys, light-floats

A *light-vessel* is a manned vessel anchored as a floating aid to navigation, from which is exhibited a light which may have any of the characteristics of a lighthouse except sectors.

A *lanby (large automatic navigational buoy)* is a very large unmanned light-buoy used as an alternative to a light-vessel to mark offshore positions important to navigation. Lanbys vary in size up to a displacement of 140 tonnes and a diameter or height of 12 metres.

A *light-float* is a boat-like structure used instead of a light-vessel or light-buoy in waters where strong tidal streams or currents are experienced. Light-floats may vary considerably in size from the size of light-vessels or lanbys down to ordinary light-buoys. They are unmanned.

The regulations concerning light-vessels are normally found in the special remarks section of the *List of Lights*. Full details of light-vessels, lanbys and light-floats may be found in the body of the *List of Lights*, provided that the structure is more than 8 metres high. Brief details are also to be found in the *Admiralty Sailing Directions*. Details are also given on the Admiralty chart, as for lights in general (*see* page 237).

Remarks on light-vessels, etc.

The following remarks refer to light-vessels and lanbys off the coast of the British Isles, also light-floats where these are listed in Volume A of the *List of Lights*. Information relating to other areas of the world may be found in the appropriate *List of Lights* or *Sailing Directions*.

1. Light-vessels, lanbys and light-floats are painted red with the name in white letters.
2. The elevation given in column 5 of the *List of Lights* is the distance from the waterline to the centre of the lantern.
3. A fixed white riding light is exhibited from the forestay, 2 metres above the rail, to show the direction in which the floating structure is swung. This direction gives a useful indication of the direction of the tidal stream.
4. If for any reason the usual light characteristics cannot be shown while on station, the riding light only is shown.
5. A light-vessel watch buoy is sometimes laid to give an indication of dragging. These buoys are conical, painted yellow, with 'LV Watch' in black letters.
6. If a light-vessel is off her proper station, the light characteristics are not shown, nor the fog signal sounded. In addition, the following signals are displayed:
   By day: Two large black balls, one forward, one aft; the International Code signal 'LO' meaning 'I am not in my correct position' should be hoisted where it may best be seen.
   By night: A fixed red light will be shown at the bow and stern; in addition, red and white flares will be shown simultaneously every 15 minutes or more frequently on the approach of traffic.
7. During fog or low visibility, on the near approach of any traffic, the bell of the light-vessel will be rung rapidly in the intervals between sounding the normal fog signals. If the normal fog signal is made by hand horn, the period of the signal is shortened as shipping approaches, becoming continuous in a dangerously close situation.
8. Neither 6 nor 7 applies to light-floats and lanbys, which are unmanned. However, an automatic shore monitoring system may be available which

keeps the position of these floating structures under surveillance. If the structure is observed to move off station, an appropriate radio navigational warning is sent out.

9. Light-vessels, lanbys and light-floats are liable to be withdrawn for repairs without notice and, in some cases, are not replaced by a relief vessel. Relief vessels usually carry the word 'Relief' or 'Reserve'.

10. Details of distress signals made from light-vessels may be found in the *List of Lights*.

Lights on oil and gas platforms, drilling rigs and single point moorings

Details of lights displayed by permanent platforms and drilling rigs may be given in the appropriate volume of the *List of Lights*. For example, in waters around the British Isles, details are given in the 'Special Remarks' section and also in the body of Volume A. Notification of the movement and position of drilling rigs is given in radio navigational warnings issued for NAVAREA I (*see* Chapter 6). Further details are given in the *Annual Summary of Admiralty Notices to Mariners*. Permanent oil and gas installations are shown on the Admiralty chart, where scale permits.

Not all light lists give full details of these lights. For example, in Volume J of the *List of Lights*, despite the fact that numerous oil rigs may be found in the Gulf of Mexico, details are not given in this volume other than a few general remarks. Recourse must be had to the appropriate charts of the area and radio navigational warnings.

The *Sailing Directions* should always be consulted for information on permanent platforms, drilling rigs, etc.

Other types of light

Details of other types of light that may be encountered at sea are given below.

Aeromarine lights. These are marine type lights in which a part of the beam is deflected to an angle of 10° to 15° above the horizon for the use of aircraft. These lights are usually listed as 'Aeromarine' in column 8 of the *List of Lights*.

Aero lights. These lights are displayed primarily for the use of aircraft and are often of greater intensity and elevation than lights used for marine navigation. Those likely to be seen from seaward are detailed in the *List of Lights;* their character (column 4) is always preceded by the word 'Aero'. These lights should always be used with caution, as any changes may not be promptly notified to the mariner.

Obstruction lights. These mark radio towers, chimneys and other obstructions to aircraft. They are not maintained for marine navigation; thus, they should be used with caution, as for aero lights. They are usually red and may be fixed, flashing or occulting.

Obstruction lights of high intensity, and likely to be visible from seaward for some distance, are listed with the character preceded by 'Aero' in column 4 and with the legend 'Obstruction' in column 8. Those of less intensity are classified as minor lights and mentioned in column 8.

Daytime lights. These are lights which are exhibited throughout the 24 hours without change of character. Information is given in column 8 of the *List of*

Lights. If by day there are any differences in the character, these are preceded by the word 'By day' in column 4. By day, the intensity may be increased.

Fog lights. The characteristics of lights shown only in reduced visibility are preceded by the words 'In fog' in column 4.

Occasional lights. These are lights exhibited only when specially needed. Examples are:

> Tidal lights, exhibited only when the tide serves.*
> Fishing lights, for the use of fishermen.
> Private lights, maintained by a private authority for its own purpose.

Notes on using lights

The following points should be remembered when using lights for navigation.

1. The characteristics of the light must *always be checked on sighting*.
2. The refraction and the height of tide may well alter the geographical range. The raising or dipping range of the light can only be approximate, and must be used with caution if being used as a position line (*see* Chapter 9).
3. Lights placed at a great height—for example, on the Spanish coast—are often obscured by cloud.
4. The distance of an observer from a light cannot be estimated from its apparent brightness.
5. The distance at which lights are sighted varies greatly with atmospheric conditions. It may be increased by abnormal refraction. It will be reduced by fog, haze, dust, smoke or rain—a light of low intensity is easily obscured in any of these conditions, and even the range of a light of great intensity may be considerably reduced. Thus ranges at which lights first appear can only be approximate. It should be remembered that there may be fog or rain in the vicinity of the light even though it is clear at the ship.
6. In cold weather, and more particularly with rapid changes of weather, the lantern glass and screens are often covered with moisture, frost or snow, which can greatly reduce the sighting range. Coloured sectors may appear more or less white, the effect being greatest with green lights of low intensity.
7. The limits of sectors should not be relied upon and should always be checked by compass bearing. At the boundaries of sectors there is often a small arc in which the light may be obscured, indeterminate in colour, or white. However, some modern sector light boundaries are defined to a much greater degree of accuracy than for older lights.
8. The limits of arcs of visibility are rarely clear cut, especially at short ranges.
9. In certain atmospheric conditions, white lights may have a reddish hue.
10. Glare from background lighting reduces considerably the range at which lights are sighted. The approximate sighting range in such circumstances may be found by first dividing the intensity of the light by 10 for minor background lighting, 100 for major background lighting, and then using the luminous range diagram (Fig. 10–3).

---

* A tide *serves* when it is at a suitable height for ships entering and leaving harbour.

BUOYS AND BEACONS

Buoys

Buoys are floating structures, moored to the bottom, used to mark channels and fairways, shoals, banks, rocks, wrecks and other dangers to navigation, where permanent structures would be either uneconomical or impracticable.

Buoys have a distinctive colour and shape, they may carry a topmark and exhibit lights; all of these are of great importance because they indicate the buoy's purpose. Buoys may also be fitted with radar reflectors and may sound bells, gongs, whistles or horns (*see* Fog signals, page 266).

Beacons

A beacon is a navigational mark constructed of wood, metal, concrete, masonry or glass-reinforced plastic (GRP), or a combination of these materials, erected on or in the vicinity of danger, or onshore, as an aid to navigation. To indicate their purpose, beacons are often surmounted by topmarks and may have a distinctive colour and may also exhibit lights. These features all have the same meaning as for buoys. Large unlit beacons are often referred to as *daymarks* (daybeacons in the USA and Canada). Beacons frequently have distinguishing marks or shapes (referred to as 'daymark' in the USA and Canada) built into their structure. Beacons may be fitted with radar reflectors. In its simplest form, a beacon is known as a *pile beacon* and consists of a single wooden or concrete pile identified only by colour and possibly a number.

Sources of information

The best guide to buoys and beacons for any area is the largest scale chart of the place concerned. The *Admiralty Sailing Directions* describe the buoyage system in use in the area covered by the volume and frequently refer in the text to individual light-buoys without giving a detailed description. Details of beacons may also be found in the *Sailing Directions*. The *Admiralty List of Lights and Fog Signals* gives details of lighted beacons, and of light-buoys of an elevation of 8 metres or more.

The International Association of Lighthouse Authorities (IALA) System

IALA is a non-governmental body which brings together representatives from the aids to navigation services of various countries to exchange information and recommend improvements.

The IALA Maritime Buoyage system covers the world in two regions, Region A and Region B, as shown in Fig. 6–1 (page 105). The only difference between the two regions is with regard to the colours of lateral marks (page 258).

The implementation of the IALA System in Region A is expected to be completed in the mid-1980s, Region B several years later.

A description of the buoyage system in Region A is set out below. For full details of the world-wide system in Regions A and B, mariners should refer to *IALA Maritime Buoyage System* (NP 735) and the relevant volume of the *Sailing Directions*, all issued by the Hydrographer of the Navy. In areas where the IALA system has not yet been implemented, it is particularly important to consult the *Sailing Directions* for details of the buoyage system in use. Dates of

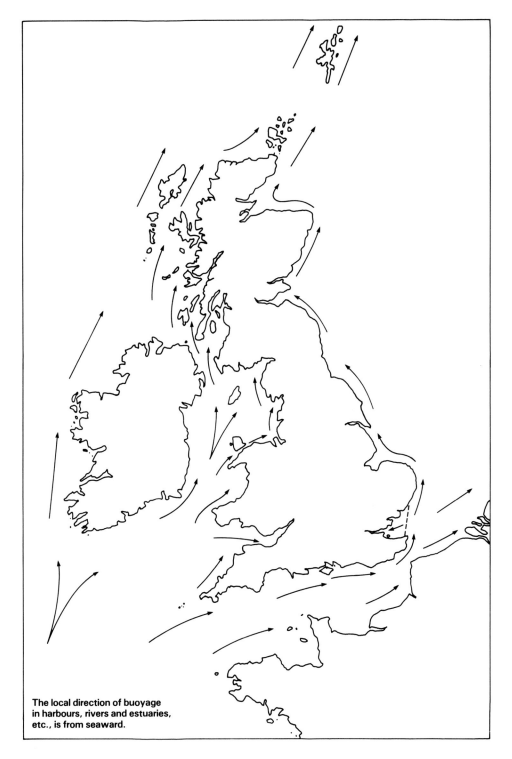

The local direction of buoyage
in harbours, rivers and estuaries,
etc., is from seaward.

Fig. 10–4.   General direction of buoyage around the British Isles

implementation of the IALA System in the two regions are given in Admiralty Notices to Mariners.

Application of the IALA System in Region A

The IALA system in Region A applies to all fixed and floating marks other than *lighthouses, sector lights, leading lights* and *marks, light-vessels* and *lanbys*. The system is used to indicate the limits of navigable channels, and to mark natural dangers and other obstructions such as wrecks (all of which are described as 'New dangers' when newly discovered) and other areas or features of importance to navigation.

Fixed marks

Most lighted and unlighted beacons, other than leading marks, are included in the system and, in general, beacon topmarks have the same shape and colour as those used on buoys.

Types of mark

The system provides *five* types of mark; lateral marks, cardinal marks, isolated danger marks, safe water marks and special marks. These are now described. Fig. 10–4 shows the general direction of lateral buoyage around the British Isles.

Lateral marks

Lateral marks (Fig. 10–5) are used in conjunction with a conventional direction of buoyage. This direction is defined in one of two ways:

1. *Local direction of buoyage.* The direction taken by the mariner when approaching a harbour, river, estuary or other waterway from seaward.
2. *General direction of buoyage.* The direction determined by the buoyage authority following a clockwise direction around continental land masses. This direction is frequently shown on the chart, particularly if there is any likely doubt about that direction, and may also be given in the *Sailing Directions*.

In some places, particularly straits, the local direction may be overridden by the general direction.

Starboard and port hand

The terms *starboard hand* and *port hand* are also used to describe lateral marks. Starboard hand means that side of the channel which will be on the right-hand side of the navigator when entering harbour, estuary or river from seaward, or when proceeding in the general direction of buoyage. Port hand means that side which will be on the left hand in the same circumstances.

Shape and colour of lateral marks

The shape of the lateral buoy is as important as its colour.

Red can-shaped buoys are generally used to mark the port hand side of the channel and green conical-shaped buoys to mark the starboard hand. If the buoy does not conform to these shapes—e.g. it is a spar or pillar* buoy, then it

---

* Pillar buoys are buoys, smaller than lanbys but much taller than the conventional can- and conical-shaped buoys, with a structure rising from the centre.

Lateral Marks used in Region A

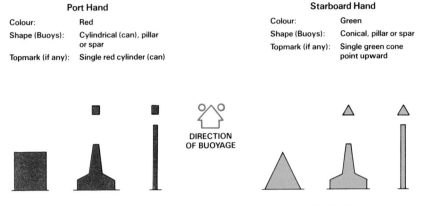

Port Hand

Colour: Red

Shape (Buoys):   Cylindrical (can), pillar
                       or spar

Topmark (if any):   Single red cylinder (can)

Starboard Hand

Colour: Green

Shape (Buoys):   Conical, pillar or spar

Topmark (if any):   Single green cone
                       point upward

LIGHTS, when fitted, may have any rhythm other than composite group-flashing (2+1) used on modified Lateral marks indicating a preferred channel. Examples are:—

Red light		Green light
Q.R	Continuous quick light	Q.G
Fl.R	Single-flashing light	Fl.G
L.Fl.R	Long-flashing light	L.Fl.G
Fl(2)R	Group-flashing light	Fl(2)G

Preferred Channels

At the point where a channel divides, when proceeding in the conventional direction of buoyage, a preferred channel is indicated by a modified port or starboard Lateral mark as follows:—

Preferred channel to starboard

Colour: Red with one broad
                       green horizontal band

Shape (Buoys):   Cylindrical (can), pillar
                       or spar

Topmark (if any):   Single red cylinder (can)

Preferred channel to port

Colour: Green with one broad
                       red horizontal band

Shape (Buoys):   Conical, pillar or spar

Topmark (if any):   Single green cone
                       point upward

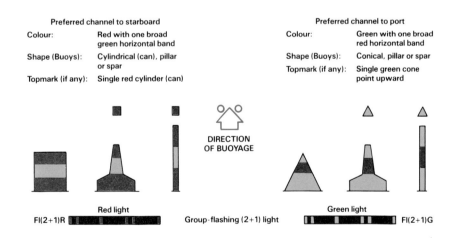

Red light		Green light
Fl(2+1)R	Group-flashing (2+1) light	Fl(2+1)G

NOTE: The colours of the buoys and lights are reversed in Region B.

Fig. 10–5.   IALA Region A lateral marks

must have a topmark of the appropriate shape and colour, red can or green cone. This topmark also applies to beacons.

By night a port hand buoy is identified by its *red* light and a starboard hand buoy by its *green* light; any rhythm may be used, except that used for a *preferred channel* buoy.

A *preferred channel* buoy is used where a channel divides into two, to indicate the *preferred route*.

If marks at the sides of a channel are numbered or lettered, the numbering or lettering should follow the conventional direction of buoyage.

Special marks (*see* page 260) with can or conical shapes but painted yellow may be used in conjunction with lateral marks for special types of channel marking.

Lateral marks in Region B

In Region B, the colours of lateral marks and their lights are reversed, but the shape remains the same; e.g. green can-shaped buoys mark the port hand side of the channel and red conical-shaped buoys mark the starboard hand.

Cardinal marks

Cardinal marks (Fig. 10–6) indicate that *safe navigable water lies to the named side of the mark*. In other words, the navigator should be safe if he passes north of a north mark, east of an east mark and so on. It may of course be safe to pass on other sides as well (e.g. a north mark may have navigable water not only to the north but also to the east and west), but the navigator will need to refer to the chart to confirm this.

A cardinal mark may be used to indicate that the deepest water in an area is on the named side of the mark, or to indicate the safe side on which to pass a danger (such as rocks, shoals or a wreck), or to draw attention to a feature in a channel such as a bend or junction, or the end of a shoal.

Black double-cone topmarks (one cone vertically above the other) are the most important feature, by day, of the cardinal marks. Cardinal marks are always painted in black and yellow horizontal bands conforming to the points of the topmarks as follows:

NORTH	Points *up*	Black *above* yellow
EAST	Points *out*	Black *about* yellow
SOUTH	Points *down*	Black *below* yellow
WEST	Points *in*	Black *between* yellow

The points of the triangles always indicate the position of the black section of the structure relative to the yellow.

Cardinal marks do not have a distinctive shape, but the buoys are normally pillar or spar.

When lighted, a cardinal mark exhibits a *white* light; its characteristics are based on a group of quick (Q) or very quick (VQ) flashes which distinguish it as

Cardinal Marks

Topmarks are always fitted (when practicable)
Buoy shapes are pillar or spar

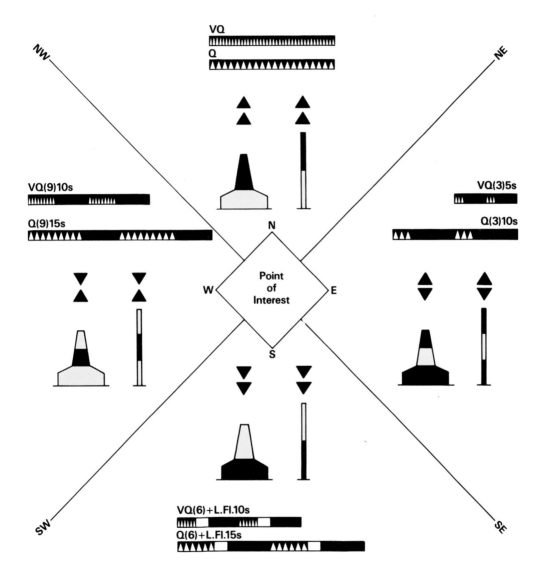

NOTE: Cardinal Marks are the same in Region B

Fig. 10–6.   IALA Region A cardinal marks

a cardinal mark and indicate the quadrant. The rhythm follows the pattern of a clock face as follows:

NORTH	Continuous flashing	Twelve o'clock
EAST	3 flashes in a group	Three o'clock
SOUTH	6 flashes in a group followed by a long flash	Six o'clock
WEST	9 flashes in a group	Nine o'clock

Isolated danger marks

Isolated danger marks (Fig. 10–7) are erected on, or moored on or above, an isolated danger of limited extent surrounded by navigable water. On the chart, the position of the danger is the centre of the symbol or sounding indicating that danger; the symbol for the buoy will be slightly displaced.

A *black double sphere topmark* (one vertically above the other), is, by day, the most important feature.

The colours used are *black with one or more red horizontal bands*. The shape of an isolated danger buoy may be either pillar or spar.

When lighted, an isolated danger mark exhibits a white flashing light showing a group of two flashes (Fl(2)).

Safe water marks

Safe water marks (Fig. 10–7) are used to indicate that there is navigable water all around the mark. Such a mark may be used, for example, as a mid-channel or landfall mark.

Safe water marks have an appearance quite different from danger marking buoys. First, they are *spherical* in shape. Secondly, they are the only type of mark to have *vertical stripes* (red and white). If pillar or spar buoys are used, then these should have a *single red sphere topmark*.

Lights, if any, are *white*, using isophase, occulting, one long flash every 10 seconds, or Morse 'A' rhythm.

Special marks

Special marks (Fig. 10–7) are not primarily intended to assist navigation but are used to indicate a special area or feature usually referred to on the chart or in the *Sailing Directions*, for example:

Ocean Data Acquisition Systems (ODAS) marks.

Traffic separation marks where use of conventional channel marking may cause confusion.

Spoil ground marks.

Military exercise zone marks.

Cable or pipeline marks, including outfall pipes.

Recreation zone marks.

A channel within a channel, for example a deep draught channel in a wide navigable estuary where the normal limits are marked by red and green lateral marks. The deep channel boundaries would be indicated by yellow buoys of the appropriate lateral mark shape, or the centreline would be marked by yellow spherical buoys.

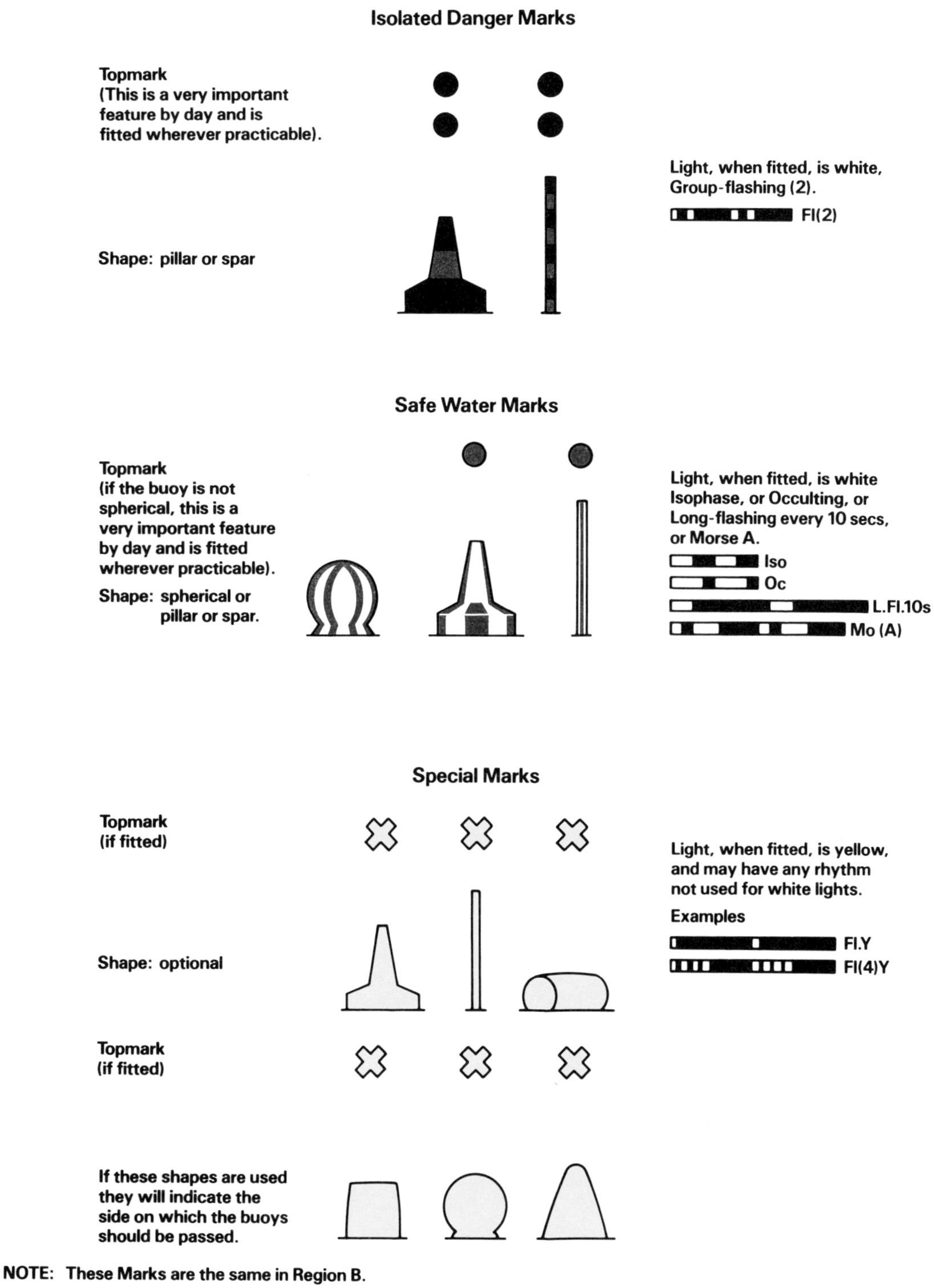

Isolated Danger Marks

Topmark
(This is a very important feature by day and is fitted wherever practicable).

Light, when fitted, is white, Group-flashing (2).

Fl(2)

Shape: pillar or spar

Safe Water Marks

Topmark
(if the buoy is not spherical, this is a very important feature by day and is fitted wherever practicable).

Shape: spherical or pillar or spar.

Light, when fitted, is white Isophase, or Occulting, or Long-flashing every 10 secs, or Morse A.

Iso
Oc
L.Fl.10s
Mo (A)

Special Marks

Topmark
(if fitted)

Shape: optional

Topmark
(if fitted)

Light, when fitted, is yellow, and may have any rhythm not used for white lights.

Examples

Fl.Y
Fl(4)Y

If these shapes are used they will indicate the side on which the buoys should be passed.

NOTE: These Marks are the same in Region B.

Fig. 10–7.   IALA Region A other marks

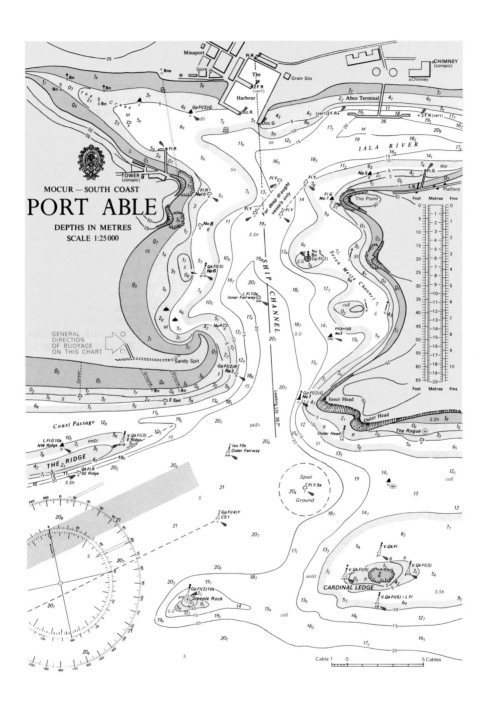

Fig. 10–8.   Chart of Port Able

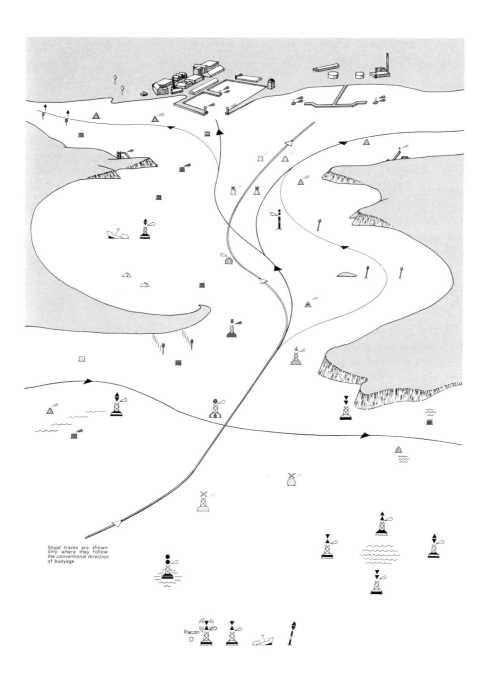

Ships' tracks are shown only where they follow the conventional direction of buoyage

Racon D

Fig. 10–9. Perspective view of Port Able

Special marks are always *yellow* in colour. If lit, *yellow* is used, and of any rhythm other than those used for the white lights of cardinal, isolated danger and safe water marks. The shape is optional, but must not conflict with that used for a lateral or safe water mark.

New dangers

A *new danger* is a newly discovered hazard to navigation not yet shown on charts, nor included in the *Sailing Directions* nor sufficiently promulgated by Notices to Mariners. The term includes naturally occurring obstructions such as sandbanks or rocks, or man-made dangers such as wrecks.

A new danger is marked by a lateral or a cardinal mark in accordance with the region rules. If the danger is considered to be especially grave, at least one of the marks will be duplicated as soon as practicable by an identical mark to give extra warning until notice of the danger has been sufficiently promulgated.

If a lighted mark is used for a new danger, it will have an appropriate cardinal (white) or lateral (red or green) quick or very quick light.

A new danger may also be marked by a racon (*see* Chapter 15), coded Morse 'D', showing a signal length of 1 mile on the radar display.

Buoyage around the British Isles

A charted representation of buoys and marks used in Region A (Fig. 10–8, p.262) shows the entrance to an imaginary port in the British Isles and the method of buoyage. Opposite is a perspective view of the same port (Fig. 10–9), which shows what the navigator should see by day and which marks are illuminated by night. It will be noted that a new danger, not yet on the chart, is visible south of the entrance to the harbour.

Charted buoy and beacon symbols

Fig. 10–10 illustrates the symbols used on fathoms and metric charts to display the IALA System for Regions A and B.

USING FLOATING STRUCTURES FOR NAVIGATION

The use of light-vessels, lanbys and light-floats for fixing the ship's position must always be subject to caution, taking care that all other data tie in, e.g. the DR/EP, the recorded depth of water and so on. After a strong gale has been blowing in the area, a floating structure may have dragged. It would be dangerous to rely on it for fixing the ship. Sometimes, however, the floating structure may be the only visual aid available (apart possibly from buoys), in which case the mariner has little alternative, but in such circumstances he must always proceed with caution.

If shore marks are available and identifiable, these should be used in preference to floating marks (but *see* (4) below).

If reliable radio fixing aids (e.g. SATNAV, Decca, *see* Volume III) of known error are available within the area concerned, these may be used in preference to floating marks, provided that the degree of accuracy of the radio aid concerned is adequate for the task in hand (but *see* (4) below). A radio aid fix from Decca or SATNAV may be accurate enough for coastal navigation, but not accurate enough for pilotage waters.

The IALA Maritime Buoyage System

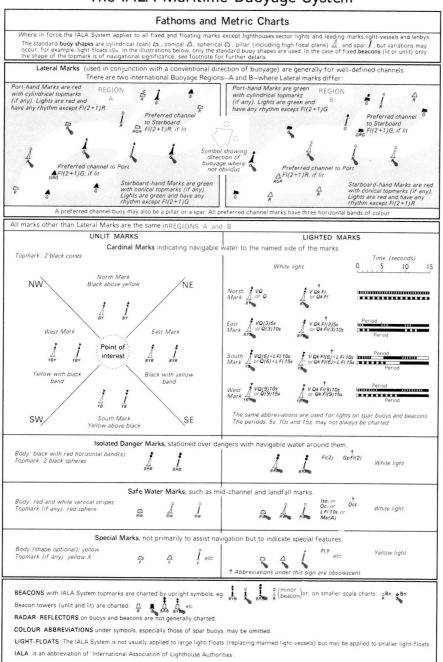

Fig. 10–10.   IALA System, charted symbols for buoys and beacons

The various factors which should be taken into account when deciding how reliable the position of one of these structures may be, are set out below:

1. Most light-vessels, lanbys and light-floats are anchored by a long scope of cable and therefore the size of their swinging circle around the charted position may be considerable. The position of the floating structure moves around its charted position depending on the scope of cable, the charted depth, the height of tide, the strength and direction of the tidal stream, current and wind.

2. Under certain conditions of weather and tidal stream, light-vessels are subject to sudden and unexpected sheers. It is therefore unwise to pass them close aboard.

3. Gales in the area could well have caused the structure to drag or break adrift, and warning signals to that effect may not have been made.

4. The structure may have been moved in any case to take account of extending shoals; a warning signal or notice to that effect may not have been received. Thus, a fix by shore objects will not necessarily give a safe position relative to those shoals.

5. If the structure is not large enough to be quoted in the *List of Lights* (i.e. it is less than 8 metres high), then it should be treated like any other buoy.

Buoys

The position of buoys and small-size floating structures must always be treated with caution even in narrow channels. In deciding how reliable their positions are, account should be taken of those same five factors set out above for light-vessels, etc. Remember in particular that buoys can quite easily drag or break adrift; that they are frequently moved as a shoal extends; and that they may not always display the correct characteristics.

Remember also that the chart symbol can only show the approximate position of the buoy mooring, as there are practical limitations in placing and keeping buoys in the exact position.

Buoys should not be treated as infallible *aids* to navigation, particularly when in an exposed position. Whenever possible, navigate by fixing from charted shore objects; use the echo sounder; check the DR/EP against the position; *use* but *do not rely* implicitly on buoys.

FOG SIGNALS

Information concerning fog signals may be found in complete detail in the *Admiralty List of Lights and Fog Signals*. Brief details are also given on the chart.

Types of fog signals

The following types of fog signals are likely to be encountered.

Diaphone. The diaphone uses compressed air to issue a powerful low note with a characteristic 'grunt' at the end of the note (a brief sound of suddenly reduced pitch). If the fog signal does not end in this 'grunt', the Remarks column (8) in the *List of Lights* will mention it.

Horn. The horn uses compressed air or electricity. Horns exist in many forms, differing greatly in sound and power. Some forms, particularly those at major fog signal stations, simultaneously produce sounds of different pitch which are often very powerful. Some produce a single steady note, while others vary continuously in pitch.

Siren. The siren uses compressed air and exists in many forms varying greatly in sound and power.

Reed. The reed uses compressed air and emits a weak (particularly if hand-operated) high-pitched sound.

Explosive. This signal produces short reports by means of firing explosive charges.

Bell, gong, whistle. These may be operated by machinery, producing a regular character; by hand, giving a somewhat irregular character; or by wave action, sounding erratically. Bells, gongs and whistles are frequently used as fog signals on buoys.

Morse Code fog signals

Morse Code fog signals consist of one or more characteristics of the Morse Code. In a similar manner to lights, the abbreviation for Morse (Mo) may be included in the abridged description of fog signals; e.g. Horn Mo (N) 90s, Siren Mo (A) 120s. Oil and gas production platforms often use a Morse Code fog signal; those off the British Isles and the north coast of France use Horn Mo (U) 30s.

Using fog signals for navigation

Fog signals give invaluable warning of danger but their use for navigation is limited. In the vicinity of fog signals, make full use of available aids, e.g. radar, radio aids, soundings. Place lookouts in positions (e.g. bow and aloft) where noises in the ship are least likely to interfere with the hearing of a fog signal.

Sound travels through air in an unpredictable way. The following points should therefore be noted when using fog signals for navigation:

1. Fog signals may be heard at greatly varying distances; the strength of the signal is no guide to the range, nor does a change of intensity necessarily indicate a similar change of range.
2. The apparent direction of a fog signal is not always a correct indication of the true direction.
3. If a fog signal is a combination of high and low notes, one of the notes may be inaudible in certain atmospheric conditions.
4. There are occasionally areas around a station in which the fog signal is quite inaudible.
5. Fog may exist a short distance from a station and not be observable from it, so that the signal may not be operated.
6. Some fog signals cannot be started on a moment's notice.

CHAPTER 11
Tides and Tidal Streams

This chapter deals with the causes and effects of the tides, in theory and in practice, and with tidal streams and currents, and the *Admiralty Tide Tables*.

Tides. Tides are periodic vertical movements of the water on the Earth's surface.

Tidal streams. In rising and falling the tides are accompanied by periodic horizontal movements of the water called tidal streams. (In American usage, tidal stream is called tidal current.)

TIDAL THEORY

Tides are caused by the gravitational pull of a heavenly body on the Earth and on the water over the Earth. The magnitude of the pull is defined in Newton's *Universal Law of Gravitation*, which states that, for any two heavenly bodies, a force of attraction is exerted by each one on the other, the force being:

1. Proportional to the product of the masses of the two bodies.
2. Inversely proportional to the square of the distance between them.
3. Directed from the centre of the one to the centre of the other.

This law may be expressed as

$$F \propto \frac{m_1 \, m_2}{d^2}$$

$$\ldots \textbf{11.1}$$

where F is the force, m_1 and m_2 the masses of the two bodies and d their distance apart.

The two heavenly bodies having the greatest tide-raising effect are the Sun and the Moon, while the effect of other heavenly bodies is negligible.

The Earth–Moon System

The Earth and Moon may be considered as forming an independent system rotating about a common centre of gravity known as the Earth–Moon barycentre (Fig. 11–1, p.270). The barycentre lies on a line joining the centres of gravity of the Earth and Moon at a point about 1000 miles below the Earth's surface.

The Earth describes a very small ellipse about the Earth–Moon barycentre, while the Moon describes a much larger ellipse about the same barycentre, taking $27\frac{1}{2}$ days approximately to complete one orbit.* As explained in Volume II of this manual, the Moon revolves around the Earth with respect to the Sun approximately once every $29\frac{1}{2}$ days. This period is known as the *lunar month*.

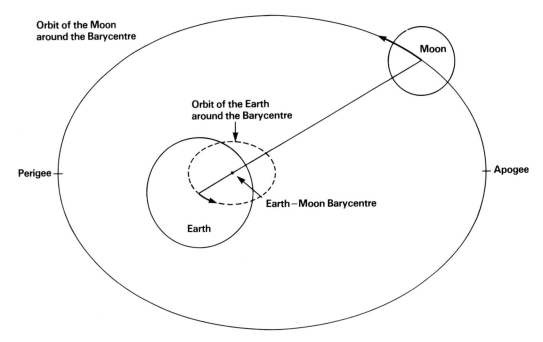

Fig. 11–1.   The Earth–Moon system

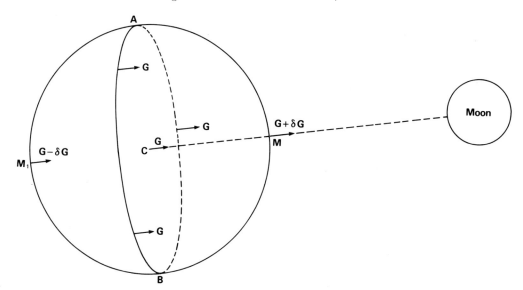

Fig. 11–2.   The gravitational force of the Moon acting on the Earth

* In a similar manner, the Earth–Moon barycentre describes, an elliptical orbit around the Earth–Sun barycentre (Fig. 11–13) located inside the Sun. It takes one year ($365\frac{1}{4}$ days approximately) for the Earth to complete one orbit around the Sun.

The gravitational force

The gravitational force of the Moon acts on the Earth as a whole affecting the structure of the Earth itself, on the atmosphere and on the water on the Earth's surface, and it is this latter phenomenon which is relevant when considering the causes of tides.

In Fig. 11–2, MM_I is the diameter of the Earth on the line joining the centres of the Earth and Moon, M being the point on the Earth's surface directly under the Moon and known as the *sublunar point*. M_I is on the opposite side of the Earth away from M and is known as the *antipode*. A and B are two points on the great circle whose plane is perpendicular to MM_I, and at all points on this circle the distance from the Moon may be considered as the same* as that from the centre of the Earth. Hence the gravitational force exerted by the Moon anywhere on AB is the same and is denoted by G. At M the distance to the Moon has decreased; thus, the gravitational force acting at M is increased by a small amount δG, while at M_I the gravitational force has decreased by a similar amount. Thus, the total gravitational force acting at M is $(G + \delta G)$ and that at M_I is $(G - \delta G)$.

Assuming for our purpose that the Earth is a smooth sphere completely covered by water, the force acting on the waters may be considered as the *difference* between the gravitational force G acting at the centre of the Earth and the actual force anywhere else on the Earth's surface; this is shown in Fig. 11–3.

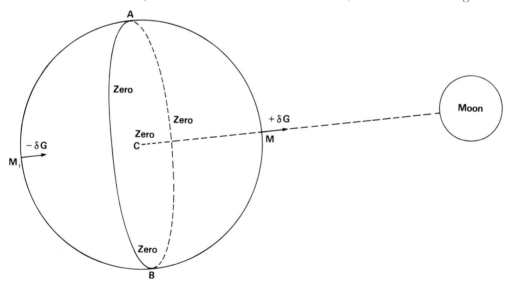

Fig. 11–3. The differential gravitational force on the Earth's surface (1)

It will be observed that, at the antipode M_I, the differential gravitational force is negative, i.e. $-\delta G$. This is equivalent to saying that the differential force at M_I is positive but acting in the opposite direction, as shown in Fig. 11–4.

---

* The distance of A and B from the Moon is very slightly more than that at C but, as the radius of the Earth is small compared with the distance of the Moon (1:60 approximately), this fact may be safely disregarded.

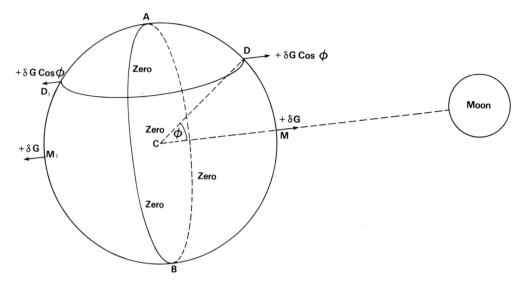

Fig. 11–4.   The differential gravitational force on the Earth's surface (2)

At some other point D on the Earth's surface (Fig. 11–4), the differential force acting on the waters at this point must be somewhere between δG and zero. If D is $\phi°$ above the sublunar–antipodal plane, then the differential gravitational force at D is equal to $\delta G \cos \phi°$. Similarly, at $D_{/}$ the force is also equal to $\delta G \cos \phi°$, but acting in the opposite direction.

The tide-raising force

If once again it is assumed that the entire surface of the Earth is covered with a uniform layer of water, these differential forces may be resolved into a vertical component at right angles to the Earth's surface and a horizontal component directed towards the sublunar or antipodal points, as shown in Fig. 11–5.

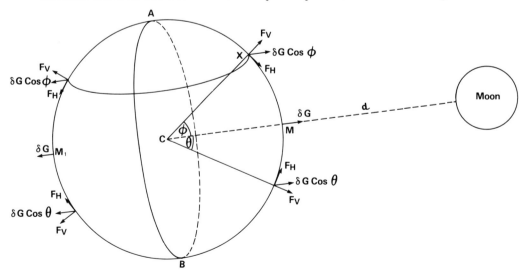

Fig. 11–5.   Resolution of the differential forces

The vertical force is only a very small portion of the Earth's gravity, so that the actual lifting of the water against gravity is infinitesimal. It is the horizontal component which produces the tides, by causing the water to move across the Earth and pile up at the sublunar and antipodal points until an equilibrium position is found. The horizontal component of the differential gravitational forces is known as the *tide-raising* or *tractive force*. Its magnitude at a given point (X in Fig. 11–5) may be expressed as:

$$F_H \propto \frac{3}{2} \times \frac{m_2 r}{d^3} \sin 2\phi \qquad \qquad \text{. . . 11.2}$$

where F_H is the magnitude of the tide-raising (horizontal) force;

 m_2 is the mass of the Moon;

 r is the radius of the Earth;

 d is the distance between the Earth's and Moon's centres;

 ϕ is the angle at the centre of the Earth between the line joining the sublunar and antipodal points, and the line joining the Earth's centre and X.

It should be noted that the tide-raising force caused by the Moon varies directly as the mass of the Moon and the radius of the Earth, and is inversely proportional to the *cube* of the distance between Earth and Moon.

The effect of the tide-raising or tractive force is illustrated in Fig. 11–6.

The tide-raising force is zero at the sublunar and antipodal points M and M_1 and along the great circle AB the plane of which is perpendicular to MM_1. The maximum tide-raising force may be found along the small circles EF and GH, which are 45° from the sublunar point and antipode respectively.

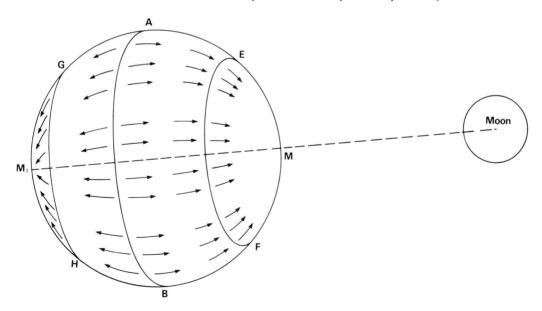

Fig. 11–6.   The effect of the tide-raising force

Equilibrium is reached when the tides formed at the sublunar and antipodal points are at such a level that the tendency to flow away from them is balanced by the tide-raising force. The tide caused in these circumstances is known as the *lunar equilibrium tide* (Fig. 11–7), with a *high water* at M and M_1 and a *low water* at A and B.

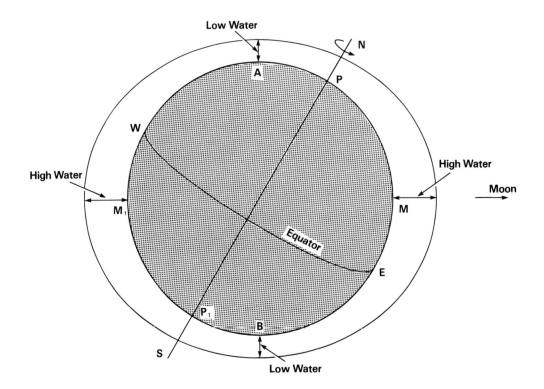

Fig. 11–7.   The lunar equilibrium tide

Effect of Earth's rotation

Fig. 11–8 shows the tide-raising effect on the Earth when the Moon is above the Earth's equator, i.e. declination* 0°.

The Earth rotates relative to the Moon once every lunar day of 24 hours 50 minutes approximately and thus, during this period, an observer at point M will experience two high waters once every 12 hours 25 minutes, interspersed with two low waters also 12 hours 25 minutes apart. This is illustrated in Fig. 11–9.

High water takes place shortly after the Moon's transit (upper and lower) of

---

* Declination is defined in Volume II. It is the angular distance of a heavenly body north or south of the celestial equator, and corresponds to latitude on the Earth.

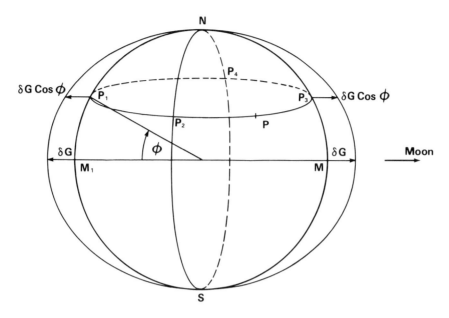

Fig. 11–8.   The effect of the Earth's rotation

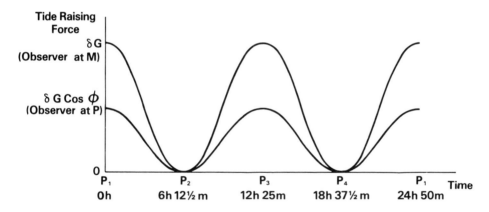

Fig. 11–9.   The lunar equilibrium semi-diurnal tide, declination 0°

the meridian* of the place. The slight delay is a side effect of the Earth's rotation.

The *range* of this equilibrium tide at the equator—that is, the difference in height between successive high and low waters—is less than 1 metre.

When the declination is zero, the tide-raising forces on the equator will be equal. At any other point P on the Earth's surface north or south of the equator, the tide-raising forces will still be equal but not so great as at the equator, and will vary approximately with the cosine of the latitude. The time intervals

* This is the time at which the Moon crosses the meridian of the place and is described in Volume II.

between successive high and low waters will still be the same as those on the equator, 6 hours $12\frac{1}{2}$ minutes approximately.

Such tide-raising forces, producing two equal maxima and two equal minima per lunar day at equal time intervals, are termed *semi-diurnal* (one cycle per half-day). When the Moon's declination is zero, the tide-raising forces are semi-diurnal for all latitudes.

Change of Moon's declination

The effect of the Moon's declination is shown in Fig. 11–10. The maximum tide occurs as before at the sublunar and antipodal points M and M_I. At any point P on the Earth's surface, not only are the heights of successive high and low waters different, the time intervals also change, as illustrated in Fig. 11–11. This effect is known as the *diurnal inequality*, a phenomenon commonly found in tides.

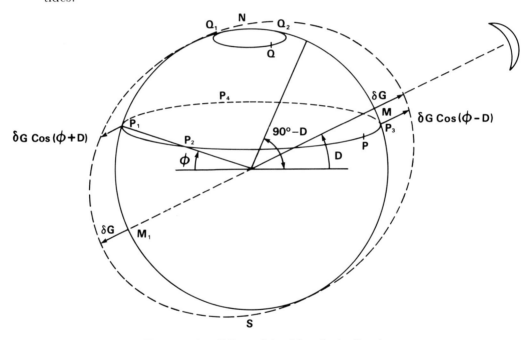

Fig. 11–10. Effect of the Moon's declination

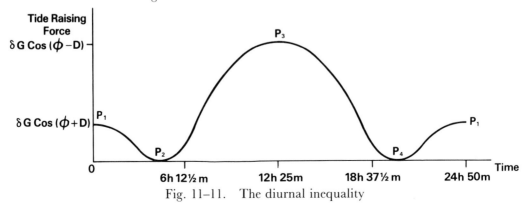

Fig. 11–11. The diurnal inequality

At another point Q on the Earth's surface (Fig. 11–10), where the latitude is greater than 90° minus the Moon's declination, the tide-raising force never reaches zero. This effect is illustrated in Fig. 11–12.

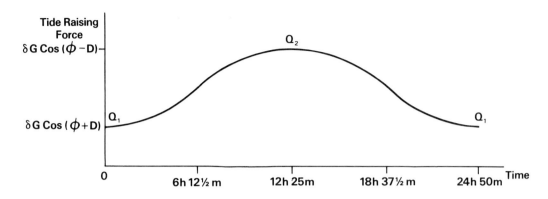

Fig. 11–12.   The diurnal tide

At Q there is only one high water and one low water every lunar day, and this type of tide is called *diurnal* (one cycle per day). The Moon's declination changes from a maximum* north to a maximum south and back again once every $27\frac{1}{3}$ days approximately; thus, a similar effect on the tide caused by the Moon's declination alone will be experienced roughly every fortnight.

The distance of the Moon

As the Moon rotates around the Earth (Fig. 11–1) approximately once every $27\frac{1}{2}$ days, the tide-raising force is strongest when the Moon is closest to the Earth, that is, at *perigee* (perigean tide). The tide-raising force is weakest when the Moon is furthest away, that is, at *apogee* (apogean tide). The variation in the Moon's distance can cause a difference in the lunar tide-raising force of between 15% and 20%; thus, tides at perigee are likely to be appreciably higher than those at apogee.

The Earth–Sun system

The Earth and Sun may be considered as forming another independent tide-raising system rotating around the Earth–Sun barycentre (Fig. 11–13, p.278).

Although the Sun has a much greater mass than the Moon, the Sun's tide-raising force is nevertheless only about 45% that of the Moon. This is because the tide-raising force is inversely proportional to the *cube* of the distance.

The tide-raising effects of the Sun on the Earth are similar to those of the Moon, though of lesser magnitude. Thus, the tides caused by the Sun will vary according to:

1. *The Earth's rotation.* The solar day is approximately 24 hours; thus, the solar equilibrium semi-diurnal tide, when the sun's declination is zero, will have

* Over an 18.6 year cycle, the Moon's maximum monthly declination oscillates between about $18\frac{1}{2}°$ and $28\frac{1}{2}°$ and back again.

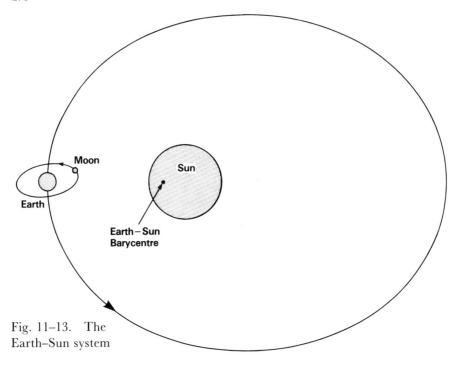

Fig. 11–13. The
Earth–Sun system

two high waters 12 hours apart, interspersed with two low waters also 12 hours apart. The time interval between successive high and low waters will be 6 hours.

2. *Change of Sun's declination.* The Sun's declination changes much more slowly than that of the Moon and reaches a maximum of about $23\frac{1}{2}°$ north and south of the equator on about 22nd June and 22nd December respectively, these dates being known as the *solstices*.

3. *The distance of the Sun.* It takes the Earth about 1 year, $365\frac{1}{4}$ days approximately, to complete its elliptical orbit around the Sun. *Perihelion*, when the Earth is closest to the Sun, occurs about 2nd January, and *aphelion*, when the Earth is furthest away, is about 1st July. Thus, the Sun's tide-raising force will be at its maximum in January and at its minimum in July. The variation in this force is, however, very small indeed, of the order of 3%.

Springs and neaps

When the tide-raising effects of the Moon and Sun are combined, they sometimes work together and sometimes against each other.

Spring tides

Twice every lunar month, the Moon and Sun are in line with each other and with the Earth, as shown in Fig. 11–14.

At new Moon, the Moon is passing between the Sun and the Earth; the Moon and Sun are said to be acting in *conjunction*. About $14\frac{3}{4}$ days later, at full Moon, the Earth is between the Moon and Sun, which are now acting in *opposition*.

The net result in both cases is a *maximum* tide-raising force, producing what is known as a *spring tide*. At springs, therefore, higher high waters and lower low waters than usual will be experienced, these occurring at about the time of new and full Moon.

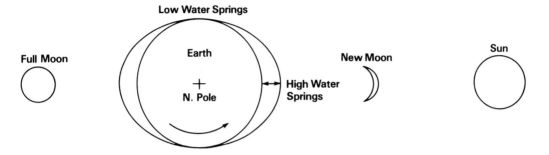

Fig. 11–14.   Spring tides

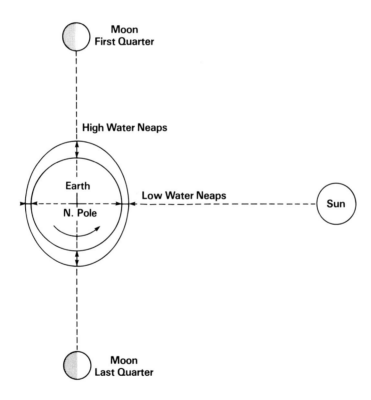

Fig. 11–15.   Neap tides

Neap tides

Twice every lunar month, i.e. about every $14\frac{3}{4}$ days, the Moon and Sun are at right angles to each other, as shown in Fig. 11–15. At these times the Moon and Sun are said to be in *quadrature*.

This situation occurs when the Moon is in the first and last quarters, and at this time the lunar and solar tide-raising forces are working at right angles to each other. The net result in both cases is a *minimum* tide-raising force, producing what is known as a *neap tide*. At neaps, lower high waters and higher low waters than usual will be experienced, these occurring at about the time of the first and last quarters of the Moon.

Frequency of springs and neaps

From the foregoing it may be seen that two spring tides will occur each lunar month interspersed with two neap tides, the interval between successive spring and neap tides being about $7\frac{1}{2}$ days. This phenomenon is found at many places in the world, although other inequalities sometimes occur to alter these timings.

It is usual for springs and neaps to follow the relevant phase of the Moon by two or three days. This is because there is always a time-lag between the action of the force and the reaction to it, caused by the time taken to overcome the inertia of the water surface and friction.

Springs and neaps will occur at approximately the same time of day at any particular place, since the Moon at that time is in a similar position relative to the Sun.

Equinoctial and solstitial tides

When the declinations of the Moon and the Sun are the same, the tide-raising force of each will clearly be acting more in concert than when the declinations are not the same.

At the *equinoxes* in March and September, when the declinations of Moon and Sun are both zero, the semi-diurnal luni-solar tide-raising force will be at its maximum, thus causing the *equinoctial* tides. At these times, where semi-diurnal tides are concerned, spring tides higher than normal are experienced.

At the *solstices* in June and December, when the declinations of Moon and Sun are both at maximum, the diurnal luni-solar tide-raising force will be at its maximum, thus causing the *solstitial* tides. At these times, diurnal tides and the diurnal inequality are at a maximum.

Note: As explained on page 277, the Moon's declination changes rapidly over a 4 week period. It can be at any value at the actual *equinox* or *solstice*, although it is bound to reach zero or maximum declination respectively within a few days.

Priming and lagging

It was explained earlier that the effect of the Earth's rotation and that of the Moon relative to each other is to cause a high water at intervals of about 12 hours 25 minutes. The effect of the Earth's rotation and that of the Sun relative to each other is to cause a (smaller) high water at intervals of about 12 hours. Thus, when the effects of both Moon and Sun are taken together, the intervals between successive high and low waters will be altered.

When the Moon is in a position between new/full and quadrature, the Sun's effect will be to cause the time of high water either to precede the time of the Moon's transit of the meridian or to follow the time of the Moon's transit. This is known as *priming* and *lagging* and is illustrated in Fig. 11–16.

The tide is said to *prime* when the Moon is between the new and the first quarter, and between full and the last quarter; high tide then occurs *before* the Moon's transit of the meridian.

The tide is said to *lag* when the Moon is between the first quarter and full, and between the last quarter and new; high tide then occurs *after* the Moon's transit of the meridian.

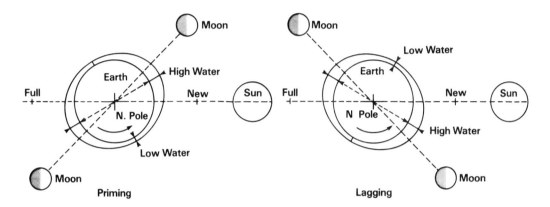

Fig. 11–16.   Priming and lagging of the tides

Summary of tidal theory

Tidal theory may be summarised as follows.

The semi-diurnal tide-raising force is maximum when the Moon's declination is nil, and minimum when the Moon's declination is at its greatest. The diurnal tide-raising force is nil when the Moon's declination is nil and maximum when the Moon's declination is greatest. The same is also true of the effect of the Sun's declination but, whereas the Moon's declination attains a maximum value north or south of the equator every 15 days or so, the Sun only reaches a maximum twice a year, in June and December at the solstices.

As the orbits of the Moon around the Earth and the Earth around the Sun are elliptical, changes in their distances from the Earth cause variations in the tide-raising force, that for the Moon being significant, that for the Sun being minimal.

Spring and neap tides occur at intervals of about 14 to 15 days, caused by the Moon and Sun either working together at full and new Moon (springs) or against each other at first and last quarters (neaps).

The Sun's tide-raising force is always a great deal less than that of the Moon, approximating to some 45% on average.

THE TIDES IN PRACTICE

In practice, the tides may differ considerably from the luni-solar equilibrium tide just discussed. This is because of the size, depth and configuration of the ocean basins, land masses, the friction and inertia to be overcome in any particular body of water, and so on.

For an appreciable tide to be raised in a body of water, it is essential to generate a large enough tide-raising force. To achieve this, the body of water must be large. The great oceans of the world—the Pacific, the Atlantic and the Indian Ocean—are large enough to permit tides to be generated, although none of these tides appears to be a single oscillating body, but rather a number. The natural period of oscillation is the decisive factor in determining whether the water responds to the diurnal or the semi-diurnal tide-raising force or a mixture of the two. Hence, tides in practice are often referred to as being semi-diurnal, diurnal or mixed.

The Atlantic tends to be more responsive to semi-diurnal forces; thus, tides on the Atlantic coast and around the British Isles tend to be semi-diurnal in character (two high waters and two low waters per day) and are more influenced by the phases of the Moon than by declination. Large tides occur at springs near full or new Moon. Small tides occur at neaps near the quarters. The largest tides of the year occur at springs near the equinoxes when the Sun and Moon are on the equator.

The Pacific is on the whole more responsive to the diurnal forces, and so tides in this part of the world tend to have a large diurnal component. In these areas, the largest tides are associated with the greatest declination of Sun and Moon, that is, at the summer and winter solstices. Areas in the South-west Pacific off New Guinea, off Vietnam and in the Gulf of Tonking, and in the Java Sea are predominantly diurnal.

Mixed tides, where the diurnal and semi-diurnal tide-raising forces are both important, tend to be characterised by a large diurnal inequality (Fig. 11–11). This may be apparent in the heights of successive high waters, low waters or both. Occasionally the tide may even be diurnal. Such tides are common along the Pacific coast of the United States, the east coast of West Malaysia, Borneo, Australia and the waters of South-west Asia.

The Mediterranean Sea and the Baltic, as bodies of water, are too small to enable any appreciable tide to be generated. The Strait of Gibraltar is too restricted to allow the Atlantic tides to have any appreciable effect other than at the extreme western end. The maximum tides are to be found in the Adriatic, where they are predominantly mixed, with a diurnal inequality at high and low water. The range may exceed 0.5 metre in several places in the Adriatic, but is rarely greater than 1 metre.

Shallow water and other special effects

As a tidal wave enters shallow water, it slows down. The trough is retarded more than the crest; thus, there is a progressive steepening of the wave front accompanied by a considerable increase in the height of the wave. This distorts the timing, in that the period of rise becomes shorter than the period of fall. These shallow water effects are present to a greater or lesser degree in the tides of all coastal waters.

The amplitude (height) of the tidal wave increases even more as it travels up an estuary which narrows from a wide entrance. This may result in a very large tide such as those to be found in the Bay of Fundy in Nova Scotia, the Severn Estuary and around the Channel Islands.

Where a river is fed from such an estuary with a large tidal range, a phenomenon known as a *bore* (Old English—*eagre*) may be found. The crest of the rising tide overtakes the trough and tends to break. Should it break, a bore occurs in which half or more of the total rise of the tide occurs in only a few minutes. Notable bores are in the Severn, Seine, Hooghly and Chien Tang Kiang.

At certain places, shallow water effects are such that more than two high waters or two low waters may be caused in a day. At Southampton, for example (Fig. 11–17), there are two high waters with an interval of about 2 hours between them. Further west, at Portland, the predominating factor is a double low water (Fig. 11–18, p.284). Double tides also occur on the Dutch coast and at other places. The practical effect of this is to create a longer *stand** at high or low water.

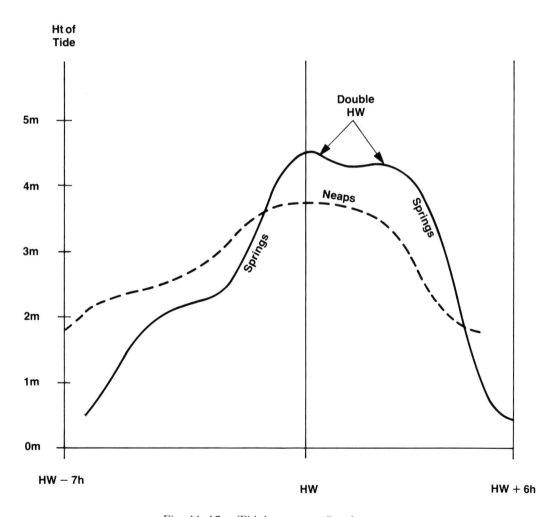

Fig. 11–17.   Tidal curves at Southampton

* The *stand* of the tide is the period at high or low water between the tide ceasing to rise (fall) and starting to fall (rise).

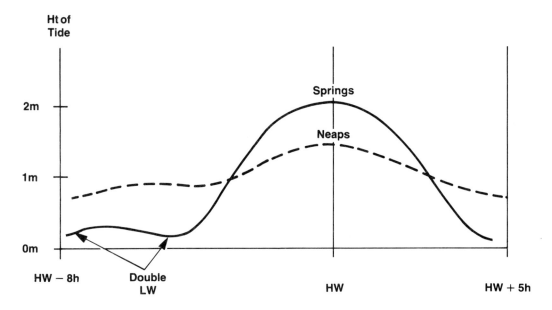

Fig. 11–18.   Tidal curves at Portland

Because of the distortion of the tidal wave caused by shallow water effect, special curves based on low water have had to be prepared for determining the height of tide on the south coast of England between Swanage and Selsey. The curves and instructions for their use are to be found in Volume 1 of the *Admiralty Tide Tables*. The tidal curve at Southampton, a standard port, is also based on low water because of the complexity of the tide around high water.

Meteorological effects on tides

Meteorological conditions which differ from the average will cause corresponding differences between the predicted and the actual tide. Variations in tidal heights are mainly caused by strong or prolonged winds and by unusually high or low barometric pressure. Differences between predicted and actual times of high and low water are caused mainly by wind.

Statistical analysis indicates that 1 standard deviation (*see* Chapter 16) of the differences between observed and predicted heights and times amounts to 0.2 metre and 10 minutes respectively.

Barometric pressure

Tidal predictions are computed for average barometric pressure. A difference from the average of 34 millibars can cause a difference in height of about 0.3 metre. A low barometer will tend to raise sea level and a high barometer will tend to depress it. The water level does not, however, adjust itself immediately to a change of pressure and it responds, moreover, to the average change in pressure over a considerable area. Changes in level due to barometric pressure seldom exceed 0.3 metre but, when Mean Sea Level is raised or lowered by strong winds or by storm surges, this effect can be important.

Effect of wind

The effect of wind on sea level—and therefore on tidal heights and times—is very variable and depends largely on the topography of the area. In general, it can be said that wind will raise sea level in the direction towards which it is blowing. A strong wind blowing straight onshore will pile up the water and cause high waters to be higher than predicted, while winds blowing off the land will have the reverse effect. Winds blowing along a coast tend to set up long waves which travel along the coast, raising sea level where the crest of the wave appears and lowering sea level in the trough. These waves are known as *storm surges* and are discussed below.

Seiches

Abrupt changes in meteorological conditions, such as the passage of an intense depression or line squall, may cause an oscillation in the sea level known as a *seiche*. The period between successive waves may be anything between a few minutes and about 2 hours and the height of the waves may be anything from 1 centimetre or so up to 1 metre.

Positive and negative surges; storm surges

A change in sea level is often caused by a combination of wind and pressure, such changes being superimposed on the normal tidal cycle. A rise in sea level is often referred to as a *positive surge* and a fall as a *negative surge*. A *storm surge* is an unusually severe positive surge.

Both positive and negative surges may appreciably alter the predicted times of high and low water, often by as much as 1 hour.

A positive surge will have the greatest effect when it is confined to a gulf or bight such as the North Sea. It rarely increases the general sea level height by more than 1 metre, although greater heights are not unknown (*see* below on storm surges). In a bight such as the North Sea, northerly winds will raise the general sea level at the southern end, causing a positive surge.

Negative surges are of great importance to large vessels navigating with small under-keel clearances. These surges are most evident in estuaries and areas of shallow water, and appear to occur when strong winds are tending to blow water out of a bight or similar area. For example, in the North Sea, strong southerly winds will tend to cause a negative surge in sea level at the southern end. Falls in sea level of up to 1 metre are not uncommon, while falls of as much as 2 metres have been recorded.

Storm surges occur in bights or estuaries when the speed of the tidal wave is reduced by shallow water effect to that of the speed of the storm. The tidal wave is thus being 'fed' by the storm and gradually increases in amplitude. In certain circumstances, it may attain a considerable height—3 metres is not unknown and, if this peak occurs at high water springs, considerable flooding and damage may be caused along the coastline.

A storm surge may be anticipated when an intense depression moves at a critical speed across the head of a bight with storm force winds blowing into the bight. Such surges have been experienced in the southern North Sea and in the Bay of Bengal. They may be preceded by an abnormal stand at low water.

Seismic waves (tsunamis)

A *seismic wave* or *tsunami* (often popularly but erroneously called a 'tidal wave') is usually the result of an undersea earthquake which sets up waves entirely unconnected with the tides. These waves travel with great rapidity in the deep waters of the oceans, reaching speeds of over 400 knots, a wavelength of over 100 miles (thus, a period of about $\frac{1}{4}$ hour) and a height of only $\frac{1}{2}$ to 1 metre. On reaching shallow water, however, they increase rapidly in height, often reaching destructive proportions. Heights of 15 to 17 metres have been recorded.

The first wave is often preceded by a very rapid lowering of the water level, a warning that the tsunami will arrive in a few minutes. The tsunami typically consists of a series of waves, the second and third being higher than the first, the rest gradually decreasing over a period which may be as little as a few hours and as long as several days.

Tsunamis usually originate in the earthquake zones of the Pacific basin and travel for enormous distances. They have been known to reach the English Channel, although by that time the amplitude has fallen to just a few centimetres.

TIDAL PREDICTION

To predict with accuracy the height of tide at any place, extensive tidal observations must be carried out and the results analysed.

Harmonic constituents

The tidal observations at a place are analysed and used to identify a number of constituent parts making up the tide-raising forces at that place. The tide-raising forces may be considered as the resultant of a large number of harmonic cosine curves, the periods and relative amplitudes of which can be calculated from astronomical theory. Some 400 harmonic constituents have been calculated but, in practice, it is unnecessary to use so many. As many as 60 are used for major tidal stations.

If a periodic force such as a tide-raising force is applied to a body of water, that water will respond by oscillating with the same period. The response is, however, modified by topographical conditions which can retard or advance the tidal wave, and raise or lower the amplitude. There is *some* response to all the harmonic constituents of the tide-raising force and *no* regular response to other forces.

The harmonic constituents are given symbols from which their general significance may be deduced. For example, the letter M is used for lunar constituents, S for solar constituents, the subscript 1 for diurnal and the subscript 2 for semi-diurnal components.

Principles of harmonic tidal analysis

The longer the period of tidal observation at a place, the better the analysis is likely to be. Because of the various cycles involved, a period of 18.6 years, equal to the longest cycle, is desirable if all the necessary harmonic constituents are to be identified. However, for *standard port* predictions in the *Admiralty Tide Tables*, the general rule is for at least 1 complete year's observations to be analysed; this allows an adequate number of constituents to be identified with sufficient accuracy. At *secondary ports*, analysis of at least 1 month's observations is the aim, as this permits the identification of the four major harmonic constituents.

The four principal constituents with which the user will come into contact are:

M_2 The principal lunar semi-diurnal constituent. This component permits calculations of the amplitude caused by a theoretical Moon in circular orbit around the Earth at the average speed of the real Moon, halfway between apogee and perigee and at an average northerly or southerly declination.

S_2 The principal solar semi-diurnal constituent. This component permits calculation of the amplitude caused by a theoretical Sun in similar circumstances to that for the Moon above.

K_1 A luni-solar declinational diurnal constituent. This component allows for part of the Moon's and Sun's declination.

O_1 A lunar declinational diurnal constituent. This component allows for the remainder of the Moon's declination.

Each harmonic constituent has a speed, an amplitude and a phase. The speed is given in degrees per hour, one complete cycle being 360°. Details of the four main constituents are given in Table 11–1.

Table 11–1

CONSTITUENT	NO. OF CYCLES PER DAY	SPEED (DEGREES PER HOUR)	TIME TO COMPLETE 1 CYCLE
M_2	2	28°.98	12 h 25 min
S_2	2	30°	12 h 00 min
K_1	1	15°.04	23 h 56 min
O_1	1	13°.94	25 h 50 min

The *amplitude H* is equal to half the range, the range being the difference in height between the maximum and minimum of each oscillation.

The phase of a constituent is its position in time in relation to its theoretical position as deduced from astronomical theory. The tide-raising forces do not act instantaneously (*see* page 280, frequency of springs and neaps); thus, each constituent has a *time* or *phase lag g*.

The purpose of tidal analysis is to determine the amplitude H and the phase lag g.

Tidal prediction

Tidal prediction is carried out by electronic computer using an appropriate number of harmonic constituents. In many places, for example Portsmouth, the shallow water constituents are very complex and additional corrections have to be applied. The authority for the observations, constants and predictions, the method of prediction and the year of observation are all shown in the *Admiralty Tide Tables*.

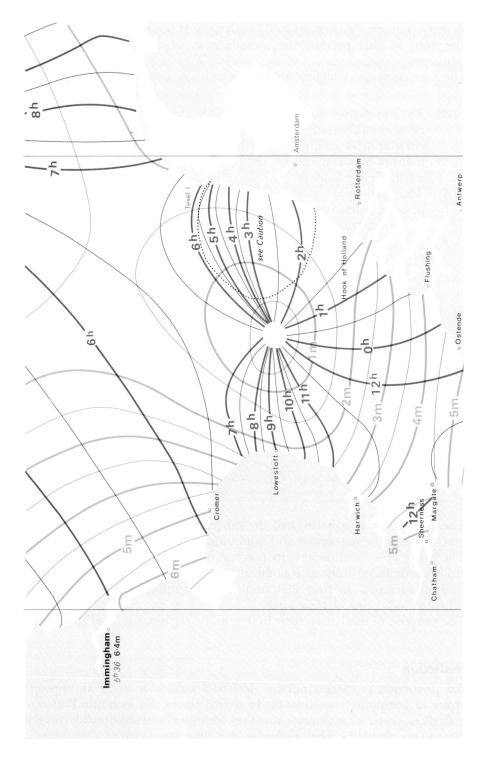

Fig. 11-19.   Co-tidal, co-range chart

Simplified Harmonic Method of Tidal Prediction (NP 159)

Provided that the four main harmonic constituents M_2, S_2, K_1 and O_1 are known, the user may obtain his own curve of predicted tidal heights, using the various forms in the *Simplified Harmonic Method of Tidal Prediction*. This method calculates the M_2 and S_2 semi-diurnal components, the shallow water corrections (if applicable) and the K_1 and O_1 diurnal components, combining all these to determine the predicted tidal curve for the place. Full instructions are given in NP 159.

M_2, S_2, K_1 and O_1 are tabulated in the *Tide Tables* for most standard and secondary ports and are referred to as *harmonic constants*. The daily values of these four components, which are determined by the position of the Moon and Sun, are also tabulated. These latter values have been amended to include a number of minor semi-diurnal and diurnal harmonic constituents.

In some areas of the world, an apparent seasonal variation may occur in the larger harmonic constants M_2 and S_2, both for amplitude and for phase. This phenomenon may be found in areas where there is a large seasonal variation in sea level, or where there are marked meteorological changes as is the case with the monsoons. It has also been found in other parts of the world such as the British Isles. It is only possible to identify the effects if at least one complete year's tidal observations have been made.

Such seasonal change must be taken into account when extracting the harmonic constants for a relevant port from the *Tide Tables*.

As mentioned above, NP 159 permits the inclusion of shallow water effect. To this end, data on shallow water corrections are included in the *Tide Tables*. At certain ports with large shallow water effects, the change in Mean Sea Level can be quite significant, dependent on the date relative to springs, and this needs to be taken into account when using NP 159. Details are given in the *Tide Tables*.

A variation of this method of tidal prediction may also be carried out on a pocket calculator, in preference to the graphical solution using NP 159. Full details are given in the *Tide Tables*. A calculator with a polar rectangular conversion facility is particularly useful. Details are also given in the *Tide Tables* on the use of programmable calculators for this method of prediction.

Co-tidal charts

Co-tidal and co-range charts show lines of equal time and range of tides (Fig. 11–19). They are available for certain areas around the world—the British Isles (and in particular the Dover Strait and southern North Sea), the Malacca Strait, the Persian Gulf. Such charts provide a means of predicting tidal information in the open sea in these areas. Instructions for their use with an example are provided on the charts, and exercises on their use are given in Volume V of this manual.

Co-tidal lines (12h, 11h, 10h, etc.) are drawn through points of equal Mean High Water Interval (MHWI). MHWI is the mean time interval between the passing of the Moon over the meridian of Greenwich and the time of the next high water at the place concerned. Co-range lines (5m, 4m, 3m, etc.) are drawn through positions of equal mean range (MSR). MSR is the difference in level between Mean High and Low Water Springs and is given in metres.

Co-tidal lines tend to radiate outwards from an *amphidromic* point* while co-range lines surround it. Near amphidromic points in the areas covered by these charts, the range of the tide may alter considerably within a short distance.

Such charts are of great importance to deep-draught ships with small under-keel clearances navigating the areas concerned. The reliability of the information depends on the accuracy and number of tidal observations made in the area concerned. Since it is difficult to position tide-gauges in suitable sites, offshore data often depend more on interpolation from inshore stations than on direct measurement; thus, **the data must be used with caution**.

TIDAL STREAMS AND CURRENTS

A careful distinction must be drawn between *tidal streams* (sometimes referred to as 'tidal currents' in the US and elsewhere) and *currents* (called, in some countries, 'non-tidal' currents). In practice, a combination of tidal stream and current is frequently experienced.

Tidal streams are horizontal movements of the water in response to tide-raising forces and may be predicted for any period in the future. *Currents*, on the other hand, are caused by meteorological factors such as wind and barometric pressure, by oceanographical factors such as water of differing salinity or temperature, and by topographical factors such as irregularities in the sea-bed. The assessment of currents is set out in Chapter 8. Ocean currents are discussed in Volume II of this manual.

In rivers and estuaries, there is often a permanent current caused by the flow of river water; such currents are included in the tidal stream tables.

Types of tidal streams

Tidal streams are of two main types, *rectilinear* and *rotary*. The first has only two directions (with perhaps small variations), which may be called the *flood* (the incoming tidal stream) or the *ebb* (the outgoing tidal stream) or, preferably, east-west going, north-south going, etc. Rotary tidal streams are continually changing in direction; they rotate through 360° in a complete cycle. The rate of the tidal stream usually varies throughout the cycle, with two maxima in approximately opposite directions interspersed with two minima about halfway between the maxima in time and direction.

In port approaches, estuaries, channels and straits, where the direction of the flow of the tidal stream is constricted by the surrounding land and shoals, the tidal streams are rectilinear. Offshore, where such restrictions no longer exist, the tidal streams are rotary.

Tidal streams, like tides, have semi-diurnal and diurnal components (including a diurnal inequality) and may be analysed harmonically or non-harmonically. In European waters, tidal streams are for the most part of the same type as the tides, that is, they are semi-diurnal in character. The rates of the stream are related to the range of the tide, and the times of slack water are related to but not necessarily identical with the times of high and low water at

---

* An amphidromic system is a tidal system, the centre of which is known to be an amphidromic point where the range of the tide is nil or very small, increasing outwards. The times of high and low water progress clockwise or anticlockwise around the centre.

the nearest standard port. For example, at Devonport, the turn of the tidal stream occurs within about an hour of the times of high and low water. However, further out into the open waters of the English Channel south of Plymouth, slack water occurs at about half-tide, that is, about 3 to $3\frac{1}{2}$ hours before and after high water at Devonport. Indeed, along open coasts, it is more usual for slack water and the turn of the tidal stream to be at half-tide rather than at high and low water.

Tidal stream data

Tidal streams which are semi-diurnal in character may be predicted by reference to a suitable standard port and are displayed in tables printed on the published chart. There is no necessity for daily predictions to be published. These tables show the rate and direction of the predicted tidal stream of springs and neaps by reference to the time of high water at a suitable standard port. The rate at times other than at springs and neaps may be found by interpolating between the two.

In other parts of the world, such as the Malacca and Singapore Straits, where the diurnal inequality of the tidal stream is large, the above procedure is not possible. Daily predictions for important areas are published in the *Admiralty Tide Tables and Tidal Stream Tables*, Volumes 2 and 3 (*ATT*). Harmonic constants for some tidal streams are also published in all three volumes so that predictions may be made using NP 159.

Tidal stream atlases

Where the tidal stream may be related to a standard port and when there are sufficient data, atlases are available showing rates and directions over a wide area. Such atlases, showing the tidal streams in pictorial form, are available for all the waters around the British Isles, and also for other parts of the world such as the west coast of France and Hong Kong. Certain countries may make the use of such atlases compulsory for ships proceeding to and from their ports; for example, US Port Authorities require their port and tidal current tables, charts and diagrams to be held by visiting ships.

Instructions for the prediction of the rate of tidal stream are given inside the front cover of the atlas.

RN ships are also issued with *Home Dockyard Ports—Tides and Tidal Streams* (NP 167), which covers the home dockyards Portsmouth, Devonport, etc. The information supplements that given in the *Tide Tables* and *Sailing Directions*. The publication also contains information on eddies and slack water.

Tidal stream observations

The observation of tidal streams presents greater difficulties than the observation of tides. However, in the case of tidal streams, the degree of accuracy necessary for tidal prediction is unnecessary as well as impracticable. For example, the tidal stream tables to be found on charts around the British Isles are, generally speaking, based on a series of observations extending over a period of 25 hours. In the case of coastal observations, any residual current is removed before the tables are compiled. As mentioned earlier, the permanent current in rivers and estuaries is included in the tables.

Because of the rapidly changing effects of sea-bed topography on the direction and rate of the tidal stream, it is often impossible to give more than an indication of how a ship will be affected by tidal streams when on passage. In a narrow channel, for instance, the stream may be running at 3 knots in the centre with virtually no stream or even a stream running in the opposite direction, at the edges of the channel: the stream may vary from nil to 3 knots in the navigable part of the channel. Tidal stream predictions for any given position in the channel should be correct for that position, but may well be incorrect for a position a few yards either side. While the tidal stream predictions must be accurate enough for navigational purposes, the methods of prediction are not required to be so complex as for tidal predictions.

Tidal streams at depth

It is sometimes of interest to HM Ships, deep-draught merchant ships, oil rig operators, and those engaged in underwater operations, to know how the tidal streams may vary in strength and direction from the surface down to lower depths. Published tidal stream data normally refer to the uppermost 10 metre layer of the sea, which is that layer of particular interest to the average ship. Tidal streams at greater depths tend to be very similar to those on the surface* until a depth is reached approximating to three-quarters the total depth although times of turn may be different (usually early but occasionally late) by as much as 1 hour compared with those on the surface. Tidal streams then fall away in strength to a value which may be about 50% to 60% of the surface rate at about 1 metre above a smooth sea-bed, and also change direction slightly by about 10° to 20°. In the bottom few centimetres of depth, tidal streams may undergo a marked change from those on the surface.

Published data are available for surface and sub-surface tidal streams in the Strait of Gibraltar (NP 629). Data are also available for a few other areas of the world from the Hydrographer. Some of the data are available, in relevant operating handbooks, to HM Ships only. Commercial companies usually apply direct to the Hydrographer or the Institute of Oceanographic Science for whatever information they may require.

Eddies, races and overfalls

Eddies, tide-rips, overfalls and races are different forms of water turbulence caused by abruptly changing topography of the sea-bed, the configuration of the coastline, the constriction of channels or sudden changes in tidal or tidal stream characteristics.

An *eddy* is a circular movement of water, the diameter of which may be anything from a few inches to a few miles. For an example of the latter, *see* the *Tidal Stream Atlas of the Approaches to Portland*, where there is an anti-clockwise eddy of the tidal stream east of Portland between 1 hour after and 5 hours after high water at Devonport.

An *overfall* is another name for a *tide-rip* and is caused by a strong stream near

---

* This situation may be quite different in ports which are fed by river water in addition to the tides, e.g. Devonport. The strength and direction of the stream may vary considerably with depth, this being dependent on the amount of fresh water flowing down-river, and the depth to which it penetrates.

the sea-bed being deflected upwards by obstructions on the bottom, thus causing a confused sea on the surface.

A *tidal race* is an exceptionally strong stream, usually caused by the constriction of water passing round a headland or where tidal streams from different directions converge. The tidal stream atlas for Portland shows an almost permanent race south of Portland Bill.

Where the effect of eddies, etc. are of a permanent nature, they are taken into account when predicting tidal streams.

ADMIRALTY TIDE TABLES (ATT)

A brief description of the *Admiralty Tide Tables* is given in Chapter 7.

Standard ports

Each volume of the *Tide Tables* has a selected number of *standard ports*, a total of about 240 in all three volumes. For standard ports in the British Isles and Commonwealth, observed tide-gauge readings have been made, where possible, over at least a year. The harmonic constants for these ports are computed from the analysis of the readings. Changes in Mean Sea Level, which are included in the standard port data, are observed and analysed where possible over at least a 3 year period. Predictions for most standard ports outside the British Isles are obtained from National Authorities. The method of prediction is not always known but it may be assumed that the predictions should be adequate for normal navigational purposes in reasonable weather.

In Volume 1, *European Waters including Mediterranean Sea*, each standard port has a diagram from which the height and time other than at high water may be predicted. In Volume 2, *The Atlantic and Indian Oceans*, and Volume 3, *The Pacific Ocean and Adjacent Seas*, one standard curve covering all the standard ports is included at the beginning of the volume. An explanation of the use of the diagram is given in the instructions for the use of the tables in each volume. The four main harmonic constants for the standard ports are also tabulated in all three volumes.

Secondary ports

Each volume of the *Tide Tables* has a selected number of *secondary ports*, there being about 8000 in all three volumes. Generally speaking, tidal information on a secondary port is based on that at a nearby standard port and is tabulated as time and height differences from the standard port. The four main harmonic constants are also tabulated in all three volumes for about 5000 secondary ports. Predictions for secondary ports are made by applying time and height differences to predictions at the relevant standard port, or by using the four harmonic constants and NP 159. The data on which the differences are based are variable in quality; where possible, observations have been carried out over at least 15 and preferably 30 days. Where this is not the case, the harmonic constants are annotated accordingly.

The standard port on which the secondary port is based has similar tidal characteristics, to ensure that the average time and height differences for the secondary port are as accurate as possible. In some cases, therefore, a standard port has been chosen which is very remote from the secondary port. For example, a number of secondary ports in Antarctica are based on Galveston, Texas. In other cases, the tides at a secondary port cannot be referred to any standard port, and the tide must be predicted using the harmonic constants and NP 159.

Using the *Tide Tables*

The time and height of high and low water, and the height of the tide at times between high and low water, may be found from the *Tide Tables* for all standard and secondary ports. Full instructions on using the tide tables are given. Suitable exercises may be found in Volume V of this manual.

High and low water at secondary ports

The times of high and low water at secondary ports are obtained by applying the tabulated time differences to the daily predictions for the relevant standard port. Where the tide is mainly semi-diurnal in character, the differences are tabulated for Mean Spring and Neap levels at the standard port. When the diurnal inequality is large, the tabulations are made for Mean Higher and Mean Lower, High and Low water (*see* page 297).

For certain ports, no suitable standard port is available and predictions must be made using NP 159. The *Tide Tables* are annotated accordingly.

Height of tide at times between high and low water

ATT, Volume 1. Intermediate times and heights are best predicted by the use of the Mean Spring and Neap curves* given for each standard port. For secondary ports, where there is little change of shape between adjacent standard ports, and where the duration of rise or fall at the secondary port is not very different from the relevant standard port, intermediate times and heights may be found by using the Mean Spring and Neap curves for the relevant standard port.

Between Swanage and Selsey, the tide is of great complexity and special curves and instructions are provided.

At some other secondary ports, where indicated in the tables, NP 159 should be used.

ATT, Volumes 2 and 3. The standard curve may be used for all ports provided that:

1. The duration of the rise or fall of the tide is between 5 and 7 hours.
2. There is no shallow water correction.

If either of these criteria is not met, NP 159 should be used.

Offshore areas and places between secondary ports

Tidal predictions for offshore areas and stretches of coastline between secondary ports should be obtained by the use of co-tidal charts (*see* page 289), if these are available.

---

* The neap curves in *ATT*, Volume 1 have been adjusted to allow the calculation of intermediate heights and times and do not, therefore, reflect the true relationship between spring and neap tides at the relevant standard port.

Admiralty Tidal Prediction Form (NP 204)

The Admiralty Tidal Prediction Form is a form designed for the majority of time and height calculations. Copies of the form are to be found in the back of the *Tide Tables* volumes, and further copies in booklet form may be obtained from Admiralty Chart Depots and Agents.

Supplementary information in the *Tide Tables*

Supplementary information provided in the *Tide Tables* in addition to that already mentioned in this chapter is as follows:

> Heights of chart datum relative to Ordnance Datum in the United Kingdom (Volume 1 only).
>
> Heights of chart datum relative to the land levelling system in countries outside the United Kingdom (Volume 1 only).
>
> Tidal levels at standard ports.
>
> Astronomical arguments for use with the semi-graphic method of harmonic analysis of 30 days tidal observations (NP 112).
>
> Tidal stream tables (Volumes 2 and 3 only).

LEVELS AND DATUMS

Datum of tidal prediction

Soundings on Admiralty charts are given below the level of chart datum, which is defined in Chapter 6 (page 115). By international agreement, chart datum is defined as a level so low that the tide will not frequently fall below it. The datum for tidal predictions must be the same as the datum for soundings, to ensure that the total depth of water is equal to the charted depth plus the height of the tide. The levels at which datums have been established at standard ports vary widely, however, and the datums do not conform to any uniform tide level. Modern practice is to establish datum at or near the level of Lowest Astronomical Tide (LAT, *see* below), but Table V in the *Tide Tables* should always be referred to when planning passages, etc. as this shows many datums different from LAT. For areas where the Hydrographer of the Navy is the surveying authority, datums have been adjusted to approximate to LAT.

It is always advisable to check that chart datum and the datum for tidal predictions are the same. This can easily be done by comparing the tide levels printed on the chart with those in the *Tide Tables*.

Chart datum and land survey datum

To determine how tidal levels vary along any given stretch of coastline, all levels must be referred to a common horizontal plane. Chart datum is not a suitable reference because it is dependent on the range of the tide. In Great Britain, the Ordnance Datum at Newlyn may be regarded as a suitable horizontal plane and should be used if comparisons of absolute height are required. On large- and medium-scale charts for which the Hydrographer is the primary authority, the panel giving tidal heights may also tabulate the difference between chart and ordnance datums for the area. Other countries have their own land survey datums; some of these are listed in Table IV of Volume 1 of the *Tide Tables*.

If absolute heights are required at a point on the coast where no tidal data are given, or where there is no connection to land survey datum, they should be obtained by interpolation from heights obtained from places on either side where data are available.

Tide levels and heights

A number of these are shown in Fig. 11–20.

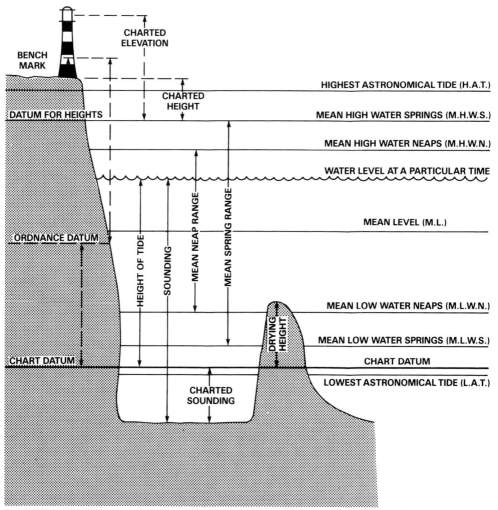

Some old charts show Bench Marks which may be based on Ordnance or Chart Datum

Fig. 11–20.   Tide levels and heights

Heights

Heights on Admiralty charts are given above a particular vertical datum. This is Mean High Water Springs in areas where the tides are semi-diurnal and Mean Higher High Water where there is a diurnal inequality. Mean Sea Level is used in places where there is no tide. (*See also* Chapter 6, page 119.)

Tide levels

These levels are all referred to chart datum, which is the same as the zero of tidal predictions. Definitions of various levels are set out below.

Highest Astronomical Tide (HAT), Lowest Astronomical Tide (LAT). These are the highest and lowest levels respectively which can be predicted to occur under average meteorological conditions and any combination of astronomical conditions. HAT and LAT are not the extreme levels which can be reached; storm surges (page 285) may cause considerably higher and lower levels to occur. The values of HAT and LAT are obtained by inspection over a period of years.

Mean High Water Springs (MHWS), Mean Low Water Springs (MLWS). The height of Mean High Water Springs is the average of the heights of two successive high waters during those periods of 24 hours (approximately every fortnight) when the range of the tide is greatest. This is computed throughout the year when the average maximum declination of the moon is $23\frac{1}{2}°$. The height of Mean Low Water Springs is the average height obtained from two successive low waters during the same period.

Mean High Water Neaps (MHWN), Mean Low Water Neaps (MLWN). The height of Mean High Water Neaps is the average throughout the year, as above, of the heights of two successive high waters during those periods (approximately every fortnight) when the range of the tide is least. The height of Mean Low Water Neaps is the average height obtained from two successive low waters during the same period.

Mean Tide Level* (MTL). Mean Tide Level is the mean of the heights of MHWS, MHWN, MLWS and MLWN.

Mean Sea Level* (MSL). Mean Sea Level is the average level of the sea surface over a long period, preferably 18.6 years, or the average level which would exist in the absence of tides.

Mean Higher High Water (MHHW). The height of Mean Higher High Water is the mean of the higher of the two daily high waters over a long period of time. When only one high water occurs in a day, this is taken as the higher high water.

Mean Lower High Water (MLHW). The height of Mean Lower High Water is the mean of the lower of the two daily high waters over a long period of time. When only one high water occurs on some days, $\triangle$ is printed in the MLHW column of the *Tide Tables* to indicate that the tide is usually diurnal.

Mean Higher Low Water (MHLW). The height of Mean Higher Low Water is the mean of the higher of the two daily low waters over a long period of time. When only one low water occurs on some days, $\triangle$ is printed in the MHLW column of the tide table to indicate that the tide is usually diurnal.

Mean Lower Low Water (MLLW). The height of Mean Lower Low Water is the mean of the lower of the two daily low waters over a long period of time. When only one low water occurs on a day, this is taken as the lower low water.

---

* The Mean Level (ML) tabulated in the *Tide Tables* is Mean Tide Level in Volume 1 and Mean Sea Level in Volumes 2 and 3. Mean Sea and Tide Levels at any one place may differ because of distortion in the tidal curve resulting from shallow water effects.

The average values of MHWS, MHWN, MLWS, MLWN, MHHW, MLHW, MHLW and MLLW vary from year to year in a cycle of approximately 18.6 years. The tide levels shown in Table V of the *Tide Tables* are average values over the whole cycle.

CHAPTER 12
Coastal Navigation

Navigational passages must be carefully planned. Everyone is liable to make mistakes; over three-quarters of all groundings are attributable to human error of some kind. A sound passage plan may not prevent a grounding, but it does reduce the chances of making mistakes.

This chapter takes the reader through the various stages of a coastal passage: the preparatory work, making the plan and finally the execution. The chapter concludes with remarks on passages in fog and thick weather and navigation in coral waters.

PREPARATORY WORK

There are many points that the navigator must consider before undertaking a coastal passage.

Charts and publications

All the charts and publications necessary for the passage must be selected and assembled.

Charts

The charts to be used are selected by studying the *Catalogue of Admiralty Charts* (NP 131) and the relevant *Admiralty Sailing Directions*. HM Ships may also need to study the *Catalogue of Classified and Other Charts* (NP 111) for classified charts. Remember that the largest scale charts *appropriate to the purpose* (*see* page 121) should always be used; for a coastal passage, a series of overlapping medium-scale charts are provided. A small-scale chart is also required covering the whole passage; the intended track throughout the voyage should be plotted on it. If possible, the whole route should be shown on one small-scale chart.

All the charts must be corrected up to date for Permanent, Temporary and Preliminary Notices to Mariners, radio navigational warnings and relevant Local Notices. Consult the *Chart Correction Log* (NP 133A, 133B); it should be up to date for all charts and folios held on board.

Extract the charts from the relevant folios and list them in the Navigating Officer's Work Book* in the order in which they will be used.

---

* Any hard-bound lined A4 size book will suffice as a Work Book.

Certain miscellaneous charts may also be required. These include *Symbols and Abbreviations Used on Admiralty Charts* (Chart Booklet 5011); co-tidal and co-range charts; passage planning charts; practice and exercise area charts; charts of surveyed areas, offshore oil and gas operations, fishery limits, etc.

In some overseas areas, charts of other national Hydrographic Offices may be required, particularly the large-scale ones (*see* page 102).

Publications

Relevant publications (which must be corrected up to date) include the following:

> *Admiralty Distance Tables.*
> *Admiralty Sailing Directions.* These are a mine of useful information for passage making. They give information on ports; recommended routes; meteorological conditions including gales and fog; conspicuous fixing marks; sketches and photographs of the coastline and suitable navigational marks; tidal and tidal stream information.
> *The Nautical Almanac* (for times of sunrise, sunset, etc.).
> *Admiralty Tide Tables.*
> Tidal stream atlases.
> Co-tidal atlases.
> *Home Dockyard Ports—Tides and Tidal Streams* (HM Ships only).
> *Admiralty List of Lights.*
> *IALA Maritime Buoyage System.*
> *The Mariner's Handbook.*
> *Annual Summary of Admiralty Notices to Mariners.*
> *Admiralty List of Radio Signals* (particularly Volumes 2, 5 and 6).
> IMO (International Maritime Organisation) *Ships' Routeing*, details of which may also be found in *Sailing Directions*, *The Mariner's Handbook*, the *Annual Summary of Admiralty Notices to Mariners*, and on the charts (including passage planning charts).
> *The Decca Navigator Operating Instructions* and *Marine Data Sheets* for ships so fitted.
> Fleet Operating Orders, procedures and programmes (HM Ships only).
> Navigational Data Book.
> Department of Transport *A Guide to the Planning and Conduct of Sea Passages.*
> IMO *Recommendation on Basic Principles and Operational Guidance Relating to Navigational Watchkeeping.*

Information required

In addition to the information given on the charts, the Navigating Officer will need to find details of some or all of the following items from the publications available.

> The distance between ports of departure and destination.
> The likely set and drift to be experienced on passage resulting from the combined effects of tidal stream, current and surface drift.
> Times and heights of the tide along the route.
> Advice and recommendations along the route obtainable from the *Sailing Directions.*

Routeing and traffic separation schemes to be encountered along the route.

Past, present and likely future weather; in the event of bad weather, the likely diversionary ports or anchorages.

Duration of daylight and darkness; times of sunset and sunrise, etc.

Radio aids available during the passage.

Likely ship's draught, fore and aft, at the beginning, during and at the end of the passage, and the requirements for under-keel clearance.

Search and Rescue arrangements along the route.

All necessary information should be noted in the Navigating Officer's Work Book.

Appraisal

Having assembled all the necessary information, the Navigating Officer carries out an appraisal of the passage. He will need to study the charts covering the route and its vicinity and the lights likely to be sighted. Some of these lights may be positioned outside the limits of the selected charts. At the same time, the *Sailing Directions* covering the area concerned must be consulted. A good plan is to tab the pages relevant to that part of the coast off which the ship will pass, inserting references to the latest supplement and to corrections listed in Part IV of the Weekly Notices to Mariners. Study the relevant portions of the *Sailing Directions* in conjunction with the charts, *List of Lights*, tidal publications, *List of Radio Signals*, local orders, etc. to obtain a clear mental picture of what may be expected along the route—the appearance of the coastline and suitable navigational marks, dangers, tidal streams, radio aids, etc. Such study will also provide information on port traffic signals, signal stations and local weather signals, depths of water over bars at harbour entrances, details of anchorages, berths, landing places and other local information. The charts should be annotated accordingly, e.g. brief descriptions of light structures and conspicuous buildings, the colour of cliffs, suitable fixing marks.

Relevant information should be noted as necessary in the Work Book.

PLANNING THE PASSAGE

Choosing the route

Having established the dangers along the route in relation to the draught of the ship, the Navigating Officer is now in a position to decide on the precise route to be taken. There are a number of factors which may affect the choice of route and the timing of the passage.

1. *Times of departure and arrival.* These may be subject to tidal considerations and also to port restrictions of various kinds (working hours, etc.). Courtesies to the country being visited (gun salutes, official calls, etc.) are also factors that need to be taken into account.
2. The possibility of *fog or low visibility*, particularly in narrow waters, and the effect this will have on passage speed.
3. The likelihood of *bad weather* along the route, the direction from which it is likely to come, the effect on passage speeds, whether it may be necessary to

seek shelter, or heave to, etc. A passage to leeward of the coast (e.g. an island) in the prevailing weather is preferable to a passage along the windward side.

4. *Ships' routeing and traffic separation schemes* may apply along part of the route. Traffic separation schemes are discussed later in this chapter, and are dealt with in detail in Part 6 of Volume III of this manual.

5. The presence of *fishing vessels/fleets* along the route. Concentrations of fishing vessels should be avoided if possible.

6. A requirement to pass through *narrow or ill-lit channels*. By adjusting the times of arrival or departure, or the passage speed, it may be possible to avoid passing through such channels at night. An alteration of a few revolutions during the night watches will often ensure that the vessel arrives at the start of a particular passage at dawn. The possibility of breakdown (main engines, steering gear, compasses, etc.) in such areas must be borne in mind.

7. *Focal points for shipping*. Traffic bottlenecks and density of shipping must be taken into account. If the coast is on the starboard hand, the planning of the track should allow sufficient room to be able to alter course to starboard to avoid other shipping and still be navigationally safe. A ship may often be forced repeatedly to starboard by heavy traffic and sometimes the only way to counter this is by means of a bold alteration to seaward as soon as traffic density allows.

8. *Operations or exercises*. Where possible, these must be planned in advance and the times allowed for. For example:

   Replenishment at Sea.
   Rendezvous with other ships.
   Flying operations.
   Weapon exercises and any need to avoid exercise or range areas while on passage.
   Damage control exercises.
   Machinery (including steering gear) breakdown exercises.
   Equipment (including compasses) breakdown exercises.
   Ship handling exercises and Officer of the Watch manoeuvres.
   Seaboat (man overboard) exercises.
   Full power trials.
   Oil-rig patrols.
   Fishery protection assistance.

9. *Speed, endurance and economical steaming*. There may be restrictions on the speed allowed to save costs on fuel. If the passsage is long, there may be a need to refuel while on passage to avoid falling below laid down fuel margins required for operational or safety reasons.

10. *Clearance from the coast, and under-keel clearances*. These are discussed later in this chapter.

11. *Territorial limits*. Territorial limits claimed by countries are given in the *Annual Summary of Admiralty Notices to Mariners* and are updated from time to time in the Weekly Notices. HM Ships and their aircraft should keep clear of these limits if intending to exercise, otherwise diplomatic clearance will have to be obtained.

12. *Mined areas (see* the *Annual Summary of Admiralty Notices to Mariners).* There are a few minefields still in existence from the Second World War; they are not believed to be any more dangerous from mines than from any other of the usual hazards to navigation whilst on passage. However, certain areas are still highly unsafe with regard to anchoring, fishing or any other form of submarine or sea-bed activity. Details of these may be found in the relevant *Sailing Directions.*

It is always possible for minefields to be laid in times of tension between nations; thus, there is no guarantee that minefields may not be encountered at some time or other.

Clearance from the coast and off-lying dangers

When coasting, the general rules to be followed are:

1. Be sufficiently close in to identify shore objects easily.
2. Be far enough off to minimise the risk of running ashore as a result of error or machinery breakdown.
3. Keep in a safe depth.

When deciding the distance to pass from the coast and from off-lying dangers, the track chosen should be such that, if fog or mist should obscure the coastal marks, the ship may still be navigated with the certainty that she is not running into danger. As a general principle, a course parallel to dangers should be chosen rather than one converging with them.

The following points should be borne in mind when laying off the ship's track on the chart.

1. When the coast is steep-to and soundings fall away sharply, pass at a distance of 1½ to 2 miles. At this range, objects will be easily recognised in normal (10 miles) visibility.
2. When the coast is shelving, pass outside that depth contour line which gives the ship an adequate safety margin beneath the keel.

    Ships drawing less than 3 metres (10 feet) should aim to pass outside the 5 metre (3 fathom) line.

    Ships drawing between 3 and 6 metres (10 and 20 feet) should aim to pass outside the 10 metre (5 fathom) line.

    Ships drawing between 6 and 10 metres (20 and 33 feet) should aim to pass outside the 20 metre (10 fathom) line.

    Ships drawing more than 10 metres (33 feet) should pass in a depth of water which gives a safe allowance under the keel (*see* p.308).
3. Unmarked dangers near the coast, where fixing marks are adequate, should be passed at least 1 mile distant provided there is sea-room.
4. Light-vessels, lanbys, light-floats, and buoys should be passed at 5 cables (½ mile) provided there is sea-room.
5. Unmarked dangers out of sight of land should be passed at about 5 to 10 miles, dependent on the time interval since the last fix and the tidal stream or current likely to be experienced. By night this distance should be increased.

Remember that distances may have to be adjusted for the prevailing weather (a greater depth of water will be needed in rough weather to allow for the

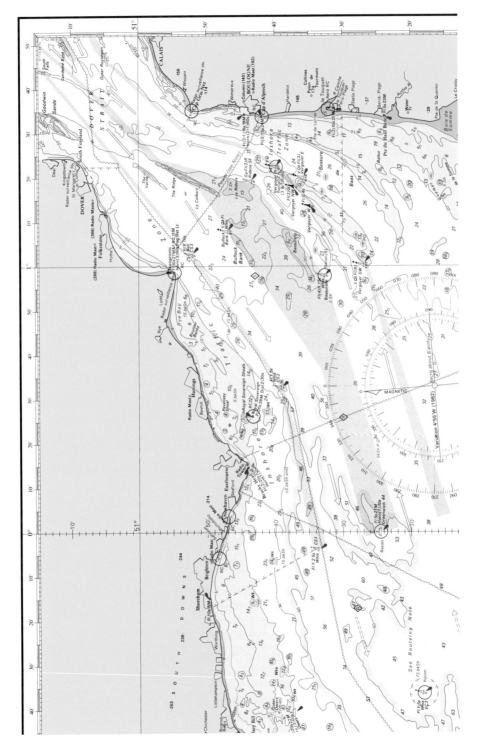

Fig. 12–1.   Traffic separation schemes, one-way lanes and inshore traffic zones

scend), tidal stream, etc., the nature of the coast, the off-lying dangers, and the opportunities for fixing. The height of tide may also be a factor which should be taken into account when considering a safe depth.

Ships' routeing and traffic separation schemes

Details of ships' routeing and traffic separation schemes (TSS) adopted by IMO (the International Maritime Organisation) may be found in *Ships' Routeing*, published by IMO. IMO is a United Nations organisation set up to deal with international regulations and recommendations relating to maritime safety (including navigation) and pollution.

The subject matter of routeing and TSS is also dealt with in some detail in Part 6 of Volume III of this manual. Details of the traffic separation schemes on Admiralty charts are given in the *Annual Summary of Admiralty Notices to Mariners*, which also lists the national authority for schemes not adopted by IMO. Further information may also be found in the *Sailing Directions*, *The Mariner's Handbook* (NP 100) and on passage planning charts. Brief details, sufficient for those planning navigational passages, are given below.

The aim of ships' routeing is to increase the safety of navigation in areas where the density of traffic is heavy, or where the traffic converges, or where restricted sea-room prevents freedom of manoeuvre. To achieve the aim, some or all of the following measures are in force.

1. *One-way traffic lanes*, separated by a zone which ships are not normally allowed to enter other than those crossing the lane (Fig. 12–1). In narrow passages and restricted waters, a separation line may be used instead of a zone to allow a greater width of navigable water in the lanes. Opposing streams of traffic may sometimes be separated by natural obstructions, e.g. Le Colbart or The Ridge in the Dover Strait.
2. *Inshore traffic zones (ITZ)* to separate local and through traffic (Fig. 12–1). These inshore zones may be used by local traffic proceeding in any direction and are separated from traffic in the adjacent one-way system by a separation zone or line.
3. Approaches to focal points, e.g. port approaches, entrances to channels and estuaries, landfall buoys, etc., may be split into different *sectors*, each sector having its own traffic separation scheme (Fig. 12–2, p.306).
4. The routeing of traffic at places where routes meet may be dealt with by means of a *roundabout* (Fig. 12–2), the traffic proceeding around a central point or separation zone in an anti-clockwise direction, or a *junction*. An alternative method is to end the one-way systems before they meet. The area enclosed by the end points is called a *precautionary area* (Fig. 12–2) to emphasise the need to navigate with caution and may be indicated by the symbol $\triangle$.
5. Other methods of routeing are deep water (DW) routes for deep-draught ships (the least depth along the recommended route may be displayed on the chart), two-way routes, recommended tracks and routes and areas to be avoided. Through traffic of medium and shallow draught must keep away from DW routes and avoid inconveniencing very large vessels on these particular routes.

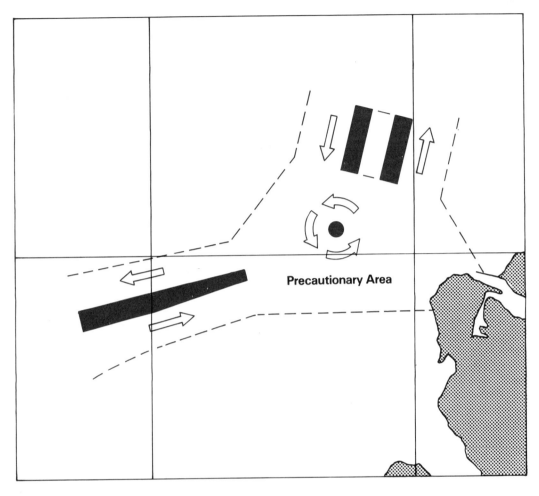

Fig. 12–2.   Sectors, roundabouts, precautionary areas

Conduct of ships in traffic separation schemes

The conduct of ships in traffic separation schemes adopted by IMO is governed by Rule 10 of the *International Regulations for Preventing Collisions at Sea, 1972*, as amended in 1983, and this is set out below.

Rule 10
Traffic Separation Schemes

(*a*) This rule applies to traffic separation schemes adopted by IMO.
(*b*) A vessel using a traffic separation scheme shall:
     (i) proceed in the appropriate traffic lane in the general direction of traffic flow for that lane;
    (ii) so far as practicable keep clear of a traffic separation line or separation zone;

(iii) normally join or leave a traffic lane at the termination of the lane, but when joining or leaving from either side shall do so at as small an angle to the general direction of traffic flow as practicable.

(c) A vessel shall so far as practicable avoid crossing traffic lanes, but if obliged to do so shall cross as nearly as practicable at right angles to the general direction of traffic flow.

(d) Inshore traffic zones shall not normally be used by through traffic which can safely use the appropriate traffic lane within the adjacent traffic separation scheme. However, vessels of less than 20 metres in length and sailing vessels may under all circumstances use inshore traffic zones.

(e) A vessel, other than a crossing vessel or a vessel joining or leaving a lane shall not normally enter a separation zone or cross a separation line except:
  (i) in cases of emergency to avoid immediate danger;
  (ii) to engage in fishing within a separation zone.

(f) A vessel navigating in areas near the terminations of traffic separation schemes shall do so with particular caution.

(g) A vessel shall so far as practicable avoid anchoring in a traffic separation scheme or in areas near its terminations.

(h) A vessel not using a traffic separation scheme shall avoid it by as wide a margin as is practicable.

(i) A vessel engaged in fishing shall not impede the passage of any vessel following a traffic lane.

(j) A vessel of less than 20 metres in length or a sailing vessel shall not impede the safe passage of a power-driven vessel following a traffic lane.

(k) A vessel restricted in her ability to manoeuvre when engaged in an operation for the maintenance of safety of navigation in a traffic separation scheme is exempted from complying with this Rule to the extent necessary to carry out the operation.

(l) A vessel restricted in her ability to manoeuvre when engaged in an operation for the laying, servicing or picking up of a submarine cable, within a traffic separation scheme, is exempted from complying with this Rule to the extent necessary to carry out the operation.

Rule 10 is intended to minimise the development of collision risks by separating opposing traffic flows, but the other Rules also apply. **The fact that a ship is proceeding along a route does not give that ship any special privilege or right of way.** When risk of collision is deemed to exist, the collision regulations apply in full.

The one-way traffic lanes are mainly for through traffic, which should not normally use the inshore traffic zone.

Special rules and recommendations may apply to certain areas (*see* the relevant *Sailing Directions* and passage planning guide); e.g. for Ushant, see the *Channel Pilot* (NP 27), also the *English Channel Passage Planning Guide*, Chart 5500).

A number of traffic separation schemes have not been adopted by IMO. The regulations governing their use are laid down by the national authority establishing them. These rules may not only modify Rule 10, but also other Rules of the 1972 regulations. Details may be found in the appropriate *Sailing Directions* or on the charts concerned. (*See also* the *Annual Summary of Admiralty Notices to Mariners*.)

Certain traffic separation schemes may lay down rules on which routes or parts of routes may be used by vessels carrying hazardous or noxious cargoes. The latter are defined in the MARPOL Rules, the international regulations set up to prevent oil pollution of the sea. Details are given in the relevant *Sailing Directions*, the appropriate passage planning chart and *The Mariner's Handbook*.

Ships should, as far as practicable, keep to the starboard side in two-way routes, including DW routes.

Under-keel clearances

All ships have to be navigated at some time or other in shallow water, and an appropriate safety margin under the keel must be allowed. Vessels with draughts approaching 30 metres have to navigate considerable distances in coastal waters with a minimum depth below the keel.

As a ship proceeds through shallow water, she experiences an interaction with the bottom, more often known as *shallow water effect* and quantified in terms of *squat*. The ship's speed in shallow water leads to a lowering of the water level around her and a change in trim, which together result in a reduction in the under-keel clearance. These phenomena are extensively covered in BR 67(3), *Admiralty Manual of Seamanship*, Volume III.

Squat is extremely difficult to quantify; the following figures must be used *with caution*, but they serve as a useful guide.

Squat may be expected to occur when the draught/depth of water ratio is less than 1:1.5, e.g. for a ship drawing 6 metres, a depth of water of 9 metres or less, or for ships drawing 30 metres, a depth of water of 45 metres or less.

The following rules of thumb are available:

$$\text{squat} = 10\% \text{ of the draught} \qquad OR$$
$$= 0.3 \text{ metres for every 5 knots of forward speed} \qquad OR$$
$$= \frac{V^2(\text{knots})}{100} \text{ metres}$$

(usually an over estimate for fine warship hulls, but suitable for merchant ships with fuller forms)

whichever is the greatest.

EXAMPLE

A ship drawing 6 metres is proceeding at 10 knots in less than 9 metres of water; what is the likely squat?

$$\text{squat} = 10\% \text{ of } 6 \ = 0.6 \text{ m} \qquad OR$$
$$= 0.3 \times \frac{10}{5} = 0.6 \text{ m} \qquad OR$$
$$= \frac{10^2}{100} \qquad = 1 \text{ m}$$

Thus, squat is likely to be about $\frac{1}{2}$ to 1 metre. Allow the greater figure.

Similarly, a ship drawing 30 metres at 10 knots in less than 45 metres of water might expect her squat to be of the order of 3 metres.

Additional under-keel allowances may have to be made for the following:

1. Reduced depths over pipelines which may stand as much as 2 metres above the sea-bed.
2. Reduced depths due to negative surges which may be as much as 1 to 2 metres, as described in Chapter 11.
3. Increased draught due to rolling or pitching. For example, a large ship with a beam of 50 metres can be expected to increase her draught by about $\frac{1}{2}$ metre for every 1° of roll. The trim of the ship is also likely to be affected by shallow water effect, and allowance must be made for any increased draught.
4. Inaccuracies in charted offshore depths and predicted tidal heights.
5. Inaccuracy in the estimated draught if coming to the end of a long passage.
6. Alterations in the charted depth since the last survey. This applies to areas where the bottom is known to be unstable, and particularly those parts of the world where *sandwaves* (*see* below) are a common occurrence, such as the southern North Sea including the Dover Strait, parts of the Thames Estuary, the Persian Gulf, the Malacca and Singapore Straits, in Japanese waters and in the Torres Strait.

Sandwaves in water are rather like sand dunes on land. The sea forms the sea-bed into a series of ridges and troughs which are believed to be more or less stationary. The size can vary tremendously, from the ripples seen on a sandy beach by the water's edge to sandwaves up to 20 metres in amplitude and several hundred metres between peaks. In the southern North Sea, sandwaves rising 5 metres above the general level of the sea-bed are quite common.

Details of known sandwave areas will be found in the relevant *Sailing Directions* and are also marked on the charts. Sandwaves may be expected to occur in shallow seas where there is relatively fast water movement and where the sea-bed is of a sedimentary type, usually sand. General remarks on sandwaves are given in *The Mariner's Handbook*. Ships navigating in sandwave areas with little under-keel clearance must proceed with the utmost caution.

From time to time a considerable under-keel allowance may be necessary. When planning a passage through a critical area, ships should take advantage of such co-tidal and co-range charts as are available; nevertheless, as already mentioned in Chapter 11, the *data from such charts must be used with caution*, since offshore data more often depend on the interpolation of inshore data than on direct measurement.

Various authorities may lay down an *under-keel allowance* for certain areas. In coastal waters, these apply especially to deep-draught ships. The figure usually takes into account an allowance for squat up to a particular speed. For example, in the Dover Strait, a *static under-keel allowance* of about 6.5 metres should be arrived at, including a squat allowance for speeds up to 12 knots.

The difference between the calculated depth of water and the ship's draught when stopped must be equal to or more than the static under-keel allowance. Thus, the least charted depth a ship should be able to cross in safety may be found as follows:

under-keel + 'static' draught = least charted + predicted height
allowance   depth   of tide

Port Authorities also issue a minimum under-keel clearance which must be observed by all ships under way regardless of squat or height of tide. For example at Portsmouth, when under way in the harbour or the approaches, ships should have at least 2 metres under the keel at all times.

The passage plan

The following procedure should be followed when planning a navigational passage. Details, calculations, etc. are entered in the Work Book. Try to keep the plan as simple as possible; the more complicated it is, the more likely it is to go wrong.

Times of arrival and departure

1. Determine the distance between departure and destination from the *Admiralty Distance Tables*. Add an amount, which may vary between 1–2% and 10%, to allow for all the likely divergences from the shortest navigable route as previously mentioned, e.g. operational or exercise requirements, under-keel clearances, traffic separation schemes, etc.
2. Consider the factors affecting the timing of the passage in terms of hours gained or lost (usually the latter). These are often operational or exercise requirements.
3. Consider the factors which may be calculated in terms of speed rather than time: the overall effect of tidal stream, current and weather.
4. Calculate the time to be taken on passage, taking into account any restriction on speed which may have been imposed, e.g. a requirement to proceed at economical speed in order to save fuel. Allow something in hand for unforseen eventualities; the amount will vary depending on the nature of the passage. With all other factors allowed for, a figure of between $\frac{1}{2}$ and 1 knot over the required passage speed, or 1 to $1\frac{1}{2}$ hours per day in hand, is a reasonable allowance. Distance divided by total passage time gives the speed of advance (SOA) required. The time in hand at various SOAs may then be calculated if desired; this also gives a cross check against the calculations.
5. Determine the Estimated Time of Departure (ETD) and the Estimated Time of Arrival (ETA). The SOA or the route may have to be adjusted to make the ETA and ETD convenient. Cross-check that this does not place the ship in a narrow or ill-lit channel at a bad time. If it does, the ETA, the ETD or the SOA will have to be adjusted, or the risk accepted. Do not forget to allow for any change in zone time while on passage.

The allowance for all these matters is illustrated below.

Torbay to Bishop Rock	129	miles
add for divergence from the route	4	
total planning distance	133	miles
delaying time for exercises and operations en route	3	hours

overall effect of tidal stream throughout
    the passage   nil
weather: likely weather, force 3–4 from
    the south-west, estimate that it will set
    ship back an average of $\frac{1}{4}$ knot against
overall speed restriction owing to the need
    for economical steaming   15 knots
allow for unforseen eventualities $\frac{1}{2}$ knot against

Time to allow for the passage is:

$$\frac{133}{15 - (\frac{1}{4} + \frac{1}{2})} + 3 \text{ hours}$$

$$= 12\tfrac{1}{4} \text{ hours (rounded to nearest } \tfrac{1}{4} \text{ hour)}$$

$$\text{SOA} = 10.86 \text{ knots (133 miles in } 12\tfrac{1}{4} \text{ hours)}$$

Once the passage time has been calculated, the ETA and ETD may be determined, e.g.

ETD   13 0800 (−1)

ETA   13 2015 (−1)

The passage chart

Having established suitable times for departure and arrival, plot the intended track (*see* Note below) throughout the passage on a small-scale chart. In Fig. 12–4 (page 313) the plan for a passage from Torbay to Bishop Rock shows:

> Distance from destination along the track; this provides a valuable cross-check against the overall planned distance which should be amended if necessary, with times and SOA adjusted as appropriate.
> The times of alterations of course.
> Suitable time intervals along the track, e.g. 1600/13.
> Tidal streams and, if relevant, currents.
> Areas and times where it is planned to conduct operations or exercises; the *position* of the ship at the start of these operations or exercises and her *intended movement* during them (PIM) should be drawn on the chart.
> Times of sunrise, sunset, moonrise, moonset, periods of darkness along the track.
> Positions where radio fixing aid chains (e.g. Decca) may change.

Note: keep the track to multiples of 5 or 10 degrees where possible. This makes life easier for the Officer of the Watch, the helmsman and others concerned.

Relevant data should then be extracted from the Work Book and summarised in the Navigating Officer's Note Book (S548A or equivalent). This is illustrated in Fig. 12–3 (page 312).

The overall plan must ensure that the needs of the ship's departments are met.

```
┌─────┬──────────────────────────────────────────────────────┐
│     │ TORBAY – BISHOP ROCK                                   │
│     │ MONDAY 13 APRIL (-1)                                   │
├─────┼──────────────────────────────────────────────────────┤
│     │ Distance  133 M.                                       │
│     │ ETD  0800 (-1) 13 April                                │
│     │ ETA  180° BISHOP ROCK 9 miles 2015(-1) 13 April        │
│     │ Overall SOA  10·86 kn.                                 │
├─────┼──────────────────────────────────────────────────────┤
│     │ Time in hand                                           │
│     │ 11 kn.    12 hrs. 5min.    10 min. in hand             │
│     │ 12        11 hrs. 5min.    1 hr. 10 min.               │
│     │ 13        10 hrs. 15min.   2 hrs.                      │
│     │ 14        9 hrs. 30 min.   2 hrs. 45 min.              │
│     │ 15        8 hrs. 50 min.   3 hrs 25 min.               │
├─────┼──────────────────────────────────────────────────────┤
│     │ Proceeding at 15 knots allows for:                     │
│     │   operations / excercises    : 3 hrs                   │
│     │   overall tidal stream       : nil                     │
│     │   In hand for unexpected                               │
│     │   eventualities              : ½ kn                    │
│     │   Weather: wind S.wly                                  │
│     │            10-15 kn          : ¼ kn                    │
├─────┼──────────────────────────────────────────────────────┤
│     │ Tides, Tidal Stream data; Neaps 13 April.              │
│     │ DOVER  13 Apl.(-1) Range 3·4m.                         │
│     │       0712  5·3m.     0146  1·8m.                      │
│     │       1952  5·3m.     1437  1·9m.                      │
│     │ DEVONPORT 13 Apl (-1)                                  │
│     │       0115  4·4m.     0746  2·1m.                      │
│     │       1415  4·2m.     2026  2·1m.                      │
│     │ TORBAY 13 Apl (-1)                                     │
│     │       0145  3·7m.     0748  1·9m.                      │
│     │       1445  3·5m.     2029  1·9m.                      │
│     │ Ht. of tide on sailing 2m.                             │
│     │ Tidal stream                                           │
│     │ 0800-1100 : S&W going: average 0·7kn. with.            │
│     │             max 1-1¼kn. off Start at 0915              │
│     │ 1100-1200 : Slack turning East.                        │
│     │ 1200-1700 : East going, average 0·8kn. against.        │
│     │             max 1-1¼kn. at 1400.                       │
│     │ 1700-1800 : Slack turning West.                        │
│     │ 1800-2015 : S&W going: average 0·9kn. with.            │
│     │             max about 1-1¼kn. at 2000.                 │
├─────┼──────────────────────────────────────────────────────┤
│     │ Sunrise/Sunset etc.                                    │
│     │        CT   Sunrise   Sunset   CT        Moon          │
│     │ 13 Apl. 0551(-1) 0625(-1)  2014(-1) 2048(-1) sets 0421(-1)│
│     │        Moon in first quarter                           │
├─────┼──────────────────────────────────────────────────────┤
│     │ Exercises / Operations.                                │
│     │ 1000-1600 : exercises/operations iaw planned           │
│     │ programme.                                             │
│     │ PIM 1000-1600. 251° 6·8kn. This allows                 │
│     │ 3½ hrs in hand at 15 knots.                            │
└─────┴──────────────────────────────────────────────────────┘
```

Fig. 12–3.   Coastal passage plan: NO's Note Book

Fig. 12–4.   Coastal passage: the passage chart

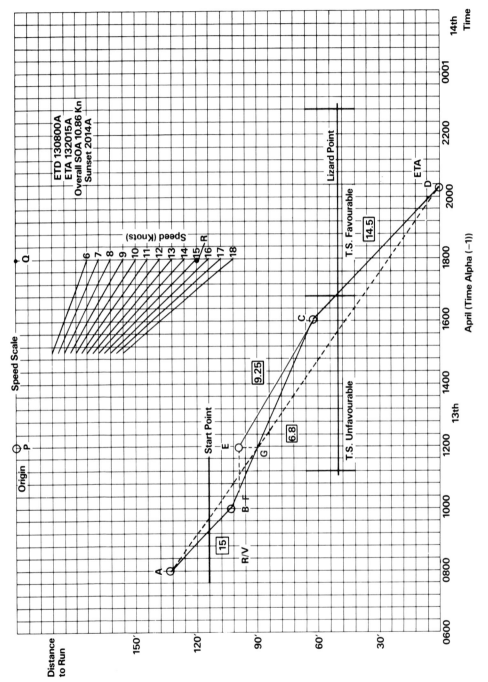

Fig., 12–5.   The passage graph

The passage graph

Having determined the ETA and ETD and prepared the small-scale chart, the navigator may draw up a passage graph. This is an invaluable aid to the planning and the execution of a passage of any distance or complexity.

Constructing the graph (Fig. 12–5)

1. Plot the time along the X axis and distance to run (DTR) along the Y axis, using the largest possible time and distance scales for the graph.
2. Construct the speed scale as follows:

   (*a*) Choose a convenient point of origin *P*, and a convenient horizontal time scale *PQ*, using the time scale of the graph; e.g. in Fig. 12–5, *PQ* is the equivalent of 6 hours.

   (*b*) Plot vertically downwards from *Q* the distances run for each speed required during the time selected, using the distance scale of the graph; e.g. the distance run in 6 hours at 15 knots is 90 miles; thus, *QR* = 90 miles.

   (*c*) The slope of the line joining these points to the origin *P* represents the SOA at the scale of the graph.

Using the passage graph as an aid to planning

The passage from Torbay to Bishop Rock (Figs 12–3 and 12–4) is drawn up on the graph as follows:

1. Plot *A*, the ETD (13 0800A) against the DTR, 133′.
2. Plot *D*, the arrival point, ETA 13 2015A. It may often be advisable to use an 'arrival gate' (*see* page 329) in preference to the final ETA.
3. Join *AD* by means of a pecked line. The slope of *AD* gives the overall SOA required, in this case 10.86 knots. *AD*'s slope may be measured against the speed scale using a parallel ruler.
4. Plot horizontal lines at the appropriate DTRs to represent important navigational features (e.g. Start Point at 114′ and Lizard Point at 51′ to go).
5. If necessary, plot vertical lines representing favourable and unfavourable tidal stream 'windows' (e.g. off the Lizard, the tidal stream is not favourable until about 1700 on 13th April). This is particularly important in difficult waters with strong tidal streams such as the Pentland Firth or Dover Strait.
6. Plot rendezvous (r/vs), exercises, etc. Point *B* is an r/v at 13 1000A, *B*━━━▶ *C* a 6 hour exercise period with a low SOA. If a zero SOA is required, as is sometimes the case during an exercise period, the slope of the graph will be horizontal.

   If planning for a group of ships, the graph may also be used to select suitable rendezvous times and positions.
7. Find the speed required for each section of the passage, by joining the relevant points *A*, *B*, *C*, *D* on the graph and measuring the slopes to determine the SOA. The SOA between *A* and *B* is 15 knots; between *B* and *C* it is 6.8 knots; and between *C* and *D* it is 14.5 knots.
8. The graph may also be used to find the ship's position at selected times, including sunrise and sunset, and these may be cross-checked against the passage chart as necessary.

Large-scale charts

1. Plot the intended track and time on the selected large-scale charts in sequence of use. Part of the track is illustrated in Figs 12–6 and 12–7 (page 318). Mark the DTR to the destination at suitable intervals.
2. In addition, plot:
    Times of alteration of course and speed.
    Tidal streams (and currents if applicable).
    Times and ranges of raising or dipping lights.
    Sunrise and sunset.
    Where to change charts.
3. Take the small-scale chart, passage graph and appropriate harbour plans (*see* Chapter 13) to the Captain for approval. Advise on the writing up of the Captain's Night Order Book (*see* page 165). Be prepared to adjust the plan for last minute changes to the ship's programme.

EXECUTION OF THE PASSAGE PLAN

The execution of the passage plan must involve a well-organised bridge procedure to detect any error in sufficient time to prevent a grounding. In open waters, it is normally sufficient to proceed from point to point, fixing the ship's position at intervals. The permissible deviation from the track, and the speed of the ship, determine the frequency and required accuracy of the fixes. The choice of fixing method depends upon the accuracy and reliability of the systems available, the time between successive fixes, and the time taken to fix. This in turn will depend, in part, on the accuracy and reliability of the ship's navigational equipment: compasses, logs, radars, etc.

The Navigating Officer plots the course of a modern Fleet destroyer

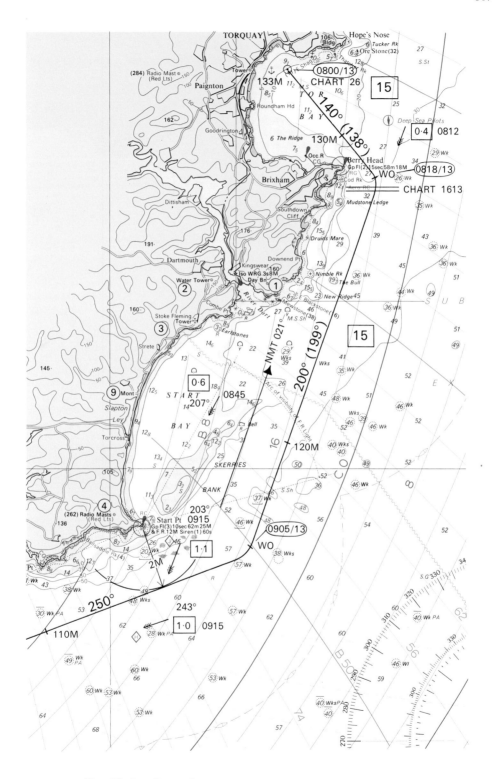

Fig. 12–6. Coastal passage plan: large-scale chart (1)

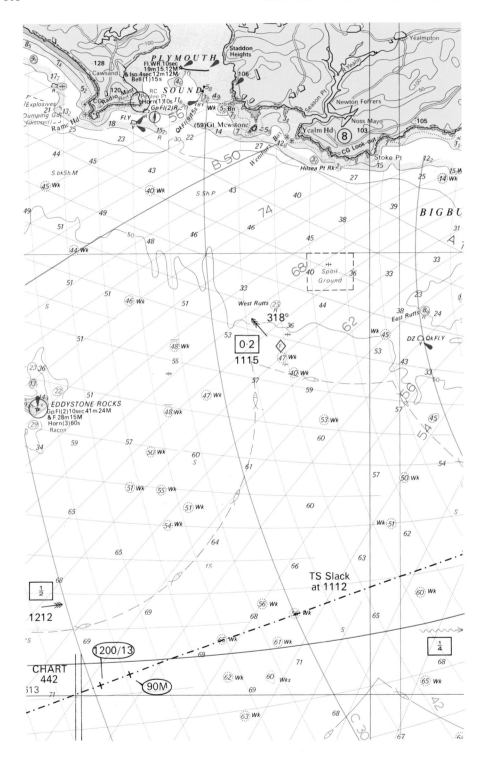

Fig. 12–7.   Coastal passage plan: Large-scale chart (2)

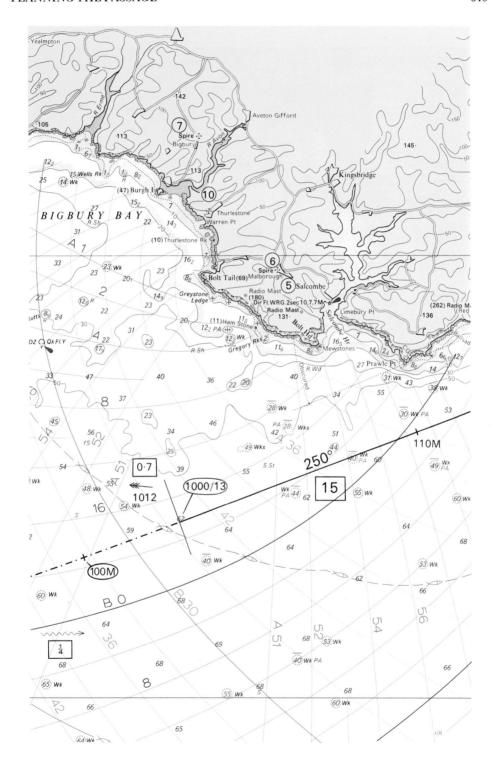

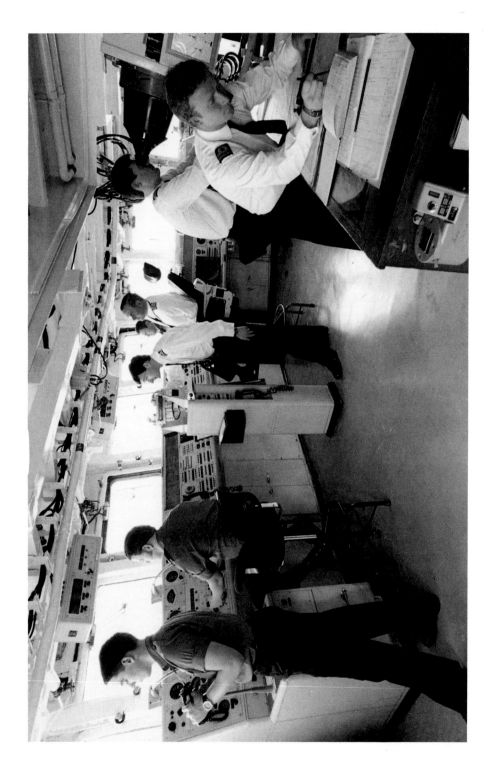

The bridge of a modern destroyer: the Command team at work

Method of fixing

The standard method of fixing on a coastal passage is by visual compass bearings, while maintaining a DR and EP ahead of the ship. Visual fixing, plotting the position, frequency of fixing, time taken to fix, keeping the record and establishing the track are all covered in Chapter 8 in the section on 'Chartwork on Passage'.

A back-up or secondary method of fixing should also be available, which may be used to cross-check or monitor the standard method. This is usually radar or a radio fixing aid such as Decca.

In restricted visibility, when it becomes no longer possible to use visual bearings, radar fixing usually becomes the standard method, with a radio fixing aid such as Decca being used as an independent (secondary) check. When radar ranges are being used, consider the use of the parallel index technique as described in Chapter 15. Sometimes the visibility is such that a mixture of visual bearings and radar ranges will be used as the standard method, with a radio fixing aid as a back-up.

The echo sounder is a further check against any possible error and its use must not be overlooked. In coastal waters, particularly when the range of the tide is large, an allowance should also be made for the height of tide.

If there is doubt about the ship's position when close to danger, it is usually wise to *stop* the ship and establish the position before proceeding.

Selecting marks for fixing

Chapter 9 refers to the selection of likely marks for fixing. A study of the chart together with the *Sailing Directions* usually reveals a number of marks suitable for fixing, visually and by radar.

For example, a study of the *Channel Pilot* reveals that, in addition to those objects such as lighthouses, prominent headlands, left- and right-hand edges, off-lying rocks and islets, the following conspicuous objects in Figs 12–6 and 12–7 (pages 317, 318) may be seen between Berry Head and Yealm Head:

1. Day beacon at Dartmouth.
2. Water tower at Dartmouth.
3. Stoke Fleming church tower.
4. Two tall radio masts, 1 mile north-west of Start Point.
5. Radio mast, 1 mile north-west of Bolt Head.
6. Malborough church spire.
7. Bigbury church spire.
8. CG lookout south-east of Yealm Head.

A *conspicuous object* is a natural or artificial mark which is outstanding, easily identifiable and clearly visible to the mariner over a large area of sea in varying light. Conspicuous objects are indicated on the chart by the legend written alongside the feature in bold capital letters, e.g. **TOWER, SPIRE, HOTEL**, etc. On older charts, the term 'conspic' may still be found, printed alongside a conspicuous feature. Buildings are sometimes blocked in on the chart in black, but only a few of these may be conspicuous.

Other objects, not necessarily conspicuous may also be found suitable for fixing: e.g. the monument at Slapton Ley (9), or Thurlestone church tower (10).

It is often helpful to write on the chart a brief description of the object, taken from the *Pilot* or *List of Lights*. For example, Start Point lighthouse is a white round granite tower, 28 metres in height. Bolt Head is a very prominent headland connected to Bolt Tail by a high ridge faced by abrupt, dark rugged cliffs.

The topography of the chart, together with the *Pilot* (including photographs and sketches) will also usually reveal a number of suitable marks for fixing, both man-made and natural: e.g. steep-to river valleys, road and railway bridges, peaks of hills and mountains, cliff edges and so on. The topography itself may frequently be a guide to the identification of objects—particularly when there are two similar objects close together of which only one is visible. Chimneys, flagstaffs, radio masts, and even churches, can cause confusion if there are a number in close proximity, and great care must be taken when 'shooting up'. The radio masts north-west of Bolt Head in (5) above are a good example of this.

Chimneys, flagstaffs and radio masts are also objects which are liable to change (removal or installation) without notification, particularly flagstaffs.

Visual fixing by night is often dependent on the various lights available and these will be clearly marked on the chart. It is extremely important to check the characteristics of lights on first sighting for correct identification. It may be advisable to use a stopwatch to time the period. If the characteristics of a light have been changed, this will usually be notified in Part V of the Admiralty Notices to Mariners *before* Part II. Do not forget there may be other lights outside the limits of the chart in use which may be seen. For example, the Lizard Light (Fig. 12–4) can be seen up to 50 miles away when the meteorological visibility is of the order of 20 miles, provided that the height of eye permits. Even when the height of eye is insufficient, the loom may well be seen at this range.

Fixing using radar, radio fixing aids and beacons

Radar and radar beacons (racons and ramarks) are dealt with in full in Chapter 15. Coastal radio aids are fully dealt with in Volume III of this manual; these include Decca, Loran-C, Hyper-Fix, MFDF radio beacons and directional radio beacons. Particulars of stations and their coverage are given in *Admiralty List of Radio Signals (ALRS)* Volume 2 (radio and radar beacons) and Volume 5 (Decca and Loran-C).

When planning a coastal passage, the coverage of these aids needs to be taken into account and decisions made as to their usefulness.

Modern radio aids give the mariner his position with sufficient accuracy to make a landfall and then proceed to port, regardless of the visibility. The aids must, however, be used intelligently, as the accuracy and range which may be obtained from these systems vary considerably.

The accuracy of the radio aid fix depends on three things:

1. The distance of the observer from the transmitter(s).

For hyperbolic fixing systems such as Decca and Loran-C:

2. The position of the observer relative to the base-line joining the pair of stations in use.

3. The angle of intersection of the hyperbolic position lines emanating from the stations.

When using radio aids, it is important to be on guard against the vagaries of radio wave propagation. At night, for example, ground and sky waves from a transmitter can interfere with each other to such an extent that the effective range of the system is very much reduced (e.g. MFDF) or 'lane slip' occurs (e.g. Decca), giving unreliable fixes. This 'night effect' is particularly severe at dawn and dusk.

Radio waves are usually subject to refraction when crossing the coast. This can cause a radio wave from a radiobeacon to be deflected by as much as 5°. With an aid like Decca, the error is published by the company as a *fixed error* correction. Decca readings are also subject to *variable errors* caused by variations in the propagation effect of the atmosphere, and these may change from hour to hour, although the maximum extent is usually predictable.

At best, MFDF is unlikely to give a bearing accurate to within ± 3°, and this only within about 100 to 150 miles of a radiobeacon by day. The range is very severely reduced at night to about 75 miles. In many cases the maximum range of radiobeacons (*see ALRS*, Volume 2) is only of the order of 50 miles. Aero radiobeacons suitable for marine use tend to have a longer range.

The accuracy obtainable from Decca is affected by the time of day and the season of the year in addition to those factors already mentioned. Under favourable conditions, the system is capable of giving a position accuracy correct to within ± 50 metres (95% probability*) up to 100 miles from the master station; but at longer ranges out to 350 miles and at poor angles of cut of the position lines, fixing accuracy in full daylight may be far less precise, of the order of ± 2000 metres (95% probability). At dusk and at night, dependent on the time of year, the order of accuracy may be even further reduced, dependent on the range of the master station and the angle of cut of the position lines. It is important to apply the variable error correction taken from the tables in the Decca operating instructions to establish the likely position circle. For example, at night in midwinter at maximum range from the master station (240 miles), in the SW approaches to the United Kingdom, the radius of the position circle generated by a Decca fix can be as much as 6 miles in extent (95% probability).

Ground wave ranges from Loran-C of from 800 to 1000 miles are usual, depending on transmitter power, receiver sensitivity and attenuation over the signal path. Errors vary from about ± 15 metres to ± 75 metres at 200 to 500 miles from the master station, increasing to ± 150 metres at 1000 miles. Within the ground wave coverage shown in *ALRS*, Volume 5, fixing accuracy can generally be expected to be within ± 500 metres (95% probability).

Information obtained from radio aids can be misleading and should always be checked whenever possible with position lines or fixes obtained from visual observations, or with fixes obtained from a different radio aid (e.g. Decca may be cross-checked with radar and vice versa). A fix from a radio aid which is markedly different from the EP must be carefully weighed up, particularly if it is unconfirmed by other fixing means.

* The principles of probability as they affect navigation are set out in Chapter 16.

Navigational equipment

It is important to ensure that the ship's navigational equipment is working correctly and at optimum efficiency. Not only should performance be checked before sailing but it should also be checked at regular intervals (once a watch or more frequently) throughout the passage and, in particular, before entering narrow or ill-lit channels or other hazardous areas. Particular items of equipment for which performance should be closely monitored are compasses, radars and radio fixing aids. Compasses and radio fixing aids are subject to random errors, while the performance of radars may deteriorate without warning.

Compasses

Methods of ascertaining gyro-compass error or deviation in the magnetic compass are explained in Chapter 9. The chart should always be studied for suitable transits which may be used to check the gyro error or magnetic compass deviation, and these should be noted on the chart or in the Note Book. In Fig. 12–6, for example, the following transits can be used to check the compass error just before an alteration of course and afterwards when steady on the new track.

◄—— Berry Head	φ	◄—— Downend Point	203½°
Dartmouth Water Tower	φ	◄—— Mew Stone	287°
◄—— Start Point	φ	◄—— Prawle Point	249°
◄—— Prawle Point	φ	◄—— Bolt Head	280½°

Keeping clear of dangers

Clearing marks and bearings, vertical and horizontal danger angles and radar clearing ranges may be used to keep clear of a danger. These measures are also discussed in Chapters 13 and 15.

Clearing marks and bearings

Clearing marks are selected objects, natural or man-made which, when in transit, or just *open** of each other, define a clearing line which leads clear of danger. In Fig. 12–6, ——► Berry Head 021° open of ——► Downend Point leads east of Skerries Bank (i.e. Berry Head should be 'kept' to the right of Downend Point). Provided a ship takes care not to go inside this line, i.e. the bearing of Berry Head NMT 021°, but keeps the marks 'open', she will pass clear of the danger.

When clearing marks are not available, a line of bearing may be drawn on the chart through a clearly defined shore object to pass a safe distance from a danger. This line of bearing is called a *clearing bearing* and is illustrated in Fig. 12–8. Provided the bearing of the church is kept not less than (NLT) 260° and not more than (NMT) 272°, the ship will pass safely between the wreck to the north and the shoals to the south on the way in to the anchorage.

---

* Marks are said to be *open* when they are not exactly in transit (*see* page 349).

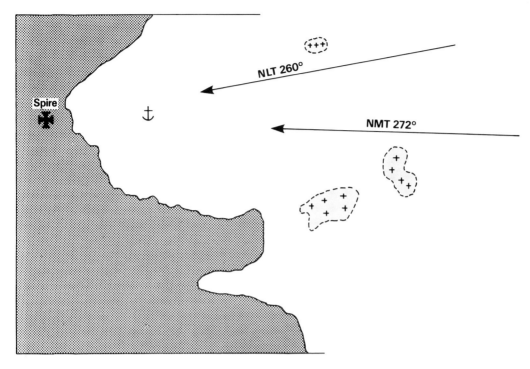

Fig. 12–8.   Clearing bearings

Vertical and horizontal danger angles

Vertical and horizontal danger angles may be used to ensure the safety of the ship in vicinity of dangers.

Vertical danger angles

It is required to pass 5 cables clear of a rock distant 3 cables from a lighthouse, height 29 metres above MHWS. MHWS is 5.5 metres above chart datum and the predicted height of tide is 4.0 metres.

This is shown in Fig. 12–9 (p.326). The height of the light above sea level is 29 + 5.5 − 4.0 = 30.5 metres. With centre the lighthouse and radius 8 cables, describe an arc of a circle. *Norie's Nautical Tables* (Distance by Vertical Angle) will give the angle subtended between the lantern and sea level from any point on the arc of the circle. For a corrected height of 30.5 metres and a range of 8 cables, the angle is 1°11′.

Set this angle on the sextant. Provided the reflected image of the lantern appears *below* sea level, the ship is outside the arc of the circle and in safety.

If the height of the tide is not allowed for, and the height of the light as printed on the chart is used instead, the ship will be further from the light than is apparent, except in the unlikely event of sea level being above Mean High Water Springs.

In the above example, if 29 metres is used for the height, the vertical angle is 1°7′. For an actual height of 30.5 metres, 1°7′ gives an actual range of 8.5 cables.

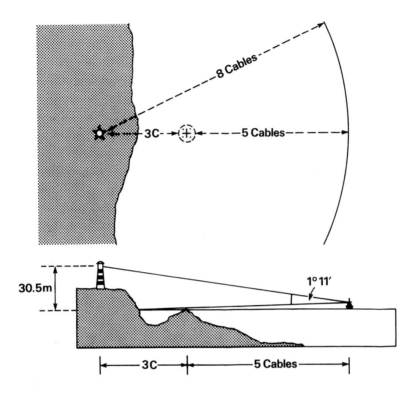

Fig. 12–9.   Vertical danger angle

Horizontal danger angles

The horizontal angle between two objects on shore may be used in a similar way. Objects should be chosen lying approximately the same distance on each side of the danger to be cleared (Fig. 12–10). The chart should be marked at the distance considered safe to pass, and lines should be drawn from the objects to the mark. The angle thus formed is measured and, if the angle subtended by the objects is less than that measured, the ship is outside the danger and in safety.

In Fig. 12–10, the horizontal danger angle for a clearance of 5 cables from the rock is plotted as 78°. So long as the horizontal angle between the lighthouse and the CG lookout remains less than 78°, the ship is outside the danger circle.

If the angle of 78° is set on the sextant, the CG lookout will appear to the left (the 'wrong side') of the lighthouse when the actual angle between the objects is less than 78°, i.e. when the ship is outside the danger circle.

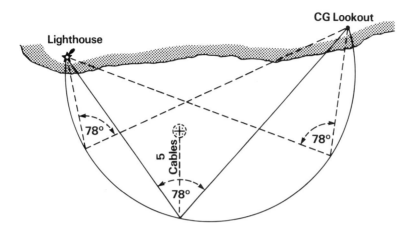

Fig. 12–10. Horizontal danger angle

Radar clearing ranges

The use of radar for keeping clear of dangers is discussed in Chapter 15.

PRACTICAL HINTS

Various 'wrinkles' or useful hints when executing a coastal passage are set out below.

Calculating the distance that an object will pass abeam

It is a help to be able to determine the distance a ship will pass an object abeam on a certain course, and by how much the course may have to be changed in order to pass the object a desired distance away. An allowance must be made for any tidal stream etc. across the track.

An abeam distance of approximately 1 mile (BC in Fig. 12–11, p.328) is subtended by an angle of 1° (angle BAC) at a distance of 60 miles (AB).

From this rule of thumb may be deduced other useful data, e.g.

An abeam distance of 2 cables is subtended by an angle of 1° at a distance of 12 miles $\left(\dfrac{12}{60} \times 10\right)$.

An abeam distance of $\frac{1}{2}$ cable is subtended by an angle of 1° at a distance of 3 miles $\left(\dfrac{3}{60} \times 10\right)$.

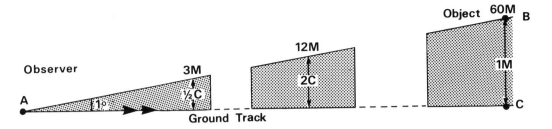

Fig. 12–11.   The abeam distance subtended by an angle of 1°

EXAMPLE

A light is sighted 10° on the bow at an estimated distance of 12', and it is desired to pass 4' from the light. What is the clearance from the light on the present course and what alteration of course is necessary?

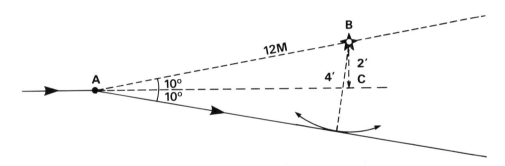

Fig. 12–12.   Alteration of course required to pass at a given distance

If the ship remains on the present course (Fig. 12–12), the distance of the light when it is abeam, *BC*, will be $\left(10 \times \dfrac{12}{60}\right) = 2$ miles.

At 12' the estimated offing per degree is 12/60 = 1/5 mile. To pass 4' off, therefore, alter course 10° outwards from the present course to bring the light $4 \times 5 = 20°$ on the bow.

The time of arrival

Circumstances nearly always tend to make a ship late rather than early and, for this reason, it is always wise to allow something in hand for unforseen eventualities (*see* page 310). Remember that, when speed has to be adjusted to arrive at the correct time, there are two factors to be allowed for:

1. The time already lost or gained when the decision to adjust speed is made.
2. The time the ship will continue to lose or gain if tidal stream and weather, etc. remain unchanged.

Any error in estimating the time on passage may readily be seen by comparing the actual time with the planned time shown on the chart.

Adjustments in speed may then be made as necessary; the passage graph (Fig. 12–5, page 314) is a very useful aid in this respect. To monitor the ship's progress, proceed as follows:

1. Fix the ship, measure the DTR, plot the position on the graph; e.g. position *E*, 131200A, DTR 99′.
2. Measure the time ahead/astern of the plan (e.g. *EF*, 1 hour 24 minutes *astern*).
3. Measure the distance ahead/astern of the plan (e.g. *EG*, 10′ *astern*).
4. An increase in the speed of advance is clearly needed; the graph enables this to be found quickly and easily.
5. Joint point *E* to the next required position, in this case point *C*, the end of the exercise period.
6. Determine the revised SOA by measuring the slope of *EC* against the speed scale, in this case 9.25 knots.
7. Adjust speed as requisite.

To ensure a precise time of arrival without having either to crawl over the last few miles or to proceed with unseemly haste, *gates* should be established some distance before the actual point of arrival through which one should aim to pass at a particular time. In a destroyer or a frigate, an ETA should be aimed at a position some 12 to 15 miles from the official arrival point, say 1 hour before the actual ETA. It is then a relatively simple matter to adjust the speed to make the right time of arrival. For example, if the official time of arrival is 0900, a gate may be set up 12 miles to go at 0800. If the ship is 5 minutes late at the gate, it is immediately apparant that an SOA of only 13.1 knots is required (an increase in speed of just over 1 knot) to make the ETA precisely. A further gate at around 0830 will confirm the accuracy of the calculations and, if any adjustment is necessary, it is bound to be a small one.

In the larger ship, entering ports like Devonport or Portsmouth, two gates will almost always guarantee an ETA correct to within a few seconds; for example, Gate 1 may be 11 miles to go, 1 hour before ETA, SOA 12 knots; Gate 2 at 3 miles to go, 20 minutes before ETA. The second gate, requiring an SOA of only 9 knots to the entry point, permits the necessary adjustments to bring the ship down to a suitable manoeuvring speed for entry (of the order of 6 to 8 knots). For other ports, the timing or positioning of the gates may be adjusted depending on the desired speed at entry.

Buoys and light-vessels

The use of buoys and light-vessels for navigation has already been covered in detail in Chapter 10. When shore marks are difficult to distinguish because of distance (the Thames Estuary for example) or thick weather, buoys and light-vessels must often be used instead. Treat light-vessels, lanbys and light-floats with a proper degree of caution; never rely exclusively on buoys.

When not to fix

On occasions when only mountain summits or distant or inconspicuous marks are visible, an apparent fix may give a position widely different from the EP. If there is no reason to distrust the EP, a fix in these circumstances should be treated with caution. Objects which are distant or difficult to distinguish should either be 'shot up' precisely or disregarded.

Tidal stream and current

When navigating along the coast, an indraught into a bay or bight is common. Sometimes there is an indraught at one end and an outdraught at the other.

Currents, tidal streams and tides are affected by the wind. Take care, however, to distinguish between wind effect on the current or tidal stream and wind effect on the ship; it is easy to confuse the two.

Wind often has a marked effect on the time of change of the tidal stream, as much as 1 to 2 hours. Wind also affects both the time of change and the height of tide.

Tidal stream data must always be used with caution; particularly at springs, tidal streams experienced are frequently different from those calculated.

The record

An example of keeping the navigational record in the Navigational Record Book (S3034) is given in Chapter 8.

Any gyro error or total error correction should be shown in the 'Remarks' column. The suffixes G, T, or C (indicating Gyro, True or Compass) should be used as appropriate. All transits should show both the observed and the true bearings.

Other details concerning the stationing of ships in company, manoeuvres, wind, tidal stream or current, soundings, alterations of clocks and so on should all be entered in the 'Remarks' column.

When courses and speeds are recorded as 'various'—for example when entering or leaving harbour, carrying out manoeuvres or Replenishment at Sea, full details and times of courses and speeds should be recorded on automatic recording equipment or entered in the Record Book for Wheel and Engine Orders (S580), so that a complete record is available from which the track may be accurately reconstructed if required. Do not forget the value of the plotting table or AIO computer in establishing the DR (Chapter 8) and the use of tape recorders for records.

At the end of each passage, the Navigating Officer should carry out an analysis of the navigational records to obtain data about the ship's performance under different conditions, and to provide a basis for subsequent similar passages. Such information should be summarised in the Work Book and the Navigational Data Book (S2677).

Flat and featureless coastlines

When it is necessary to make a flat coast with few prominent marks (such as the Dutch coast north of Scheveningen), where radar may not be of much assistance in identification, it is sound navigational practice to aim at a point perhaps 10 or 15 miles to one side of the required position. The required direction for the alteration of course on sighting the coast is immediately known and, while running parallel to the coast, objects may be identified and a fix obtained. The availability of radio fixing aids such as Decca may obviate the need for aiming to one side, but remember the errors to which this type of aid may be subject.

The echo sounder is frequently of great assistance in such circumstances in giving warning of the coast's proximity.

Fixing by night

It is surprising how much coastline may be identified visually at night for fixing purposes. It should not be assumed that navigational lights are the only visual method of fixing available. Islands often stand out well on dark clear nights or may be clearly visible by moonlight. For example, those in the Eastern Archipelago, which are not particularly well lit, can frequently be seen quite clearly.

Altering course

Before altering course, always look along the bearing of the new course to see that it is clear. Arrange also for a responsible officer or rating to look along the appropriate quarter to see that no ship is overtaking from that direction.

When rounding a point of land very close to the ship which is to be kept at a constant distance during the turn, put the rudder over by an amount corresponding to the diameter of the turn required, a little before the point is abeam. Subsequently adjust the rudder angle so that the object remains abeam throughout the turn.

'Wheel over' bearings

Some mariners prefer to use cardinal (000°, 090°, etc.) or half-cardinal (045°, 135°, etc.) bearings to determine the moment of 'wheel over' when altering course on a coastal passage. Others prefer to use a beam bearing. Others use a

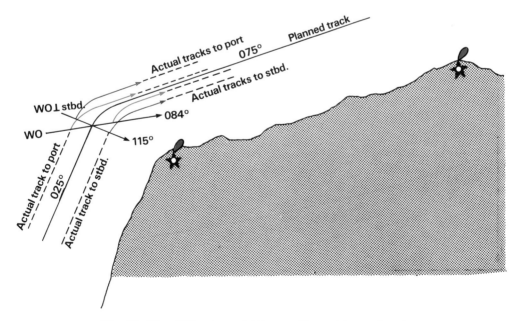

Fig. 12–13. 'Wheel over' (1): specific and beam bearings

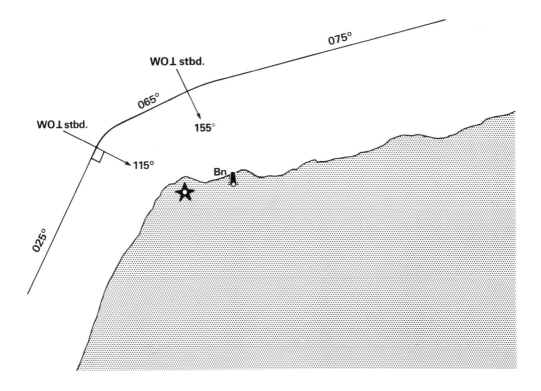

Fig. 12–14. 'Wheel over' (2): beam bearings

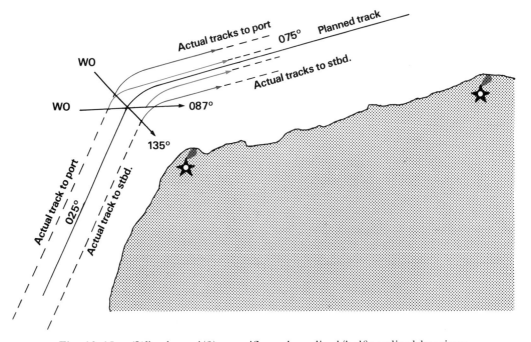

Fig. 12–15. 'Wheel over'(3): specific and cardinal/half-cardinal bearings

specific bearing closely related to the next course. All three methods have their uses.

As explained in Chapter 13, it is particularly important in pilotage work to use a 'wheel over' bearing which is as parallel as possible to the new course, as shown in Fig. 12–13. This gives the best prospect of achieving the new track. Such bearings, however, are not always available on a coastal passage.

Beam bearings are very convenient and easy to remember. This method suffers from two disadvantages:

1. If the ship is off track to start with, the ship may end up off track by as much or more than previously (Fig. 12–13).

2. Rounding a headland may from time to time require more than one alteration of course and perhaps more than one abeam object, depending on the tracks chosen (Fig. 12–14).

Cardinal and half-cardinal points (Fig. 12–15) are also easy to remember and may be convenient. This method may be of particular value on routes where traffic separation schemes do not permit the use of beam bearings. The method suffers from the disadvantage, similar to beam bearings, that if the ship is off track to start with, the ship will end up off track by as much or more than previously if the bearing is not nearly parallel to the new course. Moreover, a bearing abaft the beam may be 'wooded' (i.e. not visible from the pelorus). In any case, it is preferable not to have to look astern for a 'wheel over' bearing when altering course.

If the bearing of a single object is changing rapidly, as in Figs. 12–13 to 12–15, a useful running fix may be obtained. The time interval for a large change of bearing is short; thus, the error in the estimated run between bearings should be small.

Entering shallow water

Do not navigate in shallow water at high speed, particularly if in close company with other ships. *Shallow water effect* (page 308) may cause flooding in own ship if it has a low freeboard. In addition, a severe *interaction effect* with other ships may be experienced over several hundred metres.

A frigate or destroyer of 3500 tonnes at 15 knots will begin to experience more than normal interaction or shallow water effect in depths of less than 39 metres. The depth at which more than normal interaction or shallow water effect may begin to be experienced may be found from the formula:

$$\text{depth (metres)} = \text{speed (knots)} \times 0.17 \sqrt[3]{\text{Displacement(tonnes)}} \qquad \ldots \textbf{12.1}$$

For a supertanker of $\frac{1}{4}$ million tonnes deadweight, at 10 knots, the depth is 107 metres. A large fast ship (50,000 tonnes at 18 knots) can experience steering problems in such conditions sufficient to cause alarm.

PASSAGES IN FOG AND THICK WEATHER

The main consideration in fog is usually the proximity of shipping and the need to avoid getting into a close quarters situation (*International Regulations for*

Preventing Collisions at Sea, 1972 (Rule of the Road), Rule 19). The use of radar for collision avoidance is discussed in Chapter 17.

The navigation of coastal passages in fog is hardly more difficult than in visual conditions due to radar and radio fixing aids. There may be a reduction in fixing accuracy by having to change from visual means to radar or radio fixing aid, and this may be a limiting factor when considering a passage through an area where there are a number of navigational hazards. There is a further limitation in the event of unreliability or breakdown of radar or radio aid equipment, and in the effect of random errors in the fixes. In times of war or international tension, such aids may not be available or may be subject to jamming.

The necessity for keeping a good EP reinforced by soundings is therefore most important in fog. A series of visual fixes taken up to the moment a ship enters fog, especially in areas of strong tidal stream such as the English Channel, will give a very clear indication of the likely future ground track.

The record (page 330) of similar passages in clear weather is likely to be of sound value in navigating safely and accurately in fog and thick weather. The record should include the estimated times on each course and the estimated currents and tidal streams, together with the actual results experienced. The reasons for any discrepancies should be investigated at the end of every passage, so that adjustments may be made to minimise such errors on subsequent occasions.

It should be remembered that, in thick weather when there is little or no wind, estimates of tidal streams and currents may be relied on to a greater extent than in rough weather.

The speed of the ship is an important factor. Although at very low speeds the ship is much affected by tidal streams and currents, the advantage of higher speed must be balanced against other dangers, such as risk of collision.

The visibility in fog should be estimated whenever possible, and the ship's speed adjusted accordingly. Visibility of buoys can be ascertained by noting the time or range of passing a buoy and the time or range it disappears in the fog. Visibility circles, thus estimated and plotted around succeeding buoys, will show when the latter may be expected to appear. When it is seen that the ship is about to enter fog, always note the approximate bearing, distance and course of any ships in sight; and, if possible, obtain a fix.

Before entering fog

1. Reduce to a safe speed (Rule of the Road, Rules 19 and 6).
2. Operate radar and radio fixing aids (Rule of the Road, Rule 7). Ensure the charts in use are annotated for suitable radar fixing marks.
3. Consider closing up and operating the blind pilotage/safety team (Chapter 15).
4. Station lookouts. Lookouts should be in direct telephonic communication with the bridge, or should be supplied with portable radios or megaphones. Forecastle lookouts should be taught to indicate direction by pointing with the outstretched arm.
5. Operate the echo sounder, and give instructions for depth reporting.
6. In the vicinity of land, have an anchor ready for letting go.

7. Order silence on deck.
8. Close watertight doors and assume the appropriate damage control state in accordance with the ship's Standing Orders.
9. Start the prescribed fog signal.
10. Warn the engine room.
11. Decide if it is necessary to connect extra boilers, diesels or gas turbines.
12. Memorise the characteristics of fog signals which may be heard. Remember that sound signals on some buoys are operated by wave motion and are thus unreliable.
13. Make sure that the siren is not synchronising with those of other ships, or with shore fog signals.
14. Should radar not be working efficiently, be prepared to take DF bearings of radiobeacons and of other ships operating radio in the vicinity.
15. If in any doubt about the ship's position, alter course at once to a safe course, parallel to or away from the coast.

Visibility

If there is better visibility from the upper deck or masthead than from the bridge, a relative bearing of an object sighted from either of these positions (and especially a beam bearing) will almost certainly improve the EP.

When fog is low-lying, the masts or smoke of ships in the vicinity may frequently be seen above the fog; hence the need for a lookout as high as possible.

Practical considerations for passages in fog

If a long passage is being undertaken, for example from Portsmouth to New York, there is little advantage in taking departure for the Atlantic voyage from Bishop Rock rather than, say, St Catherine's Point (Fig. 12–16, page 336). The distance from St Catherine's to the Bishop is of the order of 200 miles while that from the Bishop to New York is more than 2900 miles. It makes little difference to the landfall off New York whether the last fix on leaving the United Kingdom was 2900 or 3100 miles from the destination. There is therefore little reason, except for such matters as operational necessity, for embarking on a point to point coastal passage in fog to be followed directly by a long ocean voyage. In such circumstances it is more sensible to stand well offshore, keeping clear of navigational hazards, following the elementary jingle 'Outward bound, don't run aground'. A great deal of coastal shipping will also be avoided.

On the other hand, the navigator of a ship that is proceeding in fog from, say, Portsmouth to Devonport, is faced with the problem of knowing his position accurately enough to make a safe landfall on approaching the destination, if he has stood well offshore to avoid shipping and navigational hazards. If he has reliable radar and radio fixing aids, backed up by a good echo sounder, his navigational problems are similar whether he stays 2 miles off the coast or 20. His main concern will be to balance the avoidance of shipping against the additional distance to be steamed. If, however, radar and radio fixing aids are not available, the navigator will be in a much stronger position, as he approaches Devonport, in knowing his position at Start Point, 25 miles from

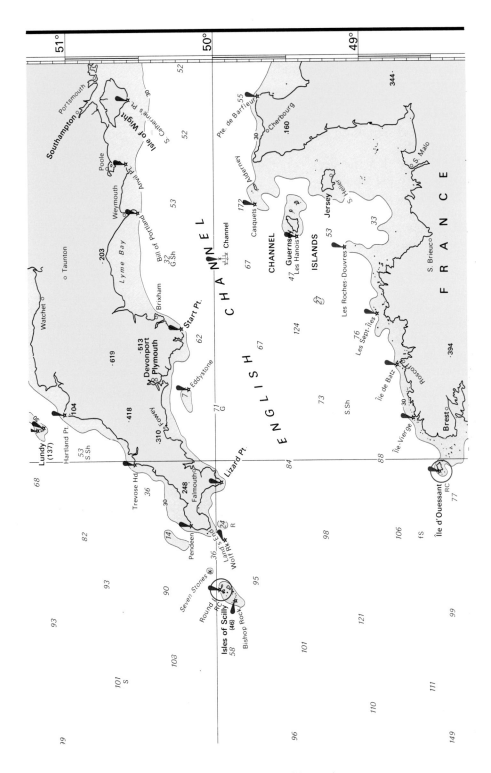

Fig. 12–16.   English Channel

Plymouth breakwater, having heard the fog signal there and checked his EP against it and the depth of water, than if his last position was off St Catherine's Point some 120 miles earlier; similarly, for his position at Start Point, if he has heard Portland Bill; and so on. Thus, in fog without radar and radio fixing aids, it is usually wiser to proceed from point to point.

Entering narrow waters in fog, such as the Dover Strait, the ship's position must be known accurately before embarking upon the passage. On approaching such waters, always consider the likely error in position and what precautions, such as the echo sounder, are available should the reckoning be incorrect. For example, on a passage from the north-east through the strait (Fig. 12–1), the ship's position must be established at South Falls in order to approach the Goodwins safely. Similarly, the position at the Goodwins must be verified in order to pass clear of the Varne. Unless reliable radar or an accurate radio fixing aid is available, the ship's position must be determined by the accuracy of the EP, and information from the echo sounder, from DF bearings and from the various fog signals. Many ships transit the Dover Strait in fog in safety with a minimum of aids, but care and prudence along the lines already discussed in this chapter are necessary.

The ship may be ahead, astern, to port or to starboard of the reckoning. The event of each possibility and its impact on the ship's navigation must be assessed. For example, to be more than 1 or 2 miles to port or starboard of track could be disastrous; alternatively, up to 10 miles to port or starboard of track could be perfectly safe, yet to be 2 miles ahead of the reckoning could be fatal. Each possibility has to be considered and adequate safeguards taken against those errors which could be dangerous.

NAVIGATION IN CORAL REGIONS

Coastal navigation in coral waters can range from relatively simple and short transits, such as those through the Balabac Strait between Palawan and Borneo, to lengthy and complex passages, such as the channel inside the Great Barrier Reef, which lies off the Queensland coast in NE Australia, over 1300 miles in length and varying in width from 40 miles at the southern entrance to a few cables at the northern end. In the more difficult parts of the Great Barrier route, navigation becomes more an exercise in pilotage than the fairly straightforward task of point to point coastal navigation.

Growth of coral reefs

Although depths over many coral reefs can remain unchanged for a long time (50 years or more), coral growth and the movement of coral debris can change depths over other reefs and shoals to a great extent. Decreasing depths from these two causes may be as much as 0.3 metre per year. Decreases due to coral debris alone have been known to exceed this rate. For example, some of the small coral heads in Darvel Bay in E Sabah grew from a depth of 14 fathoms ($25\frac{1}{2}$ metres) to within a few feet (less than 1 metre) of the surface in a period of about 70 to 80 years. The rate of growth of the massive reefs which could damage even the largest vessels is, however, only about 0.05 metre per year.

Windward channels tend to become blocked by debris and by the inward growth of the reefs, but leeward channels are usually kept clear by the ebb stream, which is often stronger than the flood and thus deposits the debris in deep water outside the reefs.

Coral reefs are frequently steep-to and depths of over 200 metres may exist within 1 cable of the reef's edge. In such circumstances, soundings are of little value in detecting the proximity of a reef. In addition, soundings may shoal so quickly that it is difficult to follow the echo sounder trace, particularly as the echo is often weak because of the steepness of the gradient. Coral usually grows to windward and is steeper on the side of the prevailing wind.

When navigating in coral waters, take into account the likely decrease in depths since the date of the survey on which the chart is based. If the survey is an old one, proceed with caution.

Navigating by eye

A common feature of coral regions is the lack of marks for fixing, particularly those ahead and astern. It frequently becomes necessary to navigate by eye.

Navigate with caution. Place lookouts aloft and on the forecastle. Use the echo sounder continuously. Coral can best be seen:
1. From the masthead.
2. When the sun is high and behind the observer and unobscured by cloud. Above 20° elevation is best.
3. When the sea is ruffled by a slight breeze. A glassy calm makes it very difficult to distinguish the colour differences between shallow and deep water.
4. When polaroid spectacles are worn. These make the differences in colour of the water, explained below, stand out more clearly.

Range of sighting

In good weather with a height of eye of about 10 to 20 metres, coral patches with depths of water less than about 6 to 8 metres should be sighted at a distance perhaps of about ½ mile. Good communications from the masthead to the bridge are essential if avoiding action is to be taken in time. Speed must be sufficiently slow so that the ship may be stopped or anchored quickly, yet high enough to maintain steerage way and cope with tidal streams and currents. A speed of about 4 to 8 knots should normally suffice.

Colour of reefs

When the water is clear, the depth over a reef may be estimated by the following colours:

LIGHT BROWN	reefs with depths of less than 1 metre.
LIGHT GREEN	reefs with depths of 2 metres or more.
DARK GREEN	reefs with depths of 6 metres or more.
DEEP BLUE	reefs with depths of 25 metres or more.

Unmarked narrow channels

In narrow channels between coral reefs, try to keep in the centre of the channel. If no marks are available, the position of the ship relative to the centre of the channel may be ascertained by placing a man on the centreline of the ship facing forward in a position where each side of the reef can be seen. With arms outstretched to the maximum extent on each side of the body, each arm is pointed down to the edge of the reef. The angle of the arms will show whether the ship is in the centre of the channel. For example, if the left arm is pointing further down than the right, the ship is to port of the centre of the channel; course should be adjusted to starboard.

Disturbed water

If the water is not clear, it will be almost impossible to see the coral reef and so navigate by eye. The only safe method is to sound ahead of the ship with boats.

Cloud patches

Cloud patches are often reflected by the sea and look exactly like reefs, although it may be possible to see their movement across the water.

If the sun becomes obscured by cloud, nearly all the reefs will disappear from view and the only safe method is to sound ahead with boats.

Cross currents and weather

Currents and tidal streams frequently set across coral channels rather than along them; examples are the inner route of the Great Barrier Reef and the Santaren Strait west of the Great Bahama Bank.

Rain squalls are fairly common in coral regions and are frequently so heavy as to obliterate everything in sight. In such circumstances, it may be prudent to stop, or anchor and wait for the weather to clear; this usually happens quickly.

Edges of coral reefs

The windward or exposed edges of coral reefs are often more uniform than the leeward edges and may also have water breaking over them; they are thus more easily seen. The leeward sides of reefs frequently have detached coral heads which are difficult to see.

Passing unsurveyed reefs

Pass on the weather side because the edges and off-lying pinnacles will be shown by the sea breaking over them.

CHAPTER 13
Pilotage

An aircraft carrier entering harbour (HMS *Illustrious* entering Portsmouth)

Within the Royal Navy, the planning and execution of pilotage is an important and demanding part of a Navigating Officer's duties. This chapter comprises a brief discussion of the regulations for pilotage for HM Ships and for merchant ships,* followed by detailed instructions for the planning and execution of pilotage.

In this book, a distinction is drawn between visual pilotage (Chapter 13) and

* To cater for a wider audience.

blind pilotage (Chapter 15); the reader should remember, however, that the two techniques are complementary to each other and are often used together.

REGULATIONS FOR PILOTAGE

HM Ships

The regulations regarding pilotage in HM Ships are laid down in *The Queen's Regulations for the Royal Navy (QRRN)* and in Volume IV of this manual. Amplifying information is to be found below.

The Navigating Officer of an HM Ship is in normal circumstances the pilot of the ship although, if he is not a specialist in navigation, the duty of pilotage devolves upon the Captain. If no navigation specialist is borne, the Captain may undertake the pilotage himself or depute any other officer in the ship to do so, although it is the usual practice for the officer appointed for navigation duties to undertake the task.

The Captain of an HM Ship is normally authorised to employ at his discretion a licensed or regular pilot for ports and channels which are difficult of access or for which charts and directions are insufficient guide, or in abnormal conditions.

Most British and Commonwealth ports are adequately charted. However, the charts of a number of foreign ports, particularly the smaller ones, are likely to be inadequate; in that case, it is usually possible to obtain suitable charts and directions from the appropriate national Hydrographic Office.

It is not compulsory for an HM Ship to take a pilot in United Kingdom ports. In Commonwealth and foreign ports, HM Ships must conform to the local regulations, which may require compulsory pilotage.

When a pilot is employed, the Captain of an HM Ship may use him in an advisory capacity or direct him to take full control of the handling of the ship. On the whole pilots are unused to the considerable power available in HM Ships and for this reason they are more usually employed in an advisory capacity.

> 'The employment of a pilot does not relieve the Captain of his responsibility for the safety of the ship, and in the event of an accident which could have been prevented by a common degree of attention on the part of the Captain or the Navigating Officer, these officers will be deemed to have neglected their duty.' (Volume IV)

Merchant ships

For merchant ships, the regulations for pilotage are laid down by the national authority or the shipping company, and in the orders for the port concerned. Recommendations on pilotage are also made from time to time by IMO.

Regulations for merchant ships frequently require compulsory pilotage, although Masters who have considerable knowledge of a particular port may be exempted for that port, as may be certain ships regularly trading on the coast concerned. In most ports, it is the usual practice for the pilot to take full control of the handling of the ship between the pilot boarding place (usually shown on the chart) and the berth. Despite the duties and obligations of a pilot, his presence on board does not relieve the Master or the Officer of the Watch from his duties and obligations for the safety of the ship. The general aim of the Master should be to ensure that the expertise of the pilot is fully supported by the ship's bridge team. The Officer of the Watch is required to co-operate closely with the pilot and keep an accurate check on the vessel's position and movements. If there is any doubt as to the pilot's actions and intentions, these should be clarified immediately. If any doubt still remains, it is up to the Master and/or the Officer of the Watch to take the appropriate action to ensure the safety of the ship.

PLANNING AND EXECUTION OF PILOTAGE

The planning and execution of pilotage, anchoring and mooring described here and in Chapter 14 assumes that the pilotage is planned and conducted by the Navigating Officer, without the assistance of a pilot.

PREPARATORY WORK

The preparatory work required is in many respects similar to that for a coastal passage (*see* Chapter 12). Full details should always be entered in the Navigating Officer's Work Book.

Charts and publications

Chart selection

Select the largest scale charts available including relevant Fleet charts (HM Ships only). Ensure the charts are corrected up to date for all Permanent, Temporary and Preliminary Notices to Mariners, radio navigational warnings and Local Notices—refer to the *Chart Correction Log and Folio Index* (NP 133A, 133B). If proceeding to a foreign port, it may be necessary to make arrangements to obtain the large-scale charts and plans published by the Hydrographic Office of the country concerned. Usually these charts and plans are available from national agencies at the larger ports and from the relevant Hydrographic Office (*see Catalogue of Admiralty Charts . . . ,* NP 131, for details). HM Ships arrange their supply through the Hydrographer, Taunton. Remember that it may be necessary to obtain larger scale charts produced by the national authority in order to enter the port concerned, e.g. the United States, Canada. (*See* the *Annual Summary of Admiralty Notices to Mariners.*)

Do not forget that extra charts for the port may have to be obtained for the following reasons:

1. The departure plan may well be different from the entry plan.
2. The blind pilotage/safety team (Chapter 15) will require their own charts.
3. It may be desirable to have an entirely separate visual fixing team to cross-check the execution of the pilotage plan; this team will also require charts.
4. It may be preferable to use additional copies, cut up into appropriate sizes, for use by the Captain and Navigating Officer instead of sketch plans in the Note Book.

5. Boats' crews may require a copy of the chart.

Publications

The following reference books should be consulted when preparing a pilotage plan:

Admiralty Sailing Directions. Information on the directions to be followed, maximum draught permissible in channels and port approaches, tidal streams, topographic details, port regulations, photographs and sketches.

Admiralty List of Lights and Fog Signals. Characteristics of lights (but not buoys), description of light structures.

Admiralty Tide Tables. Times and heights of tide.

Tidal stream atlases. Details of tidal streams at springs and neaps.

Home Dockyard Ports—Tides and Tidal Streams (HM Ships only). Recommended times of entry and departure, minimum under-keel clearances, tidal stream data.

Port Guide/Fleet Operating Orders (HM Ships only). Detailed directions, regulations, speed limits.

Navigational Data Book. Own ship characteristics (dimensions, draught, etc) turning data, etc.

Admiralty List of Radio Signals, Volume 6. Port operations, pilot services, traffic management, including communication frequencies and procedures.

Department of Transport *Guide to the Planning and Conduct of Sea Passages.* Planning, execution and monitoring of passages under pilotage.

Times of arrival and departure

The ETA and ETD were discussed in Chapter 12. Remember that the ETA and ETD may be governed by the height of tide. Operations at many ports are dependent upon the tide. The height of the tide may apply particularly to the overall depth available and to the depth of water over dangers, also to the desired minimum under-keel clearance (*see* page 308). Local Orders should be consulted.

The navigator must always know the time limits within which the entry or departure plan is valid. Tidal time 'windows' may be vital for arrival and departure, particularly for 'locking in and out', the approach to the berth and so on.

The *Sailing Directions*, the Port Guide or *Home Dockyard Ports—Tides and Tidal Streams* may give advice concerning the best time to arrive at a destination.

There are a number of other factors to be taken into account when considering the best time of day to arrive. These include:

The period of daylight.
Likely local weather.
Working hours in the port.
Movements of other shipping, including those which keep to a timetable like ferries.

Ceremonial: administrative and domestic requirements such as:
    Gun salutes.
    Official calls.
    Storing and fuelling.
    Ship's company leave.

Limiting danger lines

The water in which it is safe for the ship to navigate must be clearly shown on the chart. This is done by drawing *limiting danger lines* (LDL) (Fig. 13–1, p.346), which provide a clear presentation to the Captain and Navigating Officer of the area of safe water. The LDL may be defined as a line drawn on the chart joining soundings of a selected depth to delineate the area considered unsafe for the ship to enter.

The selected depth must obviously provide sufficient water for the ship to remain afloat, but it is important not to allow too great a safety margin to the extent that the LDL is disregarded when approached. The following factors need to be taken into account when determining the safe depth:

Ship's draught.
Predicted height of tide.
Reliability of the chart with particular reference to the charted depths
    (Chapter 6, pp.101 and 121).
The scend in the approach channel that may reduce the effective depth.
An additional margin for safety.

The choice of the charted depth of the LDL is a matter for judgement and no hard and fast rule can be laid down. If the chart has been recently surveyed on a large scale using modern techniques, a great degree of reliability can be placed upon the charted depths and the ship may be navigated safely with a minimum depth of water under the keel. In such circumstances, it will usually be safe for ships to draw the LDL for a charted depth equal to the draught of ship, plus any allowances for squat, plus 2 metres (6 feet) safety margin minus the height of tide as shown in Table 13–1.

Table 13–1.   Determining the LDL

Take	Ship's draught
Add	Squat
Add	Safety margin (usually 2 m)
Total	Above factors
Subtract	Height of tide
Obtain	Charted depth of LDL

Sometimes it may be necessary to reduce the safety margin for operational reasons.

If the area has been poorly surveyed with perhaps only a sparse number of soundings taken by lead–line many years earlier, it may not be possible to

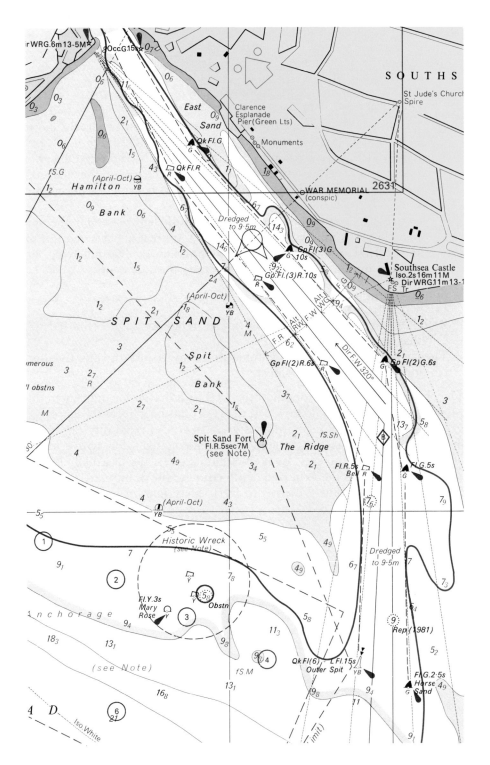

Fig. 13–1.   Limiting danger line

determine a safe LDL. It would be necessary to sound ahead of the ship using boats, while proceeding with the utmost caution.

The navigator must decide upon the LDL which he believes will keep the ship in a safe depth. An LDL approximating to $1\frac{1}{2}$ times the draught of the ship will usually be safe in the majority of cases but, as mentioned earlier this can only be a matter for judgement, taking into account all the different factors.

An LDL of 7 metres is shown in Fig. 13–1. This is for a frigate drawing 6 metres entering Portsmouth at a time when the allowance for squat is $\frac{3}{4}$ metre and the predicted height of tide is $1\frac{3}{4}$ metres. The charted depth to use when drawing the LDL is thus $6 + \frac{3}{4} + 2 - 1\frac{3}{4} = 7$ m.

Appraisal of the passage

The charts and publications should now be closely studied to obtain a clear mental picture of the passage. Information on directions, cautions, dangers and tidal streams should be extracted from the *Sailing Directions*. A brief description of any conspicuous marks should be entered on the chart. The *List of Lights* should be studied for the characteristics and appearance of light structures and beacons. A plan view of the ship's hull shape cut to the scale of the chart should be prepared, to obtain an idea of the relative sizes of the channels and harbour to the ship and the likely distances from dangers during the passage.

THE PILOTAGE PLAN

The pilotage plan must be complete in every detail. Pre-planned data are essential for a passage in confined waters. The track must be drawn on the chart, using headmarks, if possible. The position along the track must be instantaneously available from cross bearings. The safe limits each side of the track must be defined by clearing bearings. With appropriate details transcribed into a properly prepared Note Book, the Navigating Officer can give his whole attention to the conning and safety of the ship without having to consult the chart. Reports from the navigator's assistant, the echo sounder operator, the blind(safety) and/or visual fixing teams, serve to confirm (or deny) the accuracy of the navigation. If time has to be spent poring over the charts and publications during pilotage instead of conning the ship, it will be evident either that the plan has not been fully prepared, or that the Navigating Officer does not have confidence in it.

The plan must be so organised that, at each stage, the Navigating Officer recognises those factors demanding his attention with sufficient time to deal with them. For example, the plan will need to include the selection of 'wheel over' points and the observation of transits to determine the gyro error. Neither of these operations should interfere with the other. These points concern the execution of the plan rather than the planning, but consideration of such details at the planning stage will ensure a sounder plan, simpler to execute.

Selection of the track

Read the *Sailing Directions* and the Port Guide for advice on selecting the track.

The track should normally be to the starboard side of the channel as laid down in *The International Regulations for Preventing Collisions at Sea, 1972* (the Rule of the Road). This allows vessels coming in the opposite direction to pass in safety. If the ship is large relative to the size of the channel, it may be necessary to plan to use the centreline, in which case one of the following possibilities may arise:

1. The ship may have to move to the starboard side of the channel to allow room for other ships to pass.
2. Other vessels may have to be instructed by the Port Authority to keep clear (for example, such instructions are issued when large ships are entering or leaving Portsmouth).
3. Special regulations may be in force for 'vessels constrained by their draught' as defined in the Rule of the Road. Such special regulations usually only apply to the larger ships; (of the order of: draught 10 to $10\frac{1}{2}$ metres or more; length 270 metres or more; deadweight 100,000 tonnes or more).

Details of the regulations governing (2) and (3) above are usually to be found in the *Sailing Directions*. *See also* the remarks at the end of this chapter (page 379) on canal effect.

Dangers

Make sure the track chosen passes clear of dangers, and that the ship does not pass unnecessarily close to them. Dangers should already have been highlighted by the LDL. If the tidal stream is predicted to set the ship towards a danger, it is usually advisable to allow an increased margin of safety.

Tidal streams and wind

If the tidal streams across the track are likely to be large, the courses to steer to counter them should be decided beforehand. A rule of thumb for this is: at speeds of 10 to 12 knots, allow 5° for each knot of tidal stream across the course. At a speed of 5 knots, allow 10°. This rule is correct to within about 1° of the course steered for tidal streams up to 3 knots across the track.

Leeway caused by wind must also be considered. This information should be available in the Navigational Data Book. A rough rule for a frigate at slow speed is that 20 knots of wind is about equivalent to 1 knot of tidal stream. When the depth of water under the keel is restricted, leeway will be considerably reduced and this fact may often be used to advantage.

Distance to run

To assist in arriving on time, distances to run should be marked on the chart from the berth or anchorage. Distances to run should be marked at every mile over the last few miles and every cable in the last mile to anchorage or berth. This will assist in planning when to order reductions in speed.

The times at which it is required to pass through positions to achieve the ETA at the planned pilotage speed should be marked on the chart at appropriate intervals. Remember the use of planned gates as described on page 329.

Night entry/departure

If possible, the tracks chosen should be such that they can equally well be run by night as by day.

Blind pilotage

Consider the action to be taken in the event of restricted visibility. The plan should be equally safe for blind pilotage as for visual conditions. The track selected should enable the change-over from visual to blind and vice versa to be made at any time.

Radar can frequently be used to support the visual plan. This is common practice in merchant ships and warships where the pilotage team is small in numbers.

Constrictions

If the track has to pass through a constriction (for example, a narrow section of a channel) plan to steady on the requisite course in plenty of time. This is most important if there is any strong tidal stream (or wind) across the track. Furthermore, this precaution gives time to adjust to the planned track on the correct heading should the ship fail to achieve this immediately on altering course.

The Sun

Work out the bearing and altitude of the Sun likely to be experienced as dazzle during the passage. Try to avoid tracks and 'wheel over' bearings which look directly up Sun, especially at low elevations, when it may be difficult to pick up the requisite marks.

Headmarks

Suitable headmarks should be selected for the chosen tracks. Transits are best but, if these are not available from the chart, a conspicuous object should be used instead. Choose an object such as a lighthouse, pier, fort, etc. which is unlikely to be confused with anything else. Chimneys, flagstaffs, radio masts and even churches can cause confusion if there are a number in close vicinity. Flagstaffs are frequently removed or repositioned; chimneys and radio masts can change without notification. Avoid choosing objects which may no longer be visible because of changing topography.

Transits

Many harbour plans show two marks which, when kept in line, lead the ship clear of dangers or along the best channel. Such marks are called leading marks and are often shown on a chart by a line drawn from them, called a *leading line* (Fig. 13–2, p.350).

The leading line is usually shown as a full line (*CD* in Fig. 13–2) where it is safe to use the marks, and dotted elsewhere. The names of the objects and the true bearing *from seaward*, are usually written alongside the line (*see* Chart Booklet 5011, *Symbols and Abbreviations Used on Admiralty Charts*).

If the two objects chosen are seen to remain in transit (Fig. 13–3(a), p.350), the ship must be following the selected track—*BD* in Fig. 13–2. If the two objects are not in line (Fig. 13–3(b)) the ship must be off track to one side or the other.

In Fig. 13–3(b), the marks are *open*, with the monument *open right* of the beacon. This means that the observer is on or in the close vicinity of track *BE* in Fig. 13–2.

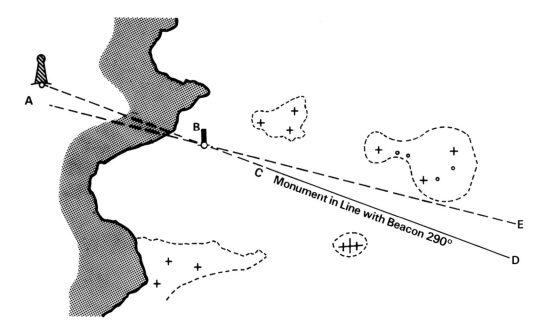

Fig. 13–2.   Leading marks, leading line

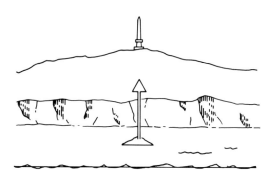

Fig. 13–3(a)   Using a transit: objects in transit

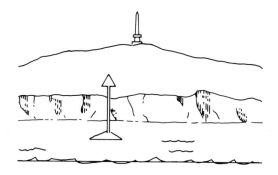

Fig. 13–3(b)   Using a transit: monument open right of beacon

The value of a transit is proportional to the ratio of the distance between the objects in transit to the distance between the ship and the nearer object. The closer the ship is to the marks, the better the transit. For example, in Fig. 13–2, if the ship is at D, the proportion is $\dfrac{AB}{BD}$. The larger this ratio the better the transit; ideally, the ratio should be 1:3 or greater. In Fig. 13–2, the ratio at D is about 1:2 and is getting larger as the ship enters harbour, so the monument and beacon form a good or 'sensitive' transit (*see* page 200).

If the chart does not show suitable leading marks, the Navigating Officer should select his own if possible.

Line of bearing

If no transit is available, a line of bearing should be used instead (Fig. 13–4).

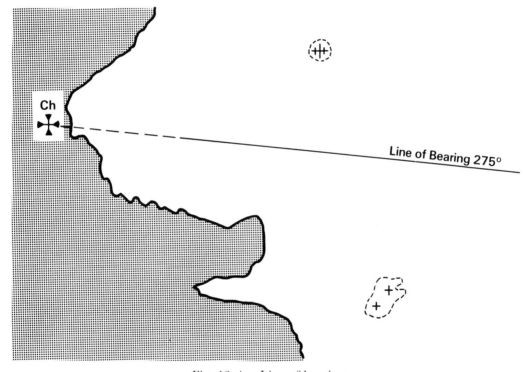

Fig. 13–4.   Line of bearing

The track is drawn on the chart to pass through some well defined object ahead of the ship and the bearing of this line noted. Provided the bearing of the object remains on the bearing noted, the ship must be on her track. If the bearing changes, the ship will have been set off the track, and an alteration of course will be necessary to regain the line of bearing.

Edge of land

Edges of land such as cliffs can be useful headmarks, particularly if they are vertical or nearly so. If the edge of land is sloping (Fig. 13–5, page 352), the charted edge is the high water mark and it is this which should be used.

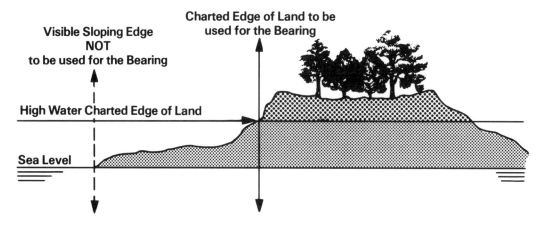

Fig. 13–5. Using the edge of land as a headmark

Distance of the headmark

The closer the headmark, the better, because it is easier to detect any change of bearing and thus whether the ship is being set off the line. One degree off the line is equivalent to a distance of about 35 yards at 1 mile, 100 yards at 3 miles, 350 yards at 10 miles.

No headmark available

If no headmark is available, a mark astern is preferable to none at all but, if no marks are available, the alternatives are:

1. *Fix and Run.* Plan to fix the ship's position as accurately as possible by bearings (taking into account any gyro error) to confirm the safety of the course. Any suitable object* on the bearing of the new track should be observed and used as a headmark when steady on the new course.
2. A *bearing lattice* (described in Chapter 9). This is easy to prepare and can be transcribed to a Note Book. Two bearings taken at the same time by the Navigating Officer at the pelorus will immediately tell him whether the ship is off track and, if so, by how much.
3. An *HSA lattice* (described in Chapter 9 and Appendix 6). This is very accurate but takes time to prepare and requires a fixing team of about three people independent of the Navigating Officer.

Altering course

When planning an alteration of course, the turning circle must be allowed for so that the ship, when steady on the new course, may be on the predetermined track. The position of the 'wheel over' is found using either the advance and transfer or the distance to new course (DNC). These terms were explained in Chapter 8 (pages 185 to 190).

---

* The object does not have to be charted. Virtually any object will do provided it is stationary and there is no likelihood of it being confused with anything else. Buildings, outcrops of rock, even trees can be used.

The turning data for a ship may be displayed in tabular or graphical form. For accurate interpolation it is easier to use the graph, drawing separate curves for advance, transfer, DNC and the time to complete the turn. This is illustrated in Fig. 13–6.

Speed 10 knots				15° of Rudder
Amount of Turn	Time		Advance	Transfer	DNC
Degrees	Min	Sec	Yards	Yards	Yards
30		50	259	57	162
60	1	20	384	178	285
90	1	50	453	338	453
120	2	30	415	515	710
150	3	10	300	645	—
180	3	40	133	711	—

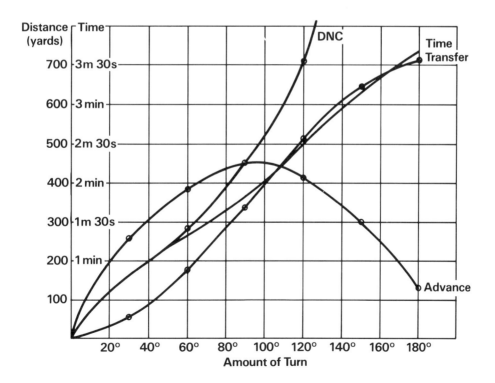

Fig. 13–6.   Turning data

Advance and transfer

The advantages of using advance and transfer are:

1. The point at which the ship gains the new track is precisely determined. This allows a better indication of the track covered by the pivot point. The path of the ship during the turn may be found by plotting the advance and transfer for intermediate angles (particularly important for the larger ship). For example, if a turn of 90° is to be undertaken, the advance and transfer for 30° and 60° as well as 90° should be plotted on the chart and the predicted path of the ship during the turn drawn.
2. The data may be used for turns up to 180°.

The disadvantage of this method is that, compared with DNC, it is slightly slower and more difficult to plot.

Distance to new course (DNC)

The advantage of using DNC is that it is simple to plot. The disadvantages are that it does not show the point where the ship completes the turn, nor can it be effectively used for turns of more than 120°.

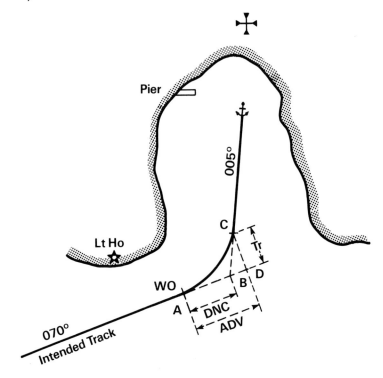

Fig. 13–7.   Turning on to a predetermined line (1)

Turning on to a predetermined line

This is illustrated in Fig. 13–7. It is desired to alter course from the 070° track to a track of 005°. *B* is the point of intersection of the two tracks. The 'wheel over' point A and the steadying point C are plotted on the chart, using the turning data relevant to the speed and intended amount of wheel. For example, using the data in Fig. 13–6, the figures for a turn of 65° are:

TIME TO TURN	ADVANCE (YARDS)	TRANSFER (YARDS)	DNC (YARDS)
1 min 24 s	400	200	305

The advance and transfer method of finding the 'wheel over' position A is as follows:

1. Project the 070° track beyond B.
2. Determine points D and C, where DC is equal to the transfer (200 yards) and DC is at right angles to the original track (070°).
3. From D lay back the advance (400 yards), to find the 'wheel over' point A.

The DNC method of finding the 'wheel over' position A consists of one step:

From B, lay back the DNC, 305 yards to find the 'wheel over' point A.

The 'wheel over' bearing at point A must be chosen with care to ensure that the ship ends up on the required track. This is illustrated in Fig. 13–8 (a) and (b), where two possible 'wheel over' bearings are shown.

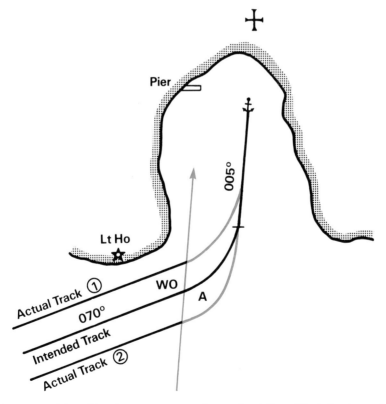

Fig. 13–8 (a).   Turning on to a predetermined line (2): 'wheel over' bearing parallel to new course

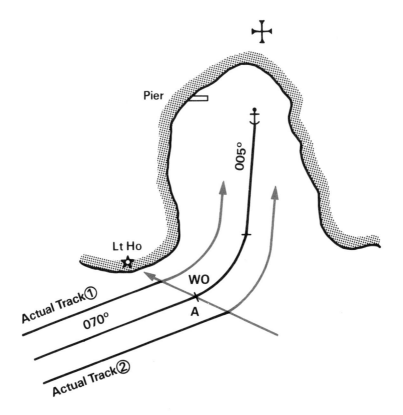

Fig. 13–8 (b). Turning on to a predetermined line (2): 'wheel over'
bearing not parallel to new course

If the 'wheel over' bearing is parallel to the new course as in Fig. 13–8 (a), the
ship will fetch up on the planned approach track, whether she is on the previous
intended track or not. If, however, the 'wheel over' bearing is not parallel to the
new course, as in Fig. 13–8 (b), a large error will result if the ship is not on the
intended track as she comes up to the 'wheel over' position.

For this reason, the 'wheel over' bearing should be as parallel to the new
track as possible. Frequently an object which has a bearing parallel to the new
track will not be available and, in such circumstances, the headmark for the
new track will generally be the best object to use.

If it is *known* that the ship is on the correct track on the run up to the 'wheel
over' position, a 'wheel over' bearing which is changing rapidly will more
precisely define the turning point than one which is changing slowly. In such
circumstances, it may be preferable to use the bearing of an object which is *not*
parallel to the new course, but care must be taken to check the bearing of the
new headmark to avoid under- or over-shooting the turn.

The bearing of an object being used to define the 'wheel over' position should
therefore:

1. Be as parallel as possible to the new track.
2. Give a high rate of bearing change.

Always have an alternative 'wheel over' bearing available.

To allow for a current or tidal stream when altering course

Allowing for a current or tidal stream when altering course is illustrated in Fig. 13–9.

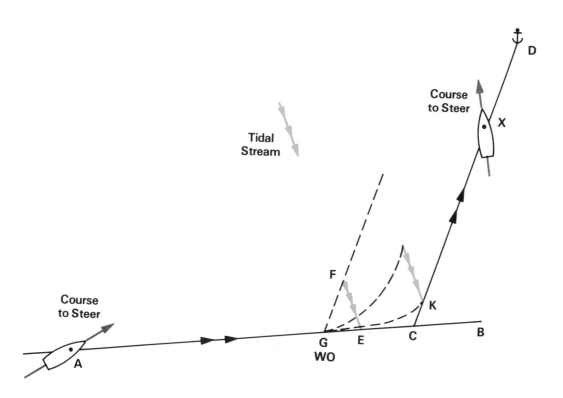

Fig. 13–9.   Turning on to a predetermined line, allowing for tidal stream

EXAMPLE

A ship at A is making good a track AB, steering to port of the ground track to allow for the tidal stream setting to the south-east. The ship wishes to turn to the line CD (where she will have to steer the course shown at X) and must therefore make an allowance for the tidal stream setting the ship to the south-east during the turn.

Determine from the turning data the 'wheel over' point E for an alteration of course equal to the difference between the ship's head at X and at A (for example, from C, lay back the DNC for this alteration to find point E).

From *E* plot, in the direction of the tidal stream *reversed*, the distance that the tidal stream will carry the ship during the time for the turn. This gives point *F*.

Draw *FG* through *F* parallel to *CD* to intersect *AB* at *G*. Point *G* is the revised 'wheel over' position to allow for the tidal stream. The ship will arrive on the line *CD* at point *K*.

Use of a single position line

Where there is no headmark or where the headmark is difficult to see, a single position line with a bearing exactly parallel to the intended approach course may be very useful when turning into an anchorage or channel. This technique involves the use of a transferred position line and is illustrated in Fig. 9–10 (page 206). Remember to time precisely the estimated ground track between the position line and the 'wheel over' point, use a stopwatch if necessary.

Keeping clear of dangers

Clearing marks and bearings, vertical and horizontal danger angles, have already been introduced in Chapter 12.

Clearing bearings

Once the track has been decided upon, clearing bearings should be drawn on the chart clear of the limiting danger line. These clearing bearings define the area of water in which it is safe to navigate.

The clearing bearing needs to be displaced from the LDL (Fig. 13–10) to such an extent that the ends of the ship (usually the bow or stern) will still be in safe water if the bridge is on the clearing bearing. But this distance should not be so great that the clearing bearing is disregarded when approached.

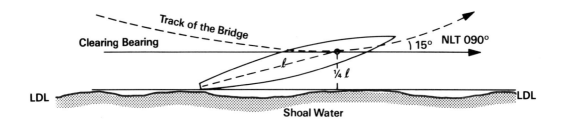

Fig. 13–10.   Displacement of the clearing bearing from the LDL

No hard and fast rule for the distance of the clearing bearing from the LDL can be laid down. It depends on the width of safe navigable water, the angle between the intended track and the LDL, the weather and tidal stream and the safety margin already allowed for in the LDL. For example, in Fig. 13–10—a fairly narrow channel where the track is parallel to the LDL—a clearing line displaced by a distance equal to $\frac{1}{4}$ of the distance ℓ between the bridge and the stern should be sufficient to keep the ship clear of danger, provided that any alteration of course away from the clearing bearing is not too great. Fig. 13–10 shows a frigate altering course away from shoal water at an angle of about 15° to the LDL, with the bridge on the clearing bearing. In such circumstances the stern is right on the LDL, so the only further safety factor 'in hand' is the additional depth margin built in to the LDL.

If there is plenty of room available, the distance of the clearing bearing from the LDL may be as much as the full distance ℓ between the bridge and the stern. This permits a 90° alteration of course away from the LDL yet still allows the stern to be in a safe depth.

Fig. 13–11.   Approaching Devonport in a large ship

If the marks are some distance away, a greater margin of safety between the clearing bearing and the LDL needs to be allowed.

Clearing bearings should be so constructed as to box in completely the safe navigable water, while ensuring that the plan remains simple and manageable (*see* Fig. 13–14 on page 367). There are two considerations:

1. Avoid restricting the ship unnecessarily.
2. Avoid using too many clearing bearings which make the plan complicated and unwieldy.

It is most important to make certain that sufficient clearing bearings are available for the shiphandling phase when the ship is approaching or leaving the berth. It is useful to have a sketch of these in the Note Book.

When navigating to very narrow limits (where even $\frac{1}{4} \ell$ is too great a margin) the cut-out model of the ship mentioned earlier will be extremely useful when considering the distance of the clearing bearing from the LDL. This is particularly important when navigating a long ship in a narrow channel which bends sharply, as is the case, for example, in the passage from Plymouth Sound through Smeaton Pass in the approach to Devonport (Fig. 13–11, page 359).

An LDL for a depth of 10 metres has been employed—draught 11 metres, plus 1 metre for squat, plus 3 metres for safety, minus 5 metres for height of tide. Clearing bearings marking the edges of safe navigable water have been drawn close to the LDL to give the maximum area in which to manoeuvre this ship. Clearing bearings are much closer to the LDL than $\frac{1}{4} \ell$. The more wheel required for a turn, the further will the stern swing out from the track, thus necessitating a greater distance of the clearing bearing from the LDL. For this reason, both turns have been planned using only 15° of wheel, the minimum that can be safely used in the circumstances.

Vertical and horizontal danger angles

If no suitable object is available for a satisfactory clearing bearing, it may be possible to use a vertical or horizontal danger angle instead. The use of these as safety angles is explained in Chapter 12 (page 325). An assistant may be required to observe the angle.

Echo sounder

The least depth expected on each leg of the plan must be known, and thought given to the course of action to be taken if the echo sounder reading falls below the least depth.

The echo sounder may also be used to provide a *clearing depth* similar in use to a clearing bearing. The LDL is based on the depth of water (page 345) but, as with a clearing bearing, a greater allowance is required for a clearing depth to ensure that the ends of the ship are always in a safe depth. For example, in Fig. 13–14 (page 367) the clearing bearings are very close to the edge of the dredged channel of 9.5 metres. This depth may therefore be used to determine the clearing depth, which is equal to the charted depth plus height of tide. For a height of tide of $1\frac{3}{4}$ metres the clearing depth would be $11\frac{1}{4}$ metres below the waterline.

It is sometimes possible to determine a single clearing depth which will suffice for the whole passage. It may often be necessary, however, to have a clearing depth for each leg and, on occasion, different depths for each side of the same leg.

Various echo sounder procedures are set out in Volume III. These cover such things as:

Depths below the keel or the waterline.
Depths in metres or fathoms.
Echo sounder operator standard reports.

Miscellaneous considerations

Gyro checks

Plan frequent gyro checks. The gyro error must be known and applied before any pilotage run is started. Before leaving a berth, if no transit is available, the gyro error may be calculated by various methods including the reduction of the cocked hat (*see* page 219).

'Shooting up'

All marks used in pilotage (headmarks, 'wheel over' and clearing marks) should be positively identified, usually by 'shooting up' (*see* page 235). In pilotage work, the most practical method is by means of transits and these should be planned beforehand, details being included in the Note Book.

Using radar to support the visual plan

Radar may often be used to support the visual plan. Examples of the uses which may be made of radar are as follows:

1. Checking the position of buoys and confirming their abeam distance.
2. Confirming that the track is being maintained (the parallel index technique—*see* Chapter 15).
3. Identifying beacons, buoys, ships, etc.
4. Confirming the 'wheel over' position.
5. Checking the distance to go to 'wheel over' along a particular track or the distance to an anchorage position.
6. Checking the distance of other ships in the vicinity.
7. Identifying the correct anchoring position.
8. 'Shooting up' marks and ships at anchor.

Point of no return

There is usually a position in any pilotage plan beyond which the ship becomes committed to the plan and can no longer break off from it and take alternative action. This position depends on many factors including the size of the ship, the weather, the narrowness and complexity of the passage, the tidal stream, etc., and must be determined during the planning. In an entry plan, the Navigating Officer needs to consider: 'Can I break off from this leg, either to anchor or to turn round and go back out to sea in safety, or does the situation commit me to continue?'

The point of no return can be a long way to seaward, particularly if the ship is large. For example in a long, deep-draught ship entering Devonport (Fig. 13–11), the point of no return is well into the Sound, south of Smeaton Pass and can in certain circumstances actually be south of the breakwater itself.

Alternative anchor berth

Suitable positions in which to anchor in case of emergency or change of plan should be considered. For example, in the plan for entry to Portsmouth Harbour (Fig. 13–14, page 367) it is advisable to have ready a plan to anchor at Spithead.

Navigating Officer's Note Book (S548A)

The relevant details of the plan should be summarised in the Navigating Officer's Note Book with a sketch (Figs. 13–12 and 13–13, pages 364, 365) so that the navigator can pilot the ship from the pelorus, using the Note Book, without recourse to charts and publications (*see* page 347).

There is no hard and fast rule as to how the Note Book should be laid out for the pilotage plan but several guidelines are set out below:

1. The book should be uncluttered and precise.
2. Sufficient information must be available to conduct the plan entirely from the book.
3. The chart or portions of the chart may be used as an alternative to the sketch and be readily available to the Captain and the Navigating Officer (*see* page 343). More than one sketch may be needed.
4. Distances from the planned track of buoys and other navigational aids should be included, as these may assist in the execution of the plan.

The Note Book must contain sufficient detail for the Navigating Officer to know:

1. The planned track and headmark.
2. If the ship is off track at any time and by how much.
3. The safety limits defined by the clearing bearings.
4. The distance to the next 'wheel over'.
5. The proximity of dangers.
6. The tidal stream.
7. The minimum depth expected on any leg.
8. The cross-checks for the next 'wheel over' point and headmark.
9. The 'wheel over' bearing.
10. The assessment of the turn to the new planned track.

A Note Book layout which has been used many times in practice and found to be satisfactory is shown in Fig. 13–13.

The Navigating Officer should always transcribe relevant details about the ship from the Navigational Data Book (S2677) into the front of his Note Book. For pilotage work, these include:

Ship's dimensions and visibility diagram (if held).
Turning data.

Reduction of speed tables for approaches to anchorages, buoys and alongside.

Special berthing information (e.g. type of catamarans required, length of brows, etc.).

The amount of cable available on each anchor. Remember that the amount of cable which can be veered is about one shackle less than that fitted.

Conning

The point on the approach where the Navigating Officer takes over the con from the Officer of the Watch, and the Captain in turn takes over from the Navigating Officer, should be planned beforehand. As a general rule, the Navigating Officer should take the con from the Officer of the Watch in sufficient time to have the 'feel' of the ship by the time the pilotage stage begins using the Note Book only (usually when the ship enters the narrow channel or anchorage approach phase).

The method of passing orders for the final shiphandling phase of the approach to the berth must be decided. Some Captains prefer to take the con themselves; some prefer to leave the Navigating Officer at the con, relaying orders through him rather than directly to the Quartermaster. If the Captain takes the con himself, he gets the feel of the ship more quickly but may lose a feel for the overall situation.

Tugs

The requirements for tugs must be decided during planning. The Tugmasters will require briefing on the intended movement plan, which should include details of how and where the tugs will be secured. For harbour entry, the position in the approach where tugs are to meet the ship should be planned.

Final stages of the plan

For the final stages of the plan, decide:

1. The time or position in the approach to:

   Close up special sea dutymen and assume the appropriate NBCD state.

   Operate the echo sounder.

   Have the anchors ready for letting go.

   Have additional boilers, diesels or gas turbines connected, second steering motor, etc.

2. The details of harbour communications, frequencies, etc.
3. The requirements for special ceremonial procedures, gun salutes, etc.
4. When to raise logs and sonar domes, secure radar sets, etc.

Submit the departure or entry plan to the Captain, including the shiphandling problems which will be encountered, including the use of tugs.

Carry out any further briefings; e.g. if berthing alongside, brief the Executive Officer, the various part of ship officers, the Marine Engineer Officer, etc.

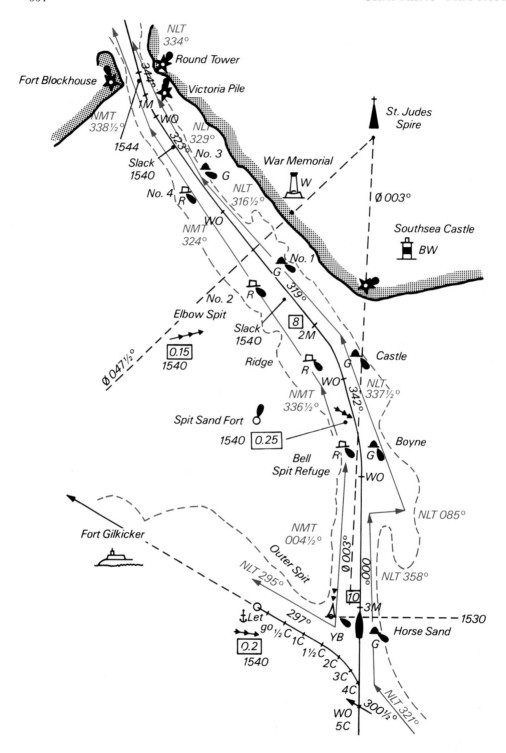

Fig. 13–12.   Pilotage plan for a frigate entering Portsmouth—the Note Book sketch

	Entry into Portsmouth, OSB – Middle Slip Wednesday 29 September (−1)		
	Distance: 3′.04 ETA OSB: 1530 (−1); alongside 1552 (−1)		
	Tides and Tidal Stream Data Neaps 27 Sept. (1/10th way to Springs) Portsmouth 29 Sept. Range 2.25M. 1009 3.9M; 1530 1.7M; 2223 4.0M. Ht. on entering harbour: 1¾ m. Tidal Streams: 0.2 kn Easterly at OSB and in Spithead, decreasing to 0.1 at Spit Refuge. Meet the ebb ¼ kn S.E., just north of Spit Refuge, slack from Elbow Spit on and in harbour entrance.		

Course/ Speed	Remarks	Dist to W.O.	Min. Depth
000° 10	On Southsea Castle Lt (St. Judes Ch., open right) Blockhouse Dir WRG φ ⟵ Spit Sand Fort 336½° Horse Sand ⊥ Stbd ½ C 1530 (−1) OSB ⊥ Port 1C War Memorial φ Spit Refuge 347°	0′.47 (2m 50s)	10.7m
342°	W.O. War Memorial 344° on War Memorial Boyne ⊥ Stbd 0.45C Spit Refuge ⊥ Port 0.7C Spit Sand Fort ⊥ Port 3.2C	0′.2 (1m 13s)	11¼ m
319° 8	W.O. Blockhouse Dir WRG φ ⟶ rt hand conspic block of flats 321° on Blockhouse Dir WRG (⟵ rt hand conspic block flats just open left) Southsea Castle 055° (2M to alongside)		 11¼ m

Fig. 13–13. Pilotage plan for a frigate entering Portsmouth—the Note Book layout

Check-off lists

It is always advisable to consider the use of check-off lists when preparing a pilotage plan. These ensure that nothing is likely to be forgotten. An example of a pilotage check-off list is to be found in Annex A to this chapter.

The plan

Fig. 13–14 illustrates part of a complete plan for a frigate entering Portsmouth using an LDL of 7 metres.

Fig. 13–12 illustrates a Note Book sketch (more than one should be used if there is much detail) and Fig. 13–13 an example of how the Note Book should be laid out (pp.364, 365).

The planned track, 'wheel over' points, LDL and clearing bearings are shown. Distances to run to the berth inside Portsmouth Naval Base are noted on the chart, together with the expected times of passing key points so as to arrive alongside at the planned time. Predicted tidal streams and planned ship's speed (*see* NP 167) and an alternative anchorage in Spithead are also shown on the chart.

For example, it may be seen that a track of 000° on Southsea Castle Light has been chosen for the first leg of the entry plan, St Jude's Church being open to the right. The track lies to the starboard side of the channel. A gyro check—the signal station at Fort Blockhouse in transit with the left-hand edge of Spit Sand Fort bearing 336½°—is available at the southern end of this leg. Clearing bearings mark the safe navigational limits on each side of the channel, the bearing of Southsea Castle Light being not less than (NLT) 358° and not more than (NMT) 004½°. The minimum depth to be expected on this first leg, allowing for the predicted height of the tide, is 10.7 metres. The ETA at the Outer Spit Buoy (OSB), which should pass 1 cable abeam to port, is 1530 (−1) on 29th September. On passing OSB, the distance to run to the berth at Middle Slip in the Portsmouth Naval Base is just over 3 miles, the ETA alongside being 1552. The ship's speed on passing OSB should be 10 knots. At this speed, and allowing for the tidal stream which is predicted to be easterly, weak, the ship should reach the next 'wheel over' position, 1 cable south of the Boyne and Spit Refuge buoys, just before 1533.

The next running mark is the War Memorial, and this may be identified by a transit with Spit Refuge buoy, bearing 347°. When the War Memorial bears 344°, course should be altered to port, passing between the Boyne buoy 0.45 cable to starboard and the Spit Refuge buoy 0.7 cable to port, to the next track of 342° on the War Memorial.

In this manner, the ship proceeds up channel and into harbour.

Fig. 13–14.   Pilotage plan for a frigate entering Portsmouth—the chart

EXECUTION OF PILOTAGE

The essence of a good plan is knowing the limits within which the ship may be navigated in safety. The essential questions which the Navigating Officer must be able to answer at all times during a pilotage passage are:

Is the ship on track?
If not, where is the ship in relation to the track and what steps are being taken to regain it?
How close is the ship to danger?
How far is it to the next alteration of course?
Are the tidal streams and depths of water as predicted?

Organisation and records

A team effort is needed to execute a pilotage plan in safety; Table 13–2 (p.370) is a recommended organisation for a frigate or destroyer. Other ships may need to modify this as necessary, dependent on the size of the ship and the team available.

The pilotage team should produce sufficient records for the ship's track to be accurately reconstructed, if required. The fixes and soundings taken through the passage should provide a series of confirmatory checks to support the visual picture and DR/EP times to support 'wheel over' bearings, etc.

Maintaining the track

An estimate of the distance off track may be made by looking along the desired bearing of the headmark and then making a direct assessment of how far the ship is off track. The distance should be quantified; for example, if it is estimated that the *required bearing* is 50 yards to the *left* of the *headmark* (Fig. 13–15), then the ship is '50 yards to *port* of track'. Remember that 1° off the track is equivalent to a distance of about 100 feet at 1 mile, $\frac{1}{2}$ cable at 3 miles.

When running a mark in a cross-tidal stream, the course steered is bound to

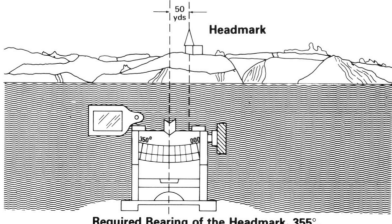

Required Bearing of the Headmark, 355°, is 50 yds to the *Left*: Ship 50 yds to *Port* of Track

Fig. 13–15.   Running a headmark: ship to port of track

Table 13–2. Pilotage organisation

CAPTAIN	In command, overall responsibility for ship safety.
NAVIGATING OFFICER (NO)	Acts as the pilot and takes over as necessary from the OOW. Executes the plan at the pelorus from the Note Book. Has ready access to the chart. Keeps the Captain fully informed on the progress of the plan. May take the bearings for his assistant to plot fixes on the chart.
OFFICER OF THE WATCH (OOW)	Filters shipping situation and informs Navigating Officer of ships which may hinder execution of the plan. Takes bearings and gyro checks as directed by the Navigating Officer. Runs the ship's routine and ceremonial and deals with matters of internal safety (of the ship). Maintains liaison with the blind safety team in the operations room.
NAVIGATING OFFICER'S ASSISTANT	Carries out the Navigating Officer's chartwork. Calls for fixes at regular and frequent intervals in order to confirm the ship's position and cross-checks the EP. Plots fixes and generates fresh DR and EP. Reports after each fix: <ul><li>its reliability: 'Good', 'Bad', or 'No fix' as the case may be;</li><li>its distance from the planned track, and course required to regain;</li><li>whether the echo sounder reports correlate with charted depth;</li><li>ETA at next 'wheel over' position.</li></ul>
BLIND SAFETY OFFICER (BSO) AND BLIND SAFETY TEAM (*see* Chapter 15)	Monitors ship's position using blind pilotage techniques as a check on the ship's navigational safety; passes navigational and anti-collision information.
NAVIGATOR'S YEOMAN	Records wheel and engine orders. A tape recorder on the bridge may be found useful.
ECHO SOUNDER OPERATOR	Makes standard reports (*see* Volume III).

differ from the planned bearing of the mark. Remember the rule given on page 348. If the correct bearing is not being maintained, the ship is off track; it must be regained by a bold alteration. When the track has been regained, a course must be steered which will counteract the tidal stream more adequately than the original one.

Do not nibble at course corrections to maintain the track and avoid making successive alterations of 1° or 2°. Alter 10° or 15° to get back on the correct track quickly, but do not overshoot.

Radar is often a useful aid in confirming whether the ship is on track or not (Chapter 15).

Running a transit

The rule for running a transit is 'Follow the front mark'. In Fig. 13–3(b) the front mark (the beacon) is to *port* of the rear mark (the monument). Therefore the alteration of course to get back on track must also be to *port*.

If the transit is *astern*, the alteration must be in the *reverse* direction, e.g. in Fig. 13–3(b) the beacon is to the *left* of the monument, therefore the alteration must be to *starboard*.

Running a line of bearing

Altering course the wrong way when running a line of bearing is a frequent cause of mistakes in pilotage. This can be avoided by the following simple rules:

1. Look down the bearing on which the headmark should be.
2. The headmark will be:
    On the mark (Fig. 13–16)   *or*
    To starboard of the bearing (Fig. 13–17, p.372)   *or*
    To port of the bearing (Fig. 13–18, p.372).
3. If the headmark is off the bearing, alter course in its direction: If the headmark is to *starboard* of the correct bearing alter course to *starboard* to regain track (Fig. 13–17).

    If the headmark is to *port* of the correct bearing, alter course to *port* to regain track (Fig. 13-18).

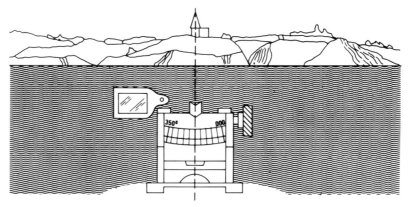

Headmark on the Correct Bearing: Ship on Track

Fig. 13–16.   Running a headmark: ship on track

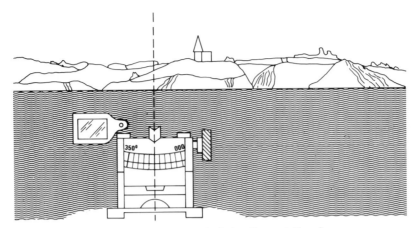

Headmark to *Starboard* of the Correct Bearing:
Alter Course to *Starboard*

Fig. 13–17.   Running a headmark: headmark to starboard of the correct bearing

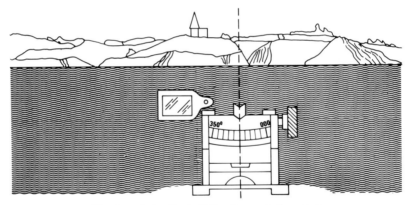

Headmark to *Port* of the Correct Bearing:
Alter Course to *Port*

Fig. 13–18.   Running a headmark: headmark to port of the correct bearing

If the mark is *astern* and the ship is running a *back bearing*, the alteration of course must be in the *reverse* direction; e.g. if the mark in Fig. 13–17 is astern and appears to the right of the required bearing, the alteration of course must be to port; if the stern mark appears as shown in Fig. 13–18, the alteration required must be to starboard.

When the mark is on the correct bearing, note a point on the landscape which is in transit with it (either in front or behind). By using this transit, it is possible to see immediately without reference to the compass whether or not the ship is being set off line.

Fix and run

This procedure is discussed on page 352. Having chosen a suitable object on which to run, obtain another one in transit with it in precisely the same way as when running a line of bearing. Radar can often be of great assistance in confirming the track.

Assessment of danger

Always be alert to the nearest and most immediate danger. This could be a ship at anchor or a buoy towards which own ship is being set by wind or tidal stream. The most immediate danger could be a ship approaching down the next leg of the route which, if she does not alter course as expected, could present a collision risk.

The chart gives warning of navigational dangers but there are other hazards—ships, yachts and small craft, emergencies such as steering gear or main machinery breakdown. The navigator must be alert to all of these matters, and be constantly thinking ahead and anticipating possible eventualities.

Identification of marks

In pilotage work, there are two quick and simple methods immediately available for the identification of shore marks.

1. A straightforward comparison of the chart with what is actually visible. Such a comparison will frequently reveal the marks to be used, without having to take a single bearing. If there is any possibility of confusion between adjacent marks (such as churches, chimneys, blocks of flats, etc.) this may have to be clarified by taking bearings.
2. Identification by means of the transits which shore marks make with the buoys marking the channel. Even if a buoy differs from its charted position by as much as 100 yards, the expected bearing of the mark to be identified will probably not vary by more than 2° or 3°; this is usually sufficient for identification purposes.

Buoys or beacons can be identified by combining a single visual bearing with a radar range of the mark.

Shipping

When altering course for shipping, take the necessary action in plenty of time. If action is delayed, the Officer of the Watch in the other ship may become alarmed and may do something unexpected and dangerous.

Do not pass too close across the bow (upstream) of anchored shipping; if possible, pass astern. The position of ships at anchor near own ship's track can be established by combining a fix with a visual bearing and radar range of the ship at anchor. With the position of the other ship on the chart, a decision can then be made to pass ahead or astern, or take some alternative action such as stopping if, for example, the anchored ship is blocking the channel.

Use of the echo sounder

The intelligent use of the echo sounder is essential to the safe conduct of pilotage. The predicted height of tide must be taken into account at all times.

Reports from the echo sounder operator or the reading on the bridge display unit must be given proper attention. If the reported depths are different from

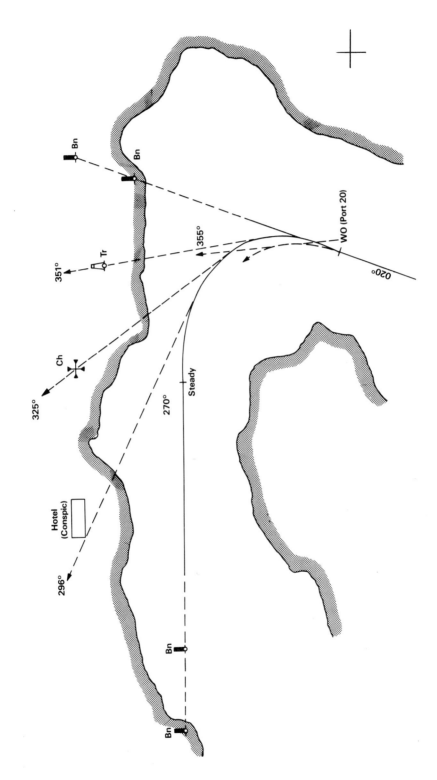

Fig. 13–19.   Monitoring a large turn in pilotage waters

those predicted, the reasons must be considered and the appropriate action taken, particularly if the depths are close to the limiting depth. It may be necessary to stop the ship and clarify the situation before proceeding further.

Altering course and speed

When turning on to a new headmark, the wheel must be put over in plenty of time. If it is put over too soon, it can be quickly eased; if it is put over too late, more wheel may not be effective. The use of excessive wheel may bring the ends of the ship closer to the clearing bearing than planned. Excessive wheel also reduces ship's speed more than originally intended and this may create problems, particularly in strong winds or when in company with other ships.

When about to turn, make sure that the ship is not tending to swing in the opposite direction to that intended. Keep the bows in hand ('smell' the turn) by using small amounts of wheel in the appropriate direction just before the turn, so that the ship 'wants' to go the desired way as soon as the wheel is put over for the turn itself. When making a large turn in a big ship, it is often advisable to use plenty of wheel initially to get the ship swinging in the right direction and then ease the wheel, otherwise the ship may 'hang' in the original direction, particularly in shallow water or when turning out of wind.

Remember that, as a general rule, ships going ahead turn more easily into wind than away from it, and allowance should be made for this.

Watch the progress of the ship during the turn to ensure that the planned track is being followed. Are objects coming up ahead on the right bearing? Does the turn look right? This is particularly important with large turns in big ships.

The monitoring of a large turn is illustrated in Fig. 13–19. A ship entering harbour on a course of 020° is required to turn 110° to port to the next leg (270°). The courses of 020° and 270° both run on a pair of beacons in transit. The track of the ship between 'wheel over' and steady is plotted using the ship's turning data. It will be seen that, once the turn has begun, the tower should come up *right ahead* on a bearing of 351°, the church on 325° and the ◄———— of the hotel (conspic) on 296°, as the ship's head swings through those particular bearings. If these bearings do not come up right ahead, the rate of turn must be adjusted. For example if, in the early part of the turn, the tower comes up right ahead on a bearing of 355°, the ship is to port of track, and is turning too fast. The wheel must be eased to bring the ship back on to track.

Before altering course, check to see that the track is clear of shipping and other obstructions. Look out on the appropriate quarter for any ship overtaking from that direction.

Always check that the wheel is put over the right way by watching the rudder angle indicator. If the wheel is put the wrong way, order 'Midships' and repeat the original order.

When altering speed, check from the shaft speed indicators or the pitch angle repeaters that speed has been altered correctly. If the shafts have been put the wrong way (e.g. astern instead of ahead), order 'Stop' and repeat the original order.

In ships where the Quartermaster is sited at the QM's console on the bridge, it is important that the above procedure should be followed and that all conning orders and replies are made in a formal manner.

Buoys

Buoys are an essential aid in pilotage, especially in narrow channels, but their positions can vary from that charted with the state of the tide. Buoys can drag, particularly if in an exposed position; they can also be repositioned to mark an extending shoal or altered channel, without immediate notification.

Use but do not trust buoys implicitly. Check the characteristics by night, and the name, number, colour or topmark by day. Fix from charted shore objects in preference to buoys, using the EP as a check. Take care in areas where it is known that channels shift and the buoys are repositioned accordingly. The charts and *Sailing Directions* may give warning of such areas, for example the channels in the vicinity of the Goodwin Sands and in the Thames Estuary.

When passing a buoy, its position may be checked by transits with two, preferably three, charted shore marks. Radar can help in the identification of buoys and in checking their positions.

Take care if the planned track leads the 'wrong side' of a buoy marking the leg of the channel, e.g. the deep-draught route for heavy ships approaching Smeaton Pass (Fig. 13–11) from Plymouth Sound which leads east of the West Mallard Buoy. It may on occasion, for example in strong winds, be preferable to aim off 2° or 3° as necessary to get the buoy on the 'correct' bow. Otherwise the ship could be set dangerously close to the buoy concerned if she is slow to turn.

The height of the tide may permit a ship to pass outside the line of buoys yet still be safe. A ship may be forced the wrong side of a buoy by other shipping. It may be better to take this course if collision cannot otherwise be avoided. In certain circumstances, it may even be better to ground than risk a collision.

Tides, tidal streams and wind

For a number of reasons, the predicted height of tide may be different from that actually experienced, perhaps by as much as 1 or even 2 metres. This is particularly dependent on the weather, as explained in Chapter 11.

Tidal streams experienced may not always agree with the predictions, particularly at springs, and the actual time of a change of direction can be as much as 1 to 2 hours different. Always check the direction and rate by noting the heading of the ships at anchor and the wash of the tidal stream past moored objects such as buoys. The eye tends to deceive; the actual strength of the stream in knots is not always as great as it appears to be.

Make an adequate allowance for cross-tidal stream and wind, because it is difficult to recover the track having been set downstream of it, especially when speed is reduced. The less the distance to the next 'wheel over' position, the larger must be the correction to regain track. If the ship is upstream of the line, there is no difficulty in regaining it.

An adequate allowance must be made for tidal streams and wind when turning; the 'wheel over' point may have to be adjusted as explained on page 357. Wind direction and strength affect not only the leeway but also the turning circle itself. A turn may have to be started early or late, using more or less wheel as appropriate, depending on the combined effects of stream and leeway on the turning circle.

Service to the Command

The Navigating Officer must anticipate the Captain's requirements and provide him with relevant information and situation reports. Such information should include:

> The headmark and its correct bearing.
> Whether on or off track. If off track, by how much, and the course required to regain.
> Distance and time to 'wheel over'.
> The minimum depth expected.
> The tidal stream and the likely effect of wind.
> Advice on the shipping situation.

Action on making a mistake

If a mistake has been made, report it immediately. If this leads to uncertainty about the ship's position, consider stopping the ship at once. The Navigating Officer must always be scrupulously honest and never try to bluff his way out of an uncertain situation. His Captain may not find him out, but the rocks and shoals will.

Checks before departure or arrival

Always observe the situation in the vicinity of the ship before leaving harbour. If alongside, the best way is to walk down the jetty checking the catamarans, the positions of adjacent ships, etc. The actual height of tide, the strength and direction of the tidal stream and the wind can be noted, and all these may lead to an adjustment of the plan.

Such a detailed check cannot be done on entering harbour, but the situation needs to be observed as accurately as possible.

Miscellaneous considerations in pilotage execution

Taking over the navigation

Take over the navigation of the ship in plenty of time. It is important to get settled in early, particularly at night or in poor visibility.

Using one's eyes

Although the execution of pilotage as presented in this chapter is a formal process involving extensive use of the compass, never neglect the eye. Use the eye to reinforce the plan; this is particularly important when assessing the actual effect of wind and tidal stream.

Making use of communications

Make full use of communications to assist in the execution of the plan. Examples are:

> Communications with the Port Authorities.
> Communications with the tugs, particularly to find out the conditions at the berth.
> Passing intentions to other shipping.

Personal equipment

The Navigating Officer should make certain that he has the necessary personal equipment available: Note Book, torch for use at night, polaroid sunglasses, binoculars, etc.

The shiphandling phase

Full details of the handling of ships are given in BR 67(3), *Admiralty Manual of Seamanship*, Volume III. Certain aspects are amplified below.

Planned speed reductions may have to be modified in the light of the conditions prevailing.

The extent to which the Navigating Officer assists the Captain in handling the ship when berthing and unberthing depends on the personal preferences of the Captain. The essential requirement is for the Navigating Officer to be fully prepared to handle the ship and to have readily available all the information pertinent to the manoeuvre—for example, the handling characteristics of the ship, the depth of water, direction and strength of tidal stream or current, length and line of berth, sea room available. During the manoeuvre he should be continuously watching the ship's movements ahead or astern, and in azimuth, and should be prepared to give the Captain the range of any object he wishes. He should ensure that the ship cannot drift unobserved into shoal water. He should check that the Captain's wheel and engine orders are correctly transmitted and obeyed. It he considers at any time that the ship is in danger, he must not hesitate to say so.

Pilotage mistakes

Mistakes often occur during pilotage. The most common ones are reflected below in a series of reminders to the Navigating Officer.

Do's

Do have the detailed planning and turning data in use cross-checked—particularly the tracks, 'wheel overs' and clearing bearings.

Do allow adequate clearances between the clearing bearing and the LDL.

Do obtain local knowledge if the charts and publications do not appear to be a sufficient guide, but always treat such knowledge with a proper degree of caution.

Do ensure that the organisation for lookouts, radar, echo sounder, etc. is adequate.

Do pay attention to the shipping situation in addition to the safe navigation, particularly in crowded harbours.

Do treat old surveys with a great deal of caution, particularly in coral regions.

Do treat the charted depths on isolated shoals with a great deal of caution. The depth could be much less than charted.

Do maintain the DR/EP from the fix up to the next 'wheel over' point; always know its time as well as the relevant bearing.

Do pay attention to the soundings and relate them to the soundings expected.

Do identify ('shoot up') the marks.

Do appreciate correctly which side of the track the ship is, and which way the correction must be made.

Do allow a sufficient correction for cross-tidal stream and wind, particularly during large turns.

Do regain track boldly. *Don't* nibble.

Do apply the gyro error correctly. *Don't* forget that the weakest point in modern gyro systems is the transmission system.

Do monitor large turns carefully throughout the turn, particularly in big ships.

Do allow plenty of room when rounding points or shoals—cutting corners can be dangerous. *Don't*, however, take a 'battleship sweep' at them—unless navigating a similarly large vessel.

Do remember the possibility of canal effect (*see* below).

Don'ts

Don't neglect the visual situation.

Don't request new courses without a visual check for navigational safety and shipping. *Don't* forget the quarter.

Don't press on in hope when there is uncertainty about the position. **Stop** instead.

Don't pass too close upwind or up tidal stream of dangers, anchored ships, buoys or other obstructions.

Don't attempt to 'cut in' ahead of other ships when approaching the harbour entrance.

NAVIGATION IN CANALS AND NARROW CHANNELS

Navigation in canals, rivers and similar narrow channels is often more an exercise in shiphandling than in pilotage. The effects on draught, speed, steering and the turning circle are much more pronounced than those experienced in more open shallow waters. The procedure when passing other ships is usually different from that in more open waters. These aspects are covered in BR 67(3), *Admiralty Manual of Seamanship*, Volume III.

When navigating in a canal, moderate speed should always be the rule to ensure that squat is not excessive. The critical speed of any particular ship in a canal, above which her steering becomes increasingly erratic because of shallow water effects, is termed *canal speed*. In the Suez Canal, for example, canal speed of the convoy is limited to about 7 to $7\frac{1}{2}$ knots and this is also related to maximum permissible draught and beam. Canal speed should never be exceeded.

Revolutions to achieve a particular ground speed will have to be higher than usual to counteract shallow water effect and the counter current set up by the ship's movement. For heavy ships this reduction in speed may be as much as 30% to 40%.

Passages through canals and other narrow channels should be planned and executed in a manner similar to other pilotage passages. The canal bank itself may be the limiting danger line and, while there may be a number of marks each side of the canal including milestones (or kilometre stones), there may often be no suitable headmark. The ship should normally be navigated in the centre of the channel so as to equalise the pressure distribution each side of the ship to prevent a sheer developing to either side. The ship should only be moved away from the centreline when it is necessary to pass ships coming in the opposite direction; the usual recommendation is to pass close aboard. Such practice helps to counteract the effect of the nearer bank and also makes it easier to regain the centre of the channel without inducing a sheer.

In some canals, the Suez Canal for example, sections are cut out of the bank to form sidings where one line of ships may be made fast while another line passes. There may be a tendency for the passing ships to veer into the siding, because of the sudden reduction of bank effect on that side of the ship, causing a collision with one of the berthed vessels. Such a tendency must be carefully guarded against.

The effects mentioned above apply mainly to large ships. Destroyers and frigates do not as a rule experience severe canal effects and can often proceed quite close to the bank of a canal, provided that speed is kept down to a moderate level.

All passages in canals must conform to local regulations, and it is essential to know and understand the local signals and communication arrangements. The *Sailing Directions* and amendments issued in Part IV of Admiralty Notices to Mariners and *ALRS*, Volume 6, are particularly important in this respect.

ANNEX A TO CHAPTER 13
Pilotage Check-off List

1. SELECT CHARTS	Largest scale.
	Fully corrected including Temporary and Preliminary Notices and warning messages.
2. SELECT PUBLICATIONS	*Sailing Directions.*
	Lists of Lights.
	Tide and tidal stream tables, etc.
3. ETA, ETD	Relevance to the pilotage plan.
4. SELECT LDL	Draw on charts for selected depth.
5. PASSAGE APPRAISAL	Clear mental picture.
	Study charts with *Sailing Directions, List of Lights*, etc.
	Note description of conspicuous objects and lights on the chart.
6. SELECT TRACKS	Starboard side of channel.
	Clear of dangers.
	Tidal stream and wind allowed for.
	Distance to go marked off.
	Suitable for night and blind conditions.
	Constrictions.
	Position of the Sun.
7. HEADMARKS	Transits.
	Line of bearing.
	Edge of land.
	Distance.
	No headmark available— bearing lattice, HSA lattice, fix and run.
8. ALTERING COURSE	'Wheel over' positions.
	Advance and transfer.
	DNC.
	'Wheel over' bearings—parallel to new course, high rate of bearing change; cross-tidal stream or current.
9. KEEPING CLEAR OF DANGER	Clearing bearings—displacement from LDL, box in navigable water.
	Vertical and horizontal danger angles.

		Echo sounder—clearing depth, depths below keel/waterline, height of tide.
10.	GYRO CHECKS	Transits, one on each leg.
11.	'SHOOTING UP'	Transits.
12.	POINT OF NO RETURN	Marked on chart.
13.	ALTERNATIVE ANCHOR BERTH	Suitable positions for emergencies/change of plan.
14.	NOTE BOOK	Relevant details of the plan. Sketch.
15.	CONNING	Navigating Officer taking over from Officer of the Watch; Captain from Navigating Officer.
16.	TUGS	How many, how secured, where to meet ship.
17.	BRIEFINGS	Captain. Other officers, warrant officers and senior ratings.

CHAPTER 14
Anchoring and Mooring

This chapter comprises detailed instructions for the planning and execution of anchoring and mooring.

In many ports or harbours, the shore authority allocates anchoring or mooring berths. There are, however, numerous occasions when the Navigating Officer is called on to select and pilot the ship to a suitable berth, particularly in out-of-the-way places visited by HM Ships.

Choosing a position in which to anchor

A number of factors have to be considered when choosing a position in which to anchor. The choice is governed very largely by matters of safety, but administrative or operational reasons may also have to be taken into account. These factors are:

> The depth of water.
> The length and draught of the ship.
> The amount of cable available.
> The type of holding ground.
> The proximity of dangers such as shoal waters, rocks, etc.
> The proximity of adjacent ships at anchor.
> The shelter from the weather given by the surrounding land.
> The strength and direction of the prevailing wind.
> The strength and direction of the tidal stream.
> The rise and fall of the tide.
> The proximity of landing places.

The depth of water

There must be an adequate depth of water under the ship at all times. If the stay is to last for more than a few hours, this safe depth must be available at all stages of the tide. A *limiting danger line* (LDL) (Fig. 14–1, p.384) must therefore be drawn for the anchorage area, taking into account the lowest height of tide during the stay.

Minimum clearance under the keel should as a rule be at least 2 metres at the lowest stage of the tide during the stay.

Swinging room when at anchor

A ship at anchor must have room to swing clear of dangers such as shoal water, rocks, etc. and also to swing clear of adjacent ships at anchor that are themselves swinging round in their berths.

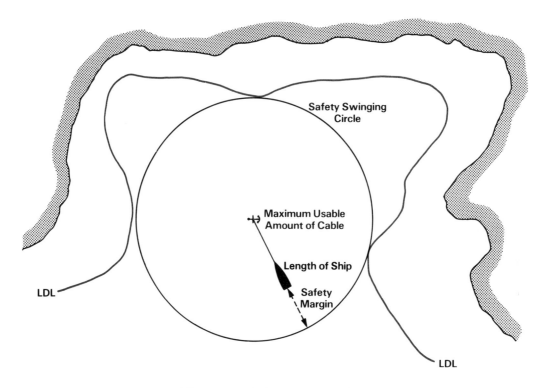

Fig. 14–1.   Safety swinging circle

Proximity of dangers

To be safe from rocks, shoals, etc., an anchorage position must be chosen so that the *safety swinging circle* (Fig. 14–1) is clear of the LDL. The radius of this circle may be obtained by adding the following:

1. The length of the ship.
2. The *maximum* amount of cable which can be veered on the selected anchor (remember that the last shackle of cable will normally be inboard of the hawse pipe). This allows for the veering of additional cable should the weather deteriorate, while still maintaining an adequate safety margin.
3. A *safety margin*. It is impossible to give any definite rule as to how near danger a ship may be anchored in safety. An ample safety margin must be allowed, in addition to (1) and (2) above. At single anchor, it is usual to allow at least one cable (1/10 mile), increased as necessary, to allow for:
   (a) The possibility that the ship may not achieve her intended anchoring position.
   (b) The likelihood of bad weather.
   (c) The likelihood of dragging.
   (d) The time between ordering the anchor to be let go and it hitting the bottom.

Anchoring by day in perfect visibility using a large-scale chart, in a flat calm with a conspicuous headmark and beam marks, should not present any great difficulty even to the inexperienced navigator. The possibility that the ship may not achieve her intended position is slight. But achieving the planned anchorage position in a minutely charted bay, at night, in a gale, with difficult marks when the final run-in is only 1 or 2 cables, is an entirely different matter.

The likelihood of dragging is dependent on: bad weather; whether the anchorage is open or sheltered; the strength and direction of the tidal stream; the nature of the bottom; the holding power of the anchor.

The ship is usually moving very slowly at the time of ordering the anchor to be let go, so the time for the anchor to reach the bottom may normally be disregarded.*

Rigid application of these considerations would preclude some anchorages which would be quite safe in good weather or in sheltered conditions or of a short duration. In such circumstances, it would be appropriate to accept a smaller margin of safety, consistent with prudence.

Suppose a ship of draught 7.1 m, length 155 m, with 10 shackles (275 m) of usable cable on each anchor, comes to single anchor. The minimum height of tide during the stay is predicted at 1.7 m. Assuming that the safety margin is $1\frac{1}{2}$ cables, her *safety swinging circle* (SSC) would be as in Table 14–1.

Table 14–1

	METRES	YARDS
Length of ship	155	170
Maximum usable cable	275	300
Safety margin	275	300
	———	———
Radius of SSC	705	770 *or* 3.85 cables

Thus, her berth must be at least 3.85 cables from the LDL. The charted depth of the LDL would be $7.1 + 2 - 1.7 = 7.4$ m, allowing for a minimum clearance of 2 m under the keel.

Amount of cable to be used

The amount of cable to be used (as opposed to the amount available) depends on a number of factors—the type of cable and anchor, the strength of the tidal stream and wind, the holding ground. This matter is discussed fully in BR 67(3), *Admiralty Manual of Seamanship*, Volume III.

The majority of HM Ships are fitted with forged steel cable and the AC 14 anchor, although minehunters and minesweepers are usually fitted with aluminium silicon bronze cable. Chapter 13 of *Admiralty Manual of Seamanship*, Volume III, gives details of the minimum amount of cable which should be laid out in various depths of water to ensure a horizontal pull at the anchor, based on the requirements of calm weather and a tidal stream of 5 knots.

* An anchor should take about 3 seconds to reach the bottom in 30 m of water. Assuming the whole operation from ordering 'Let go' to the anchor hitting the ground takes 6 seconds, a ship moving at 2 knots will only move 6 m during that time.

The amount of forged steel cable required for various depths may be calculated by the following rule, which allows a slight safety margin over the actual minimum necessary:

$$\text{amount of cable required (in shackles)} = 1\tfrac{1}{2} \sqrt{\text{depth (in metres)}} \qquad \ldots \textbf{14.1}$$

$$or \qquad = 2 \sqrt{\text{depth (in fathoms)}} \qquad \ldots \textbf{14.2}$$

For the heavier aluminium bronze cable, which requires less cable for the depth of water, the approximate rule is:

$$\text{amount of cable required (in shackles)} = \sqrt{\text{depth (in metres)}} \qquad \ldots \textbf{14.3}$$

$$or \qquad = \sqrt{1.3 \; \text{depth (in fathoms)}} \qquad \ldots \textbf{14.4}$$

The depths referred to above should normally include the maximum height of tide expected during the time the ship is at anchor. In strong winds or in very strong tidal streams, more cable will usually be required.

In good holding ground such as clay, soft chalk, sand, sand/shingle, the holding power of the AC 14 anchor is approximately 10 times its own weight. In very good holding ground such as a mixture of sand, shingle and clay or really heavy mud, the holding power may be as much as $12\tfrac{1}{2}$ times. In poor ground such as soft silty mud or shingle and shell, holding power may be as little as 6 times. Rock, coral and weed are particularly bad types of holding ground.

Distance from other ships

The anchorage position should be selected to ensure there is no danger of fouling other ships as they swing round their anchors. The *minimum* swinging radius to allow against such an occurrence (Fig. 14–2) is the length of the ship plus the length of cable veered. Thus, the distance apart of adjacent ships should be twice the minimum radius; this should be sufficient to allow the following events to take place without danger or difficulty:

1. A ship may approach and anchor in the line without finding an adjacent ship swung over the point where her anchor is to go.
2. A ship anchored in the line may weigh anchor alone without fouling other ships.
3. Two adjacent ships may swing towards each other and at the same time have their cables drawn out to their fullest extent. This is, however, most unlikely to occur since, if there is a strong wind or stream, the ships will be lying parallel and drawing out their cables in the same direction. If the ships

Table 14–2

	METRES	YARDS
Length of ship	155	170
Length of cable veered	165	180
(say, 6 shackles)	——	——
Minimum swinging radius	320	350 *or* $1\tfrac{3}{4}$ cables
Distance of ships apart	640	700 *or* $3\tfrac{1}{2}$ cables

Fig. 14–2. Minimum swinging radius for ships at anchor (1): ships at two radii apart

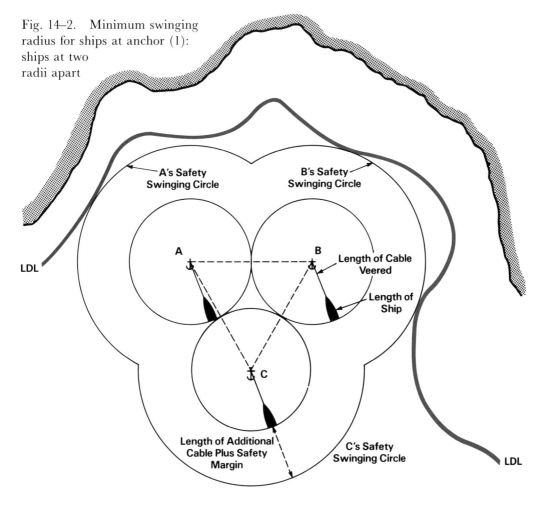

AB: Minimum Swinging Radius of A + Minimum Swinging Radius of B
BC: Minimum Swinging Radius of B + Minimum Swinging Radius of C
AC: Minimum Swinging Radius of A + Minimum Swinging Radius of C

swing in opposite directions, it is probably because the tidal stream is on the turn and almost slack, and the wind at the same time is light, so that their cables are not laid out towards one another.

The distance apart of two similar ships may be calculated as in Table 14–2. Space in harbours is often scarce and therefore it is seldom that the distance apart of two radii, to allow for the third event above, can be allowed. If the berths of adjacent ships are placed at one radius apart, however (Fig. 14–3, p.388), both the other two events can occur without difficulty. It is therefore customary to place the berths of similiar ships at one radius apart, e.g. A and B in Fig. 14–3. Ships must be on their guard against swinging towards one another, but the risk is small. However, if two ships of dissimilar classes are berthed next to one another, e.g. A and C in Fig. 14–3, the distance between their berths should be at least that of the radius required for the larger of the two ships.

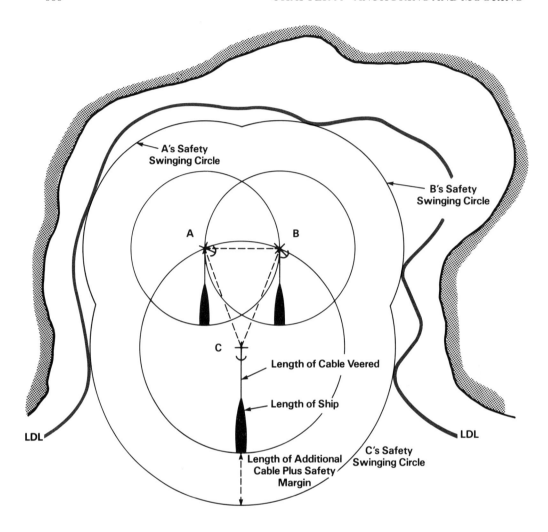

AB: Minimum Swinging Radius for A and B (Similar Ships)
AC, BC: Minimum Swinging Radius for C (the Larger Ship)

Fig. 14–3.   Minimum swinging radius for ships at anchor (2): ships at one radius apart

Reducing swinging radius

If space is particularly restricted, the distance apart of ships may be reduced by allowing a *minimum* radius (Fig. 14–4) equal to the length of the ship plus 45 metres (50 yards). In the example given above, the minimum swinging radius would be as in Table 14–3.

Care must be taken to ensure that anchor cables of adjacent ships do not foul each other, and the anchoring margin may have to be increased accordingly.

It should be noted that the safety swinging circles of the ships do not change when the swinging radius is reduced.

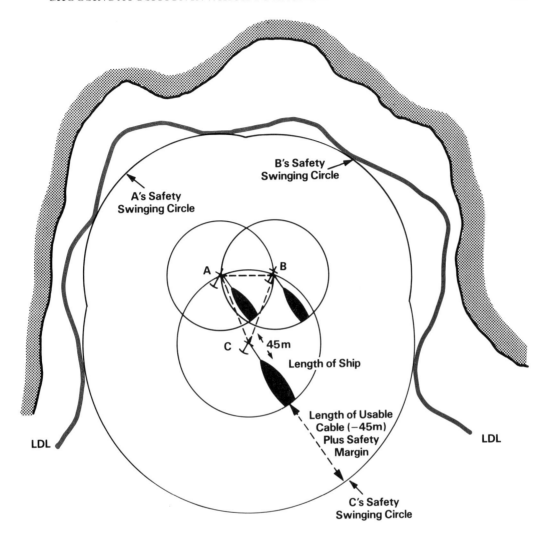

AB: Reduced Swinging Radius for A and B
AC, BC: Reduced Swinging Radius for C (C's Length + 45m)

Fig. 14–4.   Reduced swinging radius for ships at anchor

Table 14–3

	METRES	YARDS
Length of ship	155	170
Anchoring margin	45	50
Minimum radius	200	220 *or* 1.1 cables

Anchoring a ship in a chosen position

Planning the approach

Before choosing the position in which to anchor the ship, the limiting danger line should be drawn on the chart round the anchorage and its approach. The anchorage position may now be chosen taking into account the factors mentioned earlier. The anchorage plan can then be prepared.

This is illustrated in Fig. 14–5 for a frigate anchoring in Plymouth Sound. An LDL for 7 metres and a safety swinging circle (SSC) of 2.65 cables have been determined as follows:

Table 14–4

SSC		LDL	
Waterline length	120 yards	Draught	6 m
(anchor to stern)		Safety margin	2 m
7 shackles usable cable	210		——
Safety margin	200	Total	8 m
	——	Minimum height of	
Total	530 yards	tide during stay	1 m
			——
SSC	= 2.65 cables	LDL	= 7 m

1. Draw the clearing bearings to box in the approach and the anchorage. Remember to allow a safe clearance from the LDL (*see* page 358).
2. Select the headmark, and the approach course to the chosen position, clear of all dangers. A transit is preferable to a single mark (*see* page 349 for choice of headmarks). Do not allow the choice of a conspicuous headmark to override the need for a safe approach course.

   The approach course to the anchorage should be long enough to allow plenty of time to get the ship steady on the correct line. For a frigate or destroyer, the approach course may be as short as a few cables and still achieve an accurate anchorage.
3. From the position of the anchor, lay back the distance between the anchor and the pelorus (often known as 'stem to standard') to establish the 'let go' position on the chart, as shown in Fig. 14–5. This distance should be available from the Navigational Data Book and should be recorded in the Note Book.
4. From the 'let go' position, mark back the distance to run, in cables. This is usually done for every cable out to 5 cables from the anchorage and then as necessary, as shown in Fig. 14–5. One mile to go and distances at which speed is to be reduced should always be marked.
5. Select good beam marks to establish distance to go. This is particularly important for the 'let go' position. Select suitable marks for the anchorage fix.
6. Note predicted tidal stream and wind, and calculate the allowance needed for them.

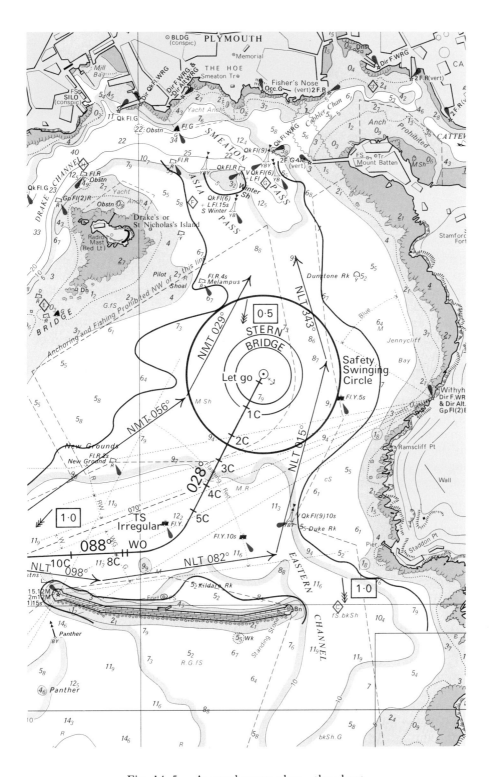

Fig. 14–5. An anchorage plan—the chart

7. Note the minimum depth expected on each leg.
8. Decide which anchor to use and what length of cable is likely to be required.
9. Mark 'wheel over' position and select 'wheel over' marks.
10. Prepare an alternative approach to the anchorage in case the run-in is fouled; prepare also an alternative anchorage is case the one selected is occupied. (This is not illustrated in Fig. 14–5.)
11. Re-check that the safety swinging circle is clear of the LDL.
12. Insert the necessary data in the Note Book, as shown in Fig. 14–6.
13. Brief the Captain on the plan and the alternative. Adjust the plan if necessary. Brief the OOW, Navigating Officer's assistant, etc.

Approach to an anchor berth: reduction of speed

It is easier to anchor in the exact berth if steerage way can be maintained up to the moment of anchoring. If ships are anchoring in company, it is essential to keep steerage way to permit ships to maintain station. For these reasons, HM Ships usually anchor with headway and lay out the cable under the ship. This method is known as the *running anchorage*.

When anchoring with headway, the speed when letting go should not be more than 2 to 3 knots over the ground. Too high a speed may strain or even part the cable, while too low a speed will prolong the operation unduly.

The alternative to anchoring with headway is to stop in the berth or just beyond it and then, having let go the anchor, go astern laying out the cable. This is known as the *dropping anchorage*; it is usually adopted by merchant vessels and, for any HM Ship anchoring independently, this method may well be more seamanlike than the running anchorage. HM Ships with underwater fittings near the forefoot are obliged to use the dropping anchorage to prevent the cable being laid out under the ship and damaging these fittings. For the same reason, these ships are not permitted to moor.

The *advantages* of the dropping anchorage over the running anchorage are:

1. The cable is laid out downwind and/or downstream (the running method being into the wind and/or stream). This is the best direction for modern anchors and cables, and there is less risk of damage to the protective bottom composition and underwater fittings.
2. There is less risk of tumbling or slewing the anchor as the ship lays back on the wind and/or stream after letting go. (When carrying out a running anchorage, this risk is reduced if the wind and/or stream are well on the bow when letting go, since the result will be to widen the bight of cable.)
3. There is less likelihood of dragging after letting go through premature snubbing by the cable officer.
4. There is less wear on the hawsepipe and cable, and less chance of damage, since the cable does not turn so sharply at the bottom of the hawsepipe while it is being laid out.
5. The ship usually gets her cable more quickly.

The *disadvantages* of the dropping anchorage as compared to the running anchorage are:

Distance	Course/ Speed	Remarks	Range of Bovisand Pier	Dist to W.O.	Min Depth
	088°	on Bovisand Pier Light			12.8m
10C	10	Breakwater⊥ stbd 1.1C	11.1C	2.1C	
		Breakwater Lt. 194°		(1m 15s)	
8C		→⊣ Fort 139½°	9.1C	0.1C	
	028°	W.O. Mount Batten Tr φ ⊱ Large conspic gasholder 033°. Bovisand Pier 9.0C. C Buoy⊥ port 0.75C throughout final part of turn. on Mount Batten Tr ⊱ Western gasholder (Large conspic gasholder open right) Ramscliff Pt.⊥ stbd 4.9C.			

Distance	Speed	→⊣ Staddon Hts. Wall	Withyhedge Beacon	Range of Mt. Batten B'water		Depth
5C		086°	065°	12.8C		14m
4C		091°	069°	11.8C		
3C		097½°	073½°	10.8C		11.6m
2C	slow ahead	104½°	079°	9.8C		
1½ C		108½°	082½°	9.3C		
1C		112°	086°	8.8C		11.1m
½ C	half astern	116°	090°	8.3C		
Let go		120°	094°	7.8C		10m

Anchorage details:	Depth:	8m + 2m tide = 10m.
	Bottom:	Mud-holding ground good.
	T.S.:	190° 0.5 knots.
	Wind:	Westerly 5–10 knots.
Port anchor.	1.5√ 12 :	5 shackles.

Anchorage Fix:	→⊣ Staddon Heights Wall Withyhedge Beacon Mount Batten Tr White Turret Building (conspic)	Depth Ship's Hd. Time

Fig. 14–6.   An anchorage plan—the Note Book

1. Shiphandling is less precise in the final stages because way is taken off the ship in the last part of the approach.
2. The cable is not laid out in a bight upwind and/or upstream as it is with a running anchorage, and so cannot absorb the strain gradually as the ship falls back on her cable. This was more important with the old Admiralty Standard Stockless anchor, where the heavier cable provided a larger share of the holding power.
3. The final moments of anchoring take longer and the operation may not look so smart as a briskly executed running anchorage.

Table 14–5.   Reduction of speed on approach to an anchor berth

Distance from Berth in Cables	Speed and Engine Orders							
	HM Ship HERMES	Invincible Class Carriers*	Assault Ships	County Class Destroyer	Sheffield Class Destroyer*	Broadsword Class Frigate*	Amazon Class Frigate*	Leander Class Frigate
10	8 knots	10 knots	8 knots	10 knots	10 knots	10 knots	10 knots	12 knots
8								
6		Slow ahead	Slow ahead					
5								
4	Stop							
3		Stop	Stop					
2¼						Slow ahead		
2	Slow astern			Stop	Slow ahead		Slow ahead	Stop
1½	Slow astern	Half astern						
1	Slow astern							
¾					Half astern	Half astern		Astern power as necessary
½							Half astern	Astern power as necessary
In Berth			Half astern	Half astern				Astern power as necessary

*For these classes of ship, information is for a dropping anchorage

A rough guide to the reduction of speed on approach to an anchor berth for various classes of ship is given in Table 14–5. Modifying factors such as wind and current must always be taken into account.

Executing the anchorage plan

Most of the remarks on the execution of pilotage (page 366) apply equally to the execution of the anchorage plan. Particular points relevant to anchoring are:

1. Check as far in advance as possible that the berth and the planned approach to it are clear. Plot anchored ships to confirm this. (*See* page 400 for an example.)
2. Keep a constant check on the speed required to meet the ETA. This is usually the time of anchoring.
3. Allow additional aim-off for cross-wind and tidal stream as the speed of the ship is reduced, in order to make good the correct line of approach. This is

particularly necessary in heavy ships, which may have to reduce speed early in the approach. This is also particularly important when executing a dropping anchorage, where the aim-off in the last few cables will need to be approximately double that for a running anchorage.

4. As a general rule, try to anchor with the wind or tidal stream (whichever is the stronger) slightly on the bow. In a frigate, the effect of 1 knot of tidal stream is roughly equivalent to 20 knots of wind (page 348).

5. Normally plan to use the weather anchor. It is sometimes better to use the lee anchor in places where the stream is so strong that the ship lies more easily to the lee anchor. The lee anchor may be used when the wind is across the stream, otherwise the ship may fall across the weather anchor in the process of getting her cable, thus causing dragging. If other ships are already at anchor, it is usually possible, by observing their cable, to see which is the better anchor to use.

6. If anchoring with the wind abeam, it is often a good plan to cant the bow into the wind using maximum rudder just before reaching the anchorage position.

7. The anchor and the amount of cable to be used are normally planned beforehand. Be prepared to adjust both of these depending on the conditions encountered.

8. When on course for the anchorage, it is usually better to give the Quartermaster the course to steer rather than to con him on to it. This leaves more time for observing marks, ships, etc.

9. Remember the sun's position (*see* page 349).

10. Information which the Captain particularly requires in addition to that given on page 377 includes:

> Depth of water.
> Nature of the bottom.
> State of the tide on anchoring.
> Rise and fall of the tide during the intended stay.
> Tidal stream on anchoring.
> Forecast and actual wind and relative direction on anchoring.
> Recommended anchor and scope of cable.
> Landing places and their distance from the ship.

11. Fix the ship on letting go the anchor—take beam bearings first for accuracy—obtain a sounding and note the ship's head and time. The sounding provides a check that sufficient cable is being used.

12. The Captain normally works the anchor flags. These are red and green hand-flags, denoting port or starboard anchor respectively. To avoid any chance of prematurely letting go the anchor, the flag should be exhibited steadily from a prominent position at 'Stand by' *for a few seconds only* before 'Let go', when it should be dropped smartly.

13. As the way is taken off the ship, the Navigating Officer must observe what the ship is doing, either by beam bearings or by objects in transit, and report this to the Captain.

14. The correct method of entering details of anchoring in the Ship's Log and Note Book is as follows:

> '*Came to port (starboard)* ⚓ *with*——*shackles in*——*metres/fathoms in No.* ——*Berth* (or *in position* ——)'.

15. The anchor bearings entered in the Ship's Log should be for the position of the anchor and not of the bridge on letting go.

16. Once the position of the anchor has been plotted, using the fix taken at the time of letting go, the direction of the ship's head at anchoring and the stem to standard distance, then:

   (*a*) The safety swinging circle should be re-plotted to confirm it is still clear of the LDL. In Fig. 14–5, the radius is 530 yards (*see* page 390).

   (*b*) The bridge and stern swinging circles should be plotted for the amount of cable veered. In Fig. 14–5 the radii are 195 and 270 yards respectively, arrived at as in Table 14–6.

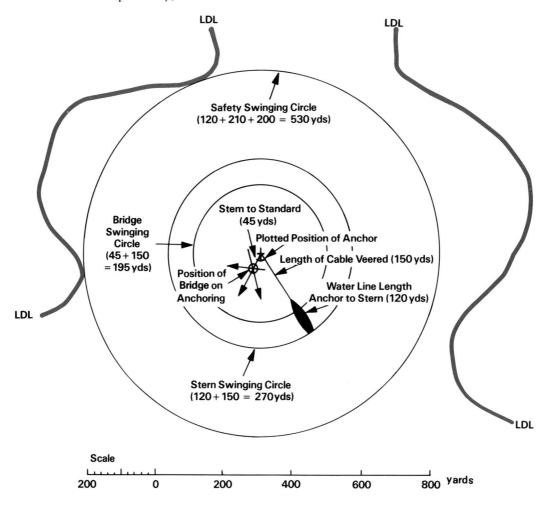

Fig. 14–7. Plotting the bridge, stern and safety swinging circles from the anchorage fix

Table 14–6

BRIDGE SWINGING CIRCLE		STERN SWINGING CIRCLE	
Length (stem to standard)	45 yards	Waterline length (anchor to stern)	120 yards
No. of shackles veered (5)	150 yards	No. of shackles veered (5)	150 yards
Radius of swinging circle	—— 195 yards	Radius of swinging circle	—— 270 yards

The plotting of the bridge, stern and safety swinging circles, using the above figures, is illustrated in Fig. 14–7.

Fixes of the position of the bridge must always lie inside the bridge swinging circle; if they lie outside, the ship must be dragging. Drawing the stern swinging circle for the amount of cable veered gives a clear indication of how much safe water there is available all round between the ship and the LDL.

(c) The distances of other ships at anchor or at buoys should be checked to confirm that there is no danger of fouling them.

Anchoring in deep water, in a wind or in a tidal stream

Fuller details of anchoring in deep water, in a wind and in a tidal stream are given in Chapter 13 of BR 67(3), *Admiralty Manual of Seamanship*, Volume III.

Anchoring in deep water

Cable must be veered (perhaps 1 shackle or even more) before letting go. The maximum safe speed of certain classes of HM Ships with cable veered is limited, while other classes, because of their underwater fittings, must stop and take all their way off, before veering cable.

When anchoring in fjords which are steep-to, with deep water reaching almost to the sides, special procedures are necessary. The bottom is often rock covered by a layer of silt and is frequently uneven. Depths can change considerably over a short distance. The holding ground is often poor. The depth of water is such that the standard rules for the amount of cable cannot be used—for example, anchoring in 60 fathoms (110 metres) requires at least $13\frac{1}{2}$ to 14 shackles. This amount of cable may not be available unless a ship so fitted is able to use both cables on one anchor. A ship with, say, 9 shackles of cable available will only be able to put about 4 shackles on the bottom in 60 fathoms (110 metres) of water. Thus, the holding power of the anchor will be considerably reduced, perhaps by as much as 60% to 70%, and account of this must be taken.

When an anchorage of this nature has to be planned, it may be preferable to assign an anchorage area of about 4 to 6 cables diameter within which the ship may anchor at her discretion, rather than allocate a precise position. It is desirable to have at least two charted soundings of about 50 fathoms (90 metres) or less within the area. If time allows, the ship should make several echo sounder passes through the area to identify the optimum position. Having found a suitable position, the ship should approach it at as slow a speed as effective steerage way will allow. Several shackles of cable may have to be veered before letting go and this should be done at minimum speed (2 to 3 knots) or when stopped in the anchorage position.

Anchoring in a tidal stream

A high contrary wind is necessary to overcome the effect of only a moderate stream; it is therefore more seamanlike to anchor into the stream. Anchoring with a following tidal stream of more than $\frac{1}{2}$ knot is not usually recommended, particularly in a heavy ship of deep draught, because of the strain on the cable and the cable holders, which is greatest as the ship swings athwart the stream.

Heavy weather in harbour

Advice on the action to be taken in heavy weather in harbour is to be found in Chapter 15 of BR 67(3), *Admiralty Manual of Seamanship*, Volume III.

Letting go second anchor

Should a gale arise while riding at single anchor, the ship will normally yaw to an extent dependent on her size and above-water design. At the end of each yaw, violent and sudden strains are brought on the cable, thus considerably increasing the chances of dragging.

To prevent dragging, either more cable should be veered on the existing anchor or a second anchor should be dropped to stop the yaw, or a mixture of these two methods should be used. Some HM Ships are fitted with only one length of cable or only one anchor, in which case they have little alternative but to veer more cable or get underway.

Remember to redraw the bridge and stern swinging circles if more cable is veered.

Dragging

Whether or not the ship is dragging may be confirmed by selecting a pair of fixed objects on the beam and in transit. Such objects need not be charted. The transit may be tested by walking along the deck to see if it opens quickly enough.

The safest method of discovering whether or not the ship is dragging is to fix by sextant angles or compass bearings. The fixes of the position of the bridge should always lie within the bridge swinging circle drawn for the length of cable veered. As mentioned earlier, if they fall outside the ship is dragging.

Anchoring at a definite time without altering speed

It is always desirable to anchor the ship at the correct or advertised time; but a drastic increase or decrease of speed may not be possible or desirable, and it is therefore as well to plan the approach in such a way that the distance remaining to be steamed can be adjusted by an alteration of course.

The following simple method of dealing with this problem enables the chart to be prepared beforehand; the navigator can see at a glance, whenever he fixes the ship's position, whether he is ahead or astern of time; and last-minute alterations of speed can be avoided.

EXAMPLE

A ship has signalled her time of anchoring at a position A (Fig. 14–8) as 0800. She proposes to approach the anchorage on a course 180°. Her speed of approach will be 12 knots, and will not be altered until the engines are stopped at 3 cables from position A.

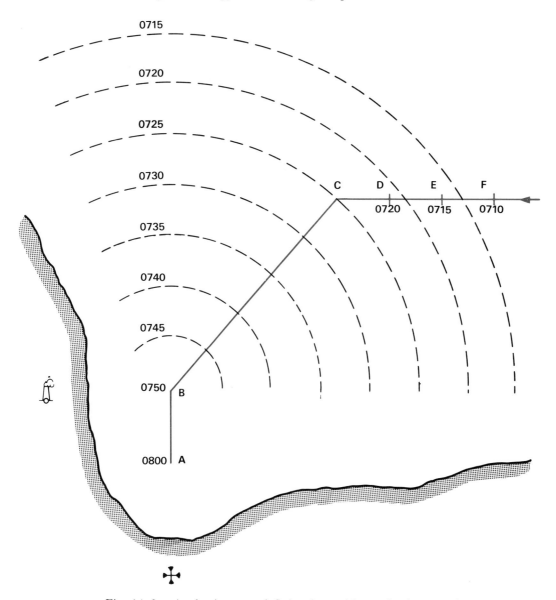

Fig. 14–8. Anchoring at a definite time without altering speed

To prepare the chart, calculate the distance the ship will run in the 10 minutes prior to anchoring, making allowance for stopping engines 3 cables from *A*.

Lay back this distance *AB* along the line of approach. *B* is then the position to be attained at 0750.

Since 5 minutes at 12 knots is equivalent to 1 mile, with centre B lay back 5-minute time circles. The chart is now prepared, and at 0710 the ship, steering 270° speed 12 knots, fixes her position at F.

At 0715 she is in position E, inside the 0715 circle. Similarly, at 0720 she is at D, inside the 0720 circle; but it is seen that at 0725 she will arrive at C, on the 0725 circle, at which time it will be necessary to steer the course CB in order to arrive at B at 0750.

Ensuring that the anchor berth is clear

When approaching an anchorage, always make sure that the anchor berth and line of approach are clear of other ships. Check the position of any ship suspected of fouling the anchor berth by one or other of these two methods:

1. Fix own position and plot the other ship by radar range and visual bearing, or take a radar range and bearing of the ship from a charted radar conspicuous object on the radar display.
2. Take a bearing of the other ship when it is in transit with a charted shore object, so obtaining a position line on which the other ship must lie. This should be done as early as possible and before altering to the approach course, so that a second or third position line may be obtained by observing the bearing of the ship in transit with other charted shore objects. The position of the other ship may then be fixed, as shown in the following example.

EXAMPLE

A ship (Fig. 14–9), steering 080° and intending to anchor in position Z by approaching the anchorage on a course 350°, suspects that a ship D is foul of her berth. At 1100 the ship is observed in transit with a chimney bearing 050°. At 1105 the ship is observed in transit with a flagstaff bearing 026°, and at 1107½ with the church bearing 000°.

From these three lines of bearing, D's position may be plotted on the chart. The position of D's anchor must then be estimated, after allowance has been made for the wind and stream at the time.

Anchoring in a poorly charted area

If there is no accurate chart of the anchorage, and the suitability of the berth is in any doubt, take careful soundings within a radius of at least 3 cables of the ship to make certain there are no uncharted rocks or dangers.

Anchoring in company

HM Ships frequently have to anchor in company and full details may be found in Volume IV of this manual and also in BR 67(3), *Admiralty Manual of Seamanship*, Volume III. Various points to remember are set out below:

1. If ships of dissimilar type are manoeuvring together, the tactical diameter which is to be used must be signalled to all ships so that they are aware how much rudder they will require, dependent on their own turning characteristics.
2. The normal manoeuvering intervals between lines of ships may have to be reduced considerably if ships are to anchor in formation.

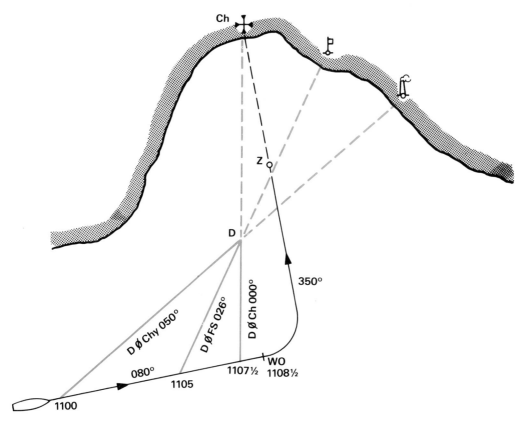

Fig. 14–9. 'Shooting up' a ship at anchor

3. A running anchorage rather than a dropping one is to be preferred. It is much easier for ships to maintain station as shiphandling is more precise. However, if some of the ships in company are obliged to carry out a dropping anchorage (page 392), then it is probably best for all ships to carry out the same procedure. This means that alterations of course together in the final stages of the approach to allow for tidal stream are likely to apply correctly for all ships. Remember that wind will have different effects when ships are dissimilar. If the same anchoring procedure is used in all ships, anchor cables will all be laid out in the same direction, so once the ships have all got their cable, they will 'look right'. In the final stages of a dropping anchorage, it becomes progressively more difficult to maintain station; the best course of action is to use the second method referred to in *Admiralty Manual of Seamanship*, Volume III—ships are ordered to anchor in the allocated berth ·'in accordance with previous instructions' as convenient.

4. When planning the anchor berths for other ships, their 'let go' bearings should if possible be clear of other ships.

5. The Senior Officer's anchor berth and those of ships in formation should be signalled early.

6. The Senior Officer's intentions (approach course, etc.) should also be

signalled early, so that other ships can prepare their own charts and appreciate what the Senior Officer is trying to achieve.

7. The anchoring formation should be taken up in good time, so that alterations of course can be made by turns together, a much simpler procedure than wheeling.

8. If possible, plan on a long run-in on the final approach course to the anchorage. This gives other ships plenty of time to settle down in their station.

9. On the final run-in, adjust course as necessary by turns of 5° or 10° to port or starboard. These alterations can be ordered in advance by flag or voice and executed as required.

10. Ships must be ready to anchor individually if ordered, and each Navigating Officer should have prepared the necessary plan to do so.

Mooring ship

Most modern HM Ships are unable to moor because of design limitations and the times when older ships are required to do so are rare. The procedure has, however, been retained and is set out below. A ship may often find it necessary to plan on letting go two anchors in predetermined positions, for example if carrying out a *Mediterranean moor*,* and the procedures set out below will generally apply.

Swinging room when moored

The object of mooring is to conserve space: the minimum swinging radius may be taken as the ship's length plus a mooring margin of at least 18 metres (20 yards). Table 14–7 gives an example.

Table 14–7

	METRES	YARDS
Length of ship	155	170
Mooring margin	18	20
Minimum swinging radius	173	190 *or* 0.95 cables

Care must be taken that anchor cables of adjacent ships do not foul each other; the mooring margin may have to be increased accordingly, dependent on the amount of cable veered on each anchor. When planning mooring berths, it must be remembered that ships may have to moor or unmoor independently, whatever the direction of the wind or tidal stream. Thus, the berths may have to be planned at an even greater distance apart. Furthermore, a safety margin of at least 1 cable from any charted danger must be added to the radius of each berth.

* A *Mediterranean moor* is a method of securing a ship at right angles to the jetty, the stern secured to it by hawsers, the bow being held by two anchors out ahead, one on each bow. (*See* Chapter 13 of BR 67(3), *Admiralty Manual of Seamanship,* Volume III for full details.)

Planning the approach

The same principles apply as for anchoring, modified as follows. The final stages of the mooring plan are illustrated in Fig. 14–10 (page 404) and show the position of each anchor relative to the stem.

1. First decide the length of each cable on each anchor when the ship is moored. As a general rule, this should be at least 5 times the depth of water. For example a ship mooring in 20 metres (11 fathoms) should use a minimum of about $3\frac{1}{2}$ shackles on each anchor. Heavy ships should always use a minimum of 5 shackles on each anchor in any case.

   One shackle is usually required to go round the bow so that the mooring swivel may be inserted. The distance between the two anchors when let go should therefore be the combined length of cable to be used on each anchor less one shackle. For example, a ship using 5 shackles on each anchor should allow a distance of $(5 \times 2) - 1$ or 9 shackles (270 yards) between the anchor positions. In Fig. 14–10, the distance of each anchor from the middled position A would be $\frac{1}{2} \times 270 = 135$ yards.

2. The direction of the line joining the anchors should coincide, if possible, with that of the prevailing wind or tidal stream; and each anchor should be sufficiently far from dangers, and from the anchors of other ships, to enable it to be weighed without inconvenience whatever the direction of the wind.

Executing the mooring plan

1. Reduce speed so that the cable on the first anchor is laid out straight and all way is taken off the ship as the second anchor is let go.

2. The second anchor can be let go from either the forecastle or the bridge. Given good marks, less than 1 mile distant, the precise moment when the bridge arrives at the correct position will be known; but even if the cable is tautly laid out, it will usually be found that the appropriate shackle, the ninth in the above example, has not reached, or is already outside, the hawsepipe when the second anchor bearing comes on. It is recommended, therefore, that the second anchor be let go by a mixture of 'bearing' and 'shackles', in an endeavour to drop it as near as possible to the right position without giving the cable officer an impossible task when middling.

   There will be occasions when middling accurately in the assigned berth is of more importance than middling with the correct number of shackles on each cable.

3. Let go the weather anchor first, in order to keep the cable clear of the stem when middling.

4. The ship must make good the correct course between anchors while the first cable is being laid out.

5. Always avoid excessive strain on the cables.

6. In order to cant the ship in the right direction for middling, the wheel may be put over about 2 or 3 shackles before letting go the second anchor, without having any appreciable effect on the berth.

7. Remember that the stem of the ship will fall well to leeward of the line of anchors when lying at open hawse.

EXAMPLE

A ship is ordered to moor with 5 shackles on each anchor in position A (Fig. 14–10). Stem to standard: 40 yards.

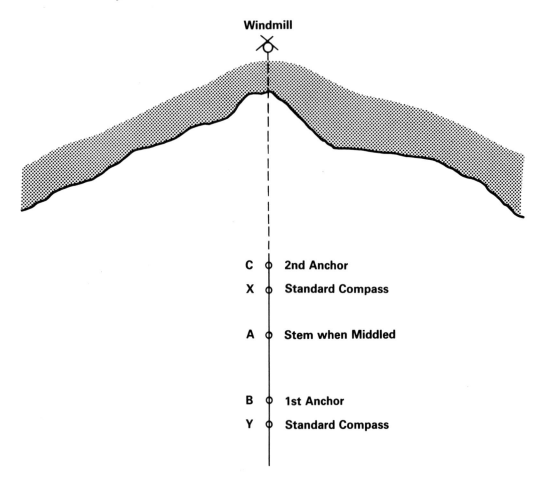

Fig. 14–10.   Mooring in a chosen position

It is decided to approach with the windmill ahead on a line of bearing. This line of bearing will be the 'line of anchors' when the ship is moored.

From A lay off $AB = AC = \dfrac{(2 \times 5) - 1}{2} \times 30$ yards $= 135$ yards

B and C will be the positions of the first and second anchors.

From B and C lay distances of 40 yards to Y and X.

Y and X are the positions of the standard compass at the moments of letting go the first and second anchor respectively.

CHAPTER 15
Radar, Blind Pilotage

This chapter contains advice on the use of radar for navigation and blind pilotage. Naval users should also be conversant with BR 1853, *Radar Manual*, which contains information necessary for a proper understanding of radar, in particular:

> The transmission of radio waves, range and range discrimination, bearing and bearing discrimination.
> The radar receiver, video signals, displays.
> Propagation and reflection.
> Capabilities and limitations.

Some of this information is amplified below.

Naval users should also refer to BR 1982, *Warning Radar Instructions*, for detailed information on the various navigational radar sets and the video distribution systems in service in the Royal Navy.

Non-Naval users should refer to standard works on radar such as *The Use of Radar at Sea*.

The chapter concludes with remarks on radar beacons, shore-based radar, and the use of radar in ice.

RADAR WAVES: TRANSMISSION, RECEPTION, PROPAGATION AND REFLECTION

Radar detection

Sufficient pulses must strike an object during one sweep of the radar to produce a detectable response, and the usual minimum for this is 6 to 8 pulses. The number of pulses N striking an object during one sweep of the aerial may be found from the formula:

$$N = \frac{BW \text{ (in degrees)}}{360} \times \frac{60}{\text{aerial rotation speed (in rev/min)}} \times PRF \quad \dots \textbf{15.1}$$

For a 3 cm radar with a beam width (BW) of 1°, aerial rotation of 24 rev/min and a pulse repetition frequency (PRF) of 1000 pulses per second:

$$N = \frac{1}{360} \times \frac{60}{24} \times 1000 = 7$$

i.e. 7 pulses every $2\frac{1}{2}$ seconds, or 168 pulses per minute.

Because the object usually has a cross-sectional area relative to the radar beam, the number of pulses will be increased and the response will therefore be improved. Thus, for a 3 cm radar, the data rate (the rate at which contact information is supplied by the radar) is high. When combined with a narrow beam and short pulses, this permits accurate bearing and range measurement. The number of pulses per aerial sweep is normally high enough to ensure positive detection.

There are, however, factors which affect detection: the reflecting area of the object, attenuation, clutter, etc. The operator must apply a *threshold level* of signal, largely determined by experience, to help him decide whether a paint represents an object or not. There is no absolute guarantee that the echoes being observed do actually indicate objects, or that objects are not hidden in the clutter. The operator may, on occasion, select as an object an echo at relatively short range which is in fact caused by noise or clutter, while at long range he may initially ignore an echo because of its apparent random nature when in fact it is an object at maximum detection range.

These factors become important where computer-based automatic detection is concerned. A receiver output level has to be selected as the threshold level. If the level is set too low, then random noise exceeding the level may be received and an object will be indicated, thus creating a false alarm. On the other hand, if the level is set too high, while there may be no false alarms, small objects giving a poor echo response may well be missed altogether.

Range discrimination and minimum range

Range discrimination equals half the pulse length and may be found from the following formula:

$$\text{range discrimination} = 164 \times \text{pulse length} \qquad \dots \mathbf{15.2}$$
$$\text{(in yards)} \qquad\qquad\qquad \text{(in } \mu\text{s)}$$

For example, the range discrimination of a radar set with a pulse length of 0.25 microseconds (μs) is 41 yards.

Minimum range, theoretically, equals the range discrimination of the set for the pulse length in use and, provided that a twin-aerial system is used, the two values should be the same. However, if a common-aerial system is used, minimum range will be approximately twice the range discrimination, owing to the momentary saturation of the receiver by the transmitted pulse. The minimum range (the ground wave) should always be noted by the user for the particular set in the prevailing conditions.

Beam width and bearing discrimination

Beam width causes distortion of the radar picture to an extent approximating to half the beam width, as illustrated in Fig. 15–1. The picture of the coastline on the radar display is a distortion of the true area, as shown by the shaded areas (it is purposely exaggerated for the sake of illustration). Small islands or rocks close to the coast, or inlets, will merge into the general echo if the beam width is large enough.

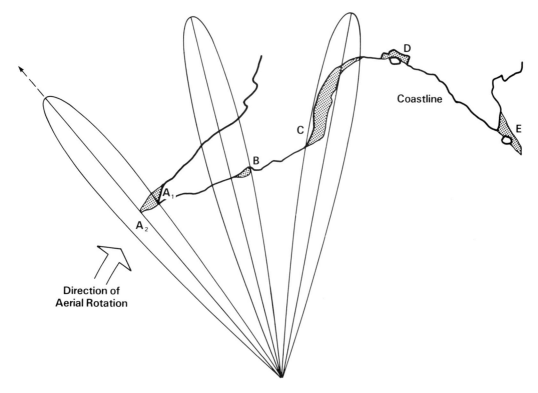

Fig. 15–1.   Distortion caused by beam width

If radar bearings of edges of the land are observed (e.g. A_2 in Fig. 15–1), they must be corrected for half the beam width.

This distortion is minimised in navigational radars by keeping the beam width, and hence the bearing discrimination, down to the order of 1°.

Video signals

Bandwidth

In a navigational radar, accurate ranging is essential; thus, the bandwidth must be wide at the expense of greater noise and loss of maximum range.

Amplification

There may be a choice of *linear* (LIN), *logarithmic* (LOG) or *processed log/lin* amplification.

LIN amplification is ideal for long-range detection and for use in calm conditions when sea clutter is minimal. Sea clutter may be suppressed by the use of swept gain, rain clutter or other block echoes by means of the differentiating circuit (*see* p.408).

LOG amplification is the best choice for short/medium-range work when a lot of sea clutter is present. The logarithmic circuit provides an inherent suppression of sea clutter which is usually better than can be achieved by the linear receiver/swept gain combination. Usually, however, there is a loss of maximum detection range.

Some radars may have a *processed log* amplification whereby the video signal retains the sea clutter suppression characteristics of the logarithmic receiver, but benefits to an extent from the high signal/noise ratio output of the linear amplifier. There is, however, a loss of maximum detection range, and straightforward linear amplification is a much better choice if there is no sea clutter present. By introducing a differentiation circuit (*see* below), a completely clutter cleared video signal may be produced.

Improvements to video signals

Measures to improve video signals are generally concerned with the removal of clutter, and some of these facilities may be available to the operator. Clutter varies with the wavelength—the longer the wavelength, the less the clutter. Clutter also varies with the height of the aerial—the higher the aerial, the greater the range of the clutter.

Automatic gain control. The gain of the amplifier is automatically reduced if the signal reaches saturation level; thus, this control is a partial answer to removing clutter from the display.

Swept gain. This control reduces the amplitude of clutter at short ranges, gain increasing with range. However, it is very easy to sweep the display clean not only of sea clutter but also of close-range echoes, like small craft and buoys, that give a poor echo response. Care must be taken not to use this control indiscriminately. Swept gain may also be known as *sensitivity time control (STC)* or *(anti-clutter) sea.*

Differentiation. The differentiation control is used to reduce the effect of rain and other blocks of unwanted echoes. The control operates at all ranges but the penalty is loss of maximum range. *Differentiation* may also be known as *fast time constant (FTC), differentiation time constant (DTC)* or *(anti-clutter) rain.*

Clipping. Clipping is a process which removes the bases of the signals to allow echoes which are close together to be seen separately on the display without having to adjust the normal controls (brilliance, focus, gain). Clipping sometimes also enables echoes to be identified which might otherwise be lost in clutter, although the differentiation control may be more satisfactory. The penalties of using the clipping control are to introduce range errors and to lose all small contacts. As with swept gain, it is dangerous to use this control indiscriminately.

Atmospheric refraction

The optical (visible) and radar horizons (Fig. 15–2) are greater than the geometric because of refraction in the atmosphere. The distance of the horizon under standard atmospheric conditions may be found from the following formulae:

$$\text{geometric horizon} \quad 1.92\sqrt{h} \text{ sea miles} \qquad \dots \textbf{15.2}$$
$$\text{optical horizon} \quad 2.08\sqrt{h} \text{ sea miles} \qquad \dots \textbf{(9.2)}$$
$$\text{radar horizon} \quad 2.23\sqrt{h} \text{ sea miles} \qquad \dots \textbf{15.3}$$

where h, the height of the aerial, is measured in metres;   *or*

$$\text{geometric horizon} \quad 1.063\sqrt{h} \text{ sea miles} \qquad \dots \textbf{15.4}$$

optical horizon $1.15\sqrt{h}$ sea miles   ... **(9.3)**

radar horizon $1.23\sqrt{h}$ sea miles   ... **15.5**

where h is measured in feet.

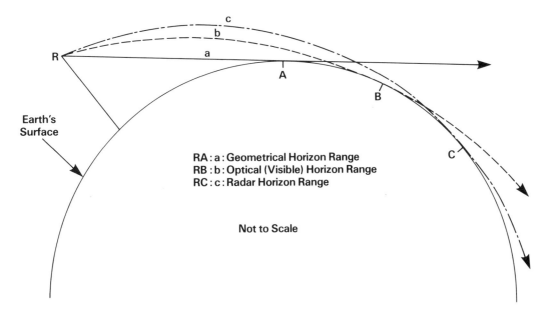

RA : a : Geometrical Horizon Range
RB : b : Optical (Visible) Horizon Range
RC : c : Radar Horizon Range

Not to Scale

Fig. 15–2.   Geometric, optical and radar horizons

Formulae **(15.3)** and **(15.5)** and the radar range/height nomograph (page 427) are all based on the assumption of a *standard atmosphere*, which approximates to the average state of the atmosphere in temperate latitudes *over the land*.

Super-refraction increases the horizon range, and thus maximum detection range, by a considerable extent. It is likely to occur when either a *temperature inversion* (an increase of temperature with height) or a *hydrolapse* (a decrease in humidity with height) is present.

A moderate degree of super-refraction is usually present over the sea because the hydrolapse in the lower levels of the atmosphere over the moist sea is normally stronger than that over the land. For *average conditions over the sea*, radar detection ranges are often increased by as much as 15% to 20%.

Sub-refraction occurs much less frequently; it decreases normal detection range through a combination of temperature and humidity which causes the radar wave to be bent upwards instead of downwards. Decrease of temperature with height may be greater than the standard lapse rate, and humidity may increase with height. Detection ranges may be reduced to the point where contacts are visible to the eye but are not displayed on radar.

A summary of types of weather, with the associated types of refraction and where these are likely to be found, is given in Table 15–1. Two charts of the world (Fig. 15–3(a) and (b)) show those areas where the meteorological conditions for super-refraction are likely to be fairly common.

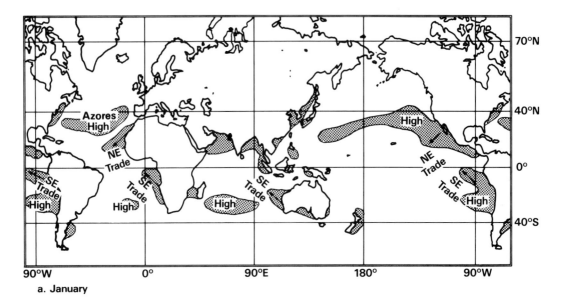

a. January

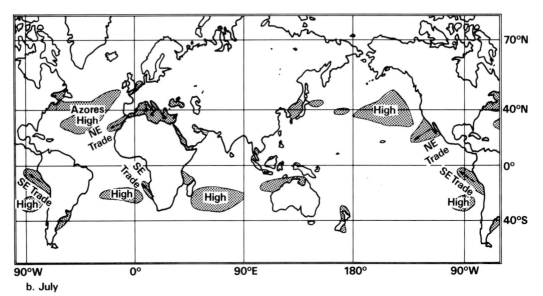

b. July

The shaded areas show where favourable conditions for super-refraction
have occurred on at least one day in five in January, (a), and July, (b).

Fig. 15–3.   Favourable areas for super-refraction

Table 15–1. Super- and sub-refraction

WEATHER	WHERE FOUND

Super-refraction

Average conditions over open sea: an evaporation duct. The air next to the water becomes damp by evaporation. If it is overlaid by drier air, a surface duct is formed practically irrespective of the type of temperature lapse. The duct may be 3 to 8 metres high, but wind will weaken and disperse it.	Everywhere in the open sea. The duct extends up to 18 metres in trade-wind zones.
Subsidence inversions. Subsiding air becomes warmer and relatively drier than the air below it. Temperature inversion and hydrolapse assist each other, causing a more pronounced duct than usual.	In anticyclonic conditions, e.g. the Azores high and the trade-wind zones. Tropical subsidence in Horse Latitudes, West Africa, Cape Verde Islands. Also found in ridges of high pressure.
Conditions in coastal waters. Offshore winds often carry warm dry air out above the cooler and damper air over the sea. The coasts adjacent to hot deserts and on the lee side of warm land masses will experience ducts.	The Mediterranean mainly in summer. Off West Africa during the Harmattan. The Arabian Sea, Bay of Bengal, Sri Lanka, Madras. The lee side of coasts in the zones of prevailing westerlies, or of north-east or south-east trade winds. In temperate zones in the ridges between depressions.
After the passage of a cold front. Cold northerly air behind a depression, blowing towards warmer waters, creates a marked hydrolapse forming a shallow evaporation duct.	In the North Atlantic, behind the cold fronts of depressions. *Note:* Polar air ariving from a westerly or south-westerly direction in the North Atlantic is likely to have only a small hydrolapse near the surface; thus, ranges are only average at best.

Sub-refraction

Conditions in the open sea with no evaporation duct. If a belt of warm air lies over the sea, a humidity inversion is formed. If this is stronger than the temperature inversion, the evaporation duct disappears, with the result that detection ranges are below average.	In relatively warm air masses over the sea in temperate regions, e.g. in a south-westerly air flow over the North Atlantic, particularly in the warm sector of a depression.
Cold wind conditions. A wind blowing from a cold land mass over a relatively warm sea may cause sub-refraction.	This condition may occur in Arctic or Antarctic regions.

The refraction conditions likely to be experienced on the passage of a frontal depression in the North Atlantic are illustrated in Fig. 15–4. In general, depressions are not favourable to long-range radar detection, whereas anticyclones and ridges of high pressure are.

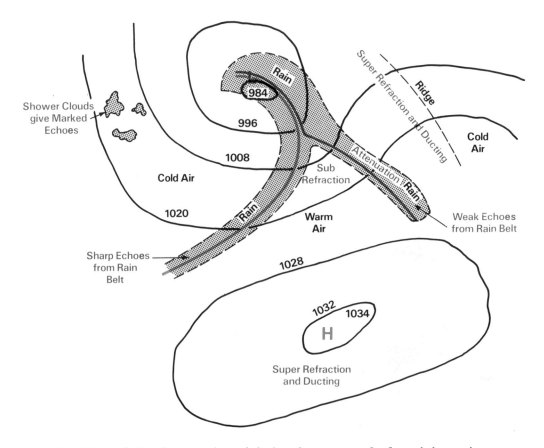

Fig. 15–4. Refraction experienced during the passage of a frontal depression.

The following effects may be experienced during super-refraction.

1. Increased clutter.
2. Multiple (second or third) trace echoes; e.g. the maximum unambiguous range of a radar set = (81,000/PRF) n miles. If the PRF is 1000, the maximum unambiguous range of the set is 81 miles. A contact at 90 miles could therefore appear on the PPI at 90 − 81 = 9 miles range.
3. Distortion in the shape of the multiple trace echoes of land masses.

Attenuation of radar waves

Absorption and scattering of radar transmissions by rain and other forms of precipitation may be considerable. Points to remember are:

1. The attenuation or weakening of the radar beam in rain may be such that objects at the far end of a rainstorm or beyond may give a much weaker echo

than expected, or may give no echo at all. The echoes from rainstorms (Fig. 15–5) can be so strong that they mask echoes from targets within the area; 3 cm radars are particularly prone to these effects. In very heavy rain such as thunderstorms, the reduction in maximum detection range may be as much as 30% to 35%, considerably more in tropical downpours. The effect is less on 10 cm radars.

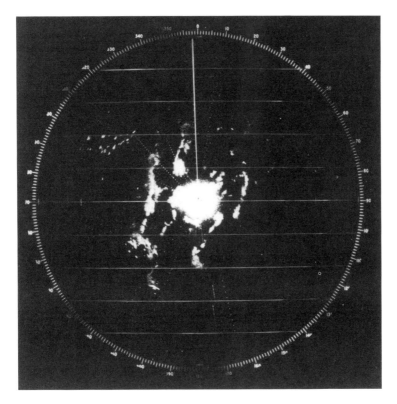

Fig. 15–5.   Shower echoes on the radar display

2. As the reflectivity of ice is less than water, the attenuation effects of hail and snowstorms are much less marked than in rain.

Appearance of weather echoes

The appearance of weather echoes on centimetric radar sets is illustrated in Figs 15–6 to 15–8. Cold fronts (Fig. 15–6) produce a band or line composed of a large number of echoes that break up and re-form as the band moves across the display. Cold fronts may be detected at long range. Warm fronts (Fig. 15–7) are varied in structure and may produce weak, diffused echoes covering a large part of the display. Fig. 15–8 is a good example of super-refraction, obtained during the summer months on 10 cm radar in the southern part of the North Sea, SE of Flamborough Head. Multiple ship echoes can be seen out to about 80 miles.

Sand/dust storms produce weak diffused echoes, particularly on 3 cm radar.

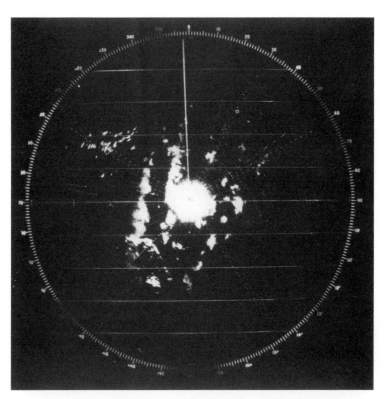

Fig. 15–6.   Cold front echoes on the radar display

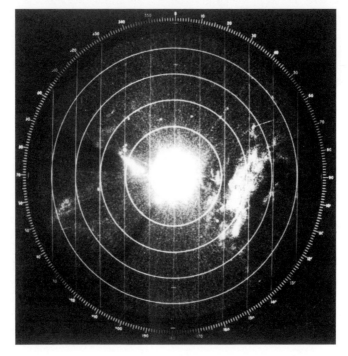

Fig. 15–7.   Warm front echoes on the radar display

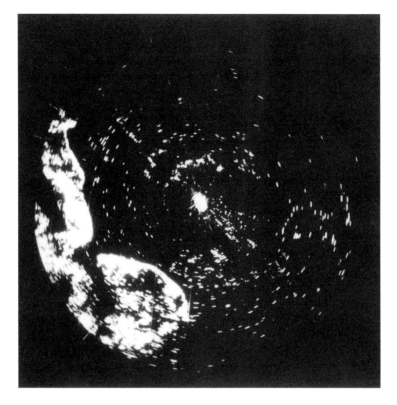

Fig. 15–8. Super-refraction on the radar display

Reflection from objects

Metal and water are better reflectors of radar than are wood, stone, sand or earth. In general, however, the shape and size of an object have a greater effect on its echoing properties than its composition. Increasing the size of an object may give a more extensive but not necessarily a stronger echo. The shape of the object dictates whether the reflected energy is diffused over a wide arc or concentrated into a beam directed back towards the radar. A flat plane may produce a very strong echo when at right angles to the radar beam but a very weak one otherwise. Curved surfaces tend to scatter the energy and thus produce a poor echo as, for example, with conical shaped lighthouses and buoys.

Corner reflectors provide a means of improving the radar response from small targets such as buoys, boats or beacons, which would otherwise give a poor echo owing to their size, shape or construction material. Fig. 15–9 illustrates a typical square corner reflector, consisting of three mutually perpendicular planes.

A *transponder* may be fitted to small units, for example helicopters, to enhance the size of the echo. A transponder consists of a separate transmitter triggered by the arrival of another transmission and transmitting on a specific frequency. The nature of the reply can be varied, one variation being *echo enhancement*, in which the transponder transmits a pulse coincident with the radar echo, so providing a much improved echo signal.

Unwanted echoes

Unwanted echoes consist, for example, of side lobes and double echoes from contacts at close range, false echoes from obstructions like masts and superstructure, and also multiple trace echoes (page 412). Such echoes are

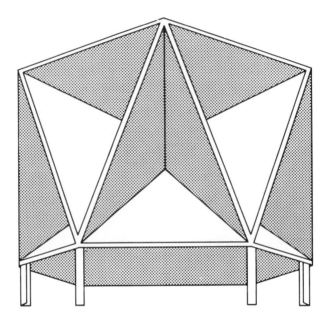

Fig. 15–9.   Typical square corner reflector

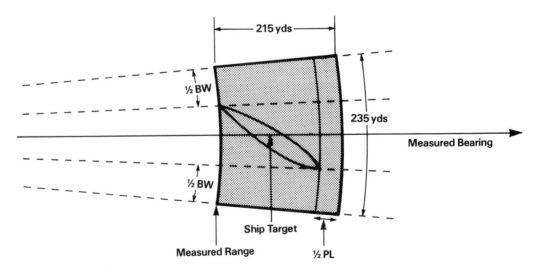

Fig. 15–10.   Radar shadow area around a ship contact

normally easy to recognise—e.g. the symmetrical nature of side lobe echoes, the double range and same bearing for double echoes.

Radar shadow

Radar shadow areas cast by mountains or high land may be extensive and may contain large blind zones. High mountains inland may well be screened by lower hills nearer the coast and thus not appear on the display.

On the display, each contact is surrounded by a *shadow area*, which is governed by the size of the object, pulse length and beam width. This is illustrated in Fig. 15–10.

A ship 200 yards long, at an angle of 30° and at a range of 4 miles, would display an echo about 215 yards in length and 235 yards in width (pulse length 0.25 microsecond, beam width 1°).

RADAR FOR NAVIGATION

The accuracy of navigation using radar depends on the accuracy of the radar in use and the correct operation of the user controls. Ranges in excess of 5 to 6 miles are rarely required for blind pilotage; therefore the radar should be adjusted for optimum performance at short range. Where available, short pulse length and narrow beam width will improve range and bearing discrimination and picture clarity. The centre spot should be in the centre and the picture correctly focused.

Displays used for blind pilotage must be set up to read in n miles and not in tactical (2000 yards) miles.

Suppression controls

As described on page 408, supression controls may be used to reduce or remove rain clutter, sea returns and side or back echoes, but care must be taken not to eliminate all small contacts. Suppression controls will need to be adjusted according to changes in the weather and sea states and also changes in the strength of the echo return from the object.

Radar and the Rule of the Road

The following points concerning *The International Regulations for Prevention of Collision at Sea, (1972)* should be remembered when using radar:

1. *Rule 5.* 'All available means' implies that radar shall be in use in or near restricted visibility, and that a watch is being kept on appropriate VHF circuits. Radar plotting must be systematic (Rule 7b).
2. *Section II, Rules 11 to 18* only apply to vessels in sight of one another.
3. *Section III, Rule 19.* If vessels cannot see each other visually, then neither has the Right of Way. This rule is strongly worded: 'Shall proceed . . .', 'Shall determine . . .', 'Shall reduce . . .', and so on.
4. The close quarters situation. *Rules 8 and 19* make it quite clear that early and substantial action should be taken to avoid a close quarters situation with another ship.

Other ships' radar

It is important to guard against making assumptions about another ship's use of radar vis-à-vis own ship, for example:

Assuming that the other ship is aware of own ship's position when in fact:
Own ship is not painting on the radar.   *or*
The other ship's radar is not operating or is not being watched.

The other ship may not be plotting own ship's track correctly: the radar bearings could be in error (page 424). This could lead the other ship to misinterpret the correct avoiding action.

Range errors

Index errors

Radar range is a function of time and is measured from the radar aerial. Ideally, the transmitter and receiver should be adjacent to the aerial but this is rarely possible. The following factors must therefore be taken into account before accurate range measurement is possible:

1. The time taken for a pulse to travel from the transmitter through the waveguide to the aerial.
2. The time between reception of the sync pulse at the input of the display timebase generator and the start of the timebase scan.
3. The time taken for an echo pulse to travel from the aerial to the receiver.
4. The time taken for the echo pulse to pass through the receiver and to be applied to the cathode ray tube.

These factors form an error called the *range index error,* which may be measured by several methods described below. Index error should be measured on each range scale before each blind passage, and should be marked on the display and applied in all fixes, cross-index ranges, etc. On some radar sets, index error may be eliminated (*see* page 424).

Other design factors

The following factors may affect range measurement in older displays, but are no longer a problem with modern solid state circuitry:

1. The calibration oscillator must be stable and at the correct frequency, otherwise the distance apart of the range calibration rings will not be correct.
2. *Linearity.* A linear display—that is, one where the physical distance between the range rings is the same—is essential for accurate ranging and parallel indexing.
3. Non-synchronisation between the range rings and the range marker.

Using the display

1. The display must be set up correctly—focus, gain and brilliance may affect ranging.
2. *Operator technique.* The largest possible scale must be used for ranging, e.g.

the 3 mile range scale is preferable to the 6 mile, the 6 mile to the 12 mile range scale, etc., as required by the range of the objects. The operator should always use a short pulse and should always range on the near side of the paint.

3. *Parallax errors.* When the display is viewed from different angles, errors are introduced by the curvature of the cathode ray tube (crt) and the separation of the plotting surface from the surface of the crt. The fitting of reflection plotters has greatly reduced these errors as does the introduction of electronic plotting and mapping lines.

4. Errors are introduced by certain controls which alter the range of the contact (e.g. 'clip').

5. Inaccuracies are caused by not using the correct range strobe for the scale in use.

Other causes of range error

Other possible causes of range error are to do with the nature of the object itself. Examples of this are:

1. Errors caused by the varied reflecting properties of different objects and their incidence to a radar beam. For example, a vertical granite cliff will give a much stronger echo than a sloping sandy beach.

2. As the tide rises and falls on a sloping coastline, the appearance of the radar picture may be very different from that indicated by the chart.

Finding the radar index error

Radar index error is the difference between radar and true range. The majority of displays under-range, therefore radar index error usually has to be added to the measured range. Radar index error is not constant and every opportunity should be taken to obtain a check. After each check, the revised error must be marked on the display and applied to all subsequent ranges. Allowance may have to be made for any range difference between the aerial and the fixing position, normally the bridge. Several methods of obtaining the index error are available; these are now described. Some methods are more accurate than others, but the use of any one method is determined by the facilities available.

Radar calibration chart

This is the most accurate method of calculating radar index error. Charts are produced by the Hydrographic Department, with additional data for certain ports, which enable a ship to fix its position to within 10 yards when at anchor or secured to a buoy. The additional data consist of curves of equal subtended angle between pairs of charted objects (Fig 15–11, page 420). The angles are measured by horizontal sextant and, for example in Fig. 15–11, a sextant angle between *A* and *C* of 40° and one between *C* and *B* of 50° would fix the ship's position at point *X*.

The true range of a radar-conspicuous mark can therefore be established from the chart and compared with a radar range taken simultaneously with the fix. Any difference is the index error. For example:

charted range	1550 yards
radar range	1530 yards
Radar index error	+20 yards

A correction of +20 yards must be applied to all radar ranges.

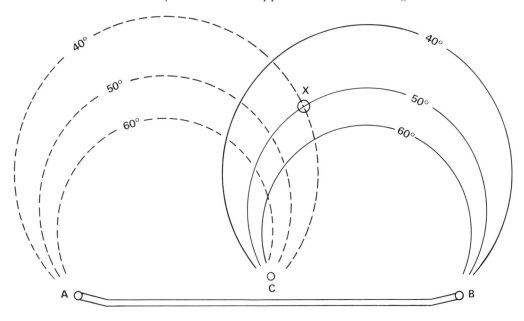

Fig. 15–11.   Curves of equal subtended angle

Use of the normal chart

If the ship is alongside in a harbour and radar-conspicuous objects are available, then charted and radar ranges of the object may be compared. The difference is the index error.

Two-mark method

The two-mark method may be used if two radar-conspicuous objects are available, the range between them is known accurately from the chart, and the ship is steaming between the marks.

Radar ranges of both objects (*A* and *B* in Fig. 15–12) are taken simultaneously as the ship crosses the line between them. Both radar ranges include index error (IE). *AB* is the charted distance between the two objects; *a* is the radar range between the ship and point *A*; *b* is the radar range between the ship and point *B*.

$$a + IE + b + IE = AB$$
$$2\,IE = AB - (a + b)$$
$$IE = \frac{AB - (a + b)}{2} \qquad \ldots \mathbf{15.6}$$

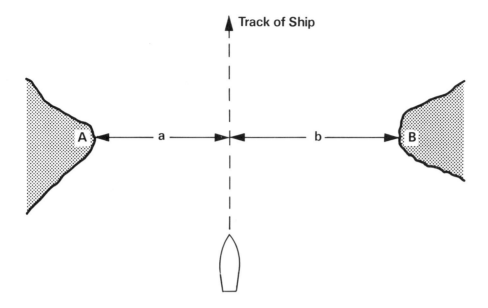

Fig. 15–12. Two-mark method

Three-mark method

When three radar-conspicuous and well charted objects are conveniently situated around the ship, radar ranges of all three objects may be taken simultaneously and range arcs from the objects drawn on the chart, producing a 'radar cocked hat', as shown in Fig. 15–13.

The index error equals the radius of the circle drawn tangential to the three range arcs.

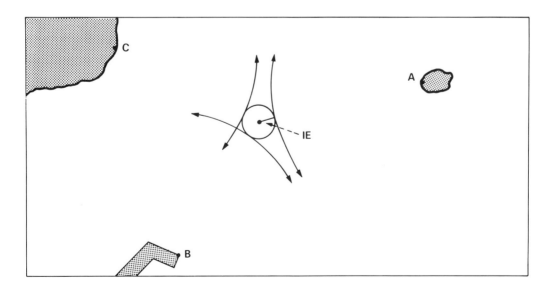

Fig. 15–13. Three-mark method

Horizontal sextant angle method

This method is carried out underway when running on a transit with a third fixing mark available on the beam, as illustrated in Fig. 15–14. A table of true range of the radar mark against sextant angle may be compiled in advance. Radar ranges are read off as the horizontal sextant angle is measured. The differences between true and radar range are then averaged to obtain the mean and the index error obtained.

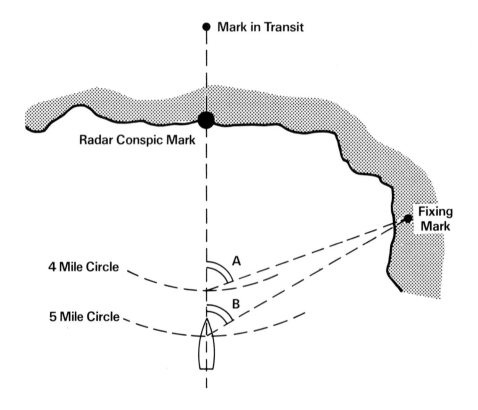

Fig. 15–14.   Horizontal sextant angle method

Two-ship method

The two-ship method involves the use of double echoes, which will usually be produced by two ships proceeding in line abreast at close range. This is illustrated in Fig. 15–15.

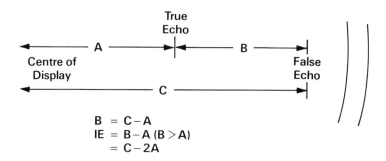

$$B = C - A$$
$$IE = B - A \ (B > A)$$
$$\quad = C - 2A$$

Fig. 15–15.   Two-ship method

Range A between own ship and the consort includes index error, but range B between the consort and the double echo does not. Thus, range B is the true range and the difference between this and the radar range A must be the index error.

Three-ship method

Three ships proceed in line abreast and simultaneously measure range from one another (Fig. 15–16).

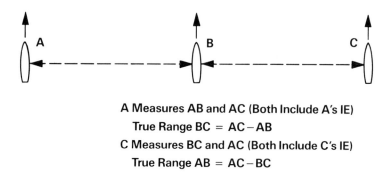

A Measures AB and AC (Both Include A's IE)
True Range BC = AC − AB
C Measures BC and AC (Both Include C's IE)
True Range AB = AC − BC

Fig. 15–16.   Three-ship method

Ship A provides true range BC and ship C provides true range AB; all three ships may thus obtain their respective index errors.

Standard set comparison method

A weapon radar set with an accurate ranging system may be established as a reference, with which a navigational radar may be compared to obtain its index error when both sets range on a given target.

Allowing for range index error

Having found the radar index error for the particular radar, the error may be allowed for as follows:

1. For some sets, the index error is noted on the front of the display and applied subsequently to all ranges taken by the operator.
2. Other sets can be adjusted by the maintenance staff. In some RN radars used for navigation, for example, any index error may be adjusted to about 5 yards and so is virtually eliminated.

Bearing errors

Causes of bearing errors

Bearing errors are invariably present and are hard to estimate, therefore radar bearings must always be treated with caution. Remember that a 1° error in bearing is equivalent to about 35 yards at 1 mile range, about 1 cable at 6 miles. Likely causes of bearing error are as follows:

1. Horizontal beam width causes an incorrect picture to be painted, (*see* page 406 and Fig. 15–1). Bearings of points of land lying across the radar beam will be distorted by approximately half the beam width.
2. Parallax errors when using an engraved cursor.
3. Incorrect centring of the display.
4. Using a longer range scale than necessary, bearings being taken too close to the centre of the display instead of near the circumference.
5. Limitations in the equipment, for example:
   (*a*) Difficulty in lining up the ship's head marker to an accuracy of less than $\frac{1}{2}°$. (This also needs to be checked after a course alteration.)
   (*b*) Difficulty in lining up the radar aerial on the masthead to an accuracy of less than 1°.
   (*c*) Error in the gyro-compass and its transmission system.
   (*d*) Backlash in the aerial training motor.
   (*e*) *Squint error.* In end-fed slotted waveguide aerials, the beam is offset from the aerial's line of sight between $\frac{1}{2}°$ and $2\frac{1}{2}°$. This is known as squint error. Squint error is at a minimum when the radar is first installed, but the oscillator frequency tends to drift with age, causing the error to vary. When the magnetron is changed, the frequency will be different and this may also also produce a significant squint error.

Bearing alignment accuracy check

At regular intervals, when using radar for navigation, the alignment of the picture and display must be checked as follows:

1. Centre the display.
2. Compare ship's head marker with the pelorus or gyro-repeater and adjust if necessary.
3. Compare the radar and visual bearings of a well defined object.
4. If a visual object is not available, compare the radar and charted bearings between two objects (Fig. 15–17).

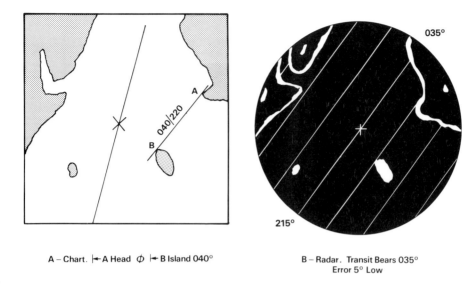

A – Chart. |← A Head Ø |← B Island 040°   B – Radar. Transit Bears 035°
                                                                    Error 5° Low

Fig. 15–17.   Checking radar alignment

A bearing accuracy check should be prepared in the planning stage of a blind pilotage run, marked on the chart and entered in the Note Book.

Comparison of 10 cm and 3 cm radars

Both 10 cm and 3 cm radars may be available for navigation and it is important to appreciate the fundamental differences between the two.

Generally, 10 cm radars have a longer pulse length and greater beam width than 3 cm radars. Thus, minimum range, and range and bearing discrimination, will be larger on a 10 cm than on a 3 cm radar. The distortion of the radar picture caused by beam width will be slightly worse.

On the other hand, because of the longer wavelength, the effects of clutter, rain, etc. will be much less on 10 cm than on 3 cm radar. Thus, in bad weather, it is quite probable that 10 cm radar will give a better picture, particularly if switched to short pulse length and wide bandwidth in order to obtain the best minimum range and range discrimination available. Long-range detection on 10 cm radar is usually better than on 3 cm, particularly when switched to long pulse.

In RN ships, the aerial of the 10 cm set is often positioned higher than the 3 cm aerial. In this case, the clutter experienced in bad weather on the 10 cm set, although not as intense as that on the 3 cm set, will extend to a greater distance (Fig. 15–18). This can mean that small targets at long range may be lost on 10 cm radar, although visible on 3 cm radar. However, as the contact closes, giving a stronger echo, it may appear through the clutter on 10 cm radar, yet disappear inside the much heavier clutter on the 3 cm radar. This is illustrated in Fig. 15–18.

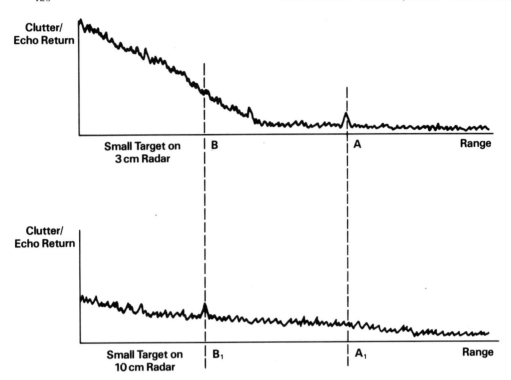

At AA₁: Target Visible on 3 cm Radar, Invisible on 10 cm Radar Because of Clutter.

At BB₁: Target Visible on 10 cm Radar, Invisible on 3 cm Radar Because of Clutter.

Fig. 15–18.   Effect of sea clutter on a small contact on 3 cm and 10 cm radar

LANDFALLS AND LONG-RANGE FIXING

Radar range/height nomograph

A useful guide to the probable maximum range of objects when the height is known, in standard atmospheric conditions, is given by the radar range/height nomograph shown in Fig. 15–19. The range R is based on the formulae **(15.3)** and **(15.5)** and may be found as follows:

$$R = 2.23 \ (\sqrt{h} + \sqrt{H}) \text{ sea miles} \qquad \ldots \textbf{15.7}$$
$$\text{i.e.} \quad H = 0.201 \ (R - 2.23 \ \sqrt{h})^2 \qquad \ldots \textbf{15.8}$$

where h, the height of the aerial, and H, the height of the target, are measured in metres;   *or*

$$R = 1.23 \ (\sqrt{h} + \sqrt{H}) \text{ sea miles} \qquad \ldots \textbf{15.9}$$
$$\text{i.e.} \quad H = 0.661 \ (R - 1.23 \ \sqrt{h})^2 \qquad \ldots \textbf{15.10}$$

where h and H are measured in feet.

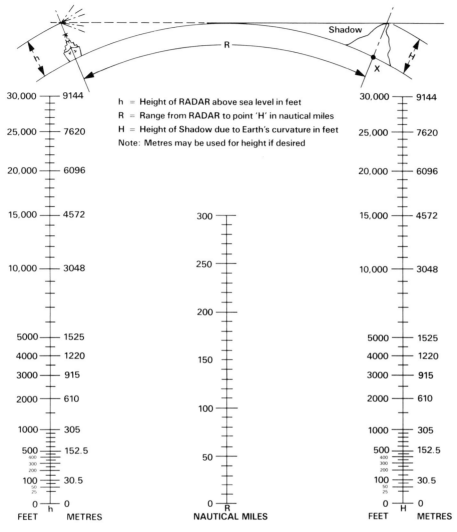

h = Height of RADAR above sea level in feet
R = Range from RADAR to point 'H' in nautical miles
H = Height of Shadow due to Earth's curvature in feet
Note: Metres may be used for height if desired

EXPLANATION

This NOMOGRAPH is an Earth Curvature Graph, corrected for refraction of the RADAR waves. It is used by passing a straight-edge through the points on two vertical lines representing known quantities and reading off the solution at the intersection of the third line with the straight-edge.

EXAMPLE

Aerial height is 100 feet.
At what range should a 7900 feet peak first be observed?

Method: Join the 100 feet mark in the left
           hand column with the 7900 feet
           mark in the right hand column.

A range of approximately 120 miles is read off at the intersection of the straight-edge with the central column.

The Nomograph is constructed for standard atmospheric conditions over land. For average conditions over the sea, detection ranges may be increased by as much as 15%.

Fig. 15–19.   Radar range/height nomograph

When considering the probable detection range of targets, two points should be borne in mind:

1. Radar will not necessarily detect an object with poor radar reflection properties at great ranges even though it may be above the radar horizon.
2. Maximum detection range is governed not only by the height of the aerial and the target but also by the power and performance of the radar set, the reflective properties of the target, and the atmospheric and sea conditions.

Long-range radar fixes

The radar/range height nomograph is a useful aid when making a landfall or fixing at long range using radar. Knowing the height of the coastline and mountains futher inland, it is possible to determine the approximate range at which these should be detected and an example is given in Fig. 15–19. Remember, however, that for average atmospheric conditions over the sea, the detection range may be increased by as much as 15%.

The likely range may also be determined from formula **(15.7)** or **(15.9)**. If, for example, the height of the aerial is 30 metres and the mountain concerned 400 metres then, from formula **(15.7)**:

$$R = 2.23 \ (\sqrt{30} + \sqrt{400}\,)$$
$$= 56'.8$$

Note: this range could be as much as 65′.3 for average atmospheric conditions over the sea, even greater in super-refraction conditions.

This indicates only that the mountain concerned should be above the radar horizon at this range (depending on the atmospheric conditions). It does not necessarily mean it will be detected at this range. Even if it is detected, it may be beyond the maximum unambiguous range of the set (81,000/PRF n miles) and so appear as a second-trace echo.

Alternatively, when an echo of high land is first detected, the height of the leading edge may be deduced from the nomograph or formula **(15.8)** or **(15.10)**. If the height of the aerial is 30 metres and land is detected at 42 miles, from formula **(15.8)**:

$$H = 0.201 \ (42 - 2.23 \ \sqrt{30}\,)^2$$
$$= 178.3 \text{ m}$$

Once the height of the leading edge of the echo has been determined in this way, the radar range position line may be plotted from the appropriate height contour level on the chart. Such long-range position lines must, however, be treated with caution because it is probable that the atmospheric conditions will be different from those on which the nomograph and formulae are based. The assessment of height may therefore be incorrect and the position line in error (Fig. 15–20), to an extent that depends on the gradient and thus the distance apart of the height contours on the chart. If, in the above example, the atmospheric conditions improve detection range by about 15%, then H ought to have been calculated for a smaller range, in this case 36′.5. (36′.5 + 15% = 42′ approx.). In which case, from formula **(15.8)**:

$$H = 118.5 \text{ m}$$

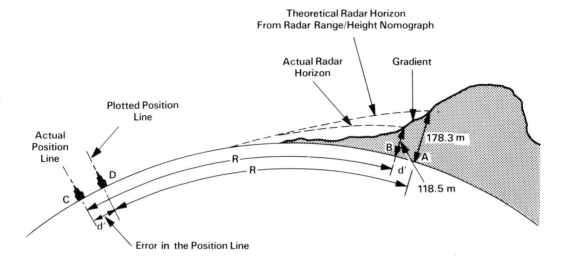

Fig. 15–20. Long-range radar position lines

This means that the radar is detecting land at a height of about 120 metres at a range of 42′ instead of 36′.5.

Using the nomograph or the formula, the observer would plot from A, the 178.3 metre contour (Fig. 15–20), the observed range R (42 miles). However, because of additional refraction, the leading edge of the mountain observed on the display is actually at B, (118.5 metres). The range R ought to have been plotted from this point, where AB equals d', the distance between the two contour lines. Thus, the error in the position line is CD, also equal to d'.

Taking into account the gradient of the height contours, d is unlikely to be large, but this will depend upon what refraction is actually being experienced. In the example given for a 15% improvement in detection range, for a gradient of about 1 in 10, the error in the position line is about $\frac{1}{3}$ mile [$10(178.3 - 118.5) = 0.32$ n mile]. For a gradient of 1 in 30 at a range of 60 miles, the error in the position line could be about $2\frac{1}{4}$ miles.

Plotting the long-range fix

Generally, it cannot be expected that the position arcs obtained at great ranges will cut in a point. As in Fig. 15–21 (p.430), they will probably do no more than indicate an area in which the ship is situated. It is advisable to plot the radar bearings of such long-range fixes as well because, although there may be inaccuracies in the bearings, they help to resolve the Position Probability Area produced by plotting the range arcs.

Note that peak E, though higher than D, is in the latter's shadow area and is therefore not visible on the display.

Any fix obtained in such circumstances should obviously be treated with caution.

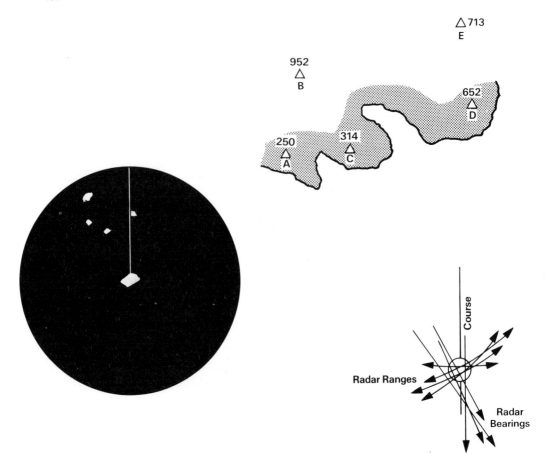

Fig. 15–21.   Fixing by radar ranges and radar bearings of long-range shore objects

The *Radar Station Pointer*

The *Radar Station Pointer* (Chart 5028), enables the Navigating Officer to plot radar echoes to the scale of the chart in use and assists in identifying these echoes with charted features. The chart is a transparent plotting sheet inscribed with radial lines from 0° to 360°. It is supplied to HM Ships in the Miscellaneous Charts Folio 317.

With the *Radar Station Pointer* orientated correctly, and with the plotted radar echoes 'fitted' on top of the charted objects, the ship's position is at the centre of the diagram.

It can also be used for:

1. Determining errors in the orientation of the radar display.
2. Laying off sextant angles as an ordinary station pointer.
3. Plotting position lines.

Instructions, and a table of approximate heights and distances at which echoes may be detected by radar under standard conditions, are printed on the diagram.

RADAR IN COASTAL WATERS

Radar is frequently used in coastal waters to supplement fixes by visual bearings. In low visibility, when shore objects are not clearly visible, fixing by radar may have to replace visual fixing altogether. Various techniques using radar in coastal waters are set out below.

Fixing by radar range and visual bearing

Fig. 15–22 shows a fix obtained by a visual bearing of a beacon from which a range has been obtained by radar. A radar range from the nearest land may also serve as a check.

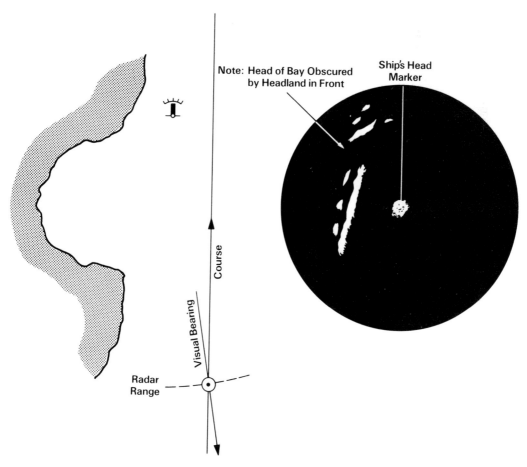

Fig. 15–22.   Fix by radar range and visual bearing

Fixing by radar ranges

Fixing using radar range arcs is normally the most accurate method of obtaining a fix using radar information alone.

Fig. 15–23 shows a fix obtained by radar ranges of two conspicuous headlands *A* and *B*, and a further headland *C* inside the bay. The position of the

buoy marking the rock D may be 'shot up' by taking a radar range and bearing
of it at the same time as the fix. It may also be cross-checked if desired by
measuring from the display the radar ranges of the buoy from headlands A, C
and E. The display shows the use that may be made of the heading marker as a
check that the ship is safely clearing the rock. It should, however, be
appreciated that, if there is a strong tidal stream setting the ship to starboard,
this could be setting the ship down on to the rock, although the ship's head may
still be pointing to the left of the buoy. Parallel index ranges (*see* page 434) on
headlands A and E are to be preferred.

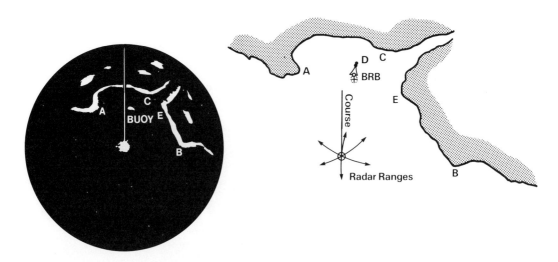

Fig. 15–23.   Fix by radar ranges of three objects

Three radar ranges should always be taken, if possible, for the radar range
fix. This should ensure that:

Objects are not misidentified.
Ranges are not read off incorrectly.
Any unresolved index error becomes apparent.

Fixing by radar range and bearing

Fig. 15–24 shows a ship off a coast which is obscured by bad visibility. A fix has
been obtained by radar range and bearing of the headland A. In spite of the
possibility of inaccuracy due to the beam width, a radar bearing has been used
because ranges of the land at right angles to the bearing A are unsatisfactory
owing to the poor radar response offered by the sand dunes. The bearing may
be corrected approximately by applying half the beam width of the radar to the
bearing obtained; in this case, it must be added.

Alternatively, a more accurate bearing may be obtained if the gain is reduced
until the headland only just 'paints' on the display. Be careful to readjust the
display to the former level for normal operation, otherwise small contacts may
be lost altogether.

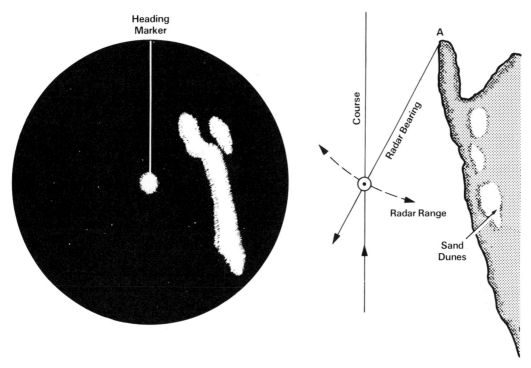

Fig. 15–24.   Fixing by radar range and bearing

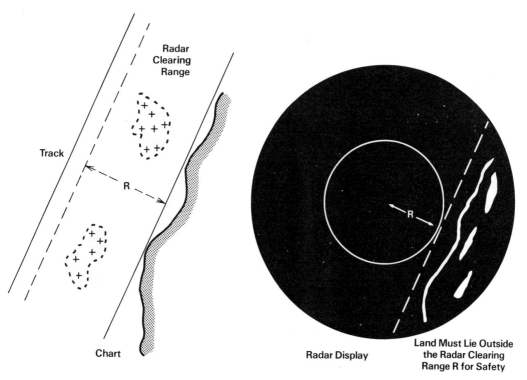

Fig. 15–25.   Use of a radar clearing range

Use of a radar clearing range

When proceeding along a coast, it is often possible to decide on a minimum clearing range outside which no off-lying dangers should be encountered. The clearing range is illustrated in Fig. 15–25, and may also be drawn on the display using the parallel index technique (*see* below). The ship must remain outside the clearing range to proceed in safety.

BLIND PILOTAGE

Blind pilotage means the navigation of the ship through restricted waters in low visibility with little or no recourse to the visual observation of objects outside the ship. The principal non-visual aid to navigation that enables this to be done is high-definition warning-surface radar, but all available non-visual aids are employed. The organisation to achieve this is called the *blind pilotage organisation*, comprising a BP team, led by a BP Officer (BPO).

Assessment of the risk involved in a blind pilotage passage

Although normally the accuracy of blind pilotage is such that a ship can be taken to an open anchorage and anchored within 50 yards of the desired place, the degree of risk involved, particularly in restricted waters, must be carefully assessed. Congestion due to other shipping, the consequences of failure of radar or other vital aids once the ship has been committed to her passage, and the number and quality of fixing marks must be taken into account.

Parallel index technique

The key to blind pilotage is the principle of the parallel index. The running of a parallel index line provides real-time information on the ship's lateral position relative to the planned track. On the chart (Fig. 15–26), a line is drawn from the

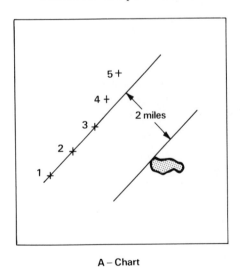

A – Chart

B – Radar Display
Range Strobe at 2 miles

Fig. 15–26.   Parallel index

edge of a radar-conspicuous object, parallel to the planned track. The perpendicular distance (or cross-index range) from the object to the track is then measured. The range strobe on the radar is then set to this range, and a solid chinagraph line drawn on the display parallel to the planned course on a scale appropriate to the range in use.

Positions 1, 2 and 3 on the chart and radar display show the ship on track at various instances up to the time that the island is abeam to starboard. Positions 4 and 5 show the ship off track to port. The exact distance off track can be measured by dividers from the radar echo of the island to the nearest point of the chinagraphed parallel index line at the scale of the display. This can be made easier by constructing scales for each range setting, as shown below, and mounting them adjacent to the display. (The crosses on the chart do not represent fixes and only appear in order to illustrate the example.)

```
0        0.25      0.5       0.75      1.0       1.25        1.5
|__|__|__|__|__|__|_____|_____|_____|_____|       1.5 miles

0        0.5       1.0       1.5       2.0       2.5         3.0
|__|__|__|__|__|__|_____|_____|_____|_____|       3.0 miles

0        1.0       2.0       3.0       4.0       5.0         6.0
|__|__|__|__|__|__|_____|_____|_____|_____|       6.0 miles
```

Radar clearing ranges

Radar clearing ranges (Fig. 15–27, p.436) are similarly drawn at the maximum or minimum distances from the radar-conspicuous objects to keep the ship clear of dangers. These are drawn as broken lines: — — —.

Course alterations

'Wheel over' positions are calculated and plotted on the chart as for visual pilotage. A radar-conspicuous mark is selected as close as possible to the 'wheel over' position. A pecked line – – – – – is then drawn through the 'wheel over' position (Fig. 15–27A) parallel to the new course, and the cross-index range measured. This 'wheel over' range is plotted on the display as a pecked line parallel to the new course. When the selected mark reaches this line, the wheel should be put over and the ship brought round to the new course, by which time the mark should be on the firm line denoting the parallel index for the new course.

The standard symbols used for parallel index lines, radar clearing and 'wheel over' ranges are shown on page 441.

Blind pilotage in HM Ships

Responsibilities

The Queen's Regulations for the Royal Navy (QRRN) state that, in normal circumstances, the Navigating Officer is the pilot of the ship although, if he is not a navigation sub-specialist, the duty of pilotage devolves on the Captain, who may either perform it himself or, at his discretion, depute any officer of the ship's complement to do so.

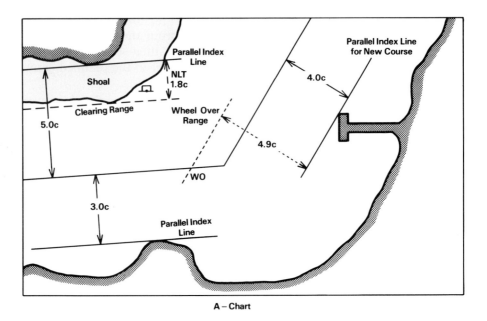

A – Chart

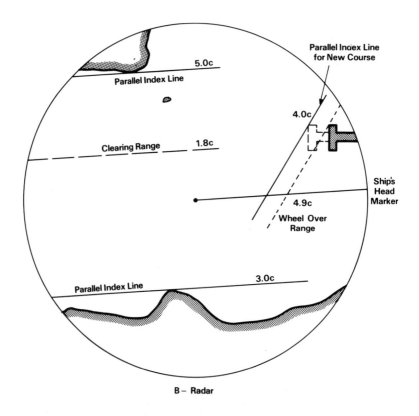

B – Radar

Fig. 15–27. Clearing and 'wheel over' ranges on the chart and the radar display

No matter what the blind pilotage organisation may be, the sub-specialist Navigating Officer (NO) is always the pilot of the ship, and thus he should also be the Blind Pilotage Officer (BPO).

Where no navigating sub-specialist is borne, the officer appointed for navigating duties should also be the Blind Pilotage Officer in normal circumstances. However, as responsibility for pilotage is clearly vested in the Captain, he may wish to delegate the blind pilotage duty to some other officer. If so, the Captain must also clearly set out in his standing orders the circumstances envisaged, to ensure that it is absolutely clear who is responsible and when. These orders must also take into account the organisation for blind pilotage in various circumstances envisaged; the organisation described below may have to be modified.

It must also be decided who is responsible for informing the Captain of the collision risk with other ships. The NO/BPO will be fully employed navigating the ship; therefore it is essential that the officer in charge of the operations room, who already has an anti-collision plot running, should be made responsible for advising the Captain and OOW on this aspect of safety.

The conduct of blind pilotage

The Navigating Officer should remain on the bridge in poor visibility and conduct the blind pilotage from there. It is essential to have another officer, who is suitable by training and experience, as a Blind Safety Officer (BSO) in the operations room, where he can monitor the blind pilotage and back up the Navigating Officer on the bridge. The BSO will need to be in touch with the surface plot to assist with the identification of radar contacts.

The essence of this arrangement is that members of the team do not change position if the visibility changes. The Navigating Officer conducts the pilotage from the bridge whatever the weather or visibility. In good visibility, the BSO acts as a useful check on the visual plan and builds up confidence in his team and the Command. In marginal visibility, the bridge team continues to make use of any visual information to supplement information from the radar. In nil visibility, the NO conducts the blind pilotage from the bridge radar display, monitored by the BSO. If reports from the NO and BSO disagree, immediate action to stop the ship may be necessary until the position has been accurately determined.

The Navigating Officer should not move from the bridge to the operations room in order to conduct the pilotage from there. This will cause delay and perhaps confusion, and can be particularly undesirable in marginal visibility, when a mixture of visual and blind techniques is required.

There may well be circumstances, particularly in large ships, where the Navigating Officer has already taken or wishes to take the con and therefore charge of the ship from the Officer of the Watch, in order to conduct the pilotage where a blind pilotage situation has already arisen or arises subsequently. In such a situation, it may be undesirable for the NO to move to the bridge radar display as indicated above. The composition and duties of the blind pilotage team must therefore have sufficient flexibility built in to cope with such circumstances. The NO may continue to con the ship from the pelorus, taking full account of the navigational and collision avoidance information he is receiving from the operations room, the bridge radar display (which should be manned by a competent officer such as the NO's assistant) and other sources, e.g. the bearing lattice team, lookouts, etc. Despite being at the con, the NO is still the pilot and the Blind Pilotage Officer of the ship and retains full responsibility for these under *QRRN*.

Blind pilotage team and duties

Blind pilotage requires a high degree of organisation and team work, so that not only are the responsibilities of individuals clearly defined but also all relevant factors may be considered while assessing the ship's position and her future movements. Suitable arrangements to achieve this are set out in Table 15–2; these may have to be adjusted depending on the class of ship, the personnel available, and the above comments.

Table 15–2. Blind pilotage organisation

PLACE	PERSONNEL	DUTY
Bridge	Captain	Overall responsibility for ship safety. May wish to con ship in certain circumstances.
Bridge	OOW	Has charge of and cons ship. In charge of lookouts and sound signals. Reports all visual sightings to Captain/NO.
Bridge	NO	Acts as Blind Pilotage Officer (BPO). Responsible for all aspects of pilotage, visual and blind.
Bridge	NO Assistant	Plots fixes, generates DR/EP. Advises on times of 'wheel over' (WO), etc. Plots visual sightings. Checks echo sounder (E/S) reports with charted depth.
As reqd	Navigator's Yeoman	Records wheel and engine orders: the running commentary from the NO/Blind Safety Officer to the Captain/OOW which includes recommended courses and speeds and information on the ship's position by radar relative to the planned track. Alternatively, this duty may be satisfied by having a continuously running tape recorder on the bridge during pilotage. It is essential to incorporate a time check at the beginning of each tape.
Bridge/ charthouse	E/S operator	Standard reports.
As reqd	Lookouts	Standard reports. Lookouts must be briefed to listen as well as look.

Table 15–2 (*cont.*)

PLACE	PERSONNEL	DUTY
Operations room	Blind Safety Officer (BSO)	Monitors ship's position as a check on the ship's navigational safety, using the most suitable display. Co-ordinates navigational and anti-collision information to bridge. Although he does not supervise surface plot, he must keep an eye on shipping situation.
Operations room	Blind Safety Officer's assistant	Plots radar fixes and other radio aids (e.g. Decca) as appropriate. Generates DR/EP. Assists in identification of marks, ships. Checks E/S reports with charted depths.
Operations room	Anti-collision plot	A suitably experienced officer or the most experienced Ops(R) Senior Rate in charge. Passes anti-collision information to bridge, co-ordinated by BSO.
Sonar control room	Sonar controller	Reports sonar information as ordered.

Planning and execution of blind pilotage

General principles

To ensure success, the ship must be accurately navigated along a pre-arranged track. In comparatively unrestricted waters, this is best done by constant fixing using radar in conjunction with other aids such as Decca and echo sounder.

In narrow waters and during the final stages of an anchorage, the delays inherent in fixing are unacceptable to the BPO. It is therefore necessary, for anti-collision and navigation in these conditions, to work directly from the radar display using a prepared Note Book; but it is still necessary to pass radar information for fixing at regular intervals as a safety check and as an insurance against radar failure.

The following principles apply:

1. The Navigating Officer should navigate or pilot the ship.
2. The Captain should have easy access to the blind pilotage position and the NO.
3. The ship should be conned from the compass platform because it is only on the bridge that the 'feel of the ship' can be retained.
4. The Captain, Blind Safety Officer, Officer of the Watch and the officer in charge of the anti-collision plot should all be carefully briefed before the passage by the NO, so that they are all entirely familiar with the visual/blind plan.

5. Navigational charts with the NO's prepared visual/blind plan must be available on the bridge and in the operations room.
6. The whole pilotage team should be exercised as frequently as possible in clear weather in visual and blind techniques. Only in this way can the necessary confidence in the system be built up which will allow runs of some complexity to be conducted safely in blind conditions.
7. The BSO should be closed up on all occasions of entering and leaving harbour and passages through narrow waters when special sea dutymen are closed up; the BP team should be regarded as part of special sea dutymen.
8. There should be good communication between the blind pilotage position and the BSO and personnel manning navigational aids fitted elsewhere.
9. All members of the team should be encouraged to admit any doubts they may have regarding the information acquired from sensors.

Blind pilotage planning

1. Normal planning considerations for selection of tracks apply. Blind and visual tracks should be the same, to enable the transition from visual to blind or vice versa to be made at any time and also to allow one plan to be used to cross-check the other.
2. The number of course alterations should be kept to a minimum to reduce the work load in redrawing parallel and 'wheel over' lines.
3. Always try to have two parallel index lines—where possible, one on each side of the track. These provide a check on measurement, mark identification and can reveal index or linearity errors.
4. Objects to be used both for parallel index lines and for fixing must be carefully selected. They should be radar-conspicuous and unchanged by varying heights of tide. Clearly mark on the chart the objects to be used for fixing and brief the assistant. Avoid if possible fixing by radar range and bearing on a single mark.
5. The range scales to be used require careful consideration. Accuracy is greater at shorter ranges but marks pass more quickly than at a distance, requiring more lines to be drawn. When operating on short-range scales, it is essential that the BPO frequently switches to longer ranges to keep aware of developing situations. Changes of range scales and parallel index marks should be pre-planned and marked in the Note Book. The stage at which charts will be changed must also be carefully considered.
6. Tidal streams and currents should be worked out and noted for calculation of courses to steer and for the calculation of EP. These should be displayed on the chart and recorded in the Note Book.
7. Expected soundings (allowing for height of tide and calibration of echo sounder) should be noted for each leg. The possibility of being early or late should also be borne in mind.
8. All hazards along the track should be boxed in by clearing ranges and their cross-index ranges listed in the Note Book.
9. Details of all lights and fog signals should be taken from the *Admiralty List of Lights*/chart and entered in the Note Book.
10. The chart should be drawn up using standard symbols (Figs. 15–28, 15–29 and 15–31), *see* Table 15–3.

Table 15–3. Blind pilotage symbols

Blind pilotage chartwork	Symbol
Parallel index lines to stay on track	———
Clearing ranges	— — —
'Wheel over' (WO) ranges	- - - - -

Use the same conventions as above for cross-index ranges.

The term *dead range* (Figs. 15–28, 15–31) is used to describe the range of a mark ahead when anchoring in a chosen position. The term may also be used when measuring the progress of a radar-conspicuous object along a parallel line, as shown in Fig. 15–31.

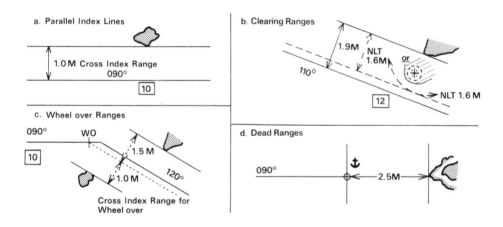

Fig. 15–28. Blind pilotage symbols

Radar-conspicuous objects such as buoys should be highlighted to enable the BPO to have a clear mental picture of what he expects to see on the display.

11. The Note Book should contain the full plan, neatly and legibly recorded in chronological order. Sketches of both chart and radar display (Fig. 15–29, p.442) can be of great assistance to the BPO in evaluating the picture. A suitable Note Book layout supplementing Fig. 15–29 is shown in Fig. 15–30 (p.443) as a guide to blind pilotage planning.

12. Tracks plotted for entering and leaving harbour should not appear on the same chart simultaneously, otherwise confusion will arise.

13. Clearing ranges should be simple, safe and easily interpreted.

14. Objects used for 'wheel overs' should be conspicuous, easily identifiable and suitably located adjacent to the track.

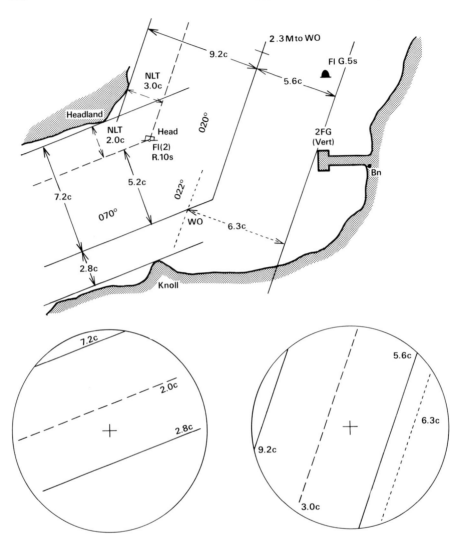

Fig. 15–29.   Blind pilotage: preparation of the chart and displays

Blind pilotage execution

1. Carry out a time check to synchronise clocks and watches.
2. On the radar display, keep one set of parallel index lines drawn up ahead of those in use. Any more will clutter the display excessively. Rub out lines as soon as they are finished with.
3. Identify contacts early (by range and bearing from charted object). An accurate EP is a most useful aid in identification.
4. Fix at frequent intervals and immediately after a change of course. DR/EP ahead. A suitable fixing procedure is:

> BPO assistant   'Stand by fix in 1 minute'
>   BPO   'Roger—using points *A, B, C*'
>   BPO assistant writes these in Note Book.

Course	Remarks Approach Speed 12 knots	Distance to Wheel-over (W.O.) miles	Minimum Depth (metres)

070°	on Pier Root Beacon
	// Port Headland 7.2C
	// Stbd. Headland 2.8C
	Head Buoy ⊥ Port 5.2C
		0.1M to W.O.	14m

W.O. to 020° (15° Port Helm)	Headmark 022° // Stbd. Jetty 6.3C		

020°	on Headmark
	// Port Headland 9.2C
	// Stbd. Jetty 5.6C
	Stbd. Hand Buoy ⊥ stbd. 5C
	
	Change to 6M range scale
	// Stbd. New Head 6.7C
		2.3M to W.O.	15.6m

Fig. 15–30. Blind pilotage: layout of Navigating Officer's Note Book

BPO/BPO assistant   'Fix now.' BPO marks the point on face of the display.
BPO assistant notes the time.
BPO then ranges off the marks drawn on display and passes these to BPO assistant.

BPO assistant   Records the ranges, plots the fix and generates fresh DR and EP.

This procedure cuts the time to take a fix and reduces the risk of a 'cocked hat' due to ship movement. It may be quicker to interpolate from the range rings rather than use the range strobe, although the latter will be more accurate.

5. *Ship's speed.* One of the factors affecting the choice of ship's speed will be the rate at which the BPO and his assistant are capable of dealing with the radar information.

6. *Commentary and conning advice.* Maintain a steady, unhurried and precise flow of information to the Command:

Distance off track/on track/course to maintain or regain.
Distance and time to next 'wheel over', new course.
Present/new course clear of shipping.
Adjacent marks or hazards, expected lights and sound signals.
Expected depth and echo sounding. Minimum depths.

When fixing and result of fix. EP to next alteration.

Manoeuvring limits (e.g. 5 cables clear to stbd, 1 cable to port).

If in any doubt, say so and if necessary stop the ship.

7. It must be appreciated that, whatever the technique employed, a drift off line is likely to be detected less readily by radar than by visual methods.

8. It is vital to pay attention to the echo sounder and the least depth expected. The nearest land is usually the bottom.

Blind pilotage exercise

To improve the reality of BP exercises in clear weather, the following points should not be forgotten:

Safe speed should be maintained.

Fixes should be recorded and plotted at the same frequency as for actual blind pilotage.

A full de-brief should take place on completion of the practice.

Blind anchorages

A blind anchorage should be planned in the same way as a visual anchorage but remember to allow 'stem to radar' instead of 'stem to standard' when plotting the 'let go' position. As shown in Fig. 15–31, parallel index lines should be used to guide the ship to the anchorage position and she must stay boxed in by clearing ranges. Distances to run can be obtained by using a dead range on a suitable object ahead, or by measuring the progress of a radar-conspicuous object along a parallel index line. Full details must be shown on the chart and in the Note Book. Distances to run must be marked on the face of the display.

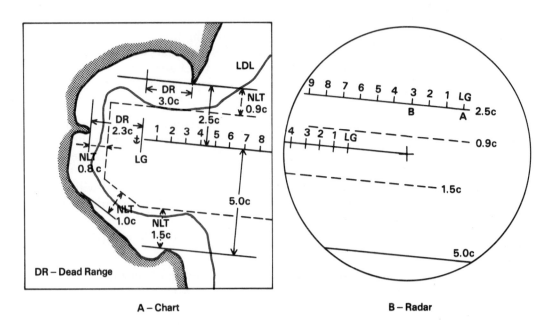

A – Chart   B – Radar

Fig. 15–31.   Blind anchorage execution

These can be backed up by the range strobe, but reliance on the strobe alone is dangerous because the reference is lost as soon as the strobe is required for any other measurement.

In Fig. 15–31, the dead range of the point of land ahead when anchoring is 2.3 cables. The distance to run to the anchorage position may be obtained by subtracting the dead range from the actual range of the point. For example, if the range of the point is 7.3 cables, the distance to the anchorage is 7.3 − 2.3 = 5 cables.

Fig. 15–31 also shows that the dead range of the point of land on the starboard side when anchoring is 3 cables. On the radar display, this point of land should 'move' along the parallel index line drawn $2\frac{1}{2}$ cables to starboard of the approach track. When the ship reaches the 'let go' position, the point of land should have reached point *A*, 3 cables beyond the abeam position *B*. The distance *AB* equals the dead range (3 cables).

Navigational records

When carrying out a blind pilotage passage, the Navigating Officer/BPO will be too busy to maintain a continuous written record. It is essential that such a record should be kept, and in comparatively unrestricted waters it is normally sufficient for this record to be kept on the chart itself by plotting fixes and noting the positions and times of alterations of course and speed and other relevant data, in addition to the record in the Navigational Record Book (S3034). This procedure, involving thorough and methodical chartwork, is in fact no different from that which should be practised during any pilotage passage.

In more restricted conditions, however, the Navigating Officer/BPO's running commentary to the Captain should be recorded on tape if possible, for example:

'No. 7 buoy fine on port bow, 8 cables—ship 50 yards to port of track—steer 136 to regain.'

In conjunction with the Navigating Officer/BPO's prepared Note Book, the chart, the recorded fixes and courses and speeds, this record should suffice for any subsequent analysis required.

Horizontal displays

Where horizontal displays are available in the operations room, the whole passage may be prepared in advance on a series of overlays, the BSO's assistant changing these at appropriate times. The drawback of this method is that all tracking and other additional marks made by the BSO are lost at each change. With most horizontal displays in use in the Royal Navy, the picture is not sufficiently precise for accurate blind pilotage and should not be used.

TRUE MOTION RADAR

There are various arguments for or against using relative motion (usually stablised 'north-up' presentation) or true motion radars for navigation. These arguments are normally to be found in standard works on radar and also in many articles in various navigational periodicals. Some general comments are set out below. Further comments on the use of radar in the collision avoidance role may be found in Chapter 17.

Advantages of true motion radar

True motion radar has two important advantages when being used for navigation, particularly in pilotage waters:

1. Ships underway may be distinguished at once by their echo trails (Fig. 15–32).
2. Echoes of stationary objects, e.g. buoys, may be distinguished by the absence of echo trails.

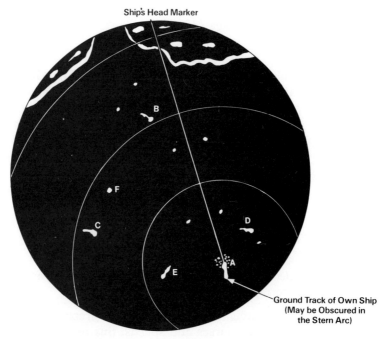

A = Own Ship Entering Harbour along a Buoyed Channel
    East-going Tidal Stream allowed for.
B, C, D, E = Other Ships Underway: Tails Indicate their Ground Tracks.
F = Ship at Anchor: Identified by Reference to the Chart.

Fig. 15–32. Identification of moving and stationary objects on a ground stabilized true motion radar

This assumes that the correct allowances for set and drift (tidal stream, wind, current and surface drift) have been made (*see* Chapter 8). It also assumes that the trail of a moving ship will be visible on the display. This depends on the size of the display, the range scale in use, speed of the target and duration of the afterglow. For example, if the 3 mile range scale is in use on a 30 cm display (5 cm to 1′) and the minimum length of echo trail required is 0.5 cm then, if the afterglow lasts for 1 minute, the minimum speed of ship that will produce an echo trail long enough for movement to be apparent is 6 knots. In 1 minute, a ship at 6 knots moves $0'.1$, which is equivalent to 0.5 cm at a scale of 5 cm to the mile.

Improved detection range ahead of the ship is also available on true motion radar, without having to change the scale, by moving own ship's position to the appropriate sector of the display (Fig. 15–32). Such a facility is often also available on relative motion radars by using the off-centring controls. Targets abaft the beam may, however, be lost and this could be important.

Disadvantages of true motion radar

The disadvantages of true motion radar for navigation are summarised below:

1. Contacts closing on steady bearings are not immediately apparent.
2. There are breaks in compilation and control every time the position is reset.
3. Adjustments to remove completely the effects of tidal stream, leeway, etc. are difficult to determine.

Shifts of picture must be carefully planned to take place after the ship has settled on a leg and has been fixed on the chart, to enable pilotage to continue by EP during the short break entailed. Shifts of picture should not be left to the last moment in case this coincides with a close quarters situation which requires constant watching.

RADAR BEACONS (RACONS AND RAMARKS)

Radar beacons are transmitters designed to produce a distinctive image on ship's radar displays, thus enabling the mariner to determine his position with greater certainty than would be possible by means of normal radar contacts. Many Lighthouse Authorities have established radar beacons at lighthouses and at other sites where it is believed they would give good service to shipping. These microwave aids to navigation usually operate initially on an experimental or trial basis and are only permanently established if the service provided is vindicated by user experience.

Details of racons and ramarks in operation are given in the *Admiralty List of Radio Signals (ALRS)*, Volume 2.

Racons

A *racon* is a radar transponder beacon which emits a characteristic signal when triggered by emissions of ships' radars. Most racons are of the *swept-frequency* kind, that is, the transponder frequency sweeps the frequency range of the marine radar band. The racon response to a ship's triggering radar pulse will therefore appear automatically on the ship's radar display. Usually, the 'racon flash' takes the form of a single line or narrow sector, extending radially towards the circumference of the display, from a point slightly beyond the spot (if any) formed by the echo from the lighthouse, etc. at the racon site (Fig. 15–33, p.448).

The range may be measured to the point at which the racon flash begins, but the figure obtained will be greater than the ship's distance from the racon; this is due to the slight response delay in the radar beacon apparatus.

Fig. 15–33.   The 'racon flash'

Other racons are termed *frequency agile*, their response always being within the bandwidth of the ship's radar receiver. They may cease to respond for a few seconds each minute to allow radar echoes otherwise obscured by the racon signal to be distinguished.

The majority of racons respond to 3 cm radar emissions, but a few respond to both 3 cm and 10 cm radar emissions.

On certain types of racon including some in British waters, the flash is composed of a Morse identification signal followed by a 'tail'. Thus Morse 'S' would show as · · · —, and 'O' – – – —. The length of the 'tail' is normally controlled by the number of characters in the Morse identification signal.

Ramarks

A *ramark* is a radar beacon which transmits independently, without having to be triggered by the emissions of ships' radars. It is otherwise similar to a racon, except that the ramark's flash gives no indication of range, as it extends from the ship's position to the circumference of the display.

There are relatively few ramarks in service throughout the world, most are in Japanese waters.

Interference from radar beacons

It may be found that, in certain circumstances, radar beacon emissions can cause unwanted interference with the normal radar display, particularly at close range. The operation of the differentiation control may reduce racon but not ramark interference to acceptable proportions, provided that the technical characteristics of the beacon have been selected with this in view.

SHORE-BASED RADAR

Shore-based radar systems may be found throughout the world, either as an aid to traffic using a port, or for the purposes of traffic surveillance or management in areas of high shipping density like the English Channel or St Lawrence River. Details of the various systems in force may be found in the relevant *Admiralty Sailing Directions* and in the *Admiralty List of Radio Signals (ALRS)*, Volume 6. Some details of surveillance systems are also given in Volume III of this manual.

Port radar systems

The aim of a port radar system is to help ships which might otherwise have to anchor to proceed in restricted or nil visibility, thus avoiding congestion and delay at the port. Such installations often operate in clear weather to assist in traffic control. The radar normally operates in the 3 cm band, often with a narrower beam width and shorter pulse length than sets fitted in ships, thus giving improved range and bearing accuracy and discrimination. The necessary VHF communications between shore and ship are also available at the control centre. The shore-based radar often covers the sea approaches to the port in addition to the approach channels. This may require remote aerial sites transmitting data to the control centre.

The shore-based system usually provides the following information to ships:

1. Information on the arrival, berthing, anchoring and departure of individual ships.
2. Information on navigational aids, navigation generally, visibility and safety.
3. Tidal information.
4. General situation and movement reports giving traffic movements, local navigational warnings and weather reports.
5. When requested, navigational information may be passed to individual ships:
     Information to bring the ship up to and through the harbour entrance.
     Accurate positioning when navigating bends.
     Warning of approaching ships.
     Position in relation to navigational marks, buoys and beacons.

Certain shore systems, dependent on the installation and siting of the radar, may also be able to provide berthing assistance in fog.

Shore based radar systems also enable the Harbour Authority to:

1. 'See' the position of all vessels underway or at anchor in the port and its approaches.
2. Check the position of all floating navigational marks: buoys, light-floats, light-vessels.
3. Check the position of any shipping casualties and arrange for the necessary tugs, firefighting and lifesaving equipment.
4. Monitor the various dredging operations being undertaken in the port and its approaches.

Positional information

Positional information is usually passed to ships from the control centre by one or other of the following methods:

1. Distance right or left of the charted radar reference line relative to the direction of progress.
2. Bearing and distance from the nearest charted object, e.g. pier, jetty, buoy, etc.

This information is normally passed by means of a running commentary from the control centre, which the ship is required to acknowledge at regular intervals. Control of the ship remains in the hands of the Captain or Master.

Reporting points within port radar systems

A number of reporting points for inward and outward bound traffic are usually designated within the area covered by the port radar system, ships being required to report to the control centre as these are passed.

The orders for the port may require the inbound ship to provide amplifying information, such as her name and nationality, intended approach channel, destination, draught, etc. Similar information is also required on departure.

Traffic surveillance and management systems

An advisory and surveillance service using shore-based radar may be used within a traffic separation scheme (*see* Chapter 12, p.305ff), where there may be an adverse combination of navigational factors. The aim of such systems is to increase the safety of navigation in hazardous areas. Navigational information is given to ships both by broadcast and by response to individual requests. Information passed to ships is usually of the following type:

1. Navigational and traffic information of immediate interest.
2. Information on the movement of ships which appear to be navigating the wrong way within a traffic separation system, contrary to Rule 10 of the Rule of the Road.
3. Urgent information, e.g. casualties, collisions, etc.

Positions are normally given by means of a range and bearing from a named navigational mark.

Aircraft, helicopters and ships may all be used to identify vessels apparently contravening Rule 10.

Position fixing assistance

Ships uncertain of their position may seek assistance from the control centre to establish their whereabouts, using a combination of VHF, DF and radar. It should, however, be remembered that, short of fitting some kind of transponder device in ships, there is often some uncertainty in the identification of any particular radar echo in poor visibility by the control centre.

Basis of operation

Traffic surveillance and management systems entail either compulsory or voluntary compliance by ships. For example, the St Lawrence Vessel Traffic Management (VTM) System is a mandatory system and applies to all vessels over gross tonnage 100. On the other hand, the English Channel and Dover Strait Ship Movement Reporting System (MAREP) together with the Dover Strait Channel Navigation Information Service (CNIS) only invite certain categories of ships to take part, as follows:

> Loaded oil tankers, gas and chemical carriers of gross tonnage 1600 and over.
> Any vessel 'not under command' or at anchor in a traffic separation scheme or inshore traffic zone.
> Any vessel 'restricted in her ability to manoeuvre'.
> Any vessel with defective navigational aids (compasses, radars, radio aids, etc.).

The radar coverage of the CNIS system is illustrated in Fig. 15–34 (p.452).

National compulsory schemes may overlap or operate side by side with voluntary ones. For example, in the south-western approaches to the English Channel (Fig. 15–35, p.453), covered by the voluntary MAREP scheme, the French regulations for the control of traffic off the north and west coasts of France and in the traffic separation scheme off Ushant are mandatory. In certain circumstances, ships already participating in the MAREP scheme may be exempt from the French regulations.

Whether the system is on a voluntary or compulsory basis, control of the ship still remains in the hands of the Captain or Master. Moreover, Rule 10 of the Rule of the Road governing the conduct of ships in traffic separation schemes (*see* Chapter 12) still applies.

Reporting points within traffic surveillance systems

A number of ship reporting points, as with port radar systems, are usually designated within the area covered by the traffic surveillance or management system. These reporting points may be at each end of the traffic separation scheme (e.g. Ushant, Casquets), or at various points within the system (e.g. the St Lawrence VTM System). Details of the information to be sent by ships may be found in *ALRS*, Volume 6, and also on Chart 5500 for the English Channel. It is usually essential that ships with any defects (e.g. 'not under command', defects in propulsion, steering or anchoring equipment, defects in navigational equipment) report the fact.

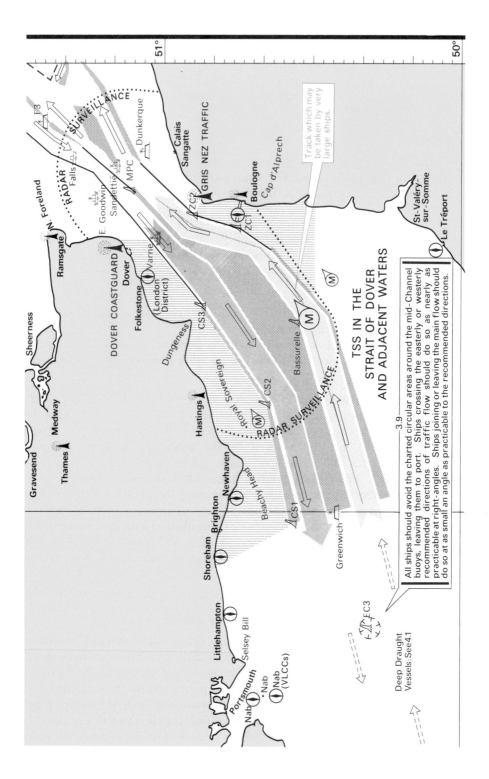

Fig. 15–34.   Radar surveillance in the Dover Strait

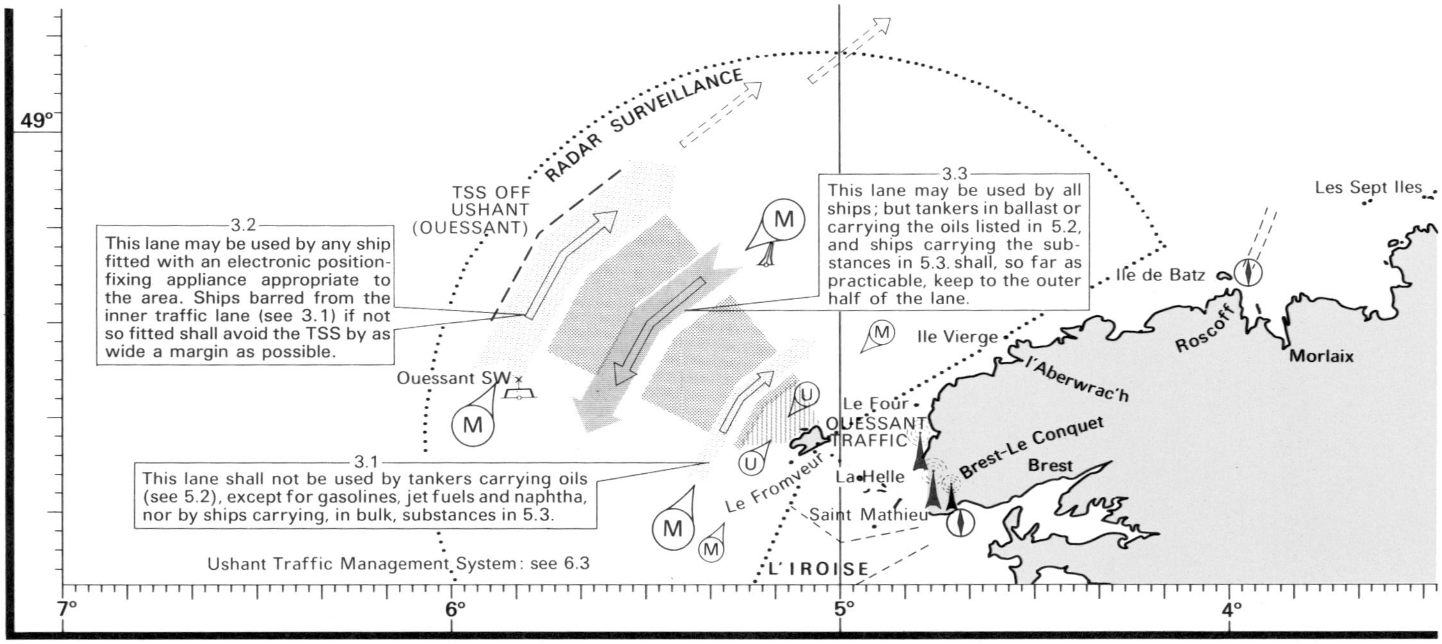
49°
7°
6°
5°
4°
RADAR SURVEILLANCE
TSS OFF USHANT (OUESSANT)
3.2
This lane may be used by any ship fitted with an electronic position-fixing appliance appropriate to the area. Ships barred from the inner traffic lane (see 3.1) if not so fitted shall avoid the TSS by as wide a margin as possible.
3.3
This lane may be used by all ships; but tankers in ballast or carrying the oils listed in 5.2, and ships carrying the substances in 5.3. shall, so far as practicable, keep to the outer half of the lane.
3.1
This lane shall not be used by tankers carrying oils (see 5.2), except for gasolines, jet fuels and naphtha, nor by ships carrying, in bulk, substances in 5.3.
Ouessant SW
Ushant Traffic Management System: see 6.3
Les Sept Iles
Ile de Batz
Roscoff
Morlaix
Ile Vierge
l'Aberwrac'h
Le Four
OUESSANT TRAFFIC
Brest-Le Conquet
Brest
La Helle
Le Fromveur
Saint Mathieu
L'IROISE
M
U

OUESSANT: ITZ AND INNER CHANNELS——3.4

French regulations prohibit navigation in the ITZ and inner channels except by: rescue and salvage tugs, local passenger ships, fishing vessels under 90m long, and pleasure craft. But other ships of under 1600 GRT may use the ITZ if SW-bound, keeping at least one mile from the nearest traffic lane, if they are bound to, or coming from, a French port on the Atlantic, Channel or North Sea coasts and are not carrying the cargoes listed in 5.2, 5.3 or 5.4.

(M) REPORTING POINTS MAREP (U) REPORTING POINTS USHANT
5·2 LIST OF OILS (MARPOL). 5·3 LIST OF NOXIOUS LIQUID SUBSTANCES (MARPOL)
5·4 MARPOL SUPPLEMENTARY LIST, FRENCH REGULATIONS

Fig. 15–35. MAREP and French traffic systems off Ushant

USE OF RADAR IN OR NEAR ICE

Ice is a poor reflector of radar waves and, for this and other reasons, radar does not always detect it in its many forms. Sole reliance must never be placed on radar for ice warning.

Nonetheless, radar can be of great assistance in giving warning of ice. In a calm sea, ice formations of most sorts should be detected on radar, from large icebergs at ranges of 15 to 20 miles down to small growlers at a range of about 2 miles. Because of the angle of incidence of the radar beam, however, smooth flat ice sends back practically no return.

In rough weather, it is unsafe to rely solely on radar when sea clutter extends beyond about 1 mile. Growlers or bergy bits large enough to damage the ship may be undetectable in the clutter until they are very close and a danger to the ship, nor will the use of swept gain necessarily reveal their presence. Small growlers may not be detected at all.

Folds of concentrated hummocked pack ice should be detected in all sea conditions at a range of at least 3 miles. The type of return from pack ice is similar to that of strong sea clutter, except that the echoes will be fixed and not continually changing.

Leads through ice will probably not show up on radar unless the lead is at least $\frac{1}{4}$ mile wide and free of brash ice. Shadow areas behind ridges are liable to be mistaken for leads.

Although ice is a comparatively poor reflector, icebergs generally give detection ranges comparable to those of land of similar height. The strength of the echo depends as much on the angle of inclination of the reflecting surfaces as on size and range.

In waters where shipping may be encountered, individual echoes should be plotted. This may help to indicate whether the echo is a ship, iceberg, bergy bit or growler. If the echo is classified as an iceberg, it should be given a wide berth to avoid the growlers which may have recently calved from it.

When using radar in coastal waters, it is quite likely that the appearance of the coastline will be greatly changed by the presence of fast ice, icebergs, etc.

CHAPTER 16
Navigational Errors

INTRODUCTION

This chapter discusses navigational errors and how the navigator may recognise and deal with them. To this end, a broad understanding is needed of the probability of errors as it affects navigation. The mathematics of one- and two-dimensional errors are set out in an annex at the end of the chapter. The quantification of particular errors in terms of distance, given certain parameters, is set out in Appendix 7.

Every time a position line is obtained from any source (celestial observation, visual bearing, radar range, radio fixing aid), the navigator must be able to judge its likely accuracy, and thus the accuracy of the ship's position obtained from the intersection of two or more of those position lines. Similarly, when determining the ship's DR position or the EP, an assessment of the likely accuracy of that position must be made.

For example (Fig. 16–1), the ship's position has been fixed at A at 0600 by celestial observations. The DR, B, and the EP, C, have been plotted on at 0700, as explained in Chapter 8. At 0700, a single visual position line DE is obtained from the oil production platform F. What position should be chosen for 0700?

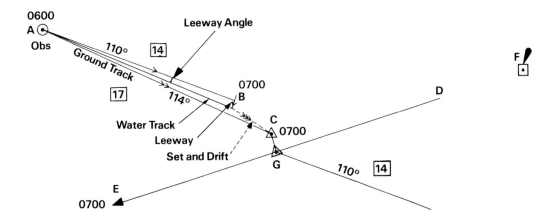

Fig. 16–1. Deriving the ship's position

The navigator may consider: 'I had a good set of stars at 0600. I have an accurate plotting table and bottom log so that the course steered and speed steamed through the water, *AB*, between 0600 and 0700 are, I think, reliable. I am not quite so sure about my estimates of leeway, set and drift, *BC*. But I know that I am on the line *DE* at 0700. I will therefore take point *G* (where *CG* is perpendicular to *DE* and so *G* is the nearest point to *C* on the line *DE*) as my 0700 EP and work from that for my estimate of future positions.'

Consider, however, the likely errors in the observed position at 0600, in the DR and the EP at 0700, and in the plotted bearing of the oil production platform at 0700. The navigator needs to take into account the following:

1. *The error in the observed position at 0600.* The practised observer can normally expect to obtain a celestial fix to within about 2 miles of the true position on almost all occasions. But a poor horizon or refraction different from the normal can cause larger errors than this from time to time.

2. *The error in the determination of the DR and the EP.* Assuming the availability of a gyro-compass whose error has been recently checked and a reliable electromagnetic bottom log, residual errors in a gyro-compass and its associated transmission system could be of the order of $\frac{1}{2}°$ to $1°$ while the error in the electromagnetic log could be as much as 1% to 2%.* Then there is the error inherent in the evaluation of leeway, tidal stream, current and surface drift. This depends as much on the quality of the available data as on the skill of the navigator in interpreting both those data and the effect of the weather.

   It is likely, therefore, that the error in the EP could be as much as 3% to 5% of the distance run since the previous fix. Occasionally the error may be more than this.

3. *Any residual but unknown error in the gyro-compass together with small but unpredictable errors in the taking and plotting of the visual bearing at 0700.* These may be as much as $±1°$.

These effects are shown in Fig. 16–2.

A position circle, radius 2 miles, is drawn around *A* to show the likely area covered by the observed position. By 0700, this position circle will have grown with time according to the errors in the course steered, the distance steamed, and errors in the estimation of leeway, and the set and rate of the tidal stream, current, etc. The bearing of the oil platform *DE* is plotted showing the $±1°$ limits. The navigator can now reduce his position circle at 0700 to the area *KLMN*.

As the chosen point *G* also lies within the area *KLMN*, this rather lengthy assessment of the position area at 0700 may seem unnecessary. The plotted bearing of the production platform might, however, fall outside the navigator's estimate of the likely position circle at 0700, e.g. *PQ* in Fig. 16–2. The navigator must then review the situation to establish what has gone wrong. Has the observed position been calculated correctly; has the DR been plotted correctly; has the production platform been properly identified? In different circumstances, the navigator may be passing close to shoals between him and

* This error assumes that the log has been correctly calibrated.

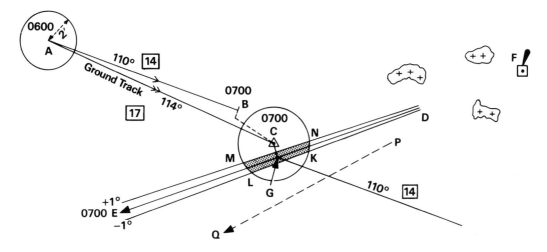

Fig. 16–2. Plotting the position, taking likely errors into account

the production platform and would be wise to choose an 0700 EP in the area *KLMN* which assumes the most 'dangerous' position, e.g. *N* in Fig. 16–2, perhaps calling for corrective action.

All practical navigational work frequently involves dealing with errors of some kind or other. The navigator needs to be able to discriminate between an error caused by a mistake, an error in a particular piece of equipment which can be allowed for in some way (e.g. an error in the gyro-compass), and an error caused at random.

NAVIGATIONAL ACCURACIES

If ships are to be navigated safely, there must always be a maximum acceptable limit to navigational accuracy. The ultimate aim in any navigational system is to ensure that the ship remains within predetermined acceptable safe limits.

Definitions

The following definitions apply.

Accuracy. Accuracy may be expressed in a number of ways which are explained later, e.g. *root mean square distance* (d_{rms}); one, two or three sigma (1σ, 2σ, 3σ); *circular error probable* (CEP). Equally and more simply, it may be expressed in terms of a percentage probability. The accuracy limits of navigation position lines, fixes, etc. should be such that there is a 95% probability that the actual position line or fix concerned is within the limit quoted.

Precision. Precision relates to the refinement to which a value is stated. For example, a celestial position line may be stated to the nearest $0'.2$ but, because of errors in refraction, personal error, etc., it may only be accurate to $\pm 2'.0$ (95% probability). Usually, there is little point in tabulating a quantity to a greater precision than the accuracy required, but calculations involving a number of fractions should not be 'rounded off' too soon, otherwise a cumulative error may be introduced.

Absolute position. The absolute position of a ship is that which defines its position on the Earth and is normally expressed in terms of latitude and longitude. Where the higher orders of accuracy are required, it is necessary to state the reference datum used.

Relative position. The relative position of a ship is a means of expressing its position with reference to a fixed point or other ship. It may be determined either by direct measurement, or by both ships using the same navigation system at the same time, or by comparison of measured absolute positions (*see* below).

Repeatability. Repeatability is the ability of the same ship or different ships to return to a particular position to the same degree of accuracy as the original ship, using the same positional sensors.

TYPES OF ERROR

There are three principal types of error: faults, systematic errors and random errors.

Faults

Faults can be caused by any of the following:

1. A blunder on the navigator's part.
2. A malfunction in the equipment. This may often be difficult to recognise. For example, a gyro may start a slow wander without setting off the alarm system and it may therefore be some time before the fault is discovered.
3. A breakdown in the equipment. This may be less serious than a malfunction, on the grounds that no information is better than the wrong information.

Faults must be guarded against. A reliable cross-check against the particular source of information is always useful. For example, radar may be used as a check against the Decca Navigator and vice versa. The DR/EP is an invaluable means of checking a position line from any source. Regular checks on the accuracy of the gyro-compass, as described in Chapter 9, may well indicate whether an error has developed, as may comparison with other gyros or with the magnetic compass. The navigator may keep a log of readings from any particular radio navigational aid to ensure that the pattern of readings is consistent. Any departure from this consistent pattern may well indicate some kind of malfunction or other fault. For example, suppose the position line readings from a radio fixing aid at equal time intervals are: 4.5, 5.2, 5.8, 7.5, 7.2, 7.8, 8.5. It should be immediately apparent that the 7.5 reading is an incorrect value as it is inconsistent with all the others.

Blunders

Blunder is the term used to describe a mistake. For example, the navigator may forget to apply the error in the compass or the deck watch, or he may apply it in the wrong direction.

Blunders are not easily revealed. Procedures need to be developed which help to eliminate them. The navigational work should always be cross-checked.

Desk-top computers and hand-held programmable calculators may be programmed with routine tasks such as astronomical sight reductions, tidal calculations, the calculation of rhumb-line and great-circle courses, etc. The interpolation involved when using tables is a frequent cause of error in navigation—this may be avoided by the use of suitable programs.

Systematic errors

A *systematic error* is one that follows some regular pattern, by which means that error may be predicted. Once an error can be predicted, it can be eliminated or allowed for.

The simplest type of systematic error is one which is constant, for example the error resulting from any misalignment between the lubber's line of the compass and the fore-and-aft line of the ship.

Other examples of systematic error are errors in the gyro-compass, the deviation of the magnetic compass, the fixed error in the Decca radio aid.* Errors in the gyro-compass may be reduced or eliminated electronically by making the necessary allowances for course, speed and latitude. The deviation in the magnetic compass may be reduced by placing small magnets and soft-iron correctors close to the compass and the residual deviation tabulated in a deviation table. Fixed errors for Decca may be found from the *Decca Navigator Marine Data Sheets* (NP 316).

Systematic errors change so slowly with time that they may be measured and corrected. It may well be, however, that certain errors, while fairly constant over a matter of hours, may then begin to change. Such errors may be termed *semi-systematic*. Examples of such errors might be: any residual error in the gyro-compass after applying the appropriate corrections; changes in dip and refraction of celestial bodies observed at low altitudes, caused by unpredictable changes in temperature and pressure.

In practice semi-systematic errors are, of necessity, treated as random errors† (*see* below).

Random errors

Other errors change so rapidly with time that they cannot be predicted. There are many causes of such errors. The taking and plotting of a visual bearing is subject to small unpredictable errors. Short-term variations in the ionosphere affect radio aid readings. A value extracted from a table is only accurate to within the limits set by the table itself. For example, if a table is expressed to only one decimal point, an extracted value of 3.4 may lie anywhere between 3.35 and 3.45.

Such errors are known as *random errors* and are governed by the laws of probability. This means that, whereas the sign and magnitude of any particular

* Whilst the fixed error remains constant in any one location, it may change considerably between relatively close positions. Thus, the error will be experienced in a moving ship as one which varies with time, the rate of change being dependent on the speed.

† It is impossible to draw a precise dividing line between random and semi-systematic errors. Similarly, it is impossible to draw a precise dividing line between semi-systematic and systematic errors. This is because the difference is to do with the time scale over which the error has occurred. It is therefore quite possible, for example, for any unknown residual error in the gyro-compass to be a random or a systematic error.

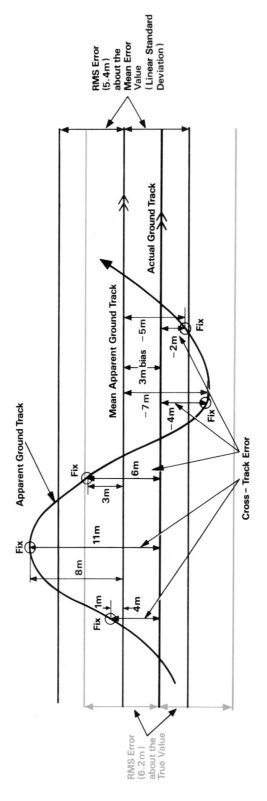

Fig. 16-3.   Errors in one dimension

random error cannot be predicted, the averaging of a number of readings can help to determine the magnitude of that error.

Composite errors

Faults, systematic (and semi-systematic) errors and random errors may exist in combination, in which case the error distribution may look like that shown in Fig. 16–4. The bell-shaped pattern of random errors is explained in the annex to this chapter.

Systematic errors shift the random distribution curve to the left or right of the correct value. A fault can be of any size, and therefore the distribution may be represented by a straight line, so adding a 'skirt' to the normal distribution.

In navigation, it is always possible for all these errors to exist in combination. Faults, systematic and semi-systematic errors can, however, be reduced, eliminated or allowed for, leaving in many cases only the random error to be dealt with. Random errors are considered as being in one or two dimensions; these are discussed below.

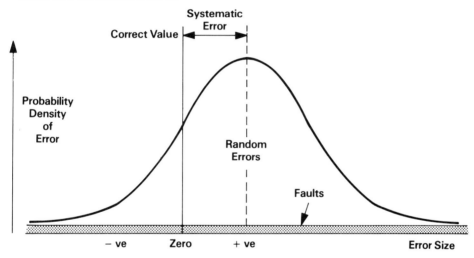

Fig. 16–4.   Combined errors

In practice, the navigator may not have the time nor the information to analyse the nature of the errors experienced, nor to calculate them. If, however, he understands these concepts, he is better equipped to determine his Position Probability Area (PPA) and his Most Probable Position (MPP). For example, he should look upon his Estimated Position (EP) not so much as a position but rather as a 95% probability circle with a radius appropriate to the situation and expanding with time. If he considers his estimate of speed along the track to be less reliable than his estimate of the ground track itself, he may decide to change his Position Probability Area from a circle to an ellipse, the longer axis being along the track.

Random errors in one dimension

Consider a ship making good an actual ground track of 090° (Fig. 16–3). Her position is fixed at various times by some navigational aid. Each fix includes random errors which cause it to fall either north or south of the actual track.

The error across the track only (cross-track error) is considered, errors to the north of track being taken as +ve and those to the south as −ve.

The cross-track error is shown at five equally spaced points along the track. The mean (cross-track) error value is:

$$\frac{4 + 11 + 6 - 4 - 2}{5} m = + 3 \text{ m}$$

This mean error value is known as the *bias*. In Fig. 16–3 it is the difference between the mean apparent ground track and the actual ground track. The bias in any given set of readings is discussed below.

Bias, however, is insufficient on its own to explain the nature of the errors. The spread of those errors also needs to be considered. The spread of errors is obtained by squaring each cross-track error, taking the average, and then taking the square root, thus obtaining the *root mean square (RMS) error*. In Fig. 16–3:

$$\text{RMS error} = \sqrt{\frac{4^2 + 11^2 + 6^2 + (-4)^2 + (-2)^2}{5}}$$

$$= 6.2 \text{ m}$$

This figure is known as the **RMS error about the true value**.

It is possible to calculate the RMS error about any other value but the only one of interest is that about the mean error value. This is referred to as the *(linear) standard deviation (SD)*.

$$\begin{array}{ll} \text{linear standard} & = \text{RMS error about} \\ \text{deviation (SD)} & \text{the mean error value} \end{array}$$

$$= \sqrt{\frac{1^2 + 8^2 + 3^2 + (-7)^2 + (-5)^2}{5}}$$

$$= 5.4 \text{ m}$$

It may also be seen that:

$$\left(\begin{array}{c} \text{RMS error about} \\ \text{the true value} \end{array}\right)^2 = (\text{bias})^2 + (\text{SD})^2 \qquad \ldots \textbf{16.1}$$

$$\text{i.e.} \qquad (6.2)^2 = (3)^2 + (5.4)^2$$

In practice, however, to determine the linear standard deviation accurately, the errors in a large number of readings are required, as explained in the annex to this chapter.

Many one-dimensional random navigational errors show a specific bell-shaped pattern (Fig. 16–4) known as a *normal distribution*. The normal distribution of errors is explained and illustrated in the annex (pp.480–1). The bell-shape of this pattern is fixed by the unbiased estimate of the linear standard deviation, which is often referred to as the *one sigma (1σ) value*, as explained in the annex. It is possible to say what percentage of errors will lie within any multiple of this standard deviation, and examples of these are set out in the annex (p.481).

In navigation, 95% probability is the value normally used to express the accuracy of one-dimensional position lines. This value may be considered for most practical purposes as being equivalent to two sigma (2σ) or twice the standard deviation (2SD). Thus, if a large number of random measurements are made which are of a normal distribution, then approximately 95% of these measurements may be expected to fall within the two sigma (2σ) value or twice the linear standard deviation about the mean value. There is a 1 in 20 chance (5%) that the position line obtained could lie outside this 2σ limit. For example, in Fig. 16–2 the navigator should now be able to recognise that:

> There is a 95% probability that the plotted bearing of the oil production platform at 0700 is accurate to within 1°, taking into account any unknown residual error in the gyro-compass and any small errors in observing and plotting. There is a 1 in 20 (or 5%) chance that the position line might lie outside this limit.

When several independent random errors are considered in conjunction, their individual standard deviations may be combined as explained in the annex (p.481):

$$\sigma = \sqrt{\sigma_1^2 + \sigma_2^2 + \sigma_3^2 + \ldots + \sigma_n^2} \qquad \ldots \textbf{16.2}$$

where σ_1, σ_2, σ_3, etc. are the individual standard deviations and σ the composite standard deviation. For example, if a ship is running a line of bearing when the accuracy of fixing is ±50 metres, assuming a 95% (2σ) probability but, due to vagaries in course keeping is only maintaining her required track to an accuracy of ±20 metres (95% probability), the combined effect of these two errors will be to produce an overall 2σ value of:

$$2\sigma = \sqrt{50^2 + 20^2} = 53.85 \text{ m}$$

The chances of the total error being as much as 70 m, which would be the case if both errors had the same sign and maximum value at the same instant, would only be 1/20 × 1/20 or 1 chance in 400. The overall error will lie within the limit of ± 54 metres on 95% of occasions. It should never be assumed that, when two random errors are involved, they must necessarily have the same sign at any particular moment.

If several small errors are combined with one which is large by comparison, the small errors can often be disregarded as having little or no practical significance. For example (*see also* p.484), the accuracy of a gyro bearing allowing for any random gyro error may be ±1°, assuming a 95% probability and normal distribution. However, the gyro bearing can only be read to the nearest $\frac{1}{2}°$, i.e. the maximum rounding-off error is ±$\frac{1}{4}°$. The gyro bearing itself can be plotted to an accuracy of ±$\frac{1}{4}°$. What is the likely total 95% error?

The standard deviations of these three values are as follows (the full details are set out in the annex, p.484):

Gyro bearing	0°.5	($2\,\sigma_1 = 1°$ ∴ $\sigma_1 = 0°.5$)
Rounding-off error	0°.15 approx.	($\sigma_2 = 0.6 \times 0°.25$)
Plotting error	0°.15 approx.	($\sigma_3 = 0.6 \times 0°.25$)

combined standard deviation $\sigma = \sqrt{(0.5)^2 + (0.15)^2 + (0.15)^2}$
$$= 0°.54$$
$$\therefore\ 2\sigma = 1°.08$$

The random gyro error of $1°$ is only increased by a negligible amount when the taking and the plotting of the bearing are also considered. For most practical purposes, the total 95% error is still only $1°$.

Bias

If a series of readings is taken, a bias in these readings about the true value may be revealed. This bias can occur for various reasons. The number of readings may be small, as in Fig. 16–3. The number of readings may be large but be taken over a relatively short time scale and may include an as yet unrevealed systematic or semi-systematic error. This systematic or semi-systematic error, which may well be constant over the time scale concerned, will be revealed as a bias, that is, a difference between the mean value of the readings and their true value.

If the errors are truly random, and if an infinite number of observations are made, then mean and true values of the readings will coincide, that is, there will be no bias. In practice, however, it is not possible to take an infinite number of readings. The navigator must always remember, therefore, that his set of readings, which appears random, may in fact be biased one side or the other of the true value.

A bias will be present in many readings from radio navigation and inertial navigation systems. Moreover, this bias will not be constant but will change with time, the rate of change of the bias depending on the type of navigational aid. For example, a 24 hour related bias will be experienced with the Ship Inertial Navigation System (SINS), Omega and also Decca. A more rapidly changing bias will also be experienced with Decca, the bias being associated with the course and speed of the ship across the Decca chain.

Random errors in two dimensions

Radial error

Although the navigator is interested in the likely error in any one position line, he is also concerned with the likely error in his fix.

Fig. 16–5 shows a situation where a ship stopped in position B has obtained a series of fixes using some navigational aid. Position A represents the mean of these fixes, the difference between the individual fix and A being shown as r_1, r_2, r_3, r_4 and r_5.

The total error between positions A and B may be regarded as being made up of one-dimensional distributions in two mutually perpendicular directions, e.g. N–S and E–W, through the mean position A. Thus, there is a component of *bias* in each of these directions, y and x, and these determine the true position B. If there is no bias, then A and B coincide.

A measure of the spread of these errors is found by calculating the *radial error* (σ_r) about the mean or true position. Radial error is known as the *root mean square (RMS) error*, or *root mean square distance* (d_{rms}) about the true or mean value. The radial error about the mean position is often referred to as the *radial standard*

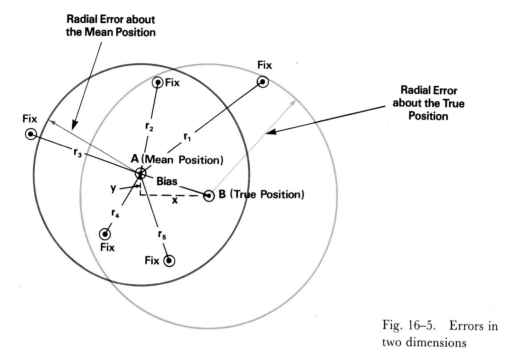

Fig. 16–5. Errors in two dimensions

*deviation** (radial SD):

$$\text{radial error about the mean position } (1d_{rms}) = \sqrt{\frac{r_1^2 + r_2^2 + r_3^2 + \ldots + r_n^2}{n}} \quad \ldots \textbf{16.3}$$

where n is the total number of individual errors. In Fig. 16–5 the radial error is shown for five values of r (r_1 to r_5). Also:

$$\left(\begin{array}{c}\text{radial error about}\\\text{the true position}\end{array}\right)^2 = (\text{bias})^2 + \left(\begin{array}{c}\text{radial error about}\\\text{the mean position}\end{array}\right)^2 \quad \ldots \textbf{16.4}$$

For example, suppose the errors around the mean position A are as follows: $r_1 = 40$ m; $r_2 = 24$ m; $r_3 = 30$ m; $r_4 = 18$ m; $r_5 = 23$ m. The bias (AB) is 19 m.

From formula **(16.3)**:

$$\text{radial error about the mean position } (1d_{rms}) = \sqrt{\frac{40^2 + 24^2 + 30^2 + 18^2 + 23^2}{5}}$$

$$\simeq 28.03 \text{ m}$$

From formula **(16.4)**:

$$\text{radial error about the true position } (1d_{rms}) = \sqrt{(19)^2 + (28.03)^2}$$

$$\simeq 33.86 \text{ m}$$

* Be careful to differentiate between linear standard deviation and radial standard deviation. Both terms are explained in the annex. The abbreviations used in this chapter are:

$$1\sigma \quad \text{linear standard deviation}$$
$$1d_{rms} \text{ or } \sigma_r \quad \text{radial standard deviation}$$

Orthogonal position lines

Orthogonal position lines are position lines (Fig. 16–6) intersecting at right angles where the individual linear standard deviations (1σ) of the error values in those position lines are the same.

The 95% circle of error around these two position lines may be found, as shown in the annex (page 487), from the formula:

$$r = 2.45\sigma \qquad \qquad \ldots \textbf{16.5}$$
$$\simeq 1.25a$$

where σ is the linear standard deviation of each position line and a is the 95% or 2σ value of the error in each.

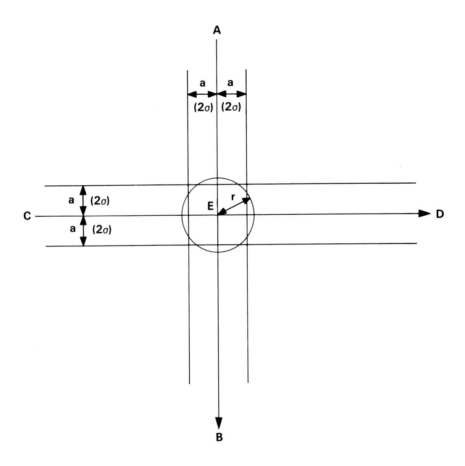

Fig. 16–6.   The 95% error circle around two orthogonal position lines

The error ellipse and the equivalent probability circle

Orthogonal position lines do not often occur in practice. It is more likely that the error distribution will be in the form of an *error ellipse* (Fig. 16–7), where the position lines do not cut at a right angle and have different standard deviations.

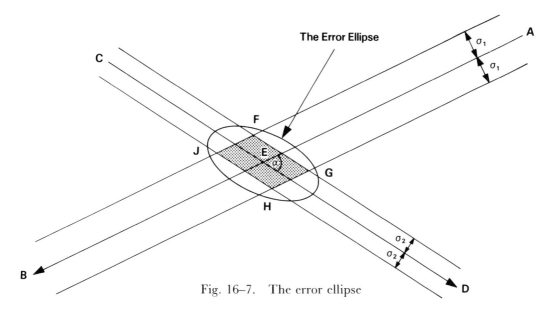

Fig. 16–7.   The error ellipse

The two position lines AB and CD intersect at E at an angle α; σ_1 is the linear standard deviation or 1σ value of the error in AB, and σ_2 is the linear standard deviation or 1σ value of the error in CD. The intersection of the standard deviation position line bands forms a *diamond of error FGHJ*.

The exact shape of the error ellipse varies with the magnitude of the errors σ_1 and σ_2 as well as the angle of cut α. The development of the 95% ellipse is explained in the annex (page 488).

It is more helpful to the navigator if this error ellipse is adjusted to form a circle around the position where the probability of error is the same as that for the ellipse. Such a circle is known as an *equivalent probability circle*.

The radial error or $1d_{rms}$ (σ_r) value of this circle may be found from the formula:

$$1d_{rms} = \operatorname{cosec} \alpha \quad \sqrt{\sigma_1{}^2 + \sigma_2{}^2} \qquad \ldots \mathbf{16.6}$$

where σ_1 and σ_2 are the individual linear standard deviations and α is the angle of cut between the two position lines. Similarly, the $2d_{rms}$ $(2\sigma_r)$ value, illustrated in Fig. 16–8 (page 468), is:

$$2d_{rms} = 2 \operatorname{cosec} \alpha \sqrt{\sigma_1{}^2 + \sigma_2{}^2} \qquad \ldots \mathbf{16.7}$$

$$= \operatorname{cosec} \alpha \sqrt{a^2 + b^2} \qquad \ldots \mathbf{16.8}$$

where $a = 2\sigma_1$ and $b = 2\sigma_2$.

The $2d_{rms}$ value is of particular interest to the navigator because its percentage probability lies between 95.4% and 98.2%, dependent on the shape of the ellipse. The navigator may therefore use the $2d_{rms}$ value for the 95% probability circle for most practical purposes as, in so doing, he is always taking a more pessimistic but safer view of the likely circle of error. An example is given later in the section on the practical application of navigational errors.

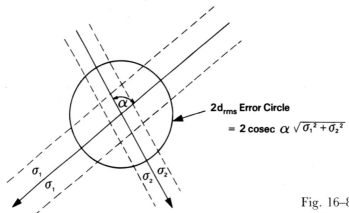

2d$_{rms}$ Error Circle

$= 2 \operatorname{cosec} \alpha \sqrt{\sigma_1{}^2 + \sigma_2{}^2}$

Fig. 16–8. The 2d$_{rms}$ error circle around the position

Circular error probable (CEP)

The navigator may encounter the term *circular error probable* (CEP) as the accuracy of navigational equipment is often expressed using this term. The CEP may be defined as being the 50% probability circle. That is to say, there is an equal chance that the position lies outside or within the circle.

When the position lines are orthogonal, the radius of the CEP approximates to 1.2σ, where σ is the standard deviation of the two position lines. The 95% probability circle may be found by multiplying the CEP radius by a factor of approximately 2.1. This factor may also be used to find the 95% equivalent probability circle from the CEP around an error ellipse, provided that the latter is not too elongated. The relationship between the CEP and the shape of the ellipse is set out in the annex (p.493).

THE PRACTICAL APPLICATION OF NAVIGATIONAL ERRORS

Allowing for faults and systematic errors

Errors arising from faults and systematic errors need to be eliminated or allowed for. Various ways of achieving this have already been discussed in this chapter and are summarised below:

1. Cross-checking one system against another. Examples are: cross-checking radar against the Decca Navigator and vice versa; cross-checking the DR/EP against a position line from any source.

2. Navigational procedures which help to eliminate mistakes, for example, cross-checking the Navigating Officer's work.
3. The reduction or elimination of systematic errors in navigational equipment such as the gyro- and magnetic compasses, radio aids, etc. Examples are:
  (a) The necessary adjustments to the gyro-compass for course, speed and latitude and the determination of any residual error by the methods described in Chapter 9.
  (b) The reduction of the deviation in the magnetic compass by means of small magnets and soft-iron correctors and the tabulation of the residual deviation.
  (c) The allowance for fixed errors in the Decca Navigator.
  (d) The allowance for personal error.

Allowing for random errors

Once faults and systematic errors have been allowed for, the navigator is left with random errors. In general, these may be expected to have a normal distribution (Fig. 16–4) and those which are rectangular (p.482) can often be disregarded because they add so little to the total random error.

As far as random errors in navigation are concerned, the accuracy limits of a position line or fix should be such that there is a 95% probability that the actual position line or fix is within the limit quoted. This means that there is always a 5% or 1 in 20 chance that the position line or fix lies outside this limit and the practical navigator always needs to bear this in mind. It is a matter of navigational prudence to choose that position in an area of uncertainty which places the ship closest to danger.

Because position lines usually cross at an angle other than a right angle and because the amount of error in individual position lines may well be different when expressed in n miles, the navigator is often left with a diamond of error and an error ellipse, as shown in Fig. 16–7. For all practical purposes, provided the ellipse is not too elongated, he may determine the radius of his 95% probability circle around his position by using the procedure described on p.489, particularly if that procedure has been programmed as suggested on p.492. Alternatively, he may use the $2d_{rms}$ formulae (16.7) or (16.8), which produce a slightly larger error circle and so err on the side of caution.

The navigator may then use the 95% probability circle in preference to the 95% error ellipse. Thus, in Fig. 16–9 (p.470) a position F may be obtained from the intersection of two position lines AB and CD, each considered accurate to $\pm1°$ (95% probability). AB and CD cut at 65° and the distances of the two objects observed* are: lighthouse 12 miles; chimney 15 miles.

One degree at 12' subtends 0'.2, at 15', 0'.25. From formula (16.8), the radius of the $2d_{rms}$ probability circle around F is 0'.35. Using formulae (16.27) and (16.28), the radius of the 95% probability circle is 0'.33.

In the special case where position lines cross at right angles and the standard linear deviations are the same, a circle of radius $1\frac{1}{4}$ times the 95% or 2σ value of the linear error is the 95% probability circle.

---

* The distances of these objects are greater than would normally be expected in coastal navigation, but they are chosen to illustrate the technique. If the two objects are 3' and 6' away, the radius of the 95% probability circle is about 230 metres.

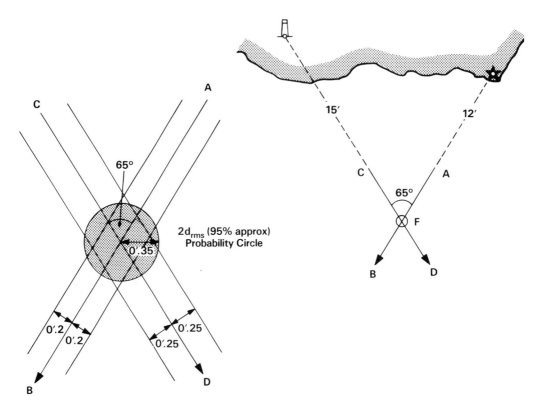

Fig. 16–9.   Plotting the $2d_{rms}$ (95% approx.) probability circle

Limits of random errors

As explained earlier, there is a 95% probability that the random error in any position line is within the two sigma (2σ) value selected; that is to say, there is a 1 in 20 chance that the position line lies outside this limit. If it appears that the error in a position line is greater than three sigma (3σ), for example from its juxtaposition with other position lines, it is more likely that the error has been caused by a mistake rather than by a random error. This is because the likelihood of there being a normally distributed random error equal to 3σ is only about 0.27% or 1 chance in 370. The likelihood of the error being as great as 4σ is only about 1 chance in 16,000.

In practice, therefore, if the random error in any one position line appears to lie between 2σ and 3σ, that position line should be treated with caution. Some kind of mistake may have been made and the possibility should be investigated. If the error appears to be greater than 3σ, then almost certainly a mistake has occurred unless there is supporting evidence to the contrary. The navigator will need to investigate the reason, for example:

He may have made a blunder such as misreading an instrument or misidentifying an object.

He may have made an incorrect assessment of the sigma values of one or more of his position lines or position areas.

His assessment of external factors such as current and tidal stream may be in error.

An unsuspected semi-systematic error may have arisen.

Most Probable Position (MPP)

The navigator is now able to determine his 95% *Position Probability Area* (PPA). PPA was defined in Chapter 8 (page 181) and four examples of finding this are given below. Within this area, he needs to choose his *Most Probable Position* (MPP) (Fig. 16–10), which he may treat as a fix, an EP or a DR dependent on the quality of the input. MPP may be defined as that position which takes into account the probability of error in each piece of positional information available.

Judgement is all-important when dealing in a practical way with errors in position lines in order to arrive at an MPP. The magnitudes of the 95% errors in the DR and the EP, and in the position lines obtained by visual observation of celestial and terrestrial objects, are largely a matter of judgement based upon experience. Some idea of the likely extent of these errors has already been given earlier in this chapter (*see* page 456) and example 4 shows how these values may be used.

Example 1

In Fig. 16–10 *E* is the ship's estimated position, considered accurate to within a radius of 3 miles (95% probability). At this time a position line *AB* is obtained, considered accurate to within 1½ miles (95% probability). The PPA will be the sector *CDFG*, the overlapping area created by the EP probability circle and the band of error around the position line.

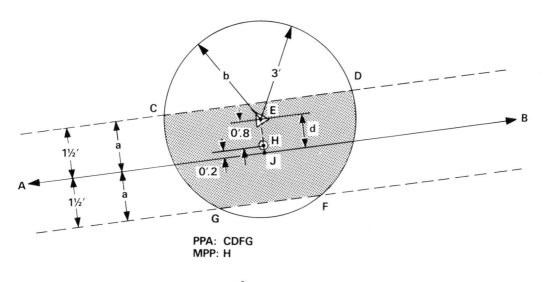

PPA: CDFG
MPP: H

Note: $HJ = \dfrac{a^2}{a^2 + b^2}\, d$

Fig. 16–10.   Position Probability Area (1): MPP within the PPA

If the overall effect of each error is considered to be of a random normal distribution, the effect of each error is proportional to the square of its size. Thus, if the likely error in the position line is a miles and that in the EP is b miles, the Most Probable Position H is nearer the position line AB at a distance:

$$\frac{a^2}{a^2 + b^2}\, d \qquad\qquad \dots \textbf{16.9}$$

where d is the perpendicular distance EJ between the EP, E, and the position line AB in Fig. 16–10.

If $a = 1\frac{1}{2}$ miles and $b = 3$ miles for a 95% probability and EJ is $1'$, then H will be:

$$\frac{2.25}{2.25 + 9} \times 1' = 0'.2 \text{ from } AB*$$

Example 2

If the position line falls outside the probability circle, although the error bands overlap (Fig. 16–11), the MPP as calculated above may fall outside the PPA.

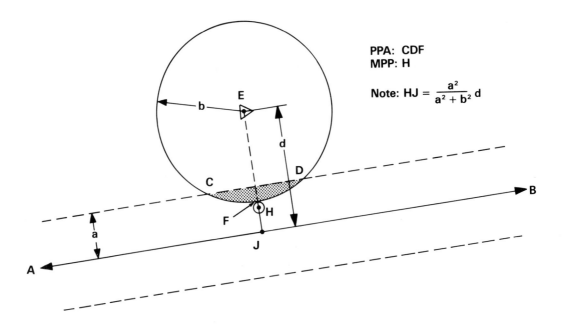

PPA: CDF
MPP: H

Note: $HJ = \dfrac{a^2}{a^2 + b^2}\, d$

Fig. 16–11.   Position Probability Area (2): MPP outside the PPA

The Most Probable Position H, as calculated above, lies outside the Position Probability Area *CDF*. Although the two areas overlap, the fact that AB lies

---

* Although an error band and an error circle may intersect, as in Fig. 16–10, it *does not always follow* that they can be combined in this way to give a better estimate of the position. Statistical confidence interval tests may indicate that the two sets of data are inconsistent with each other.

outside the probability circle around the EP means that some kind of mistake may have occurred, and so the navigator must treat the result with caution. He needs to investigate the possibility of a mistake and, if possible, resolve it. All other things being equal, he would probably choose the position *F* as the MPP. This is the point where the probability area *CDF* is closest to *H*.

Example 3

If the two error bands do not overlap at all (Fig. 16–12), then almost certainly some mistake must have occurred which should be investigated. The Navigating Officer may have erred in his estimate of the 95% probability limits, or he may have made a blunder.

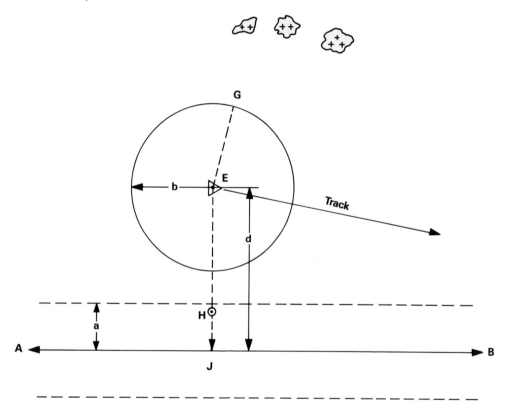

Fig. 16–12.   Position Probability Area (3): error bands do not overlap

If these matters cannot be resolved and the navigator is forced to choose between the two, his choice of position must depend on the circumstances at the time. For example, if he is in the vicinity of dangers, he should choose that position *G* which puts him closest to these. Alternatively, no dangers being present, he may choose *J*, the position on *AB* closest to *E*. On the other hand, if he decides to weight each error in proportion to its square, then he may choose *H* as the MPP, calculating this from formula **(16.9)**. In short, no hard and fast rule as to what the navigator should do can be laid down; he has to use his own judgement.

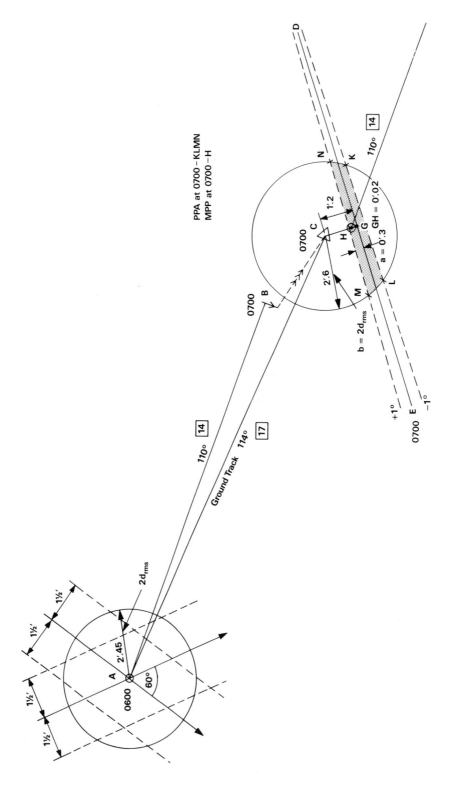

Fig. 16–13.   Plotting the position, taking probability into account

Example 4

Consider the application of the principles of probability to the example given at the beginning of this chapter (Fig. 16–1), and how these principles may be used to determine the PPA and MPP at 0700 (Fig. 16–13).

The error in the observed position at 0600

Assume this was obtained from two astronomical position lines* each considered correct to within $1'.5$ (95% probability) crossing at $60°$. Then, from formula **(16.8)**:

$$2d_{rms} = cosec\ 60°\ \sqrt{(1.5)^2 + (1.5)^2}$$
$$= 2'.45$$

At 0600, therefore, the navigator should be able to assume that there is a 95% probability that his actual position will lie within $2'.45$ of position *A*.

The error in the determination of the EP at 0700

The magnitude of the error in the EP depends upon those factors mentioned on page 456. Assuming that there is a 95% probability that the error in the EP is within 5% of the distance run since the previous fix at 0600, this error should therefore amount to 5% of $17'$ or $0'.85$.

Assuming a 95% probability, the overall error at 0700 is therefore, from formula **(16.2)**, equal to $\sqrt{(2.45)^2 + (0.85)^2}$ or $2'.59$. The radius of the position circle around *C* at 0700 is then about $2'.6$, again assuming a 95% probability.

Note: The two errors $2'.45$ and $0'.85$ must *not* be added together to obtain the combined error. The likelihood that the maximum error could be as much as $2'.45 + 0'.85 = 3'.3$ is $1/20 \times 1/20$ or $1/400$ or 0.25%. The probability that the 0700 position lies within $3'.3$ of *C* is therefore 99.75%, a much higher percentage than is needed for most practical purposes.

The error in the bearing at 0700

If the bearing of the oil production platform is accurate to within $1°$, given a 95% probability, and assuming that the distance of the platform is about $18'$, the position line *DE* will be correct to within $0'.3$. The distance *CG* may be measured, $1'.2$ (*CG* is perpendicular to *DE*).

The navigator can now reduce the position circle at 0700 to the Position Probability Area *KLMN*. The Most Probable Position *H* may be calculated, using formula **(16.9)**, as shown in the example on page 471 (Fig. 16–10).

In Fig. 16–13:

$$GH = \frac{a^2}{a^2 + b^2} \times CG$$
$$= \frac{(0.3)^2}{(0.3)^2 + (2.6)^2} \times 1'.2$$
$$= 0'.016 \simeq 0'.02$$

---

* An astronomical fix frequently comprises more than two position lines. The method of obtaining the Most Probable Position from a number of position lines that are subject to normally distributed errors is given in the annex.

Position *H* may now be plotted and the ship's future track developed from this position.

In this particular case, the EP (*G*) and the MPP (*H*) are virtually identical, so for all practical purposes the navigator may plot from *G*. It would be unwise, however, to assume that the two positions will always be so close together, as Examples 1 to 3 make clear. Each position line should be weighted to take account of its probability of error, before an assessment of the MPP is made.

ANNEX A TO CHAPTER 16
Navigational Errors

ONE-DIMENSIONAL RANDOM ERRORS

Variance and linear standard deviation

Suppose a series of observations for a single position line are taken from a radio aid (e.g. the Decca Navigator) receiver at 10 second intervals, the ship being in a fixed position. After applying any fixed error correction (which may be considered as the *bias* in that radio aid) for the area, a sample obtained from a very large number of observations might be as in Table 16A–1:*

Table 16A–1

CLASS INTERVAL OF RADIO AID READING	CENTRE OF RADIO AID LANE READING		NO. OF OBSERVATIONS		DEVIATION (APPROX.) FROM MEAN VALUE $(x - \bar{x})$	
8.195–8.205	x_1	8.20	f_1	2	d_1	−0.06
8.205–8.215	x_2	8.21	f_2	6	d_2	−0.05
8.215–8.225	x_3	8.22	f_3	17	d_3	−0.04
8.225–8.235	x_3	8.23	f_4	50	d_4	−0.03
8.235–8.245	x_5	8.24	f_5	63	d_5	−0.02
8.245–8.255	x_6	8.25	f_6	72	d_6	−0.01
8.255–8.265	x_7	8.26	f_7	76	d_7	NIL
8.265–8.275	x_8	8.27	f_8	73	d_8	+0.01
8.275–8.285	x_9	8.28	f_9	65	d_9	+0.02
8.285–8.295	x_{10}	8.29	f_{10}	52	d_{10}	+0.03
8.295–8.305	x_{11}	8.30	f_{11}	16	d_{11}	+0.04
8.305–8.315	x_{12}	8.31	f_{12}	5	d_{12}	+0.05
8.315–8.325	x_{13}	8.32	f_{13}	3	d_{13}	+0.06

Total readings $(n) = 500$

* This is a hypothetical example illustrating how random errors might occur. The example has not been derived from any particular set of radio aid readings.

A mean value $\bar{x}$ may be calculated from these readings as follows:

$$\bar{x} = \frac{x_1 f_1 + x_2 f_2 + x_3 f_3 + \ldots + x_{13} f_{13}}{f_1 + f_2 + f_3 + \ldots + f_{13}}$$ ... **16.10**

$$= \frac{(8.20)2 + (8.21)6 + (8.22)17 + \ldots + (8.32)3}{2 + 6 + 17 + \ldots + 3}$$

$$= 8.26016 \simeq 8.26$$

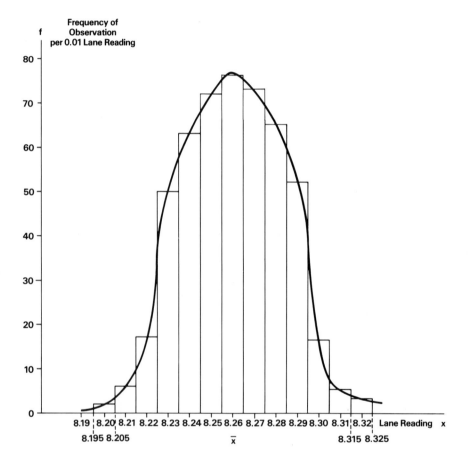

Fig. 16–14.   Histogram of lane readings against frequency of observation

If these readings are plotted against the frequency of observation in the form of a histogram (Fig. 16–14), it may be seen that the frequency of observation reduces as the readings diverge from the approximate mean value $\bar{x}$, 8.26. It may also be seen that a curve drawn through the histogram value peaks at the mean value $\bar{x}$ and is roughly symmetrical about this mean.*

* In practice, the curve may be somewhat distorted about the mean lane value and is likely to be *skewed* one way or the other.

The average error is evaluated by finding the *variance* (also known as the mean square deviation). The *variance* of a set of observations is the average of the sum (denoted by Σ) of the squares of the deviation from the mean and is given by the formula:

$$\text{variance} = \frac{\Sigma(x - \bar{x})^2}{n} = \frac{\Sigma d^2}{n} \qquad \ldots \textbf{16.11}$$

where $\quad \Sigma(x - \bar{x})^2 = \Sigma d^2 = f_1(d_1)^2 + f_2(d_2)^2 + f_3(d_3)^2 + \ldots + f_{13}(d_{13})^2$

The *standard deviation* (SD) or *root mean square (RMS) error about the mean value* of this set of observations is equal to the positive square root of the variance, i.e.:

$$\text{SD} = \sigma_n = \sqrt{\frac{\Sigma(x-\bar{x})^2}{n}} = \sqrt{\frac{\Sigma d^2}{n}} \qquad \ldots \textbf{16.12}$$

It is often more convenient to use the alternative and equivalent formula for variance:

$$\text{variance} = \frac{\Sigma x^2}{n} - \bar{x}^2 \qquad \ldots \textbf{16.13}$$

However, these readings are only a sample taken from the whole, and a better estimate of the variance and the standard deviation of all the readings is more accurately given by the formula:

$$\text{variance} = \sigma^2 = \frac{\Sigma(x-\bar{x})^2}{n-1} = \frac{\Sigma d^2}{n-1} \qquad \ldots \textbf{16.14}$$

$$\sigma^2 = \frac{1}{n-1}(\Sigma x^2 - n\bar{x}^2) \qquad \ldots \textbf{16.15}$$

The square root of this value is known as the unbiased estimate of the standard deviation and is often referred to as the *one sigma (1σ) value*:

$$1\sigma = \sigma_{n-1} = \sqrt{\frac{\Sigma(x-\bar{x})^2}{n-1}} = \sqrt{\frac{\Sigma d^2}{n-1}} \qquad \ldots \textbf{16.16}$$

$$\text{or} \qquad \sqrt{\frac{1}{n-1}(\Sigma x^2 - n\bar{x}^2)} \qquad \ldots \textbf{16.17}$$

Where n is large, as should be the case when a random sample is being considered, the difference between n and $(n-1)$ is not significant and may often be disregarded. In such circumstances, it is immaterial whether 1σ is obtained by division by n or by $(n-1)$:

In the above example, from formula (**16.16**):

$$1\sigma = \sqrt{\frac{f_1(d_1)^2 + f_2(d_2)^2 + f_3(d_3)^2 + \ldots + f_{13}(d_{13})^2}{n-1}} \qquad \ldots \; \textbf{16.18}$$

$$\simeq \sqrt{\frac{2(-0.06)^2 + 6(-0.05)^2 + 17(-0.04)^2 + \ldots + 3(0.06)^2}{499}}$$

$$1\sigma \simeq 0.02 \; \text{mean lanes}$$

From formula **(16.17)**:

$$1\sigma = \sqrt{\frac{f_1x_1^2 + f_2x_2^2 + \ldots + f_{13}x_{13}^2}{n-1} - \frac{n}{n-1} \; \bar{x}^2} \qquad \ldots \; \textbf{16.19}$$

$$= \sqrt{\frac{2(8.2)^2 + 6(8.21)^2 + \ldots + 3(8.32)^2}{499} - \frac{500}{499}(8.26016)^2}$$

$$\simeq 0.02 \; \text{mean lanes}$$

Random errors of measurement can be shown to follow the *Gaussian** distribution of normal errors which is usually referred to as the *normal probability distribution*, as shown in Fig. 16–15. Such a distribution may be considered as the limited or idealised form of the curve shown in Fig. 16–14 and only differs from it because the curve in Fig. 16–14 was based on a sample of 500 readings rather than an infinite number.

In the normal distribution curve (Fig. 16–15), errors are symmetrical about the mean distribution μ, and the probability of obtaining progressively larger errors falls off in a particular way. The area beneath the curve over a given interval measures the probability of an error occurring in that interval. The whole shape of the distribution is fixed by the standard deviation and it is possible to say what percentage of errors will lie within any multiple of sigma.

The probability density function (pdf) for the general normal distribution is

$$y = \sigma^{-1} (2\pi)^{-\frac{1}{2}} e^{-\frac{1}{2}[(x-\mu)/\sigma]^2} \qquad \ldots \; \textbf{16.20}$$

where y is the height of the curve at any point, σ is the standard deviation and μ the mean of the random variables; π and e are commonly used mathematical constants.

All values of practical significance lie between $X = -3$ and $X = +3$, as indicated in Fig. 16–15. The important figures are as follows:

50% of the errors fall within 0.674σ of the mean. The 50% error, where any individual error has an equal chance of being greater or less than this value, is often referred to as *probable error* or *linear error probable* (LEP).

68.27% of the errors fall within one sigma (1σ) of the mean. That is to say, if a large number of random measurements are made and it is known that the error

* The German mathematician Gauss (1777–1855) used the normal distribution as a model for the errors in astronomical observations.

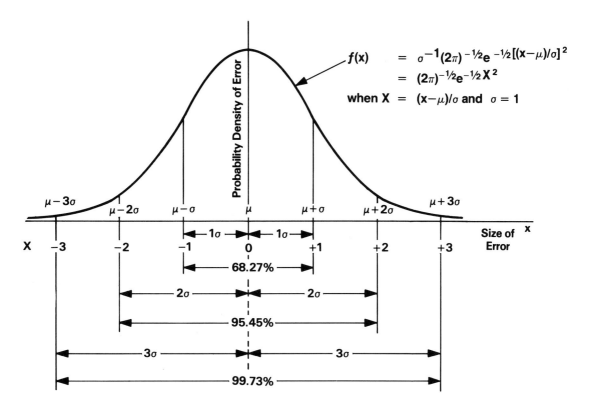

$$f(x) = \sigma^{-1}(2\pi)^{-\frac{1}{2}}e^{-\frac{1}{2}[(x-\mu)/\sigma]^2}$$
$$= (2\pi)^{-\frac{1}{2}}e^{-\frac{1}{2}X^2}$$
$$\text{when } X = (x-\mu)/\sigma \text{ and } \sigma = 1$$

Fig. 16–15.   The normal distribution of random errors

distribution is normal (Fig. 16–15), then 68.27% of these measurements may be expected to fall within 1σ value or one standard deviation from the mean.

95% of the errors fall within 1.96σ of the mean.
95.45% of the errors fall within 2σ of the mean.
98% of the errors fall within 2.33σ of the mean.
99% of the errors fall within 2.58σ of the mean.
99.73% of the errors fall within 3σ of the mean.

The 95% error is the value normally used in navigation to express the accuracy of one-dimensional position lines and this value may be considered for practical purposes as being equivalent to 2σ.

In the above example, if $1\sigma = 0.02$ mean lanes, then $2\sigma = 0.04$ mean lanes. There is a 95% probability that the actual position line lies within the limit quoted, 0.04 mean lanes. In other words, there is a 1 in 20 chance that the position line could lie outside the limit of 0.04 mean lanes.

Combining one-dimensional random errors

The total one-dimensional error at any particular instant may be found by summing algebraically the relevant individual errors. Suppose that, at a given moment, the particular errors in a navigational situation are as follows:

error in the navigation system in use   +35 m

error due to human fallibility   −27 m

error caused by the effect of the elements (wind,
    water, tidal stream, etc.)   +17 m

The total error at this moment will be +35 −27 +17 = +25 metres.

The standard deviations of several independent random errors may also be combined.

The variance of the sum (or difference) of two or more independent random variables is equal to the sum of the individual variances, i.e.

$$\sigma^2 = \sigma_1^2 + \sigma_2^2 + \sigma_3^2 + \ldots + \sigma_n^2 \qquad \ldots \mathbf{16.21}$$

The standard deviation of the sum (or difference) of these variables is as follows:

$$\sigma = \sqrt{\sigma_1^2 + \sigma_2^2 + \sigma_3^2 + \ldots + \sigma_n^2} \qquad \ldots \mathbf{(16.2)}$$

When sigma values are combined, the resultant value is much less than if the two individual values are added together. This is because the squares of the two values are added, and then the square root of the sum is taken. An example of this was given on page 463.

Rectangular errors

Random errors only follow a Gaussian or normal distribution if the error is a continuous variable. But this is not always the case. The distribution of random errors can also be rectangular.

Rounding-off errors

Many values in navigational tables are expressed to only one decimal point; thus, the error in the extracted value may be anywhere between ±0.05 about that value. Such an error is usually referred to as a *rounding-off error*.

A rectangular or continuous uniform distribution (Fig. 16–16) has the probability density function:

$$y = \frac{1}{b - a} \qquad (a < x < b) \qquad \ldots \mathbf{16.22}$$

where $\text{variance} = \dfrac{(b - a)^2}{12}$ $\ldots \mathbf{16.23}$

and $\text{SD} = \sqrt{\dfrac{(b - a)^2}{12}}$ $\ldots \mathbf{16.24}$

When a table or instrument reading to the nearest 0.1 value is being used ($a = -0.05$, $b = +0.05$), the variance and standard deviation are as follows:

$$\text{variance} = \frac{(0.1)^2}{12} = 0.000833$$

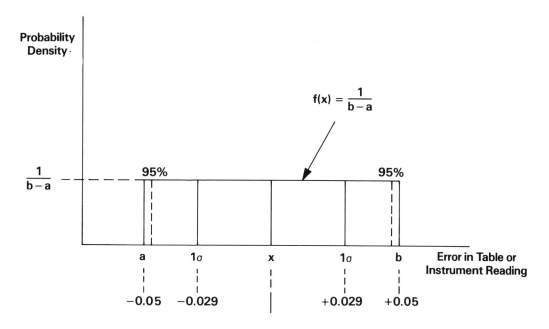

Fig. 16–16.   Rectangular error

$$\mathrm{SD} = \sqrt{\frac{(0.1)^2}{12}} = 0.029$$

The standard deviation of the error will be approx. 0.6 of the maximum error or three-tenths of the difference between the graduations. The 95% error leaves 2.5% at each end of the distribution; e.g. in Fig. 16–16 it lies between $(x - 0.0475)$ and $(x + 0.0475)$, that is to say, for all practical purposes it may be considered as being equal to half the difference between the graduations—in this case 0.05.

Effect of rectangular errors

Provided that rectangular errors of the type described above are small by comparison with a random error of normal distribution, they can often be disregarded as having no practical significance. Their effect on the total random error is small, as illustrated in the following example, which has already been summarised on page 463.

The accuracy of a gyro bearing allowing for any random gyro error is ±1°, assuming a 95% probability and normal distribution. However, the gyro bearing can only be read to the nearest ½°, i.e. the maximum rounding-off error is ±¼°. The gyro bearing itself can be plotted to an accuracy of ±¼°, once again assuming a uniform (rectangular) distribution. What is the likely total 95% error?

Accuracy of the gyro bearing

$$2\sigma_1 = 1°$$
$$\text{SD } (\sigma_1) = 0°.5$$
$$\text{variance } (\sigma_1^2) = 0°.25$$

Measuring the gyro bearing—rounding-off error
From formula **(16.23)**:

$$\text{variance} = \frac{(\frac{1}{4} - (-\frac{1}{4}))^2}{12}$$

i.e. $\sigma_2^2 \simeq 0°.021$
$$\sigma_2 \simeq 0°.14$$

Plotting the gyro bearing
From formula **(16.23)**:

$$\text{variance} = \frac{(\frac{1}{4} - (-\frac{1}{4}))^2}{12}$$

i.e. $\sigma_3^2 \simeq 0°.021$
$$\sigma_3 \simeq 0°.14$$

From formula **(16.21)**:

$$\text{combined variance} = 0°.25 + 0°.021 + 0°.021$$
$$\sigma^2 = 0°.292$$

From formula **(16.2)**:

$$\text{combined SD} = \sqrt{0.292}$$
$$\sigma \simeq 0°.54$$

As the rounding-off errors in the combination are not too large by comparison with the error in the gyro bearing, the combined standard deviation may be doubled to obtain the total 95% error:

$$\text{total 95\% error} = 1°.08$$

The random gyro error of 1° is only increased by a negligible amount when the measurement and the plotting of the gyro bearing are also considered. For all practical purposes, the total 95% error is still only 1°.

TWO-DIMENSIONAL RANDOM ERRORS

Probability heap

Consider the special case of a fix E (Fig. 16–17), which is obtained from two position lines AB, CD, crossing at right angles where the 95% error or 2σ value of each position is the same, a. Such position lines are known as *orthogonal*. Orthogonal position lines rarely occur in practice.

Each position line has its own particular error distribution which, if Gaussian by nature (Fig. 16–15), may be visualised where they intersect as a *probability heap* around the position E. The probability distribution of a single position line is a function of the area under the curve (Fig. 16–15); thus, the probability distribution of two crossing position lines is a function of the volume within the heap.

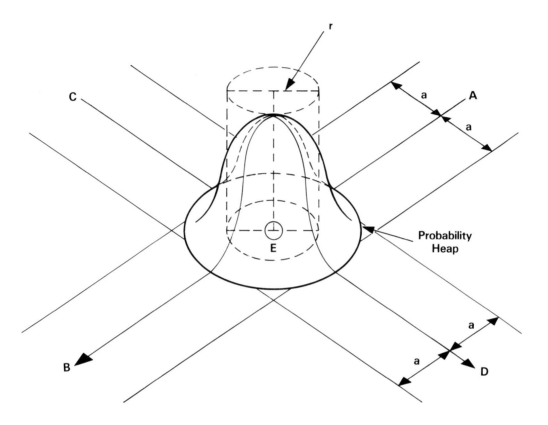

Fig. 16–17.   Error distribution of two intersecting orthogonal position lines

The circle of error

Portions of the heap cut out by cylinders of a particular radius, e.g. r in Fig. 16–17, may be removed. The proportion which the volume of the heap contained within the cylinder bears to the total volume of the heap determines the percentage error of the fix. For example, if in Fig. 16–17 the volume of the heap within the cylinder of radius r equals 70% of the total volume of the heap, then that radius r determines the 70% probability circle of the fix. Such a circle may be referred to as a *circle of error*. The *radial error* or *root mean square (RMS) error* (σ_r), is a particular case of this circle of error.

The link between percentage errors and standard deviation is *not* the same in a two-dimensional probability heap as it is in a linear distribution (page 481). This is because two sets of conditions are being met simultaneously and the probability of this occurring is less than the probability of either set being satsified individually. The probability is proportional to the volume of the heap rather than the area under the curve.

In the special case of orthogonal position lines where the linear standard deviations (1σ) are the same, the probability P (expressed as a fraction of 1, e.g. 95% is expressed as 0.95), of being within a radius r may be expressed by the following formula, which is also shown in the graph in Fig. 16–18.

$$P = 1 - e^{-r^2/2\sigma^2}$$

... **16.25**

$$\text{or} \quad P = 1 - e^{-r^2/\sigma_r^2}$$

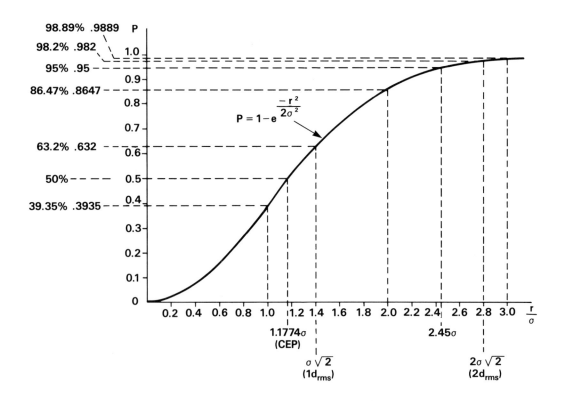

Fig. 16–18.   The circular normal distribution

The distribution of errors about the mean point has circular symmetry and the pattern of distribution is referred to as a *circular normal distribution*. The circular normal distribution may be specified in terms of the linear standard deviation (σ) in each direction. It may also be specified in terms of the radial error about the mean value.

Values of the circular normal distribution, where two position lines of equal linear standard deviation (σ) intersect at right angles, are given in Table 16A–2.

Table 16A–2

r		PERCENTAGE PROBABILITY	
1σ	$0.71\sigma_r$	39.35%	
1.1774σ	$0.83\sigma_r$	50%	*circular error probable* (CEP)
$\sigma\sqrt{2}$	σ_r	63.2%	$1d_{rms}$ *(radial error)*
2σ	$1.41\sigma_r$	86.47%	
2.45σ	$1.73\sigma_r$	95%	
$2\sigma\sqrt{2}$	$2\sigma_r$	98.2%	$2d_{rms}$
3σ	$2.12\sigma_r$	98.89%	
3.04σ	$2.15\sigma_r$	99%	

Fig. 16–6 (page 466) displays a plan view of the fix in Fig. 16–17. If the 95% or 2σ value of the linear error common to both position lines is a, then:

$$\text{when } a = 2\sigma$$
$$r = \frac{2.45a}{2}$$
$$\simeq 1.25a$$

Thus, a circle of radius $r = 1.25a$ around E provides the 95% circle of error for most practical purposes.

The relationship between CEP and other probability circles for the circular normal distribution may be determined using formula **(16.25)**. The radii of various percentage probability circles may be found by multiplying the radius of the CEP circle by the factors in Table 16A–3.

Table 16A–3

% PROBABILITY RADIUS	CEP MULTIPLICATION FACTOR
95%	2.079
98%	2.376
99%	2.578

The error ellipse

The error ellipse may be drawn by fitting an ellipse (Fig. 16–19) into an area of overlap produced by constructing bands of error around the intersecting position lines. The relationship between the ellipse probability and the width of appropriate band may be taken from Table 16A–2, for example:

Table 16A–4

ELLIPSE PROBABILITY	WIDTH OF BAND OF ERROR
50%	±1.18 linear SD (1.18σ)
95%	±2.45 linear SD (2.45σ)

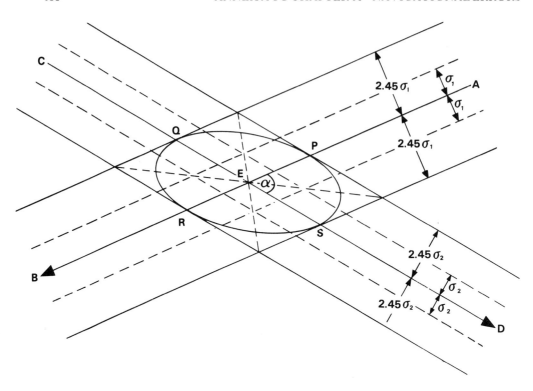

Fig. 16–19.   The 95% error ellipse

The 95% error ellipse is illustrated in Fig. 16–19. AB and CD are two position lines intersecting at E at an angle α. The linear standard deviations of AB and CD are σ_1 and σ_2 respectively.

Lines parallel to AB and CD are drawn on each side, $2.45\sigma_1$ and $2.45\sigma_2$ away from the appropriate position line.* The ellipse is now drawn to fit the parallelogram, as in Fig. 16–19, by making it pass through the points, P, Q, R, S and by making the ellipse cut the diagonals of the parallelogram approximately seven-tenths of the distance along the diagonal from the centre.

For example, if each position line is a visual bearing, then it may be said that the 95% error (2σ) value of each bearing is 1°. The standard deviation (1σ) value of the error equals $\frac{1}{2}$° and may be represented by σ_1 and σ_2 in Fig. 16–19. The actual width of this $\frac{1}{2}$° error is dependent on the distance of the fixing mark, as explained in Chapter 12.† σ_1 and σ_2 may now be expanded 2.45 times (or the $2\sigma_1$ and $2\sigma_2$ values $1\frac{1}{4}$ times approx.) and the ellipse drawn.

---

* If the 95% or 2σ values of the individual position lines are given, these may be expanded $\dfrac{2.45}{2}$, or approximately $1\frac{1}{4}$ times for most practical purposes.

† ±1° is equivalent to: ±1′ at 60′; ±0′.25 at 15′; ±0′.2 at 12′; ±0′.1 at 6′; ±0′.05 at 3′.

Equivalent probability circles

An elliptical error distribution is not particularly helpful to the navigator, who will find that it is of more practical use if he can adjust the error ellipse to form a circle (Fig. 16–20) where the probability of error is the same as that formed by the ellipse. Such circles are known as *equivalent probability circles*. The term CEP is also used (page 487) to indicate that circle within which there is a 50% probability, even though the actual error figure is an ellipse.

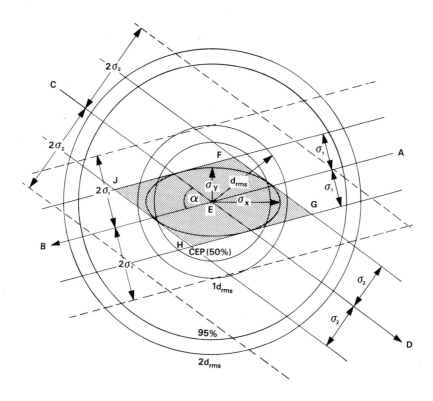

Fig. 16–20. Error ellipse and equivalent probability circles

The radial error ($1d_{rms}$) is illustrated in Fig. 16–20, together with the 1σ errors in the individual position lines. $1d_{rms}$ is equal to the square root of the sum of the squares of the 1σ error components along the major and minor axes of the ellipse:

$$1d_{rms} = \sqrt{\sigma_x^2 + \sigma_y^2} \qquad \ldots \textbf{16.26}$$

$$\text{where} \quad \sigma_x^2 = \frac{1}{2\sin^2\alpha}[\sigma_1^2 + \sigma_2^2 + \sqrt{(\sigma_1^2 + \sigma_2^2)^2 - 4\sin^2\alpha(\sigma_1^2\sigma_2^2)}]$$

$$\ldots \textbf{16.27}$$

and $\quad \sigma_y^2 = \dfrac{1}{2\,\sin^2\alpha}\,[\sigma_I^2 + \sigma_2^2 - \sqrt{(\sigma_I^2 + \sigma_2^2)^2 - 4\,\sin^2\alpha(\sigma_I^2\,\sigma_2^2)}\,]$

$$\dots \textbf{16.28}$$

$1d_{rms}$ may now be expressed in terms of σ_1 and σ_2 and the above formulae simplify to:

$$1d_{rms} = \operatorname{cosec}\alpha\sqrt{\sigma_I^2 + \sigma_2^2} \qquad\qquad \dots \textbf{(16.6)}$$

Other multiples of the radial error may also be derived by using corresponding values of σ; for example, the $2d_{rms}$ value may be calculated using the above formulae, using the 2σ error values, i.e.

$$2d_{rms} = \operatorname{cosec}\alpha\sqrt{a^2 + b^2} \qquad\qquad \dots \textbf{(16.8)}$$

$$\text{where} \qquad a = 2\sigma_I \text{ and } b = 2\sigma_2$$

$$\text{i.e.} \qquad 2d_{rms} = 2\,\operatorname{cosec}\alpha\sqrt{\sigma_I^2 + \sigma_2^2} \qquad\qquad \dots \textbf{(16.7)}$$

The numerical probabilities associated with $1d_{rms}$ and $2d_{rms}$ vary dependent on the shape of the ellipse and are given in Table 16A–5.*

Table 16A–5. d_{rms} and the shape of the error ellipse

LENGTH OF MAJOR AXIS OF ELLIPSE σ_x	PROPORTIONATE LENGTH OF MINOR AXIS OF ELLIPSE σ_y	PROPORTIONATE VALUE OF $\dfrac{1d_{rms}}{\sqrt{\sigma_x^2 + \sigma_y^2}}$	$1d_{rms}$ PERCENTAGE PROBABILITY	$2d_{rms}$ PERCENTAGE PROBABILITY
1.0	0.0	1.0	68.3%	95.4%
1.0	0.1	1.005	68.2%	95.5%
1.0	0.2	1.02	68.1%	95.7%
1.0	0.3	1.04	67.6%	96.1%
1.0	0.4	1.08	67.1%	96.6%
1.0	0.5	1.12	66.2%	96.9%
1.0	0.6	1.17	65.0%	97.3%
1.0	0.7	1.22	64.1%	97.7%
1.0	0.8	1.28	63.5%	98.0%
1.0	0.9	1.35	63.2%	98.1%
1.0	1.0	1.41	63.2%	98.2%

Provided σ_x and σ_y have been determined using formulae **(16.27)** and **(16.28)**, the radius of the probability circle may be found by multiplying σ_x ($\sigma_x \geqslant \sigma_y$) by the factors in Table 16A–6 for varying shapes of ellipse.

* *See* N. Bowditch, *American Practical Navigator*, Volume I (1977 edition), Appendix Q, Tables Q6a and Q7e.

Table 16A–6

SHAPE OF ELLIPSE σ_y/σ_x	σ_x MULTIPLICATION FACTOR		
	50% CIRCLE (CEP)	95% CIRCLE	99% CIRCLE
0.0	0.67	1.96	2.58
0.1	0.68	1.96	2.58
0.2	0.71	1.97	2.58
0.3	0.75	1.98	2.59
0.4	0.81	2.01	2.61
0.5	0.87	2.04	2.63
0.6	0.93	2.08	2.67
0.7	1.00	2.15	2.72
0.8	1.06	2.23	2.79
0.9	1.12	2.33	2.90
1.0	1.18	2.45	3.04

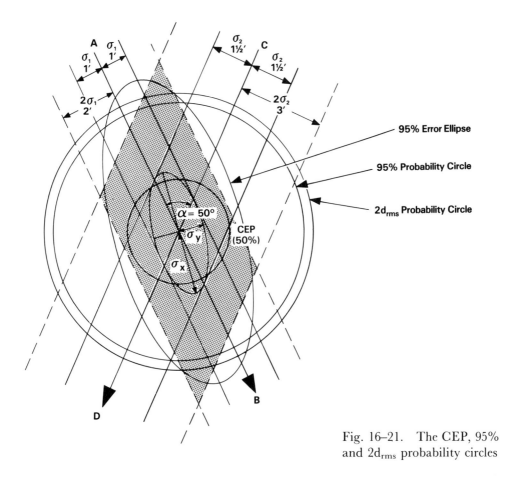

Fig. 16–21.   The CEP, 95% and 2d$_{rms}$ probability circles

For example, suppose two position lines AB and CD cross at an angle of $50°$ (Fig. 16–21), where the 1σ value of the linear error in AB is $1'$ and that in CD is $1\frac{1}{2}'$. What are the sizes of the CEP and 95% probability circles?

From formulae **(16.27)** and **(16.28)**:

$$\sigma_x = 2'.2$$
$$\sigma_y = 0'.9$$
$$\therefore \frac{\sigma_y}{\sigma_x} \simeq 0.4$$

From Table 16A–6:

radius of CEP circle $= 2'.2 \times 0.81 = 1'.8$

radius of 95% circle $= 2'.2 \times 2.01 = 4'.4$

The diamond of error formed by the 2σ (95%) linear values of the individual position lines has been shaded in Fig. 16–21 for comparison with the 95% and $2d_{rms}$ circles. The 95% error ellipse is also shown.

It is a relatively simple matter to program a desk-top computer or programmable calculator with the necessary data to obtain the radius of the 95% probability circle. Formulae **(16.27)** and **(16.28)** are required, the inputs being σ_1, σ_2 and α. The values of σ_y and σ_x and the ratio σ_y / σ_x may now be obtained. Provided the multiplication factors from the above table are also fed in to the program, the appropriate factor may be multiplied by σ_x and the radius of the 95% probability circle obtained.

The $2d_{rms}$ value, which lies between probability values of 95.5% and 98.2% dependent on the shape of the ellipse, may be deduced using formula **(16.8)**:

$$2d_{rms} \qquad = \text{cosec } \alpha \sqrt{a^2 + b^2}$$

(about the mean value)

where α is the angle of cut and a and b are the 95% (2σ) linear errors for the two position lines.

The $2d_{rms}$ about the mean value formula will always produce a slightly larger error circle than the 95% circle, the amount being dependent on the shape of the error ellipse.

The formula is much easier to use and, if no program as above is available, the navigator may for most practical purposes use the $2d_{rms}$ formula to provide the 95% probability circle. He is therefore always taking a more pessimistic but safer view of his likely circle of error.

Using formula **(16.8)** in the above example:

$$a = 2\sigma_1 = 2'$$
$$b = 2\sigma_2 = 3'$$
$$2d_{rms} = \text{cosec } 50° \sqrt{(2)^2 + (3)^2} = 4'.7$$

The disadvantage of drawing equivalent probability circles is that a position is more likely to fall within those smaller areas of the ellipse that are outside the circle than within those larger areas of the circle that are outside the ellipse.

Generally speaking, however, the equivalent probability circle is quite satisfactory for all practical purposes provided that the error ellipse is not too elongated.

Circular error probable (CEP)

A useful approximation to determine the CEP for the elliptical error is:

$$\text{CEP} = 0.615\sigma_y + 0.562\sigma_x \qquad \dots \textbf{16.29}$$

when $\sigma_x > \sigma_y$ as in Fig. 16–20. This is very accurate as long as $\sigma_y > 0.3\sigma_x$, so it is very useful for all but the most elongated of ellipses. σ_x and σ_y may be calculated using formulae **(16.27)** and **(16.28)**.

The CEP conversion factors in Table 16A–3 (page 487) may also be used for elliptical error distribution provided that the σ_y/σ_x ratio is close to 1. However, errors increase significantly both when high values of probability are desired and when the error ellipse is elongated. Fig. 16–22 shows the relationship between the CEP multiplication factor and the shape of the ellipse for a 95% probability.

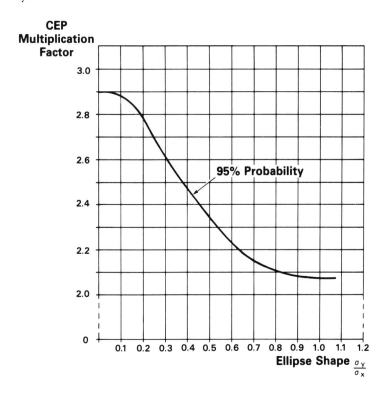

Fig. 16–22. Relationship between CEP multiplication factor and ellipse shape

It may be seen from Fig. 16–22 that the CEP multiplication factor varies between 2.08 when $\sigma_y/\sigma_x = 1$ and 2.9 when $\sigma_y/\sigma_x = 0.1$ for the 95% probability circle.

Derivation of the Most Probable Position (MPP)
from three or more position lines

The method used* to derive the Most Probable Position from three or more position lines (Fig. 16–23) is known as the *least squares, minimum variance* or *maximum likelihood* solution. It is assumed that each position line is subject to normally distributed random errors† only (Fig. 16–15) and that any faults and systematic errors have been removed or allowed for. It is also assumed that the random errors in any one position line are independent of the random errors in any other position line.

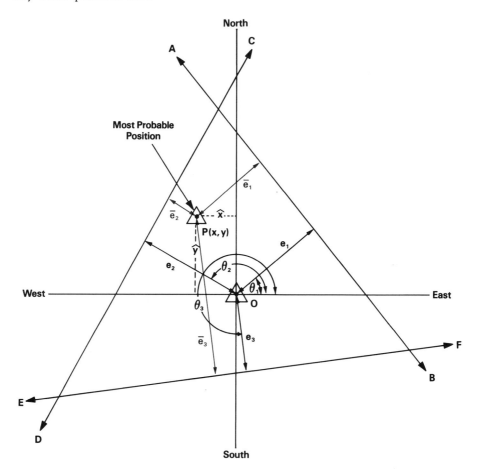

Fig. 16–23.   Derivation of the Most Probable Position from three position lines

---

* In practice, this technique has a number of limitations in that it assumes no auto-correlation on the position lines nor cross-correlation between position lines. The technique may be modified to account for these correlation effects but requires a co-variance matrix approach, rather than the relatively simple geometric solution shown here.

† The least squares method does not require the errors in each position line to be normally distributed. However, if the errors are normally distributed, the least squares estimates are also the maximum likelihood estimates.

Fig. 16–23 shows three position lines AB, CD and EF, from which any faults and systematic errors have been removed,* but that a 'cocked hat' (caused by normally distributed random errors in the position lines) still remains. O is the ship's Estimated Position and it is immaterial to the calculation whether O is inside or outside the cocked hat (but *see* Note at the end of this section). e_1 is the perpendicular distance between AB and O; e_2 is the perpendicular distance between CD and O; e_3 is the perpendicular distance between EF and O. θ_1, θ_2 and θ_3 are the angles which e_1, e_2 and e_3 respectively make with the east-west axis through O and measured from east. P is the Most Probable Position and is deduced using the least squares method. The most likely estimate of the co-ordinates of P (x, y) relative to O are $\hat{x}$ and $\hat{y}$. Thus, $\hat{x}$ and $\hat{y}$ must be found in order to establish the most likely position of P. $\bar{e}_1$, $\bar{e}_2$ and $\bar{e}_3$ are the mean error estimates between the three position lines and P. σ_1, σ_2 and σ_3 are the standard deviations of the error distributions associated with the three position lines AB, CD and EF respectively.

The most likely or best estimates of x and y—that is, $\hat{x}$ and $\hat{y}$—are given by the following equations:

$$\hat{x}C_2 + \hat{y}G = E_c \qquad \text{... 16.30}$$
$$\text{and} \quad \hat{x}G + \hat{y}S_2 = E_s \qquad \text{... 16.31}$$

where:

$$E_c = \sum \frac{e}{\sigma^2} \cos \theta$$

$$= \frac{e_1}{\sigma_1^2} \cos \theta_1 + \frac{e_2}{\sigma_2^2} \cos \theta_2 + \frac{e_3}{\sigma_3^2} \cos \theta_3 + \ldots + \frac{e_n}{\sigma_n^2} \cos \theta_n \qquad \text{... 16.32}$$

$$E_s = \sum \frac{e}{\sigma^2} \sin \theta$$

$$= \frac{e_1}{\sigma_1^2} \sin \theta_1 + \frac{e_2}{\sigma_2^2} \sin \theta_2 + \frac{e_3}{\sigma_3^2} \sin \theta_3 + \ldots + \frac{e_n}{\sigma_n^2} \sin \theta_n \qquad \text{... 16.33}$$

$$C_2 = \sum \frac{1}{\sigma^2} \cos^2 \theta$$

$$= \frac{1}{\sigma_1^2} \cos^2 \theta_1 + \frac{1}{\sigma_2^2} \cos^2 \theta_2 + \frac{1}{\sigma_3^2} \cos^2 \theta_3 + \ldots + \frac{1}{\sigma_n^2} \cos^2 \theta_n \qquad \text{... 16.34}$$

$$S_2 = \sum \frac{1}{\sigma^2} \sin^2 \theta$$

$$= \frac{1}{\sigma_1^2} \sin^2 \theta_1 + \frac{1}{\sigma_2^2} \sin^2 \theta_2 + \frac{1}{\sigma_3^2} \sin^2 \theta_3 + \ldots + \frac{1}{\sigma_n^2} \sin^2 \theta_n \qquad \text{... 16.35}$$

---

* The 'cocked hat' shown in Chapter 9 is reduced, on the assumption that the same error affects all three position lines equally. Over the time scale involved, the error in the compass may be considered as constant, affecting all three bearings equally.

$$G = \sum \frac{1}{\sigma^2} \sin \theta \cos \theta$$

$$= \frac{1}{\sigma_1^2} \sin \theta_1 \cos \theta_1 + \frac{1}{\sigma_2^2} \sin \theta_2 \cos \theta_2 + \frac{1}{\sigma_3^2} \sin \theta_3 \cos \theta_3$$

$$+ \ldots + \frac{1}{\sigma_n^2} \sin \theta_n \cos \theta_n \qquad \ldots \textbf{16.36}$$

The simultaneous equations **(16.30)** and **(16.31)** may be solved as follows:

$$\hat{x} = \frac{E_c S_2 - G E_s}{C_2 S_2 - G^2} \qquad \ldots \textbf{16.37}$$

$$\hat{y} = \frac{C_2 E_s - G E_c}{C_2 S_2 - G^2} \qquad \ldots \textbf{16.38}$$

Thus, the Most Probable Position P may be found.

Note: Provided e_1, e_2, e_3, etc. are small, i.e. each is less than about 10 miles, the position lines on the Earth will map on to the plane as straight lines with negligible distortion. If the errors are greater than 10 miles, however, equations **(16.37)** and **(16.38)** should be recalculated using the values of $\bar{e}_1$, $\bar{e}_2$ and $\bar{e}_3$ instead of e_1, e_2 and e_3 respectively. It may be necessary to carry out more than one calculation, substituting fresh values of $\bar{e}_1$, $\bar{e}_2$ and $\bar{e}_3$, although in practice one is usually sufficient unless O and P are some miles apart. If O lies some distance outside the cocked hat formed by the position lines, the navigator will need to treat the results with caution and, if possible, try to analyse why O and P are so far apart.

CHAPTER 17
Relative Velocity and Collision Avoidance

This chapter introduces the concept of relative velocity and its application to collision avoidance. The use of radar in solving collision avoidance problems is also discussed. Some simple relative velocity problems and their solutions are given. Details of the Battenberg Course Indicator, a type of mechanical plotter used within the Royal Navy to solve relative velocity and station changing problems, are given in Volume IV.

Definitions

Various terms are commonly used in the context of relative velocity and collision avoidance and also when other ships are being plotted on radar. These terms are set out below, and supplement those already described in this book, such as direction, bearing and course (Chapter 1), ground track and water track (Chapter 8), etc.

Table 17–1

SEA SPEED	The speed of own ship along the water track, expressed in knots.
GROUND SPEED	The speed of own ship along the ground track, expressed in knots.
RELATIVE TRACK OF CONTACT	The path of a radar contact as observed on a relative motion display.
TRUE TRACK OF CONTACT	The path of a radar contact as observed on a surface plotting table or on a true motion display.
ASPECT	The relative bearing of own ship from another ship, expressed in degrees 0 to 180 Red or Green relative to the other ship (Fig. 17–1, p.498). Aspect is often referred to as *angle on the bow*.
DETECTION	The recognition of the presence of a radar contact.
ACQUISITION	The selection of those radar contacts requiring a tracking procedure and the initiation of their tracking.
TRACKING	The process of observing the sequential changes in the position of a radar contact to establish its motion.

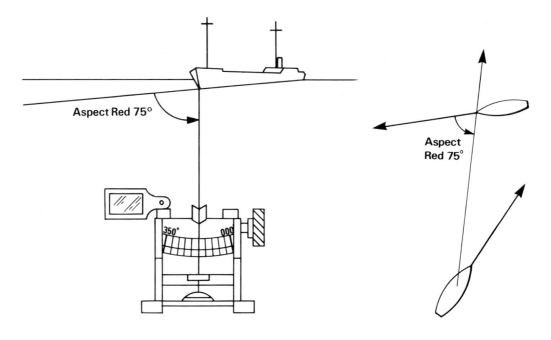

Fig. 17–1.   Aspect

PRINCIPLES OF RELATIVE VELOCITY

Relative speed

Suppose two ships are approaching each other head-on (Fig. 17–2), the speed of each being 20 knots.

Fig. 17–2.   Relative speed

Own ship may be represented by WO, the other ship by WA. The speed of one ship relative to the other is 40 knots; in other words, to an observer in one ship the other ship *appears* to be approaching at a *relative speed* of 40 knots. This relative speed may be represented by OA.

One arrowhead is used on own ship's vector, two on the other ship's vector and one arrowhead in a circle on the relative motion vector.

Relative track and relative speed

Relative speed is also dependent upon the courses being steered by each ship. For example, if the two ships are steaming in station with one another on the same course and speed, then the speed of one ship relative to the other is zero.

In order to avoid collisions between ships and also to manoeuvre ships in company safely, the terms *relative track* and *relative speed* must be understood. In Fig. 17–3 ship *G* is in sight on the starboard bow of own ship on a crossing course. If the true bearing between the two ships does not appreciably change, then in accordance with Rule 7 of the *International Regulations for Preventing Collisions at Sea, 1972* (the Rule of the Road), a risk of collision must be deemed to exist. (In such a case, under Rule 15, own ship *W* is required to give way to ship *G*.)

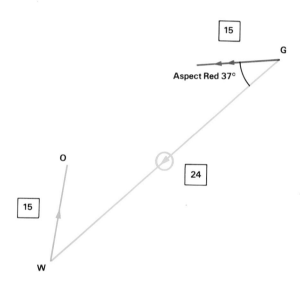

Fig. 17–3.   Relative track

If the true bearing of *G* from *W* remains steady, then to the Officer of the Watch in *W*, *G* must appear to be approaching *W* along the line *GW*. In other words, the track of *G relative* to *W* (the *relative track* of *G*) is *GW*. The *relative speed* is that speed at which *G* is approaching *W* along the line *GW*.

Fig. 17–3 illustrates the case of one ship in sight, crossing, and on a steady bearing. The collision avoidance problem is easy to solve because the bearing is steady; the relative track does not have to be computed.

If own ship is obliged to alter course to give way to another, it is important to be able to assess what effect this manoeuvre will have on the relative tracks of other ships nearby. For example, in Fig. 17–4 (p.500) own ship *W* may consider altering course 30° to starboard to avoid another ship *G*, which is approaching on a steady bearing on the starboard bow. What effect will this alteration have on the relative tracks of *H* and *J* ? Will the proposed change of course of 30° put own ship on a collision course with either *H* or *J*, or both? If it does, then a different manoeuvre may be preferable, for example a much larger alteration of course or slowing or stopping.

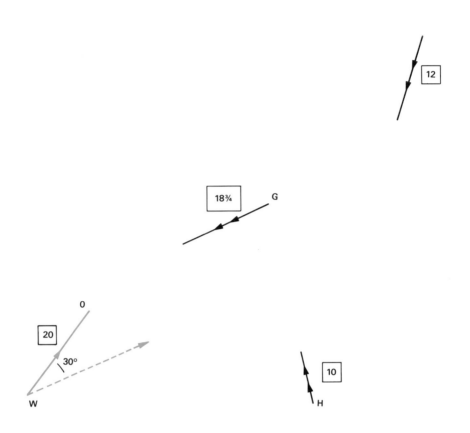

Fig. 17–4.   Manoeuvring to avoid other shipping

In order to make a proper assessment, it is necessary to find the relative track and relative speed of the other ships. It may also be necessary to find their true tracks and speed.

Comparison between relative and true tracks

Relative track

If the track of another ship (*G* in Fig. 17–5) is plotted on a relative motion radar display, the relative track of *G* will be revealed. This is because own ship remains at the centre of the display: the other ship's relative track corresponds to a combination of both movements.

At 0800 (Fig. 17–5) own ship *W* is steering 340° at 20 knots; another ship *G* bears 070°, distance 5 miles. *G*'s movement is plotted on the radar display and the following ranges and bearings are obtained:

0806	082°, 4'.1 (G_1)
0812	099°, 3'.5 (G_2)
0818	120°, 3'.3 (G_3)

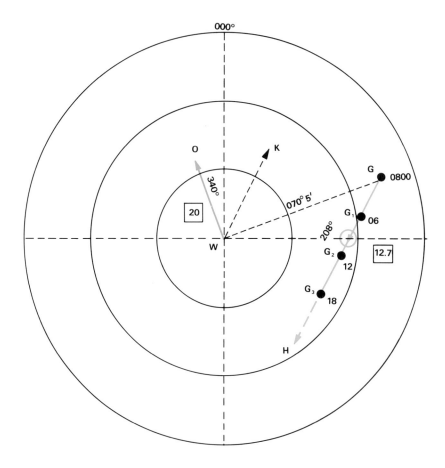

Fig. 17–5. Development of the relative track

By joining all four points on the display, G's relative track is found to be 208° (along the line GH). Between 0800 and 0818, G moves 3'.8 along GH, hence her relative speed is:

$$\frac{60}{18} \times 3'.8 = 12.7 \text{ knots}$$

It will be seen that G's relative track is leading her well clear astern of own ship. If, on the other hand, the relative track had been directly towards, as in Fig. 17–3—that is, towards the centre of the radar display, then the two ships would have been on a collision course.

This is perhaps the most important feature of collision avoidance using the relative motion display. ***If the relative track of another ship is moving directly towards own ship's position, then that ship is on a collision course.***

True track

If the track of the other ship *G* is plotted on a plotting table, taking into account own ship's track, *G*'s true track will be revealed (Fig. 17–6). This is because own ship *W* is moving over the plot in a direction and at a speed directly proportional to own course and speed. As ranges and bearings of the other ship are plotted, so the true track and speed of *G* are obtained.

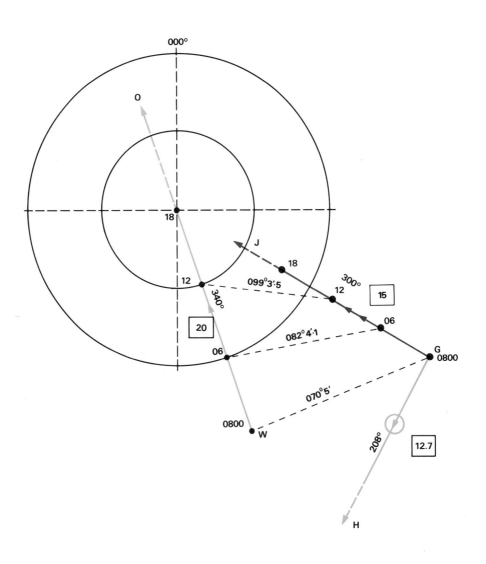

Fig. 17–6.   Development of the true track

The plotted track *GJ* is *G*'s true track and speed (300°, 15 knots). It should be noted that this is very different from *G*'s relative track and speed (208°, 12.7 knots).

The velocity triangle

Once the relative track and speed of the other ship have been found (Fig. 17–5), a *velocity triangle* (Fig. 17–7) may be used to give the other ship's true track and speed.

Alternatively, the velocity triangle may be used to find the relative track once the true track has been determined as in Fig. 17–6, or is known.

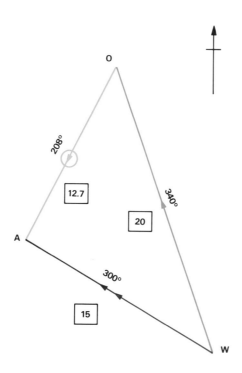

Fig. 17–7.   The velocity triangle

The velocity triangle consists of three *vectors*, each vector being a line drawn in the correct direction to represent the track, the length of the line being proportional to the speed.

Vector *WO* represents own course and speed (340°, 20 knots). A convenient scale may be chosen to represent the speed: for example, if 5 knots is to be represented by 20 mm, then own speed vector will be 80 mm long.

Vector OA represents the relative track and speed of the other ship (208°, 12.7 knots). The same scale for speed is used. OA will therefore be $(12.7/5)20 = 50.8$mm long.

Vector WA represents the true track of the other ship (300°, 15 knots). The same scale for speed is used; thus, WA will be $(15/5)20 = 60$ mm long.

Provided certain rules, as set out below, are followed, there should never be any difficulty in drawing the velocity triangle correctly, with each vector in its *correct direction*.

1. The arrowheads on *own* and the *other ship's* vectors must always *diverge* from $W—WO$ and WA in Fig. 17–7.
2. The arrowheads on the other ship's *true* and *relative* vectors always *converge* on $A—WA$ and OA in Fig. 17–7.
3. Our *own* course arrowhead *'chases'* the *relative* track arrowhead—WO 'chases' OA in Fig. 17–7.

Initial positions of ships

The initial positions of the ships do not affect the velocity triangle, which depends only on the tracks and speeds of each ship. However, the initial positions of the two ships will have very different effects on subsequent events. Suppose that, in Fig. 17–5, the other ship G had started from a position K on a bearing of 028° from own ship, instead of starting from position G. Her relative track of 208° must then pass through the position of own ship. G is therefore on a collision course.

Relative movement

When considering relative tracks, do not make the mistake of assuming that a ship points in the direction of her relative track. She is still pointing in the direction of her course, which may be very different. Visually, a ship often appears to move almost sideways, or crabwise, along her relative track.

USE OF RADAR

Radar may be used to advantage in solving collision avoidance and manoeuvring problems.

Modern radar, with its high rate of aerial rotation, gives an up to date picture of other ships' positions, their bearings and ranges. The afterglow trails on the relative motion display show the approximate relative tracks.

Radar displays

Radar data for collision avoidance may normally be obtained using the following methods of display. Detailed information on these radar displays may be found in standard works on radar.

Relative motion	north-up, stabilised.
Relative motion	course-up, stabilised.
Relative motion	course-up, unstabilised.
True motion	north-up, sea-stabilised.
True motion	north-up, ground-stabilised.

True motion   course-up, sea-stabilised.
True motion   course-up, ground-stabilised.

A brief discussion on the merits of relative or true motion radar for collision avoidance is given later in this chapter (p.509).

For collision avoidance, a stabilised method of display is generally to be preferred to an unstabilised method. Compass bearings of other ships may be read off directly and echoes do not become blurred when an alteration of course is made or when a ship yaws about her course.

The type of display used for navigational purposes usually has a mechanical bearing cursor fitted over the face of the tube. The cursor is engraved with parallel lines and can be rotated, usually by a manual control. Range is shown on the face of the tube by range calibration rings and by an electronic range strobe, which paints a circular trace and is adjusted as necessary by the range strobe control. The range to which this range strobe is set is shown on a digital read-out.

A reflection plotter, consisting of a transparent disc provided with side illumination, is fitted over the face of the display. The design of the plotter is such that parallax is eliminated, that is to say, manual plotting using a chinagraph pencil on the face of the plotter coincides with the radar picture on the face of the tube.

The calibration rings or range strobe may be used to provide the speed scale, while the rotating cursor provides the parallel lines for transferring vectors.

Modern navigational radars, such as Naval Radar Type 1007, use electronic plotting instead of the old-fashioned reflection plotter and chinagraph pencil. Tracks of specified contacts may be generated giving their course, speed, closest point of approach (CPA) and time to CPA (TCPA). Pilotage lines and markers may also be injected electronically. However, the use of such radars does *not* alter the *principles* underlying the solution of relative velocity problems discussed below.

Using the *relative motion stabilised radar display* to solve relative velocity problems

Relative velocity problems may be solved on the radar display by using the bearing cursor and range strobe and by plotting on the face of the reflection plotter. The following example uses a relative motion north-up stabilised display.

EXAMPLE

A ship bears 220°, 8 miles at 0900. Own ship's course and speed is 150°, 15 knots. Find the other ship's relative and true tracks and speeds.

1. Set the display on a suitable range scale (Fig. 17–8, p.506) to plot the relative track of the other ship.
2. Mark the initial position and the time of the other ship, on the reflection plotter (220°, 8 miles at 0900).
3. Mark the position of the other ship on the reflection plotter as accurately as possible at regular intervals to obtain her relative track, e.g.:

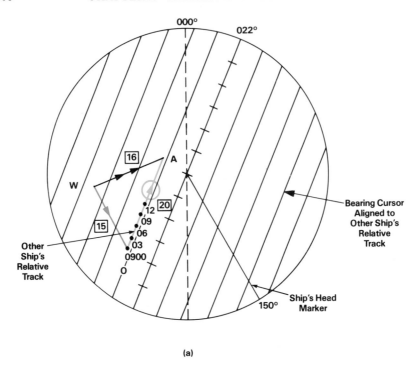

(a)

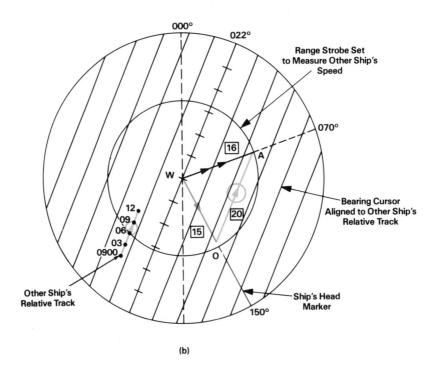

(b)

Fig. 17–8. Finding the true and relative tracks and speeds from a relative motion radar display (north-up stabilised): velocity triangles based (a) on other ship's relative track; (b) on own ship's position.

0903	222°, 7′.0
0906	226°, 6′.1
0909	229°, 5′.2
0912	237°, 4′.3

4. Measure the distance travelled by the contact between 0900 and 0912 (4 miles) and calculate the relative speed: in this case, 4 miles in 12 minutes, or 20 knots.
5. Rotate the bearing cursor to align the parallel lines to the other ship's relative track and measure this using the centre line (022°).
6. The velocity triangle may now be constructed to find the contact's true track and speed. The velocity triangle may be drawn on the other ship's relative track (already developed on the reflection plotter) or it may be based on own ship's position at the centre of the display. The two procedures are set out below.
7. *Velocity triangle drawn on the other ship's relative track* (Fig. 17–8(a))
   (a) Mark the initial position of the contact O at 0900.
   (b) Draw vector OA along the other ship's relative track (already developed for 0900–0912) to represent the contact's relative track and speed vector. A distance of 8 miles for the range scale in use on the display has been used in Fig. 17–8(a), equivalent to a 24 minute run.
   (c) Rotate the bearing cursor to own ship's course (150°) and plot own ship's course and speed vector WO (150°, 6 miles—15 knots for 24 minutes equals 6 miles).
   (d) Join and measure WA, using the bearing cursor to measure the contact's true track (070°). The distance WA over the same 24 minute period for the range scale in use equals 6.4 miles. Thus, the contact's speed is 16 knots.
8. *Velocity triangle based on own ship's position* (Fig. 17–8 (b))
   (a) Rotate the bearing cursor (alternatively use the ship's head marker) to own ship's course, and adjust the range strobe to represent own ship's speed. Draw own ship's course and speed vector WO (150°, 15 knots) on the reflection plotter.
   (b) Rotate the bearing cursor to the relative track (022°) and using the same scale draw vector OA to represent the contact's relative track and speed (022°, 20 knots).
   (c) Join and measure WA, using the bearing cursor to measure the contact's true track (070°) and the range strobe her speed (16 knots).

The first method, plotting from the other ship's position, has the advantage that it uses the existing relative track of the other ship; thus, it is a very useful method to employ when there are several contacts being plotted at the same time on the display. The second method, plotting from own ship's position, makes use of the range strobe and should be more accurate.

Radar plotting on relative and true motion displays

Radar data obtained from a stabilised or unstabilised relative motion display or a true motion sea-stabilised display may be plotted on that display as shown in Fig. 17–9, and the velocity triangle drawn.

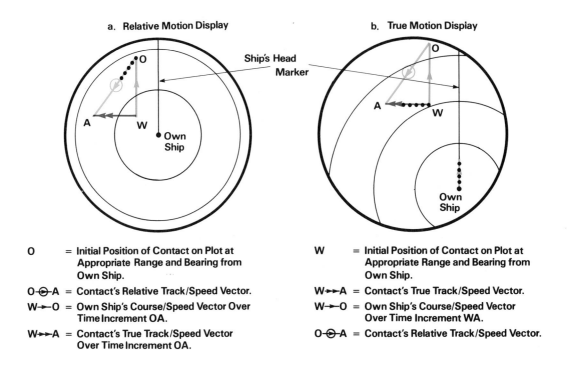

O	= Initial Position of Contact on Plot at Appropriate Range and Bearing from Own Ship.	W	= Initial Position of Contact on Plot at Appropriate Range and Bearing from Own Ship.
O-⊖-A	= Contact's Relative Track/Speed Vector.	W➤➤A	= Contact's True Track/Speed Vector.
W➤O	= Own Ship's Course/Speed Vector Over Time Increment OA.	W➤O	= Own Ship's Course/Speed Vector Over Time Increment WA.
W➤➤A	= Contact's True Track/Speed Vector Over Time Increment OA.	O-⊖-A	= Contact's Relative Track/Speed Vector.

Fig. 17–9.   Radar plotting on the relative and true motion displays

Radar limitations

The navigator must be aware of the limitations of solving relative velocity problems using radar. He may be able to draw what appears to be a precise velocity triangle (Fig. 17–9), but the data he is using are subject to error. Possible errors are:

1. *Plotting errors.* Despite the elimination of parallax, manual plotting on the face of a reflection plotter is subject to error, caused mainly by the thickness of the chinagraph pencil and the small size of the relative velocity triangles. This error should be eliminated with electronic plotting.
2. *Own ship's course and speed vector.* Both the gyro-compass and its transmission system and the bottom log are subject to errors. In RN ships, the gyro-compass should usually be accurate to ±1°, and the bottom log should usually be accurate to ±2%.
3. *Radar data.* Radar may not provide precise and consistent data, particularly with regard to range and bearing. The ship's head marker may not be lined

up correctly; the gyro-compass providing stabilisation of the radar picture is subject to error; the radar beam may be subject to squint error.

The accuracy of the data produced by the radar display will only be within certain limits. In RN ships, the usual navigational radar display has a bearing accuracy of ±1°, and a range accuracy of ±50 yards or 1% of the range scale in use, whichever is the greater. In the Department of Transport Radar Specification, the maximum permissible bearing error is 1°, while the accuracy of the variable range marker should be within 1½% of the range scale in use or 70 metres, whichever is the greater.

The cumulative effect is to cause errors in both the deduced relative and true tracks and the speeds of the contact. This is of particular importance when ships are likely to pass close to one another and also in the head-on approach. In the latter case, errors could produce a completely misleading situation, for example giving the impression that a ship is passing clear but very close down the port side when in fact it is passing down the starboard side.

The longer a contact is plotted, the more accurate becomes the assessment of the relative and true tracks. The shorter the range, the less is the effect of range and bearing errors. However, the longer a contact deemed a collision risk is plotted, the less time there is to take avoiding action.

It should not be forgotton that the relative and true tracks of a contact only tell the Officer of the Watch what was happening in the past; they do not reveal that the contact may be about to alter course or speed. If the contact alters course, there will be a time delay before this becomes evident on the radar display, and a further time delay before the new relative and true tracks can be deduced.

Relative or true motion plotting

Some general comments on the arguments for or against using relative motion or true motion radars for navigation were set out in Chapter 15 (page 446).

The advantage which a relative motion display has over true motion for collision avoidance is in giving an immediate indication of which ships are on a collision course.

On the other hand, whether or not a target is moving or stationary can usually be more quickly distinguished on a true motion display than on a relative display.

Generally speaking, from the point of view of collision avoidance, a stabilised relative motion display is usually preferable to true motion in open and coastal waters. Whether or not to use relative or true motion in pilotage waters is a matter of judgement, taking into account the situation at the time and the organisation available. The organisation in HM Ships usually includes an operations room team which deals with collision avoidance and assists with blind pilotage; thus, the need to use true motion radar displays is limited. Merchant ships, on the other hand, have fewer people to devote to these two tasks; thus, it is desirable to have both types of display immediately available. If only one type of display is available, merchant ships may prefer to use true motion radar in pilotage waters.

Aspect

When deducing another ship's true track from a plotting table (Fig. 17–6) or from the relative motion radar display (Fig. 17–8), the deduced aspect (angle on the bow)—defined earlier—of the other ship may not be the same as the visual aspect. Several factors can cause this variation. The effects on both ships of leeway, tidal stream, etc. may be different; own ship's speed input on a true motion display may not be correct; there may be a difference between the actual water or ground track of own ship and that shown on the radar display.

Always remember that the collision risk is from the approaching ship whose *bearing* is steady or does not appreciably change.

Effect of leeway

If the water track and sea speed are used as own ship's course and speed vector, the other ship's true track vector will also be her water track and sea speed, provided there is no difference in the set and drift being experienced by both ships. The difference between the deduced and visual aspects reflects the other ship's leeway and is equal to her leeway angle.

From time to time, leeway may be an important consideration, particularly if the other ship's aspect is close to zero, or if the leeway is large, as may be the case with yachts and ships in ballast.

Effect of drift and set

If the drift and set being experienced by two ships are the same, they should have no effect on the aspect, provided ground stabilisation is *not* being used. If the drift and set are not the same for each ship, then the deduced and observed aspects of the other ship will differ.

A ground-stabilised motion display may give a misleading picture in a collision situation in a tidal stream (Fig. 17–10). For the purposes of this example, it is assumed that neither ship is experiencing leeway.

At 0800, own ship W is on course and speed 000°, 12 knots, tidal stream setting 090°, 3.5 knots. Own ship's ground track is 018°, speed made good 12.5 knots. Ship G is on a steady bearing of 010° at a range of 10 miles. Her course and speed are 202°, 10 knots but, because of the tidal stream, her ground track is 182°, speed made good 9.4 knots. If no action is taken, collision will occur at point K at 0828.

On the ground-stabilised true motion display (Fig. 17–11, p.512), ship G *appears* to be on own ship's starboard bow and on an almost parallel and opposite course, the aspect being Green 8°. This is a misleading picture.

The situation, as shown on the stabilised north-up relative motion display (Fig. 17–12, p.513), is somewhat different.

Ship G is on own ship's starboard bow, crossing from starboard to port. Her aspect is actually Red 12° and not Green 8°. Such a situation should also be apparent visually and on the sea-stabilised true motion radar display.

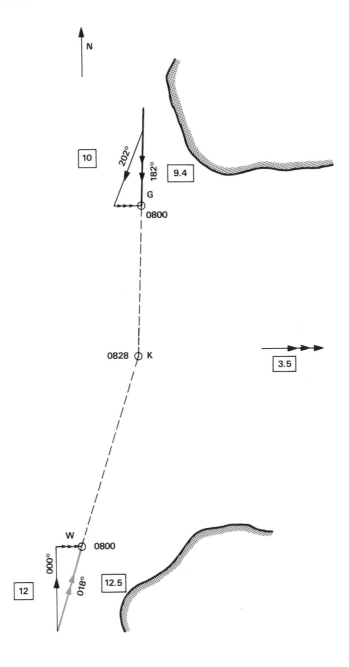

Fig. 17–10.   Collision situation in a tidal stream

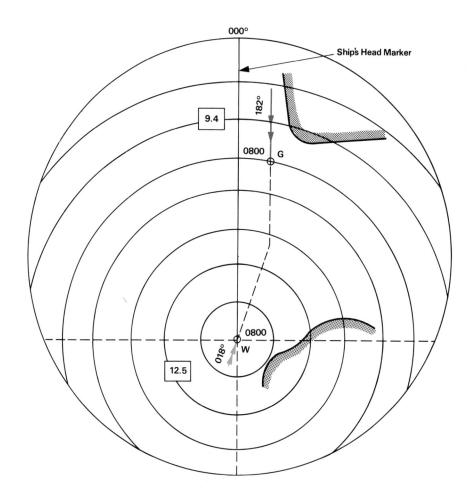

Fig. 17–11. The situation as displayed on true motion radar

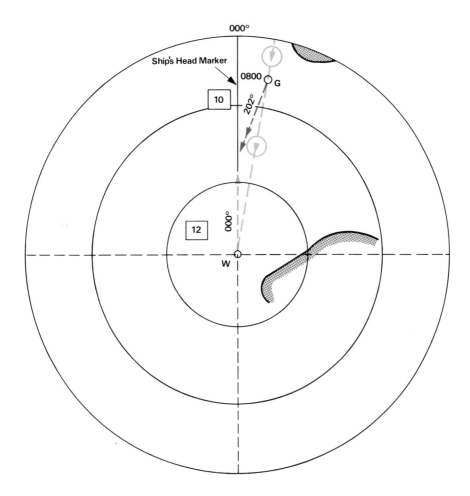

Fig. 17–12.   The situation as displayed on the relative motion radar

Automated radar plotting aids (ARPA)

A number of radars available commercially are fitted with automated or semi-automated aids to plotting and collision avoidance. Such aids to navigation are discussed in Volume III of this manual and are not dealt with in any great detail here.

The International Maritime Organisation (IMO) has set out certain standards amending the *International Convention of Safety of Life at Sea, 1974* (SOLAS '74) requirements regarding the carrying of suitable automated radar plotting aids (ARPA). Certain countries, e.g. the United States, have also enacted legislation on the subject.

A typical ARPA gives a presentation of the current situation and uses computer technology to predict the future situation. An ARPA assesses collision risk, proposed manoeuvres by own ship, etc. The following information is usually provided:

1. True or relative motion radar presentation.
2. Manual acquisition of contacts with automatic tracking of a selected number (usually about 20). Automatic acquisition is also available when contacts come within a specified range in a designated sector.
3. True or relative track and speed vectors of other ships, together with a prediction of their future positions.
4. Digital read-out on specified targets of track, speed, range, bearing, closest point of approach (CPA) and time to CPA (TCPA).
5. Automatic visible and audible warnings on targets predicted to come within a chosen CPA and TCPA.
6. The likely effect on the collision situation of a proposed manoeuvre by one's own ship.
7. Automatic ground stabilisation for navigational purposes, e.g. pilotage.
8. Selected navigational data.

The principal advantages of ARPA are a reduction in the work load of bridge personnel and fuller and quicker information on selected targets.

ARPA is not infallible, however, and must be used with caution. ARPA processes radar information much more rapidly than can be done manually, but that information is still subject to the same limitations mentioned earlier. The accuracy from inputs such as the compass and the log governs the accuracy of the displayed data. Using ARPA, the assessment from radar of the relative and true tracks of a contact is arrived at quickly, but the errors inherent in radar are still present. ARPA does not resolve the differences between the deduced and visual aspects caused by leeway and differing tidal streams, etc. The data presented are historical, and predictions are usually based on the assumption that courses and speeds of other ships will be maintained. Radar contacts can be lost or confused. Weather, especially clutter, imposes its own limitations.

The use of ARPA in inexpert hands can easily breed a false sense of security, as in such circumstances undue reliance may be placed upon the accuracy of the displayed data.

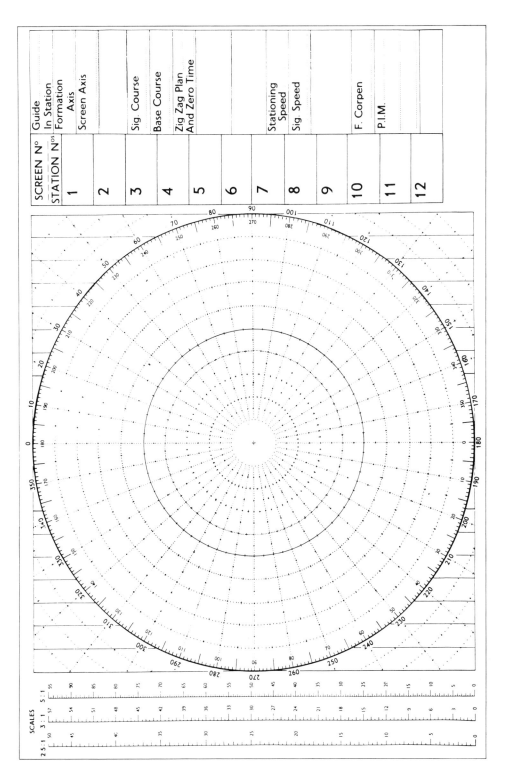

Fig. 17–13. Manoeuvring Form (S376)

SOME RELATIVE VELOCITY PROBLEMS

A number of simple relative velocity problems and their solutions is given in the following paragraphs. The conventions of the velocity triangle (Fig. 17–7)—the three rules set out on page 504—are followed; and the triangle is based on own ship's position, as in Fig. 17–8(b). The examples given are summarised in Table 17–2.

Table 17–2

EXAMPLE	TITLE	PAGE
1	Find the true track and speed of another ship from its relative movement	below
2	Find the closest point of approach (CPA)	517
3	Find the course to pass another ship at a given distance	518
4	Find the time at which two ships steaming different courses and speeds will be a certain distance apart	519
5	Open and close on the same bearing	520

These problems may be solved on radar displays, plotting tables, the Battenberg Mark 5 Course Indicator, or on plotting sheets such as the Manoeuvring Form (S376), briefly described in Chapter 7 and illustrated in Fig. 17–13 (page 515).

EXAMPLE 1   Find the true track and speed of another ship from its relative movement

Own ship's (W) course and speed are 020°, 20 knots. The following ranges and bearings of another ship G are obtained from radar as follows:

TIME	BEARING	RANGE (MILES)
0600	040°	8′
0603	038°	6′.65
0606	035°	5′.45
0609	030°	4′.25

What is the true track and speed of the other ship?

In Fig. 17–14 the positions of the echo G, G_1, G_2, G_3 are plotted relative to own ship W at the centre of the graticule or radar display.

The relative track of the other ship is along GG_3, 231°. Between 0600 and 0609, 9 minutes, the echo has moved from G to G_3, a distance of 3′.9. Thus, the relative speed of G along GG_3 is:

$$\frac{3.9}{9} \times 60 = 26 \text{ knots}$$

The velocity triangle may now be constructed to find the other ship's true track and speed. *WO*, own ship's vector, is drawn in a direction 020°, at a

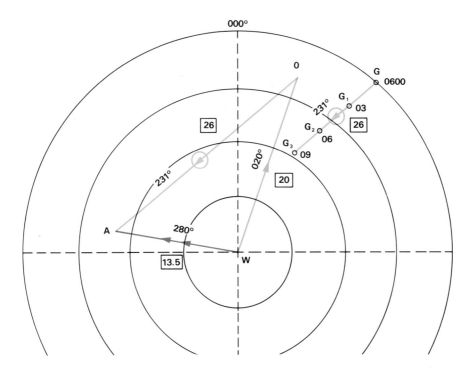

Fig. 17–14.   Other ship's true track and speed

distance equivalent to 20 knots. *OA*, the relative vector is drawn from *O* in a direction 231° at a distance equivalent to 26 knots. Vector *WA* represents the other ship's true track and speed (280°, 13.5 knots).

Note how all three rules (page 504) have been followed. *WO* and *WA* diverge; *WA* and *OA* converge; *WO* chases *OA*.

The true track and speed of the other ship is 280°, 13.5 knots.

EXAMPLE 2   Find the closest point of approach (CPA)

Given the information in Example 1, will ship G pass ahead or astern of own ship W, by what distance and at what time? How close will she come, at what time and on what bearing?

Project *G*'s relative track, *G, G₁, G₂, G₃* (Fig. 17–15, page 518), along the relative course of 231°. This track is seen to pass ahead of own ship and down the port side. When *G* is ahead, her bearing will be the same as own course (020°), and her distance WG_4 (2′.95). The distance between G_3 and G_4 may be measured (1′.4). The time of arrival at G_4 at *G*'s relative speed of 26 knots will be:

$$0609 + \frac{1.4}{26} \times 60 \text{ (minutes)} = 0612\tfrac{1}{4} \text{ (to nearest } \tfrac{1}{4} \text{ minute)}$$

G's closest point of approach (CPA) is when she reaches position G_5, WG_5 being at right angles to *G*'s relative track (231° + 90° = 321°). Measure WG_5 (1′.5).

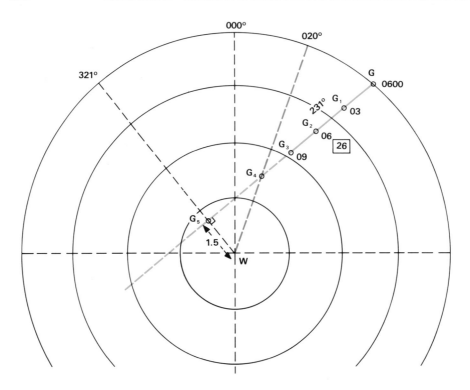

Fig 17–15.   The closest point of approach (CPA)

The total distance from G to G_5 is $7'.8$, which takes:

$$\frac{7.8}{26} \times 60 = 18 \text{ minutes at } G\text{'s relative speed of 26 knots}$$

Ship G will pass ahead $2'.95$ at $0612\frac{1}{4}$ and her closest point of approach will be on own ship's port side at 0618 on a bearing of 321° at a distance of $1'.5$.

EXAMPLE 3   Find the course to pass another ship at a given distance

Given the information in Example 1, it is decided to alter course at 0609 to ensure that ship G passes down the port side, keeping outside $3\frac{1}{2}$ miles. At the same time G alters course 5° to starboard to 285°. What is own ship's new course? What is the range, time and bearing of the new CPA?

Develop the relative track GG_3 as before (231°, 26 knots; Fig. 17–16). Own ship needs to alter course at 0609 in such a way that the relative track of G changes to keep outside $3'.5$.

Draw the arc of a circle FK, radius $3'.5$, centred on W. G's relative track from G_3 must be tangential to this circle. Construct the tangent G_3H, and measure the new relative track required ($266\frac{1}{2}°$).

Construct the velocity triangle.

1. Draw the other ship's true track vector WA (285°, 13.5 knots).
2. Through A draw the required relative track parallel to G_3H ($266\frac{1}{2}° - 086\frac{1}{2}°$).

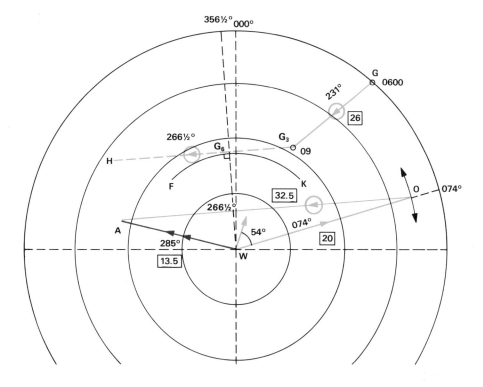

Fig. 17–16. The course to pass at a given distance

3. With centre W and radius representing own speed (20 knots), draw an arc of a circle cutting the required relative track through A, at O.
4. WO is the new course required at 0609 (074°).
5. Measure G's new relative speed OA from the speed triangle (32.5 knots).

   G's new CPA is now when she reaches G_6, WG_6 being at right angles to G's new relative track ($266\frac{1}{2}° + 90° = 356\frac{1}{2}°$). Measure G_3G_6 (2'.35). At the new relative speed of 32.5 knots, this distance will be covered in $(2.35/32.5)60 = 4\frac{1}{4}$ minutes (to the nearest $\frac{1}{4}$ minute), so G will reach G_6 at $0613\frac{1}{4}$.

   Own ship's new course at 0609 is 074°, an alteration of 54° to starboard. G's CPA is now $3\frac{1}{2}$ miles at $0613\frac{1}{4}$ on a bearing of $356\frac{1}{2}°$.

EXAMPLE 4   Find the time at which two ships, steaming different courses and speeds, will be at a certain distance apart

   Own ship's (W) course and speed are 000°, 16 knots. Another ship G on bearing 301°, 15 miles, has a true track 040° at 12 knots. When and on what bearing will ship G be 5 miles away?

   Construct the velocity triangle (Fig. 17–17, p.520).

1. Draw own ship's vector WO (000°, 16 knots).
2. Draw other ship's vector WA (040°, 12 knots).
3. Join and measure OA, the relative track and speed of the other ship G (132°, 10.2 knots).

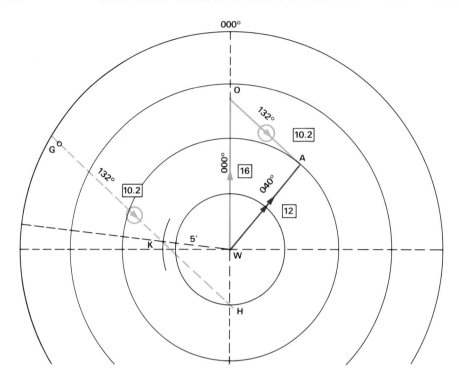

Fig. 17–17.   The time at which two ships will be a certain distance apart

Plot G's present position (301°, 15 miles) and draw in her relative track from this point GH (132°, 10.2 knots).

With centre W and radius 5 miles, draw an arc of a circle cutting GH in K. Measure GK (10'.5).

When ship G has steamed the relative distance GK (10'.5) at the relative speed (10.2 knots), she will be 5 miles away from W on a bearing of 277°. The time taken will be $(10.5/10.2)60 = 61\frac{3}{4}$ minutes (to the nearest $\frac{1}{4}$ minute).

Ship G will be 5 miles away after 1 hour $1\frac{3}{4}$ minutes, on a bearing of 277°.

EXAMPLE 5   Close and open on the same bearing

Own ship W (Fig. 17–18) is on course and speed 050°, 20 knots. Another ship G bears 330°8', true track and speed 030°, 15 knots. It is desired to close to 1 mile to identify ship G, then open out to the previous distance of 8 miles while preserving the bearing. What courses are required to close and open, and how long will each manoeuvre take?

Plot G at 330°8'. The courses which own ship W will require to steer will be those to close on a steady bearing of 330° to a distance of 1 mile, 7 miles in all, and then to open on the same steady bearing of 330°, to a distance of 8 miles, a further 7 miles. In other words, G must move to H relative to own ship, 330°, 1 mile away and then back out again to G.

Construct the velocity triangle.

1. Draw the other ship's vector WA (030°, 15 knots).

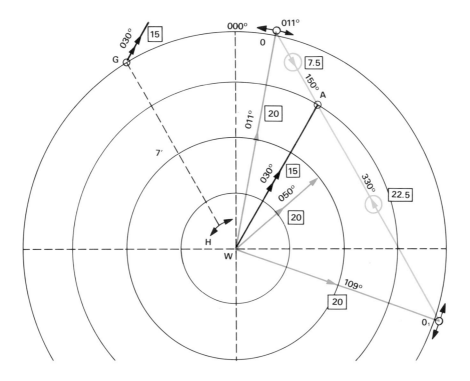

Fig. 17–18.   Close and open on the same bearing

2. Through *A* draw the required relative track, 330° − 150°.
3. From *W*, strike off an arc of a circle, radius equivalent to own ship speed of 20 knots, to cut the relative track through *A* in *O* and *O₁*.
4. Remembering the rules for the arrows:
    OA is the relative track and speed (150°, 7.5 knots) when *closing* on a steady bearing.
    O₁A is the relative track and speed (330°, 22.5 knots) when *opening* on a steady bearing.
5. *WO* is the course to steer (011°) to close ship *G* on a steady bearing.
6. *WO₁* is the course to steer (109°) to open from ship *G* on a steady bearing.

    The time to close to 1 mile will be the time to travel 7 miles at a relative speed of 7.5 knots *(OA)*: (7/7.5)60 = 56 minutes. The time to open again to 8 miles will be the time to travel 7 miles at a relative speed of 22.5 knots *(O₁A)*: (7/22.5)60 = 19 minutes (to the nearest minute).

    The course required to close to 1 mile is 011°, time taken 56 minutes. The course required to open to 8 miles is 109°, time taken 19 minutes.

CHAPTER 18
Surveying

Many Admiralty charts are to this day compiled from the sketch surveys of the last century, and the Hydrographer is dependent on many and varied sources of information in his endeavours to keep charts up to date. Opportunities often exist during the various passages and visits of HM Ships for valuable data to be collected and forwarded to the Hydrographic Department. Commanding Officers should, however, be careful to respect the territorial seas of foreign states and must obtain diplomatic clearance before embarking on anything which might be construed as surveying. Guidance can be found in *General Instructions for Hydrographic Surveyors* 0534, 0752 and 0803.

The purpose of this chapter is to explain to navigating officers of HM Ships how to carry out various kinds of hydrographic surveying work. The methods described have been kept as simple as possible, bearing in mind the limited resources generally available. The chapter starts with a discussion of those items of surveying work which the Navigating Officer may be required to undertake within a relatively short time scale. It concludes with some remarks on conducting a complete minor survey, should he have the opportunity and time, in an unsurveyed or poorly charted area.

It should be appreciated that hydrographic surveying is neither a mysterious nor very complicated art and that a lot of valuable work can be done by Navigating Officers with the relatively simple equipment to be found in any HM Ship.

Whatever is attempted, it is important that the work itself and the records later rendered to the Hydrographic Department should be honest and complete. Details of just how the work was done, what accuracy is judged to have been attained and what mistakes and omissions were made is vital if the survey is to earn its place as a worthwhile contribution to the Admiralty chart of the area. Lack of information on how the work was carried out can often lead to the discarding of work which might be sound, because it cannot be checked.

It is important to consider the cartographer who has the task of fitting the new survey to existing work. The more information that is rendered concerning scale, orientation and position, the easier it is to evaluate the work and insert it in its correct position on the chart. A survey may be an example of superb draughtsmanship and look to be of impeccable accuracy, but at the same time be virtually useless through lack of essential 'fitting-on' data.

Full instructions and advice on carrying out a survey may be found in the *Admiralty Manual of Hydrographic Surveying (AMHS)*, Volumes I and II, and the

General Instructions for Hydrographic Surveyors (GIHS), to which frequent reference will be made in the pages that follow. However, both of these publications may be somewhat forbidding to the non-professional and an attempt is made here to reduce the various surveying processes to their simplest terms. *AMHS* and *GIHS* are issued to HM Ships as part of their complete set of navigational publications and may also be purchased from Admiralty Chart Agents. Advice on rendering hydrographic notes may be found in Chapter 6.

Types of surveying work

Types of surveying work which lie within the capability of non-surveying HM Ships are listed below. Those which the Navigating Officer is more likely to find himself tackling are given first. The guidance on conducting a minor survey is put last, as the length of time it is likely to take, several days or up to a week, is not often likely to be available. Despite the listed order, the reader may find it helpful to read the last item first, as he will acquire a better understanding of the fundamental principles of surveying on which all the others depend. The pages which deal with them are given in brackets.

1. Passage sounding (below).
2. Fixing new navigational marks and dangers (below).
3. Disaster relief surveys (page 525).
4. Information on new port installations (page 526).
5. Running surveys (page 527).
6. Searches for reported dangers (page 529).
7. Tidal stream observations (page 530).
8. A complete minor survey (page 532).

It should always be borne in mind that, with hydrographic notes, disaster relief surveys, running surveys or area surveys, any information however limited is better than none. Even such brief statements as 'Harbour developments have made Chart . . . out of date', or 'Chimney (conspic) could not be seen' are useful, as they prompt the Hydrographer to write to the Port Authority concerned to seek more detailed information.

PASSAGE SOUNDING

Whenever ships are on a steady passage, particularly outside the Continental shelf but also in coastal waters which appear poorly charted, they should take every opportunity to obtain continuous lines of passage sounding. Guidance and instructions may be found in *AMHS*, Volume II, Chapter 3; *GIHS; The Mariner's Handbook* and Fleet Operating Orders. A high quality of passage sounding data is now possible with the introduction of deep echo-sounders and improved worldwide radio aids such as Omega and SATNAV.

FIXING NEW NAVIGATIONAL MARKS AND DANGERS

There are two main methods of fixing navigational marks and dangers: intersection and resection. Circumstances may dictate the use of one or the other, but intersection is preferred as being inherently the more accurate and easier to check.

To fix an object by intersection, observations, which may be angles by sextant, bearings by compass or ranges by radar, are made from fixed positions *into* the object. For resection the observations are made *at* the object to be fixed.

The fixed position from which an intersecting shot is taken may be the bridge of the ship or a boat, in which case the ship or boat must be fixed simultaneously with the observation of the shot. Best of all, the ship or boat should be fixed by horizontal sextant angles to shore marks with the object to be fixed in transit with a charted mark. This procedure should be repeated until at least three shots with different transits and a good cut have been obtained, and the fixes and shooting up angles can be plotted with station pointers to fix the object. If suitable transits cannot be found, the intersecting shot should be the sextant angle between one of the fix marks (preferably the centre to facilitate plotting with station pointers) and the object to be fixed. Alternatively, but with less accuracy, the fix and intersecting shot can be obtained by gyro bearings and/or radar ranges. Similarly, the intersecting shot may be observed from ashore using a sextant or hand bearing compass from a well defined charted object such as a beacon or breakwater head.

Resection implies the accessibility, for ship, boat or man, of the object to be fixed. This method is often suitable for fixing a buoy. A boat is taken alongside the buoy and the position fixed by horizontal sextant angles. A new beacon on a jetty may be fixed by the observer standing alongside it and taking a sextant fix. In every case, a check angle to a fourth mark must be obtained in addition to the main fix and plotted with the fix to guard against errors.

Buoys should be fixed on both ebb and flood and a mean position accepted.

An underwater danger must be fixed either by resection, with the ship or boat on top of the danger; or by intersection, the danger having been marked with a dan or pellet, possibly laid by diver.

DISASTER RELIEF SURVEYS

From time to time, earthquakes, tidal waves and hurricanes cause considerable damage to ports and anchorages. Navigational marks may have been destroyed or displaced; berths and jetties severely damaged; and the whole topography of the sea-bed may undergo considerable change with consequential alterations in the depths. HM Ships sent to the area to afford relief may well therefore find themselves carrying out essential surveys. This work may involve any of the following:

1. Helping to erect and establish the position of fresh navigational marks, e.g. beacons, leading marks, etc.; establishing any errors in position of buoys and other floating navigational aids.
2. The sounding out of approach channels, recommended tracks and leading lines for differences in depths from those charted, especially along leads and over bars. It may even be necessary to try to establish alternative approaches, setting up fresh leading marks, etc.
3. Sounding out anchorages.
4. The charting of new wrecks and other dangers to navigation which may be encountered (*see* GIHS).

5. Amendments to the *Admiralty Sailing Directions*, together with views and photographs.

Whatever the particular need, which can only be decided by the Navigating Officer on the spot, the general surveying principles set out elsewhere in this chapter will apply.

Reporting new dangers

It is of paramount importance that any new danger to navigation is reported without delay. This may be done by signal and followed up with a hydrographic note (Form H102 or H102A, *see* Chapter 6). Such reports should also include errors in the position of floating navigational aids, and lights which are unlit or whose charted or listed characteristics appear to be in error.

INFORMATION ON NEW PORT INSTALLATIONS

The following information should normally be obtained on new jetties and wharves.

1. Dimensions.
2. Height (above chart datum or MHWS).
3. Orientation.
4. Depth alongside and at 5, 10 and 20 metres off.
5. Type of construction.
6. Particular berthing and mooring arrangements (e.g. dolphins).
7. Boat landings.
8. Cranes and other facilities.

Sounding out a berth alongside a jetty

A suitable scale for this type of work is about 1:1000 (1 cm to 10 m). If the jetty is charted on a large scale, its position and orientation may be taken from the chart. If it is not charted, its position and orientation must be fixed in the field with reference to the largest scale chart available.

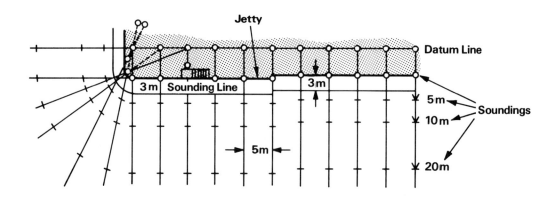

Fig. 18–1. Sounding out a berth alongside a jetty

The survey procedure (Fig. 18–1) is as follows:

1. Establish a datum line parallel to the line of the jetty and far enough back to provide sensitive transits.
2. Paint marks at 5 metre intervals along the datum line with whitewash or white emulsion. Make similar marks on the face of the jetty, to form transits with the marks on the datum line at right angles to the line of the jetty.
3. Additional marks to provide transits for lines around the corner of the jetty may also be required.
4. Poles or flags are placed or held on the white marks to enable the transits to be seen while sounding each line.
5. Soundings should be taken alongside and at 5, 10 and 20 metres off. This work is most easily done in a small dinghy at or near high water, when the tidal stream is slack. The distance of the leadsman from the face of the jetty may be obtained by distance line.
6. A line of soundings parallel with the jetty and about 3 metres off should be run, to ensure that no underwater obstructions exist which might foul a ship's bilge keels or propellers.
7. If shoal depths are found in the vicinity of the berth, sounding lines should be run parallel to the line of the berth to indicate how far these extend.
8. Details such as cranes, bollards, sheds, railway lines, etc. should be included on the plan, if time permits.

RUNNING SURVEYS

A running survey, as the name implies, is carried out whilst a ship is on passage along a coast and does not require the ship to slow down or stop. The technique can be practised on any coastal passage in well charted waters, so that the team is worked up should the need for a running survey arise later.

In a running survey, the scale, orientation and geographical position (page 533) are provided by the ship's track fixed by the most accurate means available. It is preferable to fix the ship at the beginning and end of the run and, if possible, regularly in between, by some means independent of the adjacent coast that is to be fixed. Ideal for this purpose is any suitable radio aid (e.g. SATNAV) or, if none is available, astronomical fixes. If the latter are used, however, at least three reliable observers should obtain the best agreement possible.

If the run is fixed at each end, scale and orientation for the survey are provided by the adjusted fair track between fixes. If only one fix can be obtained, scale and orientation are provided by 'fixing' by range and bearing off one well defined mark ashore. Even if the geographical position of this mark is unknown, it will provide a stationary reference point from which the ship's ground track can be found and plotted. Alternatively, scale and orientation can be provided less accurately by the water track derived from log, compass and leeway. It will help if the ship's course and speed are kept as steady as possible during a running survey.

The remainder of the running survey procedure is standard, regardless of the means used to find the ship's track. *DR stations* are established at regular intervals of about 10 minutes and selected objects ashore are 'shot up' using gyro, sextant and radar. The objects selected should be those which best define the coastline, such as headlands, river mouths, etc., off-lying islands and rocks, and any useful marks for navigation such as prominent peaks, buildings and conspicuous natural features.

To minimise 'cocked hats' at the shore objects being fixed, it is important that all observations should be made simultaneously at the instant of the DR station or, at the most, a few seconds either side. The use of several observers and recorders will make this easier.

The best way of recording radar data at the stations is by photographing the radar display. Ideally, range rings should be switched on and, if fitted, the bearing marker should be pre-set to a fixed bearing, e.g. north; if not, the ship's head marker should be used to orient the picture. In the latter case, the ship's head should be noted at the instant of each fix, as the radar display bearing graduations do not always show up well in a photograph. It is advisable to construct a simple jig of wood or Dexion strip to hold the camera square to the face of the display and properly centred. This avoids distortion of the picture and ensures consistency between photographs. Later, ranges can be read off the photographs by interpolation between the range rings and bearings read off, by aligning a protractor with the bearing marker or ship's head marker. Once the salient points of the coastline have been fixed, the radar picture can be of great assistance in filling in the shape of the coast in between.

The scale chosen should be not larger than 1:100,000 or about 18 mm to a sea mile as, even at this scale, inaccuracies will be very apparent in the plot.

In addition to the observations mentioned above, the ship should run a line of soundings and obtain photographic views at intervals along the run (*see* NP 140).

It is important that all instruments and equipment used (gyro, sextants, radar, echo sounder, etc.) are calibrated before and after the run.

Fig. 18–2 shows how, in the course of about $1\frac{1}{2}$ hours, an inadequately charted coastline of about 8 miles could be improved.

At 0800 the ship is fixed by radio aid and simultaneously fixes the lighthouse by radar range and visual bearing. The ship is then fixed by range and bearing of the lighthouse (fixes 2 to 15) at 6 minute intervals.

Numerous sextant angles and gyro bearings are taken into the selected objects ashore, either at these fixes or, to relieve congestion on the gyro, at accurately plotted DR stations in between. Observations at each station must be simultaneous or may be taken at accurately timed points and plotted from the DR between the fixes.

Photographs of the radar display, soundings and photographic views are also obtained throughout the run. If possible, the aim should be to obtain at least five shots into each object.

One of the greatest difficulties experienced is that of identifying the objects consistently as the aspect of the coastline changes with the ship's movement along it; a methodical approach to the recording is necessary to avoid muddle.

If there is no reliable charted object for a fix, such as the light in Fig. 18–2, the best object available should be chosen instead, e.g. islet A. This should be fixed as soon as possible, its geographical position being based on the ship's position which has been found by astronomical observations or radio aid (e.g. SATNAV).

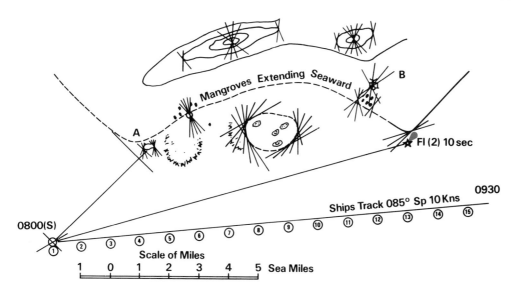

Fig. 18–2.   A running survey

Islet *A* would now be used as the datum for subsequent fixes.

As the ship proceeds along the coast, it is possible to 'hop' from one datum to another, for example from islet *A* to mosque *B*, at the same time endeavouring to establish the ship's geographical position by other means. If it is not possible to establish the geographical position in this way, the EP will have to be used, but it should be remembered that this will become progressively more inaccurate as the distance increases from the last fix. The process of 'hopping' from one datum to the next may be used on a long stretch of coast, but it is essential to tie in the ship's track to a geographical position at each end of the run.

A full report of survey should be forwarded to the Hydrographer, describing the methods used, assumptions made and results achieved.

If the scale of the published chart is suitable, the survey should be forwarded as a tracing to fit the chart; alternatively, a tracing on a selected scale should be prepared with sufficient graduations to permit accurate comparison with Hydrographic Office records.

SEARCHES FOR REPORTED DANGERS

A brief study of Admiralty charts will reveal many reported dangers or shoal soundings. Many of them prove to be false and may not be dangerous to surface navigation. The Hydrographer is obliged to chart them even though the evidence for their existence may be poor, but they can only be removed, or be more positively charted, after a systematic search has been carried out by a ship whose navigation can be relied upon.

A search out of sight of land is best conducted on an automatic plotting table provided the log is accurately calibrated. A scale of about 10 cm to 1 mile is generally adequate and the search should usually cover about 100 square miles.

The depth of water governs the distance apart of the lines of soundings, which should be spaced in accordance with the following rough rules:

general depths of 4000 m	4 miles apart
general depths of 2000 m	1 mile apart
general depths of 1000 m	$\frac{1}{4}$ mile apart

The search track must invariably be adjusted between star sights or other reliable fixes by radio aid.

If the soundings indicate shoaling, additional lines of sounding should be run to establish the least depth. If possible, an up and down wire sounding should also be taken over the shoalest part to guard against false echoes.

Sonar and a helicopter greatly enhance the value of a negative report and may also contribute to the safety of one's own ship. A good visual look out with polaroid sunglasses should also be maintained.

Fuller guidance may be found in *AMHS*, Volume II, Chapter 3 and *GIHS*.

TIDAL STREAM OBSERVATIONS

It is normally only practicable to observe tidal streams over a limited period. In the waters around the British Isles and in other areas where the tide is predominantly semi-diurnal, a single observation period of 25 hours at springs is usually enough. In areas where the diurnal inequality is large, a period of 49 hours during large tides is to be preferred. If this is not possible, sufficient measurements should be obtained to enable a description to be inserted in the *Sailing Directions* and tidal stream arrows to be shown on the chart.

Where the tidal stream is very strong, the method described below will be unsuitable but, at the very least, if the times of slack water and the direction from and to which the stream is changing are reported, a valuable contribution will have been made.

Pole current log

A pole current log should be used to measure tidal stream rates. The pole should be weighted at the base so as to float vertically with about 45 centimetres above water, the base being at a depth appropriate to the average draught of shipping using the area. A small light or reflector should be attached for night observation.

A hole should be drilled through the pole at the waterline so that the current line may be attached. This may consist of any small buoyant line, well stretched, and marked with coloured bunting every 3 metres, starting about 15 metres away from the log to allow it to be well clear of the ship before observations start (Fig. 18–3).

The log is streamed from the stern. A relative bearing plate or gyro repeat will be required to observe the direction of the pole and so deduce the direction of the stream.

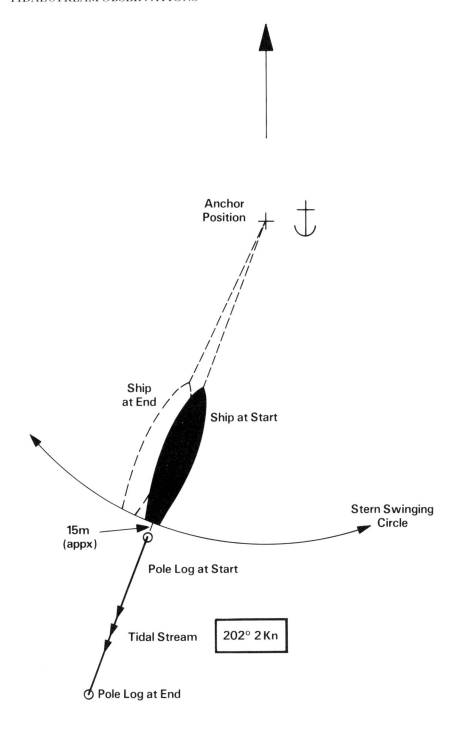

Fig. 18–3. Plotting tidal stream data

Observing procedure

Allow the current line to run out to the first mark (15 metres approx.) and start the watch as the first mark passes outboard. The line is allowed to run for 2 minutes, or 1 minute if the stream is more than $2\frac{1}{2}$ knots. When the time is up, the direction of the log and the distance run are noted. The log is then handed, and a further observation taken 1 hour later, and so on until the total time is up.

The rate of the tidal stream may be deduced from the formula:

$$30.9 \text{ m/min} = 1 \text{ knot} \qquad \qquad \dots \mathbf{18.1}$$

Recording

The following is an example of the record of observations kept. Note that the time zone used must be recorded.

ZONE TIME	LINE RUN OUT	MINUTES	RELATIVE DIRECTION OF POLE AT		SHIP'S HEAD		TRUE DIRECTION OF POLE AT	
			START	FINISH	START	FINISH	START	FINISH
1300(A)	130 m	2	R175°	G170°	021°	025°	206°	195°

The calculation of the rate and direction of the stream from the above data is best made graphically on a large-scale plotting sheet or Manoeuvring Form (S376) and is illustrated in Fig. 18–3.

The position of the anchor is plotted at the centre of the plotting sheet from which the stern swinging circle (Chapter 14) is plotted. The position of the stern relative to the anchor and the position of the pole are plotted at the start and finish of the run. The direction and rate of the tidal stream may now be calculated. Do not forget to make an allowance for the length of the stray line when plotting both the start and finish positions.

For the above data, the calculated tidal stream at 1300 is 202°, 2 knots.

A COMPLETE MINOR SURVEY

Principles of surveying

The pages that follow describe how a full survey may be conducted with limited equipment, time and resources. They start with first principles and should enable the navigator to produce a passable survey of a small area even in the unlikely event of him finding himself in a totally uncharted and unmapped part of the world. Almost always, in practice, there will be at least a chart of the area and, depending on its scale, date of publication and reliability, there will be one or more of the basic elements of control mentioned below which can be taken from it.

Control

A hydrographic survey has to present a three-dimensional picture on a two-dimensional piece of paper.

In the horizontal dimension all plotted features shown must be:

1. The correct *shape*; that is, outline features such as islands, bays and contours must be the correct shape and point features such as depths, beacons and buoys must be in the correct angular relation to each other.
2. The correct *size* or distance apart, in accordance with the stated *scale* of the survey.
3. In the correct *orientation* relative to true north.
4. In the correct *geographical position* in terms of latitude and longitude and relative to adjacent land masses and existing charts.

These four elements—shape, scale, orientation and geographical position—form the *horizontal control* of a survey and permit construction of a framework of fixed points to which the detail such as soundings, coastline and topography can be added.

Vertical control is the process whereby depths and heights are referred to the appropriate vertical datums.

Horizontal control

There are several methods of controlling the shape of the survey, but the one described here as being most suitable for a navigator carrying out a minor survey with limited equipment is the classical method of *triangulation* (Fig. 18–8, page 543). It relies on the fact that, if the three angles of a triangle are known, that triangle can only be plotted in one shape. In addition, the other three requirements of scale, orientation and geographical position are satisfied if the length and true bearing of one side and the geographical position of one of the points of the triangle are known. Triangulation takes advantage of the inherent check that the three angles of a plane triangle sum to 180° exactly.

Triangulation

To establish the framework to which the survey detail will be added, the navigator must first simplify. From the irregular coastline and topography he sees before him, he must select a number of triangulation stations, the lines of sight between them forming a series of rigidly defined geometric figures based on the triangle. Having established his main framework of relatively few stations, he then fixes more stations from these, called *sounding marks*, until he has a sufficiently dense network of control points from which his sounding boat can be fixed and from which a shore party can fix the detail of the coastline and topography.

The regular methods of triangulation and the elaborate adjustment of the observations described in *AMHS*, Volume I cannot be carried out thoroughly unless ample time and a full equipment of surveying instruments are available. As a rule, the navigator will measure all angles with a sextant and, in the small surveys with which he is generally concerned, he should reduce his system of triangulation to the simplest possible form. For this type of survey the following points should be noted:

1. The triangulation scheme should as nearly as possible enclose the area to be surveyed and the positions of the sounding marks. This conforms with one of the fundamental principles of surveying—that of working *from the whole to*

the part. By working inwards from the outer framework, errors are diminished rather than exaggerated.

2. Providing (1) above is observed, the number of triangulation stations should be the least that will provide an adequate framework to cover the area to be surveyed. For a small anchorage or harbour, half a dozen stations should suffice. From these it should be possible to 'shoot up' any additional marks required for fixing the soundings and topography.

3. The stations should be grouped so as to form quadrilaterals or polygons with central stations. By so doing, each will be connected by at least three shots from adjacent points, and a check is provided against errors of observation and plotting.

4. The stations should be sited so that most of them are intervisible, and certainly the three stations forming any one triangle should see each other.

5. The shots fixing each station should intersect at a strong angle of cut.

6. Natural marks should be used as far as possible, and efforts should be made to include in the triangulation a selection of well defined points already shown on the chart. This will greatly assist the cartographer when he has to incorporate the new survey in exisiting charted material.

7. The angles of the triangulation should be measured in the horizontal plane. It may not be possible to site all the stations at about the same level, but it should be remembered that, if the subtended angle between two objects is in the region of 90°, the error due to differing elevations is reduced to a minimum (*see* page 541 and *AMHS*, Volume I).

Scale

The choice of scale should be governed by the complexity of the area, the irregularity of the sea-bed, and the type and size of vessel likely to use the area. A more complex area requiring more detailed survey will call for a larger scale. If a large-scale chart or plan of the area already exists, it may well be advisable to use the same scale. In any case, a study of the chart folios held on board will help determine a suitable scale for a given type of area.

As a general guide a suitable scale for a coastal survey might be 1:50,000; for an anchorage or small bay 1:25,000; and for detailed work in a harbour 1:10,000 or even larger. For these large scales, much skill and very careful observations are needed to ensure accurate results, and the inexperienced surveyor will be well advised to think very carefully before undertaking any such work. The larger the scale, the longer the work will take. As a rough guide, doubling the scale trebles the time.

In choosing a scale, it is also necessary to consider the instruments available for plotting. Large sheets can be plotted with accuracy only if metal scales, straight edges and beam compasses are used. If the plot has to be made entirely with station pointers, the scale should be such that the marks of the survey are all contained within a sheet of moderate size, say about 15 inches square.

In the absence of a metal scale, there is no exact method of measuring distances on the paper and the natural scale can only be approximate. However, the relative positions of every point on the survey can be correctly plotted and the true scale can be worked out afterwards, provided the length in metres of one or more of the sides of the triangulation is stated.

The base line

All surveys depend on a 'base' for scale, and this base must be measured as accurately as possible. There are various methods by which the base line may be obtained.

1. *The published chart*

   Sometimes it is possible to use the distance on the published chart between two identifiable objects, thereby providing the scale, orientation and geographical position in one operation.

   It will be seldom, however, that the published chart is on a large enough scale for a new survey, and the distance obtained will have to be doubled or trebled. To do this, prick-off the charted length on to the plotting sheet, draw a fine line through the points on the sheet and extend it well either side of them; equal distances can then be stepped off the the left and right of the original two points as required to double or treble its length. This method is considerably more accurate with limited equipment than measuring the length on the chart on the distance scale, multiplying the distance by 2 or 3, and then re-converting into a plotting distance.

2. *Taped base*

   A base line may be taped out along the ground provided the ground is reasonably flat. The base length should be at least 300 m over flat ground—a jetty is ideal. A number of poles may have to be set up in transit, so that the various fleets of the tape are all in a straight line.

   The base should be measured at least once in each direction and the measurements should agree to within 15 cm. Any discrepancy should be noted for subsequent inclusion in data rendered at the end of the survey.

   A base even 300 m long will only plot 12 mm long at 1:25,000, and this is too short if the rest of the triangulation is to be plotted by angles alone as scale error will increase as the plot progresses away from the base. The measured base must therefore be incorporated into the triangulation by what is called the *base extension*, so that the longest side can be calculated through the successive triangles using the sine formula. The triangulation can then be plotted from the longest side as described on pages 542 to 543. The principles and some suitable layouts for base extension triangulation may be found in *AMHS*, Volume I. Fig. 18–5 (p.536) is a simple example of base extension using an even shorter measured distance.

3. *Radar base*

   Longer bases can be measured by carefully calibrated radar with reasonable accuracy, providing the marks chosen as targets give a well defined radar response and that the ship is so tightly moored as to provide unfluctuating ranges during the period of measurement. The angles between the marks and the ship must be measured at the same time, preferably with a sextant, to permit calculation of the triangle involved, as shown in Fig. 18–4 (p.536). To avoid parallax, it is important that the observer's sextant be as near vertically below the radar aerial as possible and that the observers ashore use the centre of the aerial as their mark.

4. *Subtense method*

   If it is impossible to measure a long enough base because of the rugged

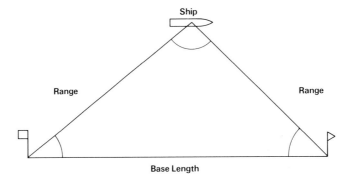

Fig. 18–4.   Determination of the base length by radar

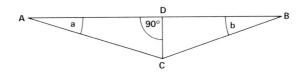

Fig. 18–5.   Determination of the base length by the subtense method

nature of the ground, the subtense method (Fig. 18–5) may be used as follows, *DC* being the measured distance.

If the distance *AB* is required, find a point *D* about midway between *A* and *B*, lay out *DC* at right angles to *AB* and measure *DC* and the angles *a* and *b*. Then, by plane geometry:

$$AB = DC\,(\cot a + \cot b) \qquad\qquad \text{...}\ \textbf{18.2}$$

AD and *DB* should not be more than about 7 times the length *DC* and the small angles *a* and *b* should be very carefully observed and plumbed directly over the marks. Observations with a number of different sextants should be taken if possible.

Orientation

The true bearing of one of the sides of the triangulation must be determined in order to orient the whole triangulation scheme. This can be done in one of the following ways:

1. From an existing large-scale chart or plan. Measure the angle between the base line or another side in the triangulation and a meridian of the chart, using the most accurate station pointers available.
2. By observing the angle subtended at one end of the line between the other end of the line and low altitude sun or stars. Accurate times must be noted

and the mean of several observations accepted. Sun or stars should be at an altitude of 10° to 30°, and the angle between the other end of the line and the sun or star as near as possible to 90°. An accuracy of ±5′ should be aimed at (*AMHS*, Volume I).

3. By observing along the line from both ends with as accurate a magnetic compass as available and then correcting for variation and accepting the mean.
4. By reference to a distant charted object. Take a bearing from the chart between an identifiable point in the survey area to another well charted point which may or may not lie in the survey area. For example, in Fig. 18–6 point *A* is a beacon in the survey area, shown also on the published chart; point *X* is a well defined hill summit some miles up the coast, also charted. The bearing *A* to *X* may be taken from the chart, the angle *XAB* observed by sextant, and hence the true bearing of the line *AB* deduced. The angle *XAB* should be as close to 90° as possible to avoid errors due to unequal elevation of the marks.

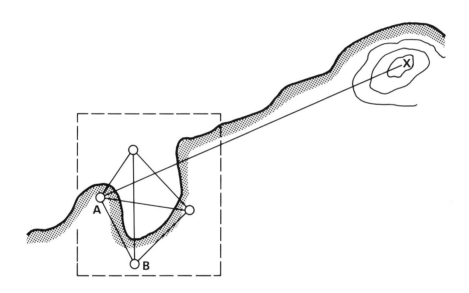

Fig. 18–6.   Orientation of the base line

5. By ship's compass.
   (*a*) Take a round of compass bearings to the various marks of the survey from the ship at anchor. Plot the bearings, radiating from a point, on a piece of tracing paper and obtain the best fit by sliding the tracing paper over the plotting sheet. Having obtained a position of the ship relative to the marks, a meridian may be drawn on the plot. The bearings must be obtained quickly as well as accurately, as the ship may move appreciably about her anchor.
   (*b*) If two of the plotted marks of the survey are so situated that the ship can be placed on the transit, the gyro bearing of one from the other can easily

be obtained. The gyro error should be found as close to the time of observation as possible.

Geographical position

Before the cartographer can incorporate a survey on to the published chart, he needs to have a means of fitting it on in the right place. Where a survey is close to the coast, its geographical position is best defined by fitting-on points. At least two, and preferably more, points should be chosen that are common to the survey and the largest scale suitable chart. Any well charted objects such as lighthouses, beacons, church towers, well defined peaks or points of land may be used. The points should be as widely spaced on paper as possible, ideally spanning the field work of the survey. If, as could happen on a featureless desert coast, suitable fitting-on points are not available, geographical position will have to be observed independently. Depending on how the ship is fitted, SATNAV, long-range electronic position fixing systems or astronomical observations may be used. Whichever method is used, the ship must be fixed relative to a mark or marks of the survey simultaneously with the observations. In the case of a SATNAV fix, where the time of fix is not known until after the pass, the ship must be anchored and fixed at frequent intervals during the pass so that the fix closest in time to the SATNAV time of fix can be used.

Vertical control

A hydrographic survey shows detail in three dimensions. Not only does it show the position of land and water features but it also gives the depth of water and the height of lighthouses and hills.

Soundings are reduced to chart datum; whenever soundings are being obtained, a record of the height of tide above chart datum must be kept so that the soundings can be reduced by the height of tide at the time (*see* page 548). The elevation of rocks and banks which dry at low water but cover at high water is measured above chart datum.

Heights are referred to Mean High Water Spring (MHWS) (or Mean Higher High Water (MHHW) where the tide is mainly diurnal).

The method of establishing chart datum in the survey area is given below (page 550).

The practical survey

Survey equipment

The items of equipment listed below should all be available to the navigating Officer of an HM Ship, or capable of being made on board. If he has sufficient notice of the opportunity or requirement to carry out a survey, it is possible that the Hydrographic Department at Taunton or any surveying ship may be able to assist with such items as surveying sextants, steel tapes, portable echo sounders or modern plastic drawing materials and instruments.

Depending on the circumstances, some items may not be needed. For instance, if a base length is derived from the existing chart, there is no need for steel tapes.

The following is a list of equipment likely to be required:

1. Sextants: two or more, preferably fitted with star or surveying telescopes.
2. A device for measuring distance on the ground. Steel tapes are ideal but linen tapes are not recommended, as they are liable to stretch perhaps by as much as 15 cm in 15 m. A very serviceable steel 'tape' may be made from a 30 m length of small diameter wire accurately measured against an engineer's steel tape on board before starting the survey and again on completion.
3. A straight edge and a measuring scale for plotting the work. An engineer's steel rule is quite adequate, as the average length of line to be measured will not generally exceed 300 mm.
4. An accurate magnetic pocket compass.
5. Station pointers. These should be graduated in minutes of arc, for plotting the fixes when sounding, etc. and also for plotting angles when laying down the framework or triangulation of the survey (*AMHS*, Volume II, Chapter 3).
6. Douglas protractors.
7. Lead lines: one for each boat. These may be made up on board, preferably fitted with a wire heart, and marked in metres or fathoms and feet depending on the units required. Lead lines should be calibrated before and after sounding when wet, and corrections for stretch made if necessary. Bearing-off spars or boat-hook staves may also be marked off for use in shallow water (*AMHS*, Volume II, Chapter 3).
8. Tide pole. This should be marked off in metres or feet dependent on the units of soundings required (page 549 and *AMHS*, Volume II, Chapter 2).
9. Ten-foot poles. Two or three poles 10 feet in length may be required for measuring short distances (*AMHS*, Volume I).
10. Materials for marks ashore. Flags, bunting, boat-hook staves, whitewash or white emulsion, guys, stakes, etc. (*AMHS*, Volume II, Chapter 1).
11. A pair of sounding boards. Any flat drawing board mounted with suitable paper will suffice.
12. One plotting sheet made of thick paper, for example the back of a clean, flat, cancelled chart. Do not use tracing cloth, as it is liable to become distorted.
13. Appropriate sounding and field books. Any conveniently sized Stationery Office note book will suffice.
14. *Admiralty Manual of Hydrographic Surveying*, Volumes I and II.
15. *General Instructions for Hydrographic Surveyors*.

Reconnaissance and planning

Plan on the largest scale chart or map available. If there is a Land Survey Office interested in the area, they will probably be able to supply maps and other data; they may be able to provide an easily recoverable base for the survey. If no adequate chart or map exists, a quick reconnaissance may be worth while to help in the planning of the triangulation. This can usually be done with sufficient accuracy in a few hours by sketches from ship or boat stations with the aid of compass and radar. If a helicopter is available, a most thorough reconnaissance of the area can be quickly obtained together with all-round oblique photographs from which to plan later. Natural objects, suitable for inclusion in the triangulation, should be picked out. The best site for a base and the method of measurement must be decided upon, and also the most suitable scale.

Marking (*AMHS*, Volume II, Chapter 1)

For shore marks, white-painted marks or boat-hook staves with flags will, with the help of natural objects, fulfil most of the requirements of a small survey. Floating marks are sometimes useful for fixing, particularly as a centre object when coastlining, and a boat on a taut moor, or a dan buoy, can often be used to advantage if the scale is not too large. A floating beacon can easily be improvised using 40 gallon oil drums.

The siting of marks requires a good deal of thought if their numbers are to be kept within reasonable limits. They must be designed to provide a good fix at any part of the survey; generally speaking, marks about every 50 to 100 millimetres on paper are desirable. Some marks sited inland can enable a boat to fix right up to the beach, but remember that the marks used in a fix should be at approximately the same elevation and as close to water level as possible.

Before finally deciding where to place marks, refer back to the section on triangulation (page 533) and *AMHS*, Volume I.

Observing

Having erected or selected all the marks for both triangulation and sounding marks, the next step is to observe all the angles of the main triangulation and those to sounding marks by sextant.

All the angles of the triangulation forming a series of triangles must be observed wherever possible. If, for some reason, it is not possible to observe one angle of a triangle, it can be derived by subtracting the sum of the other two from 180°, but this is not recommended because there is no check on the accuracy of the angles observed.

The observed angles of any triangle add up to 180° if there is no error of observation; as a general rule, a triangle should be re-observed if it does not close within 5'. When observing it is most important that the observer's eye should be exactly over the triangulation station. It is also most important that boat-hook staves carrying flags should be perfectly upright. Most errors of observation are due to the non-observance of these points.

It follows that an object like a church steeple is not suitable as a main station but is better fixed as a sounding mark by intersection (page 525). A church tower, however, with a flat roof, on which an observer can occupy a station, can be excellent providing there is a precise target such as a flagpole for shots into the tower from other stations.

The marks of a survey are seldom at the same height and therefore the angles measured are seldom truly horizontal. For example, if one mark is 4° above the horizon and the other is on the horizon, and the true horizontal angle between them is 40°, the angle between them will be 40°10'. This is termed a 'cocked-up' angle. The true horizontal angle may be obtained from the cocked-up angle by the following formula (*AMHS*, Volume I):

cos true horizontal angle = cos angular distance

$\times$ sec apparent altitude   . . . **18.3**

The error is zero if the angular distance between the two marks is 90°.

Angles should be observed to the nearest $\frac{1}{2}$ minute of arc.

Observed angles at a mark must be consistent with each other; e.g. the angle at A between B and C (Fig. 18–7 below) added to the angle between C and D must equal the angle between B and D. Check this before leaving the mark.

Use of the sine formula

Fig. 18–7 shows a quadrilateral in which the eight angles at A, B, C and D have been observed by sextant and the length of the side AB is known. In the triangle ABD the lengths of AD and BD may be found from the sine formula:

$$\frac{AB}{\sin ADB} = \frac{AD}{\sin ABD} = \frac{BD}{\sin BAD}$$

i.e. $AD = \dfrac{AB \sin ABD}{\sin ADB}$

and $BD = \dfrac{AB \sin BAD}{\sin ADB}$

Similarly, once BD is known, the other two sides BC and CD in the triangle BCD may be found.

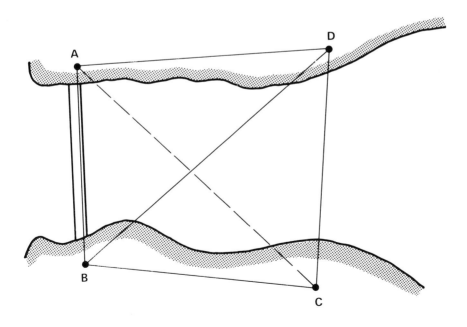

Fig. 18–7.   Triangulation

Calculation of the longest side

In the type of survey being considered here, the observed angles are plotted straight on to paper to form the triangulation rather than by computing the rectangular co-ordinates of stations and plotting on a grid. In order to minimise errors of plotting, the plot must start with the longest side. Depending on the method of base measurement used, the measured base may or may not be the longest side. If it can be so arranged, so much the better but, if the base is measured by tape, it is unlikely to be longer than about 400 metres, which will only plot at 16 mm at 1:25,000 or 40 mm at 1:10,000.

In most cases, therefore, it will be necessary to calculate the length of the longest side from the measured base through the triangulation using the sine formula (page 541 above).

Fig. 18–8 (opposite) represents a small harbour triangulation. At each of the five main stations, sextant angles between all the other four have been observed. A check has been made in the field that each of the ten component triangles sums to within 5' of 180° and any rogue angles have been re-observed.

AB is the base whose length has been measured, or calculated from a shorter measured base through a base extension scheme (pages 535–6), and whose true bearing has been found by one of the methods described above.

In this case, there is little to choose in length between AC and EC but AC is preferred as the plotting 'longest side' because calculation of its length and bearing involves fewer steps:

$$AC = \frac{AB \times \sin ABC}{\sin ACB}$$

and   the bearing AC = bearing AB + angle BAC

Nevertheless, it is prudent also to calculate AC via another route as a check on observing errors. For example, the length of AE can be found in the triangle ABE and then, in the triangle ACE, another value for the length of AC can be found. The discrepancy between the two values for AC will be due to errors in the observation of the sextant angles and, providing it is not plottable on the scale of the survey, it will be quite adequate to accept the mean of the two values.

Plotting and graduation

Having found the length of AC and converted it via the scale of the survey to a plotting distance, the plot proceeds as follows.

First, draw a line XY right across the plotting sheet on the approximate bearing of AC. Prick-off the length AC at the most convenient place along XY, then lay off the rays from A and C into the other marks B, D and E by station pointer using the long line XY as zero. Again, make these rays as long as possible to the edge of the paper to provide accurate alignment for further plotted rays.

The positions of B, D and E are now each defined by the intersection of two rays. As a check, the rays from B, D and E into all other stations should be plotted so that each station including A and C has at least three rays passing through it. The size of the resulting cocked hats will indicate the accuracy of the work.

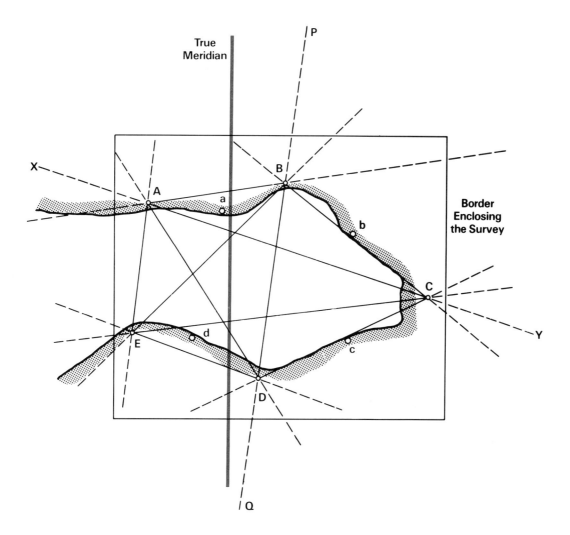

Fig. 18–8. Triangulation of a small harbour

Plotting of the rays is best done by scribing fine lines with a 'pricker' (a needle secured in a penholder makes a very serviceable one) rather than in pencil, as even with a 'chisel edge' on the pencil lead, it is virtually impossible to draw a line to coincide with the leg of the station pointer.

Once the main triangulation stations are plotted and checked, any sounding marks can also be plotted (*a, b, c* and *d* in Fig. 18–8).

The method of graduating a sheet is described in *AMHS*, Volume I Chapter 6. This cannot be done in satisfactory manner unless the necessary instruments are available. The navigator is advised to render his survey in the form of an ungraduated plan; a meridian and scales of latitude, longitude and metres will be sufficient, provided the geographical position of a plotted point is given in the title.

The plotting sheet should bear the title and scale of the survey, together with the name of the ship and the officer in charge of the surveying work. The geographical position of at least one main station, either from the chart or map, or from SATNAV or astronomical observations, should be given, and also a table of the lengths of all measured or calculated sides. The plotting sheet should be forwarded to the Hydrographer with the fair chart or tracing.

Tracing and field boards

The plotting sheet is the master plot for the survey and should be preserved from rough handling and risk of getting wet. In order to transfer the plotted points from the plotting sheet to field boards, which will be taken away in boats or used to plot the coastline, a 'prick-through' tracing is used.

A previously flattened piece of tracing paper is laid over the plotting sheet, and main stations, sounding marks, scales and meridian are pricked through. This tracing can now be used as a template for pricking through on to the field boards.

Field boards are best made by pasting cartridge or chart paper on to softwood boards or thick plywood.

Sounding (*AMHS*, Volume II, Chapter 3)

The sounding of the area of the survey is both the most important, and the most difficult, part to achieve with limited resources. The sounding must be systematic and cover the area with regularly spaced lines of sounding. Any irregularities of depth, particularly shoaling, found on these lines must be investigated by 'interlines' and, if necessary, a close examination made using a pellet as a datum.

Boat sounding

In a Navigating Officer's survey, soundings will probably be carried out using the boat's lead and line. The lead line is described in BR 67(1), *Admiralty Manual of Seamanship*, Volume I. Lead lines used for survey work should be fitted with a wire heart to ensure they do not stretch in use. The markings should be checked using a steel tape (*see AMHS*, Volume II Chapter 3.)

Procedure when sounding

A table, on which the sounding board and instruments may be placed, should be rigged across the boat in a convenient position, preferably sheltered from spray.

Prepare the sounding board before leaving the ship by ruling on it the lines along which it is proposed to sound. These should be at right angles to the general direction of the depth contours, and usually therefore at right angles to the coast. The recommended method of sounding is to run along these predetermined lines, fixing at intervals by simultaneous horizontal sextant angles (HSA). This requires considerable expertise from the whole sounding team, officers and boat's crew.

Using a largely untrained boat's crew, it is well worth while erecting transit marks ashore (Fig. 18–9) for each line to be run. The transits assist the boat to steer along a straight line and also space the lines correctly. Nothing very elaborate is required. Two men can hold the transit marks—boat-hook staves with flags—in position while the sounding line is run. If a triangulation station or sounding mark can be used as one of the transit marks, so much the better. Fixing the boat is a separate matter and is discussed below.

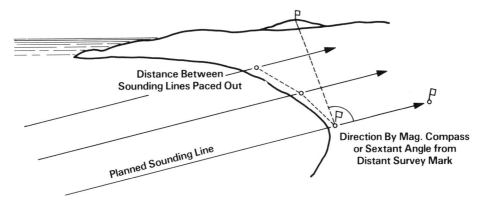

Fig. 18–9.   Sounding, using transit marks

The distance apart of lines is not very critical, but it is usual to run them some 5 millimetres apart on the sounding board. The front transit mark can be moved to the position for the next line by pacing out (or measuring by tape) the appropriate distance. The back transit may be positioned by a magnetic compass bearing, or by a sextant angle from a distant object.

Quite often it is possible to utilise a distant object (Fig. 18–10) well inland as a back transit mark; the sounding lines then become a 'star' centred on the distant object; provided it is far enough away, the lines of sounding open out very little over the area of an average survey.

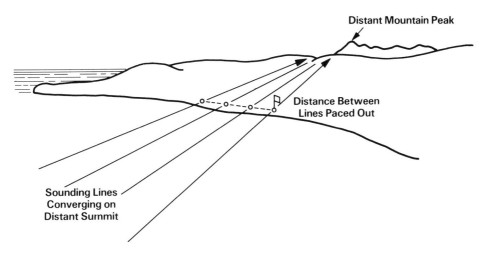

Fig. 18–10.   Sounding, using a distant object

It will be helpful to insert the relevant coastline and topographical detail on the sounding board if this has been obtained before sounding starts.

Methods of fixing the boat

As mentioned earlier, the recommended method of sounding is to run along a predetermined line, fixing by simultaneous horizontal sextant angles. There are various methods of fixing the boat at the necessary intervals along the line of soundings. These depend on the nature and scale of the survey.

Method 1. Station pointer fixes steering transits

This method was illustrated in Figs 18–9 and 18–10. The boat is steering along the planned sounding lines by means of shore transits. HSA fixing is carried out at close intervals, using two observers and one plotter. Fixes are also taken when crossing important depth contours.

If conditions are suitable, this is probably the best method for the average small harbour or anchorage survey. For advice on how to choose marks giving a strong fix, *see* Chapter 9, also *AMHS*, Volume II, Chapter 3, part 2.

If an inexperienced officer finds he cannot keep up with the plotting of the fixes while the line is being run, he can plot them at the end of the line confident that, with the help of the transit, at least the boat maintained a steady track. The same is true of Method 2 but not of Method 3.

Method 2. Transits and 'cut-off' angle

The boat is steered along planned sounding lines by means of shore transits. The transit marks must be accurately fixed relative to the triangulation and plotted on the board. Fixing is now carried out by observing at regular intervals one horizontal 'cut-off' angle between the transit and a suitably positioned shore mark.

Such a method only requires one practised observer instead of two, plus one plotter. However, as the transit forms one position line of the fix, it is essential that the boat maintains the transit. If the boat strays off the line, the amount cannot be measured and so the line must be run again.

Method 3. HSA fixes without transits

Simultaneous horizontal sextant angles are observed between three fixed marks and plotted on the sounding board using a station pointer. This method requires two observers and one plotter, all practised. The helmsman steers by compass and is conned on to the correct track by the plotter as the result of plotting each fix immediately after it is taken. To be effective, particularly in a difficult cross-tide or cross-wind, the fixes have to be plotted, and any alteration of course made, very quickly after the angles have been observed. If the plotting and conning order take longer than about 50 seconds, control will soon be lost and the line will have to be re-run. The smaller the scale and therefore the larger the interval between fixes, the more time is available for corrective conning to take effect and the easier this method becomes.

Accurate positioning of soundings

Soundings must be precisely positioned. An error in position is often more misleading than an error in depth. It is advisable to adjust the speed of the boat so that fixes are between 1 and 1½ cm apart on the sounding board and never more than 2½ cm. The density of soundings along the line should be about 4 per centimetre. This is illustrated in Fig. 18–11. The accuracy of the inking in (*see* below) is increased if fixes are spaced to allow an odd number of soundings to be inserted between them, as the centre one can be inked in first and the spaces either side more easily subdivided by eye.

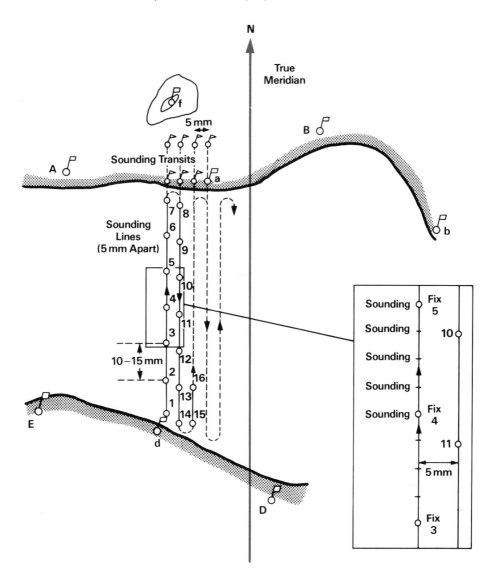

Fig. 18–11.   Fixing while sounding

The boat's speed between fixes must be constant, otherwise the intervening soundings will be plotted incorrectly. If the boat's course has to be altered, it is best to do this at the fixes and not between them.

Recording boat soundings

Each fix position should be given a consecutive fix number as it is plotted on the board. Details of the fixes and the soundings obtained should be noted in the sounding book together with the intervening soundings, as follows. Soundings are in metres and decimetres. The height of tide and reduced soundings allowing for this are shown in red.

TIME	FIX NO.	ANGLES AND SOUNDINGS			SOUNDING AT FIX
1015	3	A	a	b	
4.0 m					
		$46°21'$	$52°33'$		12_2
		12	11_8	11_6	8_2
		8	7_8	7_6	
1017	4	A	a	b	
		$56°04'$	$56°00'$		11_4
		11_2	11	10_8	7_4
		7_2	7	6_8	

Reduction of soundings

The recorded soundings must be reduced for the height of tide obtained from the tidal curve (page 551) before being plotted. The reduced sounding may also be recorded in the sounding book (*see* above) but in a different colour.

Soundings are plotted to the nearest decimetre in depths of less than 31 metres, in metres elsewhere. The general principle to be followed is that depths are never to be shown as greater than they actually are, relative to chart datum. For example, a recorded depth of 10.2 m, the height of tide above chart datum being 4.1 m, would be plotted as a reduced sounding of 6.1 m (10.2 − 4.1). A recorded depth of 37.2 m, the height of tide being 3.4 m, would be plotted as a reduced sounding of 33 m: 37.2 m − 3.4 m = 33.8 m, but, to follow the principle set out above, the depth relative to chart datum must be rounded *down* to the nearest metre (33 m).

Inking in of soundings

All significant features, particularly pinnacles and other dangers, must be precisely positioned on the sounding lines when they are inked in on the sounding board. Once these have been inserted, representative soundings should be inserted between them to provide as accurate as possible a depiction of the sea-bed's topography as allowed by the scale of the survey. Soundings should be inked in at a density of about 4 per centimetre along the sounding line.

When the soundings are being inked in, it is important to try to visualise the underwater terrain as a whole, so that areas requiring further examination may be identified and soundings which appear to be inconsistent may be queried and re-examined if necessary. If a shoal is suspected from adjacent soundings, the area concerned should be marked for interlining and cross-lining at the first opportunity. Additional soundings may also be needed to fill in any holidays.

The ship's echo sounder

It will sometimes be possible to use the ship's echo sounder to run lines of sounding.

The echo sounder must be precisely adjusted and calibrated (*see* Volume III of this manual and *AMHS*, Volume II, Chapter 3). It should be set up to read depths below the surface and the stylus speed adjusted to suit the prevailing water conditions.

Calibration should be carried out once the equipment is thoroughly warmed up. It should be carried out at the start and at the end of a day's soundings. The zero setting and speed of the recorder should be checked regularly throughout the day and noted in the sounding book.

If the moment of fixing and the fix number, together with the phase, are marked on the echo trace as well as in the sounding book and on the sounding board, the soundings may subsequently be taken off the trace at any point between fixes. The greatest care must be taken when soundings are read off and marked in. Do not forget to reduce them for the height of tide.

Echo sounder traces should be carefully preserved for forwarding with the survey report. They should be clearly marked with the following information:

> Ship's name.
> Echo sounder type.
> Sound velocity and units used.
> Scale of survey.
> Start date/time ⎫ (or appropriate fix identification with dates and
> Finish date/time ⎭ times).

The rendering of echo sounder traces with hydrographic notes is also covered in Chapter 6.

Tides

Tidal observations

Since all soundings obtained must be reduced to chart datum, a tide pole must be erected before sounding can begin. The tide pole (Fig. 18–12, p.550) consists of a length of wood with painted graduations. These graduations are usually in metres and decimetres (or feet and fifths of a foot), alternate metres (feet) being painted with black figures on a white background and white on black.

It is preferable to erect the pole at low water. The following points should be considered.

1. The readings must be relevant to the area, and not to some very local tide as in a lagoon.
2. The pole should not be too exposed to heavy weather.
3. The zero of the pole should not dry out at low water.
4. The pole should be long enough to allow readings to be made up to and including high water.
5. The pole should be positioned so that it can be easily read by the observer.
6. The pole must not move, particularly vertically, during the course of the survey and must be firmly secured, preferably to a wall, jetty or pier. If guyed

Fig. 18–12.   Tide pole, graduated in metres

to the bottom, the latter must be sufficiently firm to ensure that the pole does not sink into the ground.

7. The pole must be vertical. Any deviation from the vertical will introduce a scale error into the readings.

Tidal observations to establish chart datum may now be carried out. Observations to the nearest decimetre (or 0.2 foot) should be made every $\frac{1}{2}$ hour and, near high and low water, every 10 minutes. Observations should be obtained over a complete tidal half-cycle of at least 6 hours—that is to say, observations should include at least one high and one low water, and preferably four (*see* below).

Tidal observations will also need to be carried on during the times that the area is being sounded, so that all soundings may be reduced to chart datum.

Establishing chart datum on the tide pole

If the survey area is very remote from a standard or a secondary port, and there is no information on chart datum in the area, the lowest level to which the tide falls on the tide pole during the survey period will have to be used as chart datum.

More usually, it should be possible to establish a connection between the tide pole readings and the data for the nearest standard or secondary port, which may be obtained from the relevant volume of the *Admiralty Tide Tables*. The following method should be used (Fig. 18–13).

Observe, on the tide pole, four consecutive high and low waters. From the eight observations, deduce mean level *m* above the zero of the tide pole. Mean level will be half-way between the mean values of the high and low waters.

Determine from the *Tide Tables* the times and heights of HW and LW of the predicted tides for the relevant period for the nearest standard or secondary port. Derive the level of chart datum on the tide pole from the following formula:

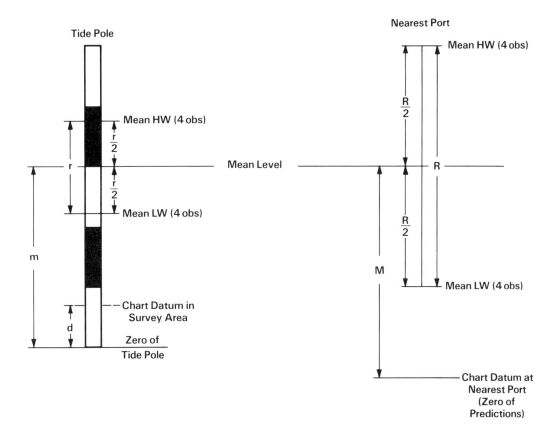

Fig. 18–13. Establishing chart datum on the tide pole

$$d = m - \frac{r}{R}M \qquad\qquad \ldots \textbf{18.4}$$

where:

d is the level of local chart datum relative to the zero of the tide pole.

m is the height of local mean level above the zero of the tide pole.

r is the range (mean HW − mean LW) at the place.

M is the height of mean level at the standard or secondary port (ML or Z_o in the *Tide Tables*) above chart datum.

R is the range of the predicted tide (mean HW − mean LW) at the nearest standard or secondary port.

All tidal observations and calculations should be forwarded to the Hydrographer with the rest of the survey. It is important that the time zone used is clearly stated throughout.

Tidal curve

While sounding is in progress, readings on the pole should be read at half-hourly intervals. Subsequently these may be plotted to the nearest decimetre against time (Fig. 18–14), having been first corrected for the value of chart datum on the tide pole.

The heights of tide obtained may then be deducted from the recorded soundings to obtain a corrected depth, reduced to chart datum.

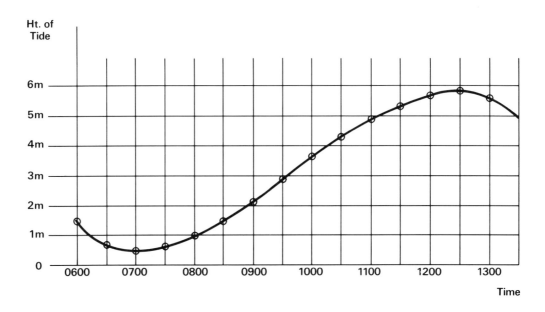

Fig. 18–14.   Tidal curve

Coastline

The coastline in a small survey can best be charted by taking a series of HSA fixes along the high water line. Provided the HW line is fairly smooth and the fixes close together (about 10 to 15 millimetres apart on the coastlining board), the coastline between fixes may be drawn in by eye. At every fix, angles are taken to three of the main triangulation stations plus a check angle to some other mark. (*See* Chapter 9, also *AMHS*, Volume II, Chapter 3, part 2 on how to select marks to obtain a well conditioned fix.)

This is illustrated in Fig. 18–15, which represents part of Fig. 18–8 enlarged. HSA fixes are obtained along the coastline from *A* to *B* and at each fix a check angle is also observed. The fix *B, D, A* is a strong one in this area as the observer is inside the triangle formed by the three marks; the angle from *D* to *E* is suitable as a check angle.

If the coastline is rugged or indented (Fig. 18–16, p.554), it will probably be best to use a sextant and ten-foot pole for fixing the detail between sextant fixes.

A ten-foot pole is a light pole at the ends of which are secured two targets whose centres are exactly 10 feet apart. The pole is held vertically or horizontally, exactly perpendicular to the line of sight from the sextant, and the angle between the target centres is measured by sextant and then converted to distance by the use of tables (*AMHS*, Volume I). For short distances, a pocket

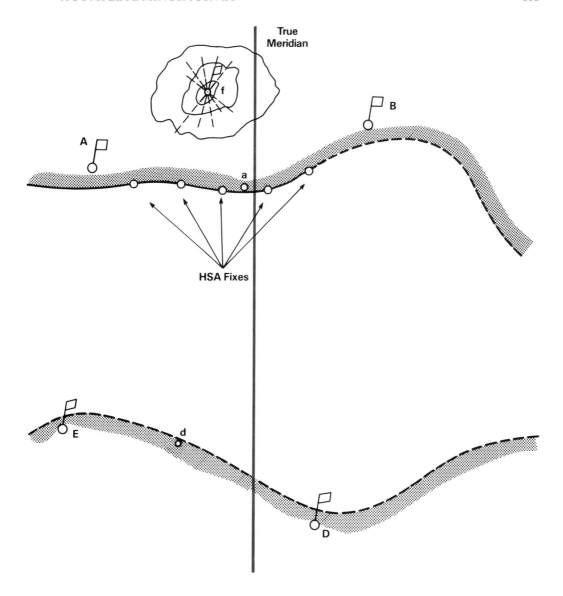

Fig. 18–15. Fixing a smooth coastline and a summit inland

compass may be used to determine the bearing of the pole from the previous position.

For example (Fig. 18–16), positions (2) to (6) may be established as follows:

1. The ten-foot pole is held vertically at position (2) and its position is fixed as described above by the observer, standing at position (1).
2. The observer moves to position (2) and the pole is then moved to position (3).
3. The vertical angle and the bearing of the pole are measured to fix position (3).

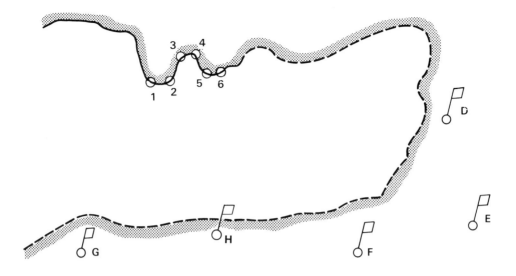

Fix 1: HSA Fix using E,H, G, Check Angle to F

Fix 2:
Fix 3:
Fix 4: } Fixes using VSA, 10 ft Pole and Pocket Compass
Fix 5:

Fix 6: HSA Fix using E,H, G, Check Angle to F

Fig. 18–16.   Fixing a rugged or indented coastline

4. This process is continued for positions (4) and (5), a fresh HSA fix being obtained at position (6).

It is inadvisable to obtain more than four or five such pole and compass positions without obtaining a proper fix by sextant angles.

A considerable amount of time can sometimes be saved by mooring a boat off the coast, fixing its position and using it as the centre object of the fix. This can save a lot of pole work.

On a steep-to, cliff-lined coast, it will probably be easier to fix the coastline by moving along in a dinghy rather than attempting to walk round the base of the cliffs.

The nature of the HW line (sand, shingle, etc.), the foreshore and the type of country immediately inshore of the HW line should be recorded in the field note book. The drawing of frequent and large-scale freehand sketches of each section of the coast is recommended to aid subsequent plotting.

Fixing navigational marks and dangers (*see* page 524)

Buoys, dolphins, ends of jetties, stranded wrecks, etc. should be fixed by bringing the boat alongside and taking angles to all visible fixing marks. In the case of buoys, this must be done on both ebb and flood and a final mean position shown.

A small buoy or pellet and a sinker should always form part of a sounding boat's equipment to provide a visual datum for the examination of any rocks or shoals which may be encountered.

Topography

It is usual to fix the topography at the same time as the coastline. This is done by means of sextant 'shots' into the object to be charted from the various fixes on the coastline. For example, the position of the summit *f* in Fig. 18–15 may be intersected by horizontal angles from coastline fixes. Rough contours or form lines may be drawn in at the same time to give an impression of the relief. Heights of natural features are difficult to obtain unless a sea horizon is available as the datum for a vertical sextant angle. Provided that the elevation can be measured accurately from the HW mark, the height of objects not too far inland may be calculated from the formula

$$\text{height in metres} = \frac{\text{distance in miles} \times \text{altitude in seconds of arc}}{111.5} \quad \ldots \textbf{18.5}$$

Do not attempt too much topography. Fix only those objects that will be of direct assistance to the mariner. It is better to have two or three easily identifiable marks (e.g. well defined summits, conspicuous buildings, etc.) correctly positioned than a large number of objects which have been inserted by eye to improve the appearance of the chart.

A lot of topography can be scaled down from existing land maps or aerial photographs. If possible, arrange to have the maps or photographs photo-reduced to the scale required.

Aerial photography

Vertical photographs from the ship's helicopter can be most useful for charting purposes and a useful aid to coastlining on the ground. Instructions for the pilot should include details of the tracks to be flown, the required flying height, the approximate lateral and fore-and-aft overlap to be obtained (usually 30% and 80% respectively), together with other considerations such as the state of tide at which the photography is to be taken. For more detailed advice, *see AMHS*, Volume II, Chapter 6.

Tidal stream observations (*see above*, page 530)

Admiralty Sailing Directions

All matter appearing in the *Sailing Directions* relevant to the locality of the survey should be carefully checked, and any new information which may be of use to the mariner should be added. This information should be recorded under the appropriate headings and in the sequence adopted in the *Sailing Directions*.

Views for the *Sailing Directions* obtained from oblique aerial photography can be most useful. The topography, prominent features and the use made of the area by shipping, together with the age of the views already published, are factors which need to be taken into account when considering the need for photographs. Full details are given in NP 140, *Views for Sailing Directions*.

Preparing the fair sheet

A tracing is the quickest way of rendering a minor survey, as the navigator is unlikely to have the materials, instruments or time to draw a fair chart in the traditional sense. Tracing paper (but not tracing cloth, which is too unstable) is satisfactory for this purpose. Ozatex, a matt surface transparent foil, is better, if it can be obtained from a surveying ship or the Hydrographic Department in time.

All the soundings, coastlining, topography, etc. obtained during the survey should be transferred to the fair sheet.

Colour washes cannot be used on tracing paper but coloured drawing inks improve the clarity of detail and light crayon may be used for the land tint if desired.

Details regarding the use of colours and symbols may be found in *GIHS* and also in Chart Booklet 5011, *Symbols and Abbreviations used on Admiralty Charts*.

If possible, the fair tracing should be graduated for latitude and longitude but, if not, then it should be enclosed within a plain border. The true meridian must be shown with the lines of the border parallel and at right angles to it.

If the sheet is not graduated, it must show a scale of metres (or feet) and/or latitude and distance and give the geographical position of one fixed point of the survey.

Report of survey

The report of survey should be rendered to the Hydrographer at the same time as the fair sheet. It should give a brief description of how the survey was carried out, notes on whether or not the least depths over shoals have been found, and comments on omissions or inaccuracies in the existing chart. It is important that full comments are made on differences between the published chart and the survey. This ensures that the cartographer is left in no doubt that detail omitted in the survey is not caused by an oversight. Other items usually forwarded as appendices to the report are set out below (*GIHS* 0918):

1. Triangulation data. Information should include a drawing of the scheme of triangulation, a list of observed angles and triangles used for the main control of the survey, and a list of observed angles used to 'shoot up' other marks.
2. Base measurements. Details of how the base was derived or measured should be forwarded.
3. Amendments to the *Sailing Directions* (*see* above).
4. Tidal observations and data. These should include details of the datum used for soundings and how it was arrived at, together with all tide readings obtained.

Shadwell Testimonial

In memory of Admiral Sir Charles F. A. Shadwell, a prize consisting of instruments or books of a professional nature of use in navigation is presented to a Naval or Royal Marine Officer for the most creditable plan of an anchorage or other marine survey accompanied by sailing directions received each year. Hydrographic notes and lines of ocean sounding can also qualify, providing they show sufficient merit and scope. Details are given in the *Navy List*.

CHAPTER 19
Bridge Organisation and Procedures

This chapter considers bridge organisation and procedures within the Royal and Merchant Navies.

More than three-quarters of navigational accidents (collisions, groundings, berthing incidents) are attributable to human error of some kind. When these accidents are analysed, it is often evident that one or more of the following factors has played a major part.

1. Poor planning.
2. Inadequate bridge organisation.
3. Unsound bridge procedures.
4. Failure to make intelligent use of the information available.

Sound navigational planning, the organisation of the bridge for certain specific tasks e.g. pilotage, and correct navigational procedures have already been covered in previous chapters.

Effective use must also be made of the considerable information available to the mariner on the bridge. The DR or EP projected from the last fix may well show up any misidentification of shore marks. Radar and radio fixing aids provide a valuable cross-check for visual fixes. The echo sounder frequently gives advance warning that the ship is being taken into shoal water. Clearing bearings will do the same. Tides and tidal stream data are essential for coastal navigation, pilotage and berthing. The errors of the compasses must be known and either applied or allowed for. Details of turning and stopping data are essential for the safe planning and execution of pilotage and berthing. The observation of the bearing of other ships, and the acquisition of their relative tracks on the radar display, will identify those ships on a collision course.

BRIDGE ORGANISATION AND PROCEDURES WITHIN THE ROYAL NAVY

These remarks serve as both instructions and guidance for Captains, Navigating Officers (NOs), Principal Warfare Officers (PWOs) and Officers of the Watch (OOWs), reminding them of important regulations and of principles on which to base their actions. They also show how the duties of these officers are interdependent.

Definitions

Certain terms (like 'command') are used throughout this section; their definitions are as follows:

COMMAND (of the ship). This is the overriding authority over the ship's movements which the Captain retains at all times. The circumstances in which he may delegate sea command to another officer are set out in BR 31, *The Queen's Regulations for the Royal Navy (QRRN)*.

CONDUCT. The direction of a team or management of a series of tasks in the performance of a function, e.g. conduct of the ship; conduct of navigation; conduct of operations. Conduct includes planning and may include execution.

CHARGE (of the ship). The authority delegated by the Commanding Officer or the officer to whom command or conduct has been delegated, to the Officer of the Watch for the safety of the ship at sea.

CONTROL. The action of a functional superior in issuing instructions and guidance in a clearly defined professional field.

CONNING. The act of giving wheel, hydroplane or engine orders.

The Captain

Command responsibilities

A number of instructions about the conduct and charge of the ship are contained in *QRRN*, with which the Captain and his officers must be thoroughly familiar. Not only may the Captain delegate sea command in certain circumstances (*see* above), he may also, in accordance with *QRRN*, delegate the conduct of navigation to the Navigating Officer and the conduct of operations in his ship or other units under his command to the Principal Warfare Officer. Advice to the Captain on delegation is to be found in Volume IV of this manual.

Further advice to the Captain on his general navigational responsibility is also to be found in Volume IV.

Charge of the ship

The articles in *QRRN* and in Volume IV of this manual concerning *charge of the ship* must be carefully studied. At sea, the Officer of the Watch alone can have charge of the ship. The Captain may, however, authorise other officers to take charge of the ship from the OOW in certain circumstances. For example, the Navigating Officer may require to take charge of the ship in the course of pilotage. When an officer other than the Captain takes charge of the ship from the OOW in this way, he automatically becomes the OOW.

Charge of the ship returns to the Captain at any time he so directs, and automatically should he give any conning order either directly or through another person. In such circumstances the Captain must ensure that there is a clearly understood division of responsibilities on the bridge. The Captain should always make it quite clear when he is taking over charge of the ship. Nothing is more likely to cause an accident than doubt on the bridge as to who has charge of the ship. For example, if while altering course the Captain wishes the OOW to use more wheel, he should give the order 'Use more wheel' and not

'Starboard 25'; if the Captain gives a direct wheel or engine order, he is in effect relieving the OOW of his responsibility for handling the ship.

At no time may the Principal Warfare Officer on his own authority take the ship out of the charge of the OOW or absolve him from his responsibilities as laid down.

Calling the Captain

The Captain's Standing Orders should leave the OOW/PWO in no doubt as to when the Captain should be called. If the OOW/PWO begins to think that the Captain should be called, the effect of the Standing Orders should prompt him to do so. The OOW should be encouraged to call the Captain if in any doubt whatsoever about the safety of the ship. The PWO should call the Captain as soon as an operational situation requiring the Captain's attention develops.

Captain's Night Order Book (S553)

It has long been the custom for the Captain to keep a Night Order Book in which he puts instructions for the OOWs and PWOs of the night watches and gives information about the special circumstances of the night. The Night Order Book should state when the Captain wishes to be called and should draw attention to his Standing Orders on calling. The Night Order Book is an essential link between the Captain and the OOW and PWO (and the NO) who should initial it on taking over their watch.

Shiphandling

This subject is dealt with in BR 67(3), *Admiralty Manual of Seamanship*, Volume III, except for certain aspects classified Restricted, e.g. turning data of HM Ships, or aspects concerning particular types or classes of HM Ships. These may be found in Volume IV of this manual.

Importance of a shiphandling plan

Shiphandling requirements should be planned in advance by the Captain jointly with his Navigating Officer and, for berthing or replenishment, with other officers concerned.

Circumstances may prove different from those which were anticipated; it is wise, therefore, not only to have prepared contingency plans but to have in mind the action to be taken to meet all reasonable eventualities — for example, a sudden change in wind strength or direction, a mechanical failure or a fouled berth.

All contingencies cannot be foreseen, however. It is worth remembering that precipitate departure from the plan increases the risk of undetected errors.

Supervision of the Navigating Officer

The Captain should supervise the work of the Navigating Officer. When under stress or when tired, it is easy to make mistakes in laying off or ordering a course.

The Navigating Officer should insist that the Officer of the Watch checks the course on the chart and carries out the duty of fixing the ship in coastal waters, reporting at once if he considers the ship is being set off her intended track.

Training of seaman officers

All seaman officers should be given every opportunity to gain bridge experience. This includes retaining charge of the ship during manoeuvres and peacetime exercises. During long periods of operations in peace or war no Captain or Navigating Officer can remain in sole charge without loss of efficiency from fatigue. A 'second eleven' must be trained and ready to take responsibility during the relatively quiet periods.

Captains are advised to take the following steps to raise and maintain the standards of all seaman officers in navigation:

1. Officers should take and work out sights during their periods off watch. The Officer of the Watch may take sights if a second Officer of the Watch is on watch.
2. On long passages seaman officers should take turns in carrying out the duties of the Navigating Officer in addition to the officer appointed.
3. On coastal passages the Officer of the Watch should plan and execute a passage for his watch between a given point of departure and a given destination compatible with the overall plan.
4. Before coming to an anchorage, another officer besides the Navigating Officer should prepare and carry out the run-in, combining this with a blind approach if appropriate.
5. A plan for departure from anchorage or berth should be prepared by the Harbour Officer of the Day.

Bridge watchkeeping non-seaman officers

Commanding Officers should make every opportunity available for their engineer, instructor and supply officers who are medically qualified to obtain Bridge Watchkeeping Certificates. This task is voluntary and must not be to the detriment of the officer's primary role nor his professional training.

The Officer of the Watch

Instructions for the Officer of the Watch at sea are to be found in *QRRN*, BR 67(3), *Admiralty Manual of Seamanship*, Volume III, and in Volume IV of this manual. These instructions may be amplified in Captain's Standing Orders.

Looking out

The Officer of the Watch should be constantly looking out ahead and on either bow and frequently astern. Whenever he leaves the position from which he can look out, he should see that someone else on the bridge is doing so for him. He should be continuously alert and be the first to spot anything new that comes into view. He must watch the bearings of *all ships in sight*, including those of giving-way vessels. This visual alertness should not be diminished in the slightest by the knowledge that lookouts are posted or that radar is operating.

The limitations of radar. The best plots and radar displays cannot be more than aids to shiphandling in a *close quarters* situation, where the human eye is still far superior in speed, accuracy and completeness of information, even at night. The tracks of ships take time to mature on a plot, and further delay occurs in reporting them to the bridge. On a relative motion radar display, the aspects of ships cannot be assessed directly and, as compared with the eye, there is a considerable delay before the fact that a ship is under wheel and altering course becomes apparent. The alert and watchful OOW should appreciate much earlier than the operations room that a dangerous close quarters situation is arising.

The OOW should keep his lookouts informed about the general situation and tell them what particularly to look for. He should always acknowledge their reports and praise them for good sightings. The efficiency of lookouts is greatly improved by the encouragement and interest of the OOW and, conversely, they will become uninterested and unreliable if ignored. This applies equally to the Lifebuoy Sentry, whom many ships call the 'stern lookout' to reflect this equally important responsibility.

Even when his ship is Guide, the OOW must keep an eye on the movements of all ships in company. To assume that attention can be relaxed because other ships *should* keep clear of the Guide is unfortunately a dangerous fallacy. The OOW must remember his next astern particularly, and ships astern of him generally, whenever he alters course or speed.

Merchant vessels often cruise at higher speeds than warships, so that it is essential, particularly in ships where the view astern is restricted, for the OOW to look astern or check with the stern lookout to discover whether there are ships coming up astern before making any alteration of course or reduction of speed.

Calls by the Officer of the Watch

The Officer of the Watch must pay particular attention to the Captain's orders about calling him. The same applies with equal force to calling the Navigating Officer. Neither the Captain nor the NO can obtain any real rest at sea unless they are confident that they will be called, and thoroughly roused if need be, as soon as they are required. The OOW should never shrink from making sure that the Captain or NO comes to the bridge if he is wanted there.

Because the weather usually changes gradually over a number of hours, the OOW may not always realise when the moment has come to inform the NO and Captain during the night of a change in the condition of the sea, etc. Such a change may affect the course and the speed made good and, if action is postponed until morning, drastic remedies may then be necessary.

An OOW will be unable to retain his Captain's confidence if his reports are sloppy or inaccurate. The basic principles which the OOW should follow are:

> First   Present the facts in a clear, logical and succinct manner.
> Second   Propose solution/make recommendation.

In this way the Captain is told what he needs to know and can make the necessary decisions.

Emergencies

There are many kinds of emergency that may arise suddenly and which will require the Officer of the Watch to act immediately. He must be thoroughly familiar with the particular action needed in each emergency. It is good practice to run over in the mind, during the quiet periods of the watch, the correct procedures for each case; then the reaction will be instant and correct in any dangerous situation.

Some of the emergencies for which the OOW should be prepared are:

> Man overboard in own or nearby ship.
> Failure of main engines in own or nearby ship, particularly in the ship next ahead.
> Failure of steering in own or nearby ship.
> Outbreak of fire.
> Approach of fog.
> Incorrect action by consorts in carrying out signalled manoeuvres.

The OOW should be equally well versed in the action required of him in the many types of emergency that may arise in war, e.g. sighting of torpedo track, detection of submarine, etc.

Equipment failures

In the event of an engine telegraph failure, the Officer of the Watch must ensure that there is immediate and direct telephone communication available between the bridge and the engine room or MCR. In certain circumstances this line must be manned continually at both ends by communication numbers who have no other duties to perform.

Compass failure

The compass alarm system in HM Ships primarily indicates a failure of the master compass only. A ship's compass transmission system alarm may also be incorporated in an integrated compass alarm and indication system. However, even with this integrated system, the possibility of a fault occurring in the overall system that does not operate the alarms cannot be completely eliminated.

A modification to the ship's compass transmission system is available to cover those ships with a Mark 19, Mark 23 or Arma–Brown gyro-compass outfit, in which an integrated system is not fitted. However, this only gives an indication of loss of power to the transmission system.

It is possible for the compass transmission system to fail and also for a fault to occur in the overall system (e.g. one introducing a slow wander) without the alarm system operating. In all ships fitted with more than one transmitting compass (gyro or magnetic), duplicate repeaters from alternative sources are provided on the bridge, at main or secondary steering positions and in the operations room. Comparison of these repeaters will serve to check the operation of the compasses and transmission system. In some bridge arrangements, due to space considerations, and in operations rooms, the repeaters can be switched to either compass. In these instances, ensure that the repeaters are switched so that both compasses are displayed.

Conning orders

It cannot be emphasised too often that wheel and engine orders must always be given very clearly and precisely, and that imprecise orders such as 'Meet her' and 'Nothing to starboard' should never be used. If the wheel is put the wrong way, the best action is to order 'Amidships', followed after a short pause by a very precisely spoken repetition of the original order. It is unwise to rebuke the helmsman at the time, because this may unnerve him and cause further errors. Similarly, if the engines are put the wrong way, the best action is to order 'Stop (both) engines' followed by a repetition of the correct order. A 'post mortem' can be held later, when the ship is clear of dangers.

Details of conning orders may be found in BR 67(1), *Manual of Seamanship*, Volume I, pages 422–423.

When the automatic (auto pilot) system is being used, the procedure to be followed by the Officer of the Watch is:

'Set course port/starboard 305'.
'Rudder limits 10/15/20 etc. degrees' (as appropriate — this ensures the ship will be turned under the required helm).

The auto pilot will then apply rudder and counter-rudder to achieve the new course. The Quartermaster reports when steering the course ordered:

'Course 305, Sir.'

Note: When the turn is more than 180° and it is intended to go the long way round, the course must be ordered in two bites, so that each bite is less than 180°.

The above sequence of events should apply to all course alterations when the auto pilot is in use. If the helmsman is on the bridge, it is important to ensure that he is not confused between a specific order to alter course and general discussion as to what the next course should be.

Action information organisation (AIO)

The Officer of the Watch should always bear in mind that the officer in charge of the operations room may have better information than he has. He should make a point, therefore, of seeking information or clarification from the operations room as necessary. Nonetheless, the OOW has the final responsibility for the safety of the ship.

When on passage or cruising, the value of information that the OOW derives from the AIO will be in direct proportion to the interest he takes in it. In order to produce a comprehensive and clear picture, the operations room must be supplied from the bridge with up to date information about signalled courses, speeds, changes of formation; with visual sightings, and visual confirmation of radar contacts. At the same time, the OOW should insist that the AIO provides him with whatever information he needs and which it is capable of providing; for instance, he should see that the AIO tracks any new ship that is detected and that her track and speed are reported, whether she is expected to pass clear and, if so, what will be her closest point of approach.

The Navigating Officer

Instructions to Navigating Officers are to be found in *QRRN* and in Volume IV of this manual. Some amplifying remarks are set out below.

Method of navigation

The Navigating Officer who is not methodical in the preparation and execution of his work will sooner or later endanger the ship. Even in familiar waters a proper plan is essential. The nearer the ship is to danger, the more frequently must the NO fix her position, so that he is quite confident that he knows precisely the track she is making over the ground. Navigation should never be done 'by eye', except in very confined waters when the ship is being piloted from the pelorus. In that case, the NO will have put all the relevant data in his Note Book, e.g. headmarks, 'wheel over' bearings, clearing bearings, transits, etc., so that he is in effect conducting the ship along a predetermined track. The NO must be on the lookout at all times, and particularly in narrow channels, for any signs of danger, such as the colour of the water, or the appearance of the waves over a shoal. If he feels from such portents that he is running into danger, he must be prepared to abandon his plan on the instant and order the ship to be stopped, or the wheel to be put hard over, as appropriate. Running the echo sounder continuously in shoal water is required by the regulations, and soundings often give the only warning that something has gone wrong with the plan. Too often the echo sounder is run without an adequate reporting organisation; a well briefed and attentive reporter is required.

It may happen occasionally that the ship is required to enter unfamiliar waters in an emergency without time for full navigational preparation. The NO should point out the risk to the Captain, who alone can decide whether the importance of the task justifies his attempting it immediately.

In doubt

If the Navigating Officer is doubtful about the position of the ship and if the possibility of grounding exists, he must tell the Captain of his misgivings and suggest that the ship be stopped at once until the position has been accurately determined.

Instructions for the Officer of the Watch

Navigating Officer's Night Order Book. The Navigating Officer must give precise orders to the Officers of the Watch as to when he is to be called. This may be done verbally or by keeping a Night Order Book or Call Book, in which navigational information can be put as well as orders for calls each night.

Bridge Emergency Orders and Bridge File. These contain information and instructions for the OOW. The NO is responsible for their compilation.

Changing of steering and conning positions. At the start of the commission, the NO should agree with the Marine Engineer Officer detailed drills for changing steering and conning positions in the event of damage or breakdown. These drills should be submitted to the Captain for promulgation in his Standing Orders. Subsequently the NO should see that they are available in brief and handy form on the bridge, and in the various steering and conning positions. He should also recommend to the Captain that the drills are exercised frequently, so that all the OOWs are familiar with them.

Use of the chart, etc. The NO must make available to the OOW the chart showing the ship's track, and must ensure that, in his absence from the bridge, the OOW attends to the navigation. The OOW must fix the ship in coastal waters and the NO must see that he enters his observations neatly in the Navigational Record Book (S3034) and on the chart, and that he also inserts them as necessary in the Ship's Log (S322). It must always be remembered that navigation is a branch of seamanship, and therefore within the province of every seaman officer. The NO must regard it as part of his duty to train inexperienced OOWs in pilotage and navigation, and to encourage the more senior ones to practise it.

The Principal Warfare Officer

The Principal Warfare Officer is not a member of the bridge team as such, and is to be found in the operations room, where he is the officer in charge. He has a very close relationship with the Command and with the Officer of the Watch.

From time to time the PWO may be given *control* of the ship (*see* page 560) by the Captain, in which case the PWO gives instructions to the OOW regarding the conduct of operations. In such circumstances, the OOW has authority to query, modify or delay carrying out any instruction which appears likely to lead to a dangerous situation.

The PWO is never to *con* (*see* page 560) the ship from the operations room unless directed to do so by the Captain when the ship is at shelter stations.

The PWO also provides the OOW with any available information, advice or intentions which may assist him in avoiding collision or grounding or other hazard.

Essential information from the operations room

To ensure that the Officer of the Watch knows the expected movements of other ships in the vicinity, and the part to be played by his own ship, it is essential that the Principal Warfare Officer keeps him fully informed at all times of what is going on. The OOW will then know what to watch for and can alert his lookouts accordingly.

Special sea dutymen

Special sea dutymen are a standing party of men who close up at specified navigational control positions when the ship is entering or leaving harbour or at times of other hazardous navigational conditions, such as replenishment at sea or when negotiating a narrow channel. When the ship is clear of harbour or other hazard they are relieved by the sea dutymen of the watch on deck. Some or all of those listed in Table 19–1 (p.568) will be needed, according to the type and class of the ship.

Special sea dutymen of other departments close up simultaneously with those of the operations department to operate equipments and provide services for which their departments are responsible.

Table 19–1

NAME	POSITION OF DUTY
Chief Quartermaster or Coxswain	At the wheel.
Quartermaster of the watch and telegraphsmen	In the forward steering position.
Quartermaster longest off watch	In the after steering position.
Screw flagmen	Aft (visible from bridge).
Boatswain's Mate of the watch	At the main broadcast system, also required for ceremonial piping.
Telephone operators	On the forecastle, quarterdeck and bridge.
Bridge messenger	On the bridge.
Blind pilotage team (radar)	As required.
Navigating Officer's Yeoman	On the bridge (recording of wheel and engine orders).
Chief Boatswain's Mate	With Executive Officer.

Standing orders and instructions

Captain's Standing Orders

Captain's Standing Orders should include sections on the conduct of the ship in harbour and at sea. A useful aide-mémoire for these orders is provided in Volume IV.

Bridge Emergency Orders

Bridge Emergency Orders should contain orders in the form of an aide-mémoire to assist the Officer of the Watch in taking the correct action in an emergency. They should be kept on cards in plastic covers or displayed on boards. Full details of the emergencies to be covered are given in Volume IV and include the following:

Man overboard.
Steering gear breakdown.
Check list for entering fog.
Machinery and telegraph breakdowns.
Compass breakdown.
Internal alarm signals, including fire.
Torpedo countermeasures.
Various helicopter operating emergencies.

Bridge File

The Bridge File should contain information of a more routine nature than in the Bridge Emergency Orders. Volume IV gives full details, including:

Extracts from Captain's Standing Orders (sea and operational sections).
Extracts from Navigation Departmental Orders.
Navigational Data Book extracts.
Navigational lights, switching arrangements.
Masthead heights.
Salvage aide-mémoire.
ASW procedures.
Submiss/subsunk orders.
Orders for domes, etc.
Bridge weapons safety guides.
Instructions on use of recognition.
Helicopter operations.
Instructions for helicopter drill (COPDRILL).
Replenishment at Sea check-off list.
List of maintainers responsible for each radar and navaid.
Leaving and entering harbour, check-off list.

Books and publications

The following list shows those books and publications which should be kept on the bridge, or should be readily available when at sea, in addition to those already mentioned above:

Fishing Vessel Log (S1176).
The Mariner's Handbook.
Admiralty List of Lights and Fog Signals
Admiralty Tide Tables
Tidal stream atlases   } of appropriate area.
Admiralty Sailing Directions
BR 45(1) and (4), *Admiralty Manual of Navigation*, Volumes I and IV.
The Nautical Almanac.
Norie's Nautical Tables.
Decca Navigator Operating Instructions and *Marine Data Sheets.*
Admiralty List of Radio Signals, Volumes 5 and 6 and associated diagrams.
ATP 3, latest edition.
ATP 10, latest edition.
Ship's Standing Orders.

Navigational Departmental Orders

A useful aide-mémoire for these orders is provided in Volume IV.

Orders for Quartermasters

There are some general instructions for Quartermasters in BR 67(1),(2),(3), *Admiralty Manual of Seamanship*, Volumes I to III. The Navigating Officer should also prepare detailed instructions for Quartermasters to cover their duties and responsibilities in harbour and at sea. A useful aide-mémoire for these orders is provided in Volume IV.

Orders for the Navigator's Yeoman

The Navigating Officer should prepare orders for his Yeoman. These should include instructions for correcting charts and publications along the lines set out in Chapter 6 (pages 135 to 138). It is important that the Navigating Officer checks his Yeoman's work frequently for accuracy and for correct dissemination of information.

A useful aide-mémoire for these orders is provided in Volume IV.

BRIDGE ORGANISATION AND PROCEDURES WITHIN THE MERCHANT NAVY

Many instructions and recommendations are available which deal with the organisation of ship's bridges and the navigational procedures to be followed in British Flag Merchant Ships. These may be found in a number of books and publications, including the following:

> The Merchant Shipping Acts.
> Statutory Instruments on merchant shipping safety.
> Department of Transport booklets (e.g. *A Guide to the Planning and Conduct of Sea Passages*).
> Department of Transport Merchant Shipping 'M' Notices.
> IMO recommendations.
> International Chamber of Shipping (ICS) and General Council of British Shipping (GCBS) recommendations (e.g. the ICS *Bridge Procedures Guide*).
> Admiralty Chart 5500, *English Channel Passage Planning Guide*.
> Company instructions.
> Port regulations.

In addition to these items, the Master of a merchant ship usually produces Master's Standing Orders and a Bridge Order Book.

Navigation safety

The following remarks on navigation safety in Merchant Ships are taken from Department of Trade (now Transport) Merchant Shipping Notice M.854 (HMSO, August 1978).

'. . . To assist masters and deck officers to appreciate the risks to which they are exposed and to provide help in reducing these risks it is recommended that steps are taken to:

(*a*) ensure that all the ship's navigation is planned in adequate detail with contingency plans where appropriate;

(*b*) ensure that there is a systematic bridge organisation that provides for
   (i) comprehensive briefing of all concerned with the navigation of the ship;
   (ii) close and continuous monitoring of the ship's position ensuring as far as possible that different means of determining position are used to check against error in any one system;

(iii) cross-checking of individual human decisions so that errors can be detected and corrected as early as possible;

(iv) information available from plots of other traffic to be used carefully to ensure against over-confidence, bearing in mind that other ships may alter course and speed.

(c) ensure that optimum and systematic use is made of all information that becomes available to the navigational staff;

(d) ensure that the intentions of a pilot are fully understood and acceptable to the ship's navigational staff.'

Bridge organisation

The following remarks on bridge organisation are taken from the ICS *Bridge Procedures Guide* (1977) which was issued as a guide to Masters and Navigating Officers.

'1.1 General

1.1.1   The competence and vigilance of the Officer of the Watch provides the most direct means of avoiding dangerous situations. However, analyses of navigational casualties show that weaknesses in bridge organisation are a contributory cause in very many cases. Well defined procedures clearly laid down in company instructions and/or Master's Standing Orders, supported by an efficient organisation, are essential.

'1.1.2   Clear instructions should be issued to cover such matters as:

(a) calling the Master . . .;

(b) reducing speed in the event of restricted visibility, or other circumstances;

(c) posting lookout(s);

(d) manning the wheel;

(e) the use of largest scale charts and navigational aids, such as echo sounder, radar, etc.;

(f) an established drill for changing over from automatic to manual steering and, if applicable, change-over from hydraulic to electric steering and vice versa;

(g) the provision of additional watchkeeping personnel in special circumstances, e.g. heavy traffic or restricted visibility.

'1.1.3   There is a clear requirement that Officers of the Watch should be in no doubt as to what action Masters expect them to take and therefore it is good practice to issue the foregoing as standing instructions, supplemented by a bridge order book.

'1.1.4   It is the responsibility of the Master to ensure that, when practicable, the departing officers 'hand-over' correctly to officers joining. Newly joined officers should read and sign Standing Orders and any other directives. It is essential they be shown how to set up and operate all appropriate bridge equipment . . .

'1.2   Passage Plan

1.2.1   The Master should ensure that a plan for the intended voyage is prepared before sailing. It is of particular importance that this procedure is adopted for that part of the voyage in coastal waters. In pilotage waters, it may be appropriate to have available a forecast of the times of alteration of course, speed and sets expected . . .

'1.3   Safety Systems — Maintenance and Training

1.3.1   In addition to the above, the Master should ensure that all safety systems (for example, life-saving appliances, fire-fighting equipment) are properly maintained and that Officers of the Watch and other crew members are trained, as appropriate, in the use of these systems. Regular drills should be carried out, especially at the early stages of a voyage.'

Principles of watchkeeping arrangements for navigational watch

The following remarks on keeping a navigational watch on the bridge of a merchant ship are taken from Department of Trade (now Transport) Statutory Instrument (SI) 1982 No. 1699, *Merchant Shipping (Certification and Watchkeeping) Regulations 1982 (Merchant Shipping: Safety* series, HMSO, 1983) Schedule 1.

'1. Watch arrangements

(*a*) The composition of the watch shall at all times be adequate and appropriate to the prevailing circumstances and conditions and shall take into account the need for maintaining a proper look-out.
(*b*) When deciding the composition of the watch on the bridge which may include appropriate deck ratings, the following factors, inter alia, shall be taken into account:
  (i) at no time shall the bridge be left unattended;
  (ii) weather conditions, visibility and whether there is daylight or darkness;
  (iii) proximity of navigational hazards which may make it necessary for the officer in charge of the watch to carry out additional navigational duties;
  (iv) use and operational condition of navigational aids such as radar or electronic position-indicating devices and any other equipment affecting the safe navigation of the ship;
  (v) whether the ship is fitted with automatic steering;
  (vi) any unusual demands on the navigational watch that may arise as a result of special operational circumstances.

'2. Fitness for duty

The watch system shall be such that the efficiency of watchkeeping officers and watchkeeping ratings is not impaired by fatigue. Duties shall be so organised that the first watch at the commencement of a voyage and the subsequent relieving watches are sufficiently rested and otherwise fit for duty.

'3. Navigation

(*a*) The intended voyage shall be planned in advance taking into consideration all pertinent information and any course laid down shall be checked before the voyage commences.
(*b*) During the watch the course steered, position and speed shall be checked at sufficiently frequent intervals, using any available navigational aids necessary, to ensure that the ship follows the planned course.

(c) The officer of the watch shall have full knowledge of the location and operation of all safety and navigational equipment on board the ship and shall be aware and take account of the operating limitations of such equipment.

(d) The officer in charge of a navigational watch shall not be assigned or undertake any duties which would interfere with the safe navigation of the ship.

'4. Navigational equipment

(a) The officer of the watch shall make the most effective use of all navigational equipment at his disposal.

(b) When using radar, the officer of the watch shall bear in mind the necessity to comply at all times with the provisions on the use of radar contained in [the applicable regulations for preventing collisions at sea].

(c) In cases of need the officer of the watch shall not hesitate to use the helm, engines and sound signalling apparatus.

'5. Navigational duties and responsibilities

(a) The officer in charge of the watch shall:
  (i) keep his watch on the bridge which he shall in no circumstances leave until properly relieved;
  (ii) continue to be responsible for the safe navigation of the ship, despite the presence of the master on the bridge, until the master informs him specifically that he has assumed that responsibility and this is mutually understood;
  (iii) notify the master when in any doubt as to what action to take in the interest of safety;
  (iv) not hand over the watch to the relieving officer if he has reason to believe that the latter is obviously not capable of carrying out his duties effectively, in which case he shall notify the master accordingly.

(b) On taking over the watch the relieving officer shall satisfy himself as to the ship's estimated or true position and confirm its intended track, course and speed and shall note any dangers to navigation expected to be encountered during his watch.

(c) A proper record shall be kept of the movements and activities during the watch relating to the navigation of the ship.

'6. Look-out

In addition to maintaining a proper look-out for the purpose of fully appraising the situation and the risk of collision, stranding and other dangers to navigation, the duties of the look-out shall include the detection of ships or aircraft in distress, shipwrecked persons, wrecks and debris. In maintaining a look-out the following shall be observed:

(a) the look-out must be able to give full attention to the keeping of a proper look-out and no other duties shall be undertaken or assigned which could interfere with that task;

(b) the duties of the look-out and helmsman are separate and the helmsman shall not be considered to be the look-out while steering, except in small ships where an unobstructed all round view is provided at the steering position and there is no impairment of night vision or other impediment to the keeping of a proper look-out. The officer in charge of the watch may be the sole look-out in daylight provided that on each such occasion:

(i) the situation has been carefully assessed and it has been established without doubt that it is safe to do so;

(ii) full account has been taken of all relevant factors including, but not limited to:

state of weather

visibility

traffic density

proximity of danger to navigation

the attention necessary when navigating in or near traffic separation schemes;

(iii) assistance is immediately available to be summoned to the bridge when any change in the situation so requires.

'7. Navigation with pilot embarked

Notwithstanding the duties and obligations of a pilot, his presence on board shall not relieve the master or officer in charge of the watch from their duties and obligations for the safety of the ship. The master and the pilot shall exchange information regarding navigation procedures, local conditions and the ship's characteristics. The master and officer of the watch shall co-operate closely with the pilot and maintain an accurate check of the ship's position and movement.

'8. Protection of the marine environment

The master and officer in charge of the watch shall be aware of the serious effects of operational or accidental pollution of the marine environment and shall take all possible precautions to prevent such pollution, particularly within the framework of relevant international and port regulations.'

Operational guidance for officers in charge of a navigational watch

Operational guidance for officers in charge of a navigational watch is set out in a Department of Transport Merchant Shipping Notice M.1102 (HMSO, March 1984) and the following is an extract:

'... Taking over the navigational watch

7. ... The relieving officer should not take over the watch until his vision is fully adjusted to the light conditions and he has personally satisfied himself regarding:

(a) standing orders and other special instructions of the master relating to navigation of the ship;

(b) position, course, speed and draught of the ship;

(c) prevailing and predicted tides, currents, weather, visibility and the effect of these factors upon course and speed;

(d) navigational situation, including but not limited to the following:

(i) operational condition of all navigational and safety equipment being used or likely to be used during the watch;

(ii) errors of gyro and magnetic compasses;

(iii) the presence and movement of ships in sight or known to be in the vicinity;

(iv) conditions and hazards likely to be encountered during his watch;

(v) the possible effects of heel, trim, water density and squat on underkeel clearance.

8. If, at the time the officer of the watch is to be relieved, a manoeuvre or other action to avoid any hazard is taking place, the relief of the officer should be deferred until such action is completed.

'Periodic checks of navigational equipment

9. Operational tests of shipboard navigational equipment should be carried out at sea as frequently as practicable and as circumstances permit, in particular when hazardous conditions affecting navigation are expected: where appropriate these tests should be recorded.

10. The officer of the watch should make regular checks to ensure that:

(a) The helmsman or the automatic pilot is steering the correct course;

(b) the standard compass error is determined at least once a watch and, when possible, after any major alteration of course; the standard and gyro-compasses are frequently compared and repeaters are synchronized with their master compass;

(c) the automatic pilot is tested manually at least once a watch;

(d) the navigation and signal lights and other navigational equipment are functioning properly.

'Automatic pilot

11. The officer of the watch should bear in mind the necessity to comply at all times with the requirements of Regulation 19, Chapter V of the International Convention for the Safety of Life at Sea, 1974. He should take into account the need to station the helmsman and to put the steering into manual control in good time to allow any potentially hazardous situation to be dealt with in a safe manner. With a ship under automatic steering it is highly dangerous to allow a situation to develop to the point where the officer of the watch is without assistance and has to break the continuity of the look-out in order to take emergency action. The change-over from automatic to manual steering and vice-versa should be made by, or under the supervision of, a responsible officer.

'Electronic navigational aids

12. The officer of the watch should be thoroughly familiar with the use of electronic navigational aids carried, including their capabilities and limitations.

13. The echo-sounder is a valuable navigational aid and should be used whenever appropriate.

'Radar

14. The officer of the watch should use the radar when appropriate and whenever restricted visibility is encountered or expected, and at all times in congested waters having due regard to its limitations.

15. Whenever radar is in use, the officer of the watch should select an appropriate range scale, observe the display carefully and plot effectively.
16. The officer of the watch should ensure that range scales employed are changed at sufficiently frequent intervals so that echoes are detected as early as possible.
17. It should be borne in mind that small or poor echoes may escape detection.
18. The officer of the watch should ensure that plotting or systematic analysis is commenced in ample time.
19. In clear weather, whenever possible, the officer of the watch should carry out radar practice.

'Navigation in coastal waters

20. The largest scale chart on board, suitable for the area and corrected with the latest available information, should be used. Fixes should be taken at frequent intervals: whenever circumstances allow, fixing should be carried out by more than one method.
21. The officer of the watch should positively identify all relevant navigation marks.

'Clear weather

22. The officer of the watch should take frequent and accurate compass bearings of approaching ships as a means of early detection of risk of collision; such risk may sometimes exist even when an appreciable bearing change is evident, particularly when approaching a very large ship or a tow or when approaching a ship at close range. He should also take early and positive action in compliance with the applicable regulations for preventing collisions at sea and subsequently check that such action is having the desired effect.

'Restricted visibility

23. When restricted visibility is encountered or expected, the first responsibility of the officer of the watch is to comply with the relevant rules of the applicable regulations for preventing collisions at sea, with particular regard to the sounding of fog signals, proceeding at a safe speed and having the engines ready for immediate manouvres. In addition, he should:
    (a) inform the master (see paragraph 24)
    (b) post a proper look-out and helmsman and, in congested waters, revert to hand steering immediately;
    (c) exhibit navigation lights;
    (d) operate and use the radar.
       [It is important that the officer of the watch should know the handling characteristics of his ship, including its stopping distance, and should appreciate that other ships may have different handling characteristics.]

'Calling the master

24. The officer of the watch should notify the master immediately in the following circumstances:
    (a) if restricted visibility is encountered or suspected;

(*b*) if the traffic conditions or the movements of other ships are causing concern;

(*c*) if difficulty is experienced in maintaining course;

(*d*) on failure to sight land, a navigation mark or to obtain soundings by the expected time;

(*e*) if, unexpectedly, land or a navigation mark is sighted or change in soundings occurs;

(*f*) on the breakdown of the engines, steering gear or any essential navigational equipment;

(*g*) in heavy weather if in any doubt about the possibility of weather damage;

(*h*) if the ship meets any hazard to navigation, such as ice or derelicts;

(*i*) in any other emergency or situation in which he is in any doubt.

Despite the requirement to notify the master immediately in the foregoing circumstances, the officer of the watch, should in addition not hesitate to take immediate action for the safety of the ship, where circumstances so require.

'Navigation with pilot embarked

25. If the officer of the watch is in any doubt as to the pilot's actions or intentions, he should seek clarification from the pilot; if doubt still exists, he should notify the master immediately and take whatever action is necessary before the master arrives.

'Watchkeeping personnel

26. The officer of the watch should give watchkeeping personnel all appropriate instructions and information which will ensure the keeping of a safe watch including an appropriate look-out . . .'

Routine bridge check lists

It is useful to have bridge check lists for routine navigational matters. The ICS *Bridge Procedures Guide* recommends the following:

'1. Familiarisation with Bridge Equipment
2. Daily Tests and Checks
3. Preparation for Sea
4. Embarkation/Disembarkation of Pilot
5. Master/Pilot Information Exchange
6. Navigation, Coastal Waters/Traffic Separation Schemes
7. Changing over the Watch
8. Navigation, Deep Sea
9. Preparation for Arrival in Port
10. Anchoring and Anchor Watch
11. Restricted Visibility
12. Heavy Weather
13. Navigating in Ice
14. Navigating in Tropical Storm Area.'

The recommended routines for coastal navigation and the preparations for arrival in port (Routine Check Lists 6 and 9) are set out below:

'6   Navigation, Coastal Waters/Traffic Separation Schemes

(*a*) Corrected charts and hydrographic publications available.

(*b*) Courses laid off well clear of obstructions.

(*c*) Following factors taken into consideration:

> advice/recommendation in the sailing directions;
> depth of water and draught;
> tides and currents;
> weather, particularly in areas renowned for poor visibility;
> degree of accuracy of navigational aids and navigational fixes;
> day-light/night-time passing of danger points;
> concentration of fishing vessels.

(*d*) Position fixed at regular intervals, particularly when navigating in, or near a traffic separation scheme.

(*e*) The position of buoys or other floating marks to be used with caution.

(*f*) Error of gyro/magnetic compasses checked whenever possible.

(*g*) Likelihood of encountering unlit, small craft at night.

(*h*) Appropriate publications consulted for effect of tidal streams and current.

(*i*) Effect of "squat" on underkeel clearance in shallow water.

(*j*) Broadcasts by any local navigational services monitored.

(*k*) Account taken of 1972 International Regulations for Preventing Collisions at Sea [as amended by Department of Transport SI 1983 No. 708*], Rule 10 when navigating in, or near the vicinity of, an IMO-approved traffic separation scheme.'

'9 Preparation for Arrival in Port

(*a*) ETA sent to pilot station at appropriate time with all relevant information required.

(*b*) Available port information, sailing directions and other navigation information, including restrictions on draught, speed, entry time, etc., studied.

(*c*) All appropriate flag/light signals displayed.

(*d*) Minimum and maximum depths of water in port approaches, channels and at berth calculated.

(*e*) Draught/trim requirements.

(*f*) Cargo/ballast re-arranged if necessary.

(*g*) Large-scale charts for port's pilotage water prepared.

(*h*) Latest navigational messages for area received.

(*i*) All hydrographic publications fully corrected up-to-date.

(*j*) Tidal information for port and adjacent area extracted.

(*k*) Latest weather report available.

(*l*) Radio check for pilot/tugs/berthing instructions.

(*m*) VHF channels for various services noted.

---

* *The Merchant Shipping (Distress Signals and Prevention of Collisions) Regulations (Merchant Shipping: Safety* series, HMSO).

(n) Availability of pilot ladder/hoist on correct side . . .
(o) Master/Pilot information exchange form prepared.
(p) All navigational equipment tested, stabilisers housed.
(q) Engines tested for satisfactory operation ahead and astern.
(r) Steering gear tested in primary and secondary systems.
(s) Course recorder, engine room movement recorder and synchronisation of clocks checked.
(t) Manual steering engaged in sufficient time for helmsman to become accustomed before manoeuvring commences.
(u) Berthing instructions, including:
          anchoring/berthing;
          which side to jetty;
          ship or shore gangway;
          size and number of shore connections;
          derricks required;
          mooring boats/mooring lines;
          accommodation ladder.
(v) Ship's crew at stations for entering harbour.
(w) Mooring machinery tested, mooring lines, etc., prepared.
(x) Adequate pressure on fire main.
(y) Internal communication equipment, signal equipment and deck lighting tested.'

Action in an emergency

The Officer of the Watch must be prepared for any emergency and the following guidelines are useful:

1. You may have to act on your own initiative.
2. Rehearse beforehand in your mind the action to be taken in an emergency.
3. Indecision and delay may make it too late.
4. Questions you need to ask yourself:

Are you keeping a good lookout, visually and on radar?
Are you taking seamanlike precautions for the circumstances, e.g. low visibility, bad weather?
Have you checked the ship's position, course and speed correctly?
Are you thinking ahead? Is a dangerous situation likely to arise which action *now* might prevent?
Have you called the Master in plenty of time?

Procedures for emergencies should be readily available on the bridge, and they should be printed on a red background. These procedures include:

Man overboard.
Steering gear breakdown.
Approach of fog.
Fire or explosion.
Machinery or compass breakdown.
Collision or grounding.
Flooding.

Boat/liferaft stations.

Search and Rescue.

Recommended procedures for 'Man Overboard' and 'Steering Failure' taken from the ICS *Bridge Procedures Guide* (Emergency Check Lists 10 and 2) are set out below. These instructions may be amplified as necessary in the particular ship.

'10   Man Overboard

(*a*) Lifebuoy with light, flare or smoke signal released.

(*b*) Avoiding action taken.

(*c*) Position of lifebuoy as search datum noted.

(*d*) Ship manoeuvred to recover person ("Williamson" turn recommended if sea-room allows).

(*e*) Lookouts posted to keep person in sight.

(*f*) Three long blasts sounded and repeated as necessary.

(*g*) Rescue boat's crew assembled.

(*h*) Master informed.

(*i*) Engine room informed.

(*j*) Position of vessel relative to person overboard plotted.

(*k*) Vessel's position available in radio room, up-dated as necessary.'

'2   Steering Failure

(*a*) Engine room informed and alternative/emergency steering engaged.

(*b*) Master informed.

(*c*) "Not under command" shapes or lights exhibited.

(*d*) Appropriate sound signal made.

(*e*) If necessary, way taken off ship.'

APPENDIX 1
Basic Trigonometry

Trigonometry is that branch of mathematics dealing with the relations between the angles and sides of a triangle and with the relevant functions of any angles.

The degree

The angle between two intersecting lines is the inclination of one line to the other, and this inclination is commonly measured in degrees and sub-divisions of a degree.

In one complete revolution there are 360 degrees. When the two arms of the angle are perpendicular, the angle is said to be a right angle, in which there are 90 degrees.

The sub-divisions of the degree are the minute and second, the relation between them being:

$$1° = 60 \text{ minutes } (')$$
$$1' = 60 \text{ seconds } ('')$$

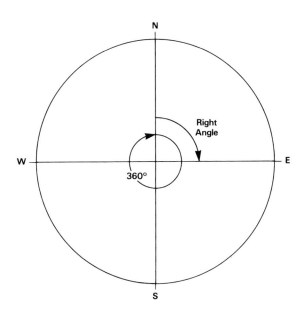

Fig. A1–1.   Degrees in one revolution

In navigation, angles are measured clockwise from north 000°, through east 090°, south 180° and west 270° to north (Fig. A1–1).

The radian

The degree is an arbitrary unit. The principles of trigonometry would not be altered if its size were chosen so that 100 degrees formed a right angle. The mathematical unit is the radian, which is defined as the angle subtended at the centre of a circle by a length of arc equal to the radius.

The number π is defined as the constant ratio of the circumference of a circle to its diameter and is approximately equal to 3.1415927 . . . From this it follows that:

1. The angle subtended by an arc equal to the radius is also constant and equal to 360° ÷ 2π, or approximately 57° 17′ 45″.
2. The number of radians in a right angle is $\frac{1}{2}\pi$.
3. The length of any arc is equal to the radius multiplied by the angle in radians.

The definitions of trigonometric functions

The right-angled triangle

In Fig. A1–2, the triangle ABC is right-angled at C; the sides BC, CA and AB are of length a, b and c respectively; and the angle CAB is of size θ. For navigational convenience AC is taken as due north so that the (true) bearing of B from A is θ.

There are six trigonometric functions. Two of these, the sine and cosine, are of fundamental importance while the other four, tangent, cotangent, secant and cosecant are derived from them. The six functions are defined and abbreviated thus:

$$\sin \theta = \frac{\text{side opposite the angle}}{\text{hypotenuse}} = \frac{a}{c} \qquad \ldots \textbf{A1.1}$$

$$\cos \theta = \frac{\text{side adjacent to the angle}}{\text{hypotenuse}} = \frac{b}{c} \qquad \ldots \textbf{A1.2}$$

$$\tan \theta = \frac{\text{side opposite}}{\text{side adjacent}} = \frac{a}{b} = \frac{a}{c} \times \frac{c}{b} = \frac{\sin \theta}{\cos \theta} \qquad \ldots \textbf{A1.3}$$

$$\cot \theta = \frac{b}{a} = \frac{1}{\tan \theta} = \frac{\cos \theta}{\sin \theta} \qquad \ldots \textbf{A1.4}$$

$$\sec \theta = \frac{c}{b} = \frac{1}{\cos \theta} \qquad \ldots \textbf{A1.5}$$

$$\operatorname{cosec} \theta = \frac{c}{a} = \frac{1}{\sin \theta} \qquad \ldots \textbf{A1.6}$$

The last four trigonometric functions are defined in terms of sin and/or cos. The last three functions are reciprocals of the first three.

In Fig. A1–2, where AC is 000° and angle CAB equals θ,

$$a = c \sin \theta$$
$$b = c \cos \theta$$

Thus, B is $c \sin \theta$ east of A and $c \cos \theta$ north of A.

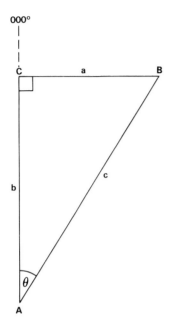 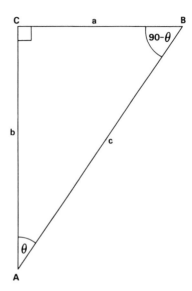

Fig. A1–2.   The right-angled triangle   Fig. A1–3.   Complementary angles

Complementary angles

Angles that add together to make 90° are said to be 'complementary'. Thus, if one angle is 34°, its complementary angle is 56°.

In any right-angled triangle the two acute angles are complementary, since the sum of the three angles, of which one is 90°, must be 180°. Fig. A1–3 shows this and also:

$$\sin \theta \quad = \frac{a}{c} \quad = \cos (90° - \theta) \qquad \text{...A1.7}$$

e.g. $\sin 34° = \cos 56°$

$$\cos \theta \quad = \frac{b}{c} \quad = \sin (90° - \theta) \qquad \text{...A1.8}$$

e.g. $\cos 34° = \sin 56°$

$$\tan \theta \quad = \frac{a}{b} \quad = \cot (90° - \theta) \qquad \text{...A1.9}$$

e.g. $\tan 34° = \cot 56°$

Trigonometric functions of certain angles

Fig. Al–4 and Table Al–1 show the relationship between the trigonometric functions of certain angles and the length of sides of right-angled triangles.

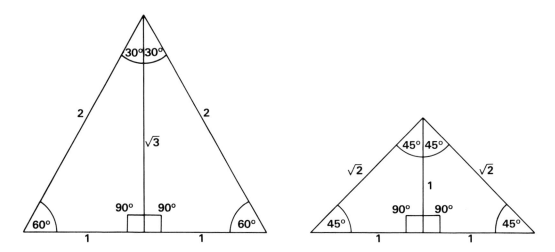

Fig. Al–4.   Trigonometric functions of certain angles

Table Al–1

θ	0°	30°	45°	60°	90°
$\sin \theta$	0	0.5	$\dfrac{1}{\sqrt{2}} \simeq 0.707$	$\dfrac{\sqrt{3}}{2} \simeq 0.866$	1
$\cos \theta$	1	$\dfrac{\sqrt{3}}{2} \simeq 0.866$	$\dfrac{1}{\sqrt{2}} \simeq 0.707$	0.5	0
$\tan \theta$	0	$\dfrac{1}{\sqrt{3}} \simeq 0.577$	1	$\sqrt{3} \simeq 1.732$	∞

The signs and values of the trigonometric functions between 000° and 360°

The definitions given earlier (Formulae **A1.1** to **A1.6**) of the six trigonometric functions for acute angles may be extended to angles up to 360° as follows.

Bearing and direction are measured clockwise from 000° to 360°. Northerly and easterly directions may be considered as +ve, southerly and westerly as −ve (Fig. Al–5). South may be said to be the equivalent of negative north and west the equivalent of negative east. Tangent, cotangent, secant and cosecant may be defined in terms of sine and/or cosine (page 582).

In Fig. A1–5, B_1 is at a distance r and on a bearing θ_1 from A, where θ_1 equals the angle θ. B_1 is $r \sin \theta$ east of A and $r \cos \theta$ north of A. The sine, cosine and tangent of the direction θ_1 are all positive, as are their respective reciprocals, cosecant, secant and cotangent.

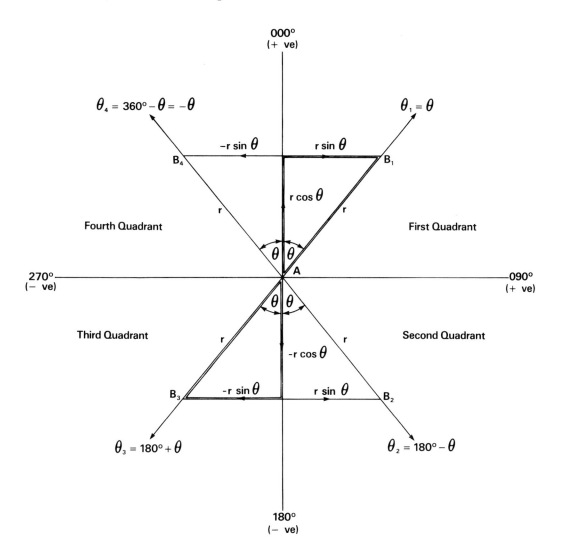

Fig. A1–5. The signs of the trigonometric functions between 000° and 360°

The six trigonometric functions (**A1.1** to **A1.6**) remain true for angles between 90° and 360°.

Bearings between 090° and 180° lie between south (−ve) and east (+ve).
Bearings between 180° and 270° lie between south (−ve) and west (−ve).
Bearings between 270° and 360° lie between north (+ve) and west (−ve).

Consider, for example, B_3, south and west of A at a distance r on a bearing θ_3 (equal to the angle $180° + \theta$). B_3 is $r \sin \theta$ west of A, which is equivalent to $-r \sin \theta$. B_3 is also $r \cos \theta$ south of A, equivalent to $-r \cos \theta$.

$$\sin \theta_3 \quad (\sin (180° + \theta)) = \frac{-r \sin \theta}{r} = -\sin \theta$$

$$\cos \theta_3 \quad (\cos (180° + \theta)) = \frac{-r \cos \theta}{r} = -\cos \theta$$

$$\tan \theta_3 = \frac{\sin \theta_3}{\cos \theta_3} = \frac{-\sin \theta}{-\cos \theta} = \frac{\sin \theta}{\cos \theta} = \tan \theta$$

The signs of the three functions, sine, cosine and tangent in the four quadrants are summarised below: the other three functions, cosecant, secant and cotangent, are reciprocals of the first three respectively, and take the same signs.

```
                                000°
    (C) – Cosine positive        |        (A) – All positive
       (sine, tangent, negative) |
270° ────────────────────────────┼──────────────────────────── 090°
    (T) – Tangent positive       |        (S) – Sine positive
       (sine, cosine, negative)  |           (cosine, tangent, negative)
                                180°
```

The mnemonic All Stations To Crewe provides a reminder of the signs of the trigonometric functions.

The value (as distinct from the sign) of any trigonometric function of an angle greater than $90°$ is equal to the value of the trigonometric function of the angle made with the north–south axis. For example, the value of sin $127°$ equals sin $53°$ ($180° - 127°$), while the value of cosine $296°$ equals cosine $64°$ ($360° - 296°$).

The signs and values of the trigonometric functions of angles in each quadrant are summarised in Table A1–2 (see also Fig. A1–5).

Table A1–2

DIRECTION	ANGLE	SINE ANGLE	COSINE ANGLE	TANGENT ANGLE
θ_1	θ	$\sin \theta$	$\cos \theta$	$\tan \theta$
θ_2	$180° - \theta$*	$\sin (180° - \theta)$ $= \sin \theta$	$\cos (180° - \theta)$ $= -\cos \theta$	$\tan (180° - \theta)$ $= -\tan \theta$
θ_3	$180° + \theta$	$\sin (180° + \theta)$ $= -\sin \theta$	$\cos (180° + \theta)$ $= -\cos \theta$	$\tan (180° + \theta)$ $= \tan \theta$
θ_4	$360° - \theta$ $(= -\theta)$	$\sin (360° - \theta)$ $= -\sin \theta$ $= \sin (-\theta)$	$\cos (360° - \theta)$ $= \cos \theta$ $= \cos (-\theta)$	$\tan (360° - \theta)$ $= -\tan \theta$

* If θ is an angle, the angle equal to $(180° - \theta)$ is known as the supplement of θ. Supplementary angles add together to $180°$.

Table A1–3, illustrated in Fig. A1–6, gives the sign and value of trigonometric functions of some angles between 90° and 360°.

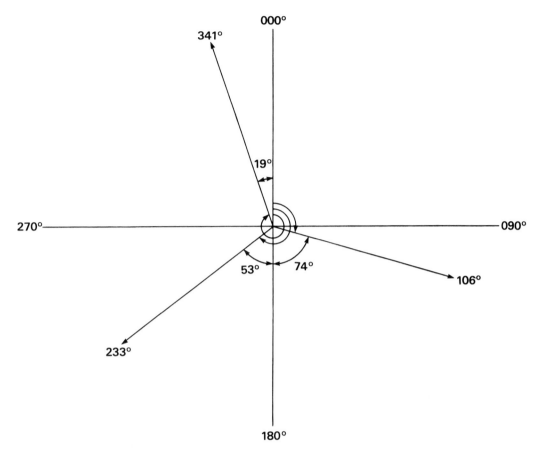

Fig. A1–6. The signs and values of trigonometric functions of angles between 90° and 360°

Table A1–3

ANGLE	SINE	COSINE	TANGENT
106°	+sin 74°	−cos 74°	−tan 74°
233°	−sin 53°	−cos 53°	+tan 53°
341°	−sin 19°	+cos 19°	−tan 19°

The sine, cosine and tangent curves

Although, in navigation, angles outside the range 0° to 360° are rarely encountered, the definitions given earlier may be extended to angles greater than 360°. The value 360° (or multiples of 360°) may be subtracted from the angle concerned to reduce it to an angle between 0° and 360°.

Negative angles may be taken as angles measured anti-clockwise from due north and brought to an angle between 0° and 360° by the addition of 360° (or multiples of 360°).

The graphs of sin θ, cos θ and tan θ may be deduced for any given range. Fig. A1–7 shows the graphs of sin θ and cos θ between −180° and +540°, and the graph of tan θ between −180° and +270°.

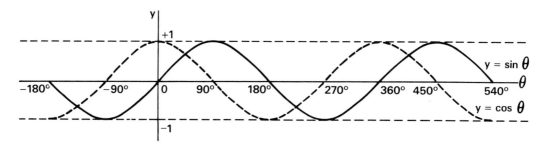

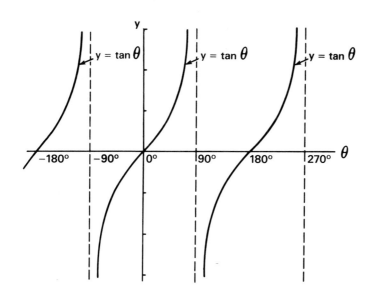

Fig. A1–7.   The sine, cosine and tangent curves

The following should be noted:

1. Both sin θ and cos θ repeat every 360°.
2. tan θ repeats every 180°.
3. In any 360°, there are two angles which have the same value for any trigonometric function, e.g.

$$\sin 35° \;= \sin 145°$$
$$\cos 134° = \cos 226°$$
$$\tan 213° = \tan 33°, \text{ etc.}$$

Inverse trigonometric functions

As there are two angles in any $360°$ which have the same value for any trigonometric function, it follows that the inverse function has more than one value. However, a calculator can only give what is called the *principal value* of the inverse trigonometric function. The principal value ranges for sine, cosine and tangent are as follows:

$$\sin^{-1}: \quad -90° \leqslant \theta \leqslant 90°$$
$$\cos^{-1}: \quad \ \ 0° \leqslant \theta \leqslant 180°$$
$$\tan^{-1}: \quad -90° < \theta < 90°$$

The principal value may not be the one required in a particular problem, and the graph of the appropriate trigonometric function should be used to determine other values. For example:

$$\sin^{-1} +0.5 \ \ = \ \ \ 30° \text{ (the angle could be } 30° \text{ or } 150°.)$$
$$\sin^{-1} -0.5 \ \ = -30° \text{ (the angle could be } 210° \text{ or } 330°.)$$
$$\cos^{-1} +0.866 \simeq \ \ \ 30° \text{ (the angle could be } 30° \text{ or } 330°.)$$
$$\cos^{-1} -0.866 \simeq 150° \text{ (the angle could be } 150° \text{ or } 210°.)$$
$$\tan^{-1} +0.577 \simeq \ \ \ 30° \text{ (the angle could be } 030° \text{ or } 210°.)$$
$$\tan^{-1} -0.577 \simeq -30° \text{ (the angle could be } 150° \text{ or } 330°.)$$

Care must be taken to ensure that the displayed angle reading is adjusted if necessary to the correct value. This may often be achieved by inspection. For example, if a bearing θ is such that $\tan \theta \simeq -0.577$, but it is also known that the bearing is in the fourth (north-west) quadrant, then the angle required must be $330°$ (and not $150°$, nor the $-30°$ given by a calculator).

Alternatively, two trigonometric functions corresponding to the displayed value may be compared. For example, if the sine of the displayed value is −ve, while the cosine is also −ve, the angle corresponding to both values can only be in the third (south-west) quadrant, where sine and cosine are both negative.

Pythagorean relationships between trigonometrical functions

By the theorem of Pythagoras, the square on the hypotenuse of a right-angled triangle is equal to the sum of the squares on the other two sides. Therefore (Fig. A1–3):

$$a^2 + b^2 = c^2$$

i.e.
$$\frac{a^2}{c^2} + \frac{b^2}{c^2} = 1$$

or
$$\sin^2 \theta + \cos^2 \theta = 1 \qquad \qquad \ldots \textbf{A1.10}$$

Further division by $\cos^2 \theta$ gives:
$$\tan^2 \theta + 1 = \sec^2 \theta \qquad \qquad \ldots \textbf{A1.11}$$

or, if **(A1.10)** is divided by $\sin^2 \theta$:
$$1 + \cot^2 \theta = \operatorname{cosec}^2 \theta \qquad \qquad \ldots \textbf{A1.12}$$

These formulae hold for all values of θ, because the square of any quantity is always positive, although the quantity itself may be negative.

Acute and obtuse triangles

There are several formulae connecting the sides and angles of acute and obtuse triangles (Fig. A1–8) and the choice of formula is governed, as a rule, by the data available and the requirements of the problem to be solved.

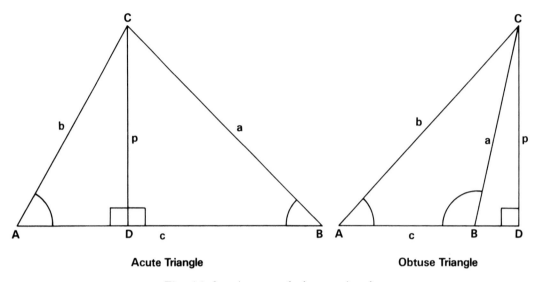

Acute Triangle   Obtuse Triangle

Fig. A1–8.   Acute and obtuse triangles

The sine formula

This formula is established by dropping a perpendicular from any vertex on to the opposite side. In Fig. A1–8, the perpendicular is CD, denoted by p. Then:

$$\sin A = \frac{p}{b}$$

also $\dfrac{p}{a} = \sin B$ (acute triangle) or $\sin(180° - B)$ (obtuse triangle) $= \sin B$

i.e. $p = b \sin A$ $p = a \sin B$

$\therefore b \sin A = a \sin B$

or $\dfrac{a}{\sin A} = \dfrac{b}{\sin B}$

Similarly, if a perpendicular is dropped from A to BC, or BC produced:

$$\frac{b}{\sin B} = \frac{c}{\sin C}$$

Hence $\dfrac{a}{\sin A} = \dfrac{b}{\sin B} = \dfrac{c}{\sin C}$ . . . A1.13

If two angles A and B and one side of the triangle are given, the third angle is $180° - (A + B)$; and the sine formula gives the remaining sides.

Fig. A1–9 shows that ambiguity arises if the formula is used for solving the triangle when two sides and an angle other than the included angle are given, the given angle being opposite the smaller side. If, for example, the sides b and c and the angle C are given, the angle found from the formula is either ABC or its supplement $AB_{1}C$, because the sine of an angle is equal to the sine of its supplement.

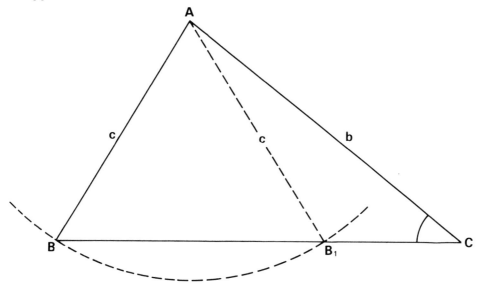

Fig. A1–9.   Ambiguity in the sine formula

The cosine formula

This formula is established by applying the theorem of Pythagoras to the right-angled triangles ADC and BDC in Fig. A1–8. Thus:

$$a^2 = p^2 + BD^2$$
$$b^2 = p^2 + AD^2$$
$$\therefore a^2 = (b^2 - AD^2) + BD^2$$
$$= b^2 - AD^2 + (c - AD)^2$$
$$= b^2 - AD^2 + c^2 - 2cAD + AD^2$$
$$= b^2 + c^2 - 2cAD$$
$$= b^2 + c^2 - 2bc \cos A \qquad \qquad \text{...A1.14}$$

In the same way it can be established that:

$$b^2 = c^2 + a^2 - 2ca \cos B \qquad \qquad \text{...A1.15}$$
$$c^2 = a^2 + b^2 - 2ab \cos C \qquad \qquad \text{...A1.16}$$

This formula is true for any triangle, but it must be remembered that, if the angle A, B or C is greater than $90°$, the angle lies in the second quadrant and its cosine is negative.

The formula gives the third side when two sides and the included angle are known, or any angle when the three sides are known.

The area of a triangle

It is known that the area of a triangle is equal to half the base multiplied by the perpendicular height. The area of the triangle ABC (Fig. A1–8) may also be found by transposing this value using the sine formula to give the following:

$$\tfrac{1}{2}\, ab \sin C \qquad\qquad\qquad\qquad \textbf{...A1.17}$$

$$\tfrac{1}{2}\, bc \sin A \qquad\qquad\qquad\qquad \textbf{...A1.18}$$

$$\tfrac{1}{2}\, ca \sin B \qquad\qquad\qquad\qquad \textbf{...A1.19}$$

Functions of the sum and difference of two angles

The trigonometric functions of combined angles may be determined. For example, the sine, cosine and tangent of the angles $A + B$ in Fig. A1–10 may be found as follows.

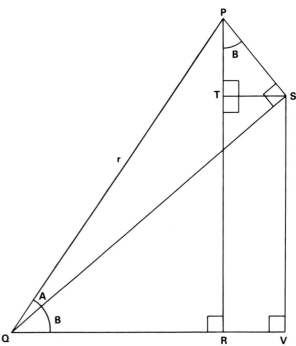

Fig. A1–10.   The sum of two angles

PQR is a triangle right-angled at R. The line QS divides the angle Q into the angles A and B. PS is a perpendicular from P to QS and SV is a perpendicular from S to QV. ST is the perpendicular from S to PT. The angle SPT equals the angle B.

$$r \sin (A + B) = PR = PT + TR = PS \cos B + SV$$
$$= r \sin A \cos B + QS \sin B$$
$$= r \sin A \cos B + r \cos A \sin B$$
$$\therefore \sin (A + B) = \sin A \cos B + \cos A \sin B \qquad\qquad \textbf{...A1.20}$$

$$r \cos (A + B) = QR = QV - RV = QS \cos B - TS$$
$$= r \cos A \cos B - PS \sin B$$
$$= r \cos A \cos B - r \sin A \sin B$$
$$\therefore \cos (A + B) = \cos A \cos B - \sin A \sin B \qquad \ldots \textbf{A1.21}$$

$$\tan (A + B) = \frac{\sin (A + B)}{\cos (A + B)}$$
$$= \frac{\sin A \cos B + \cos A \sin B}{\cos A \cos B - \sin A \sin B}$$

Dividing top and bottom by $(\cos A \cos B)$:

$$\tan (A + B) = \frac{\tan A + \tan B}{1 - \tan A \tan B} \qquad \ldots \textbf{A1.22}$$

We may find $\sin (A - B)$, $\cos (A - B)$, $\tan (A - B)$ from these three formulae by remembering that $\sin (-B) = -\sin B$, $\cos (-B) = \cos B$ and $\tan (-B) = -\tan B$, and substituting these values. Thus:

$$\sin (A - B) = \sin A \cos B - \cos A \sin B \qquad \ldots \textbf{A1.23}$$
$$\cos (A - B) = \cos A \cos B + \sin A \sin B \qquad \ldots \textbf{A1.24}$$
$$\tan (A - B) = \frac{\tan A - \tan B}{1 + \tan A \tan B} \qquad \ldots \textbf{A1.25}$$

Double and half-angle formulae

If A is equal to B, it follows from formulae (**A1.20**), (**A1.21**) and (**A1.22**) that:

$$\sin 2A = 2 \sin A \cos A \qquad \ldots \textbf{A1.26}$$
$$\cos 2A = \cos^2 A - \sin^2 A \qquad \ldots \textbf{A1.27}$$
$$= 1 - 2 \sin^2 A$$
$$= 2 \cos^2 A - 1$$
$$\tan 2A = \frac{2 \tan A}{1 - \tan^2 A} \qquad \ldots \textbf{A1.28}$$

In terms of the half-angle these formulae become:

$$\sin A = 2 \sin \tfrac{1}{2}A \cos \tfrac{1}{2}A \qquad \ldots \textbf{A1.29}$$
$$\cos A = \cos^2 \tfrac{1}{2}A - \sin^2 \tfrac{1}{2}A \qquad \ldots \textbf{A1.30}$$
$$= 1 - 2 \sin^2 \tfrac{1}{2}A$$
$$= 2 \cos^2 \tfrac{1}{2}A - 1$$
$$\tan A = \frac{2 \tan \tfrac{1}{2}A}{1 - \tan^2 \tfrac{1}{2}A} \qquad \ldots \textbf{A1.31}$$

Sum and difference of functions

The above formulae, relating to *the sines and cosines of sums and differences,* may be combined to give other formulae which relate to *the sums and differences of sines and cosines.*

By adding **(A1.20)** and **(A1.23)**, and writing P for $(A + B)$ and Q for $(A - B)$ so that A is equal to $\frac{1}{2}(P + Q)$ and B to $\frac{1}{2}(P - Q)$:

$$\sin (A + B) + \sin (A - B) = 2 \sin A \cos B$$

i.e. $\quad \sin P + \sin Q = 2 \sin\frac{1}{2}(P + Q) \cos\frac{1}{2}(P - Q) \qquad \ldots \textbf{A1.32}$

By subtracting **(A1.23)** from **(A1.20)**:

$$\sin (A + B) - \sin (A - B) = 2 \cos A \sin B$$

i.e. $\quad \sin P - \sin Q = 2 \cos \frac{1}{2}(P + Q) \sin \frac{1}{2}(P - Q) \qquad \ldots \textbf{A1.33}$

By using formulae **(A1.21)** and **(A1.24)**, it can be shown that:

$$\cos P \ + \cos Q = 2 \cos \tfrac{1}{2}(P + Q) \cos \tfrac{1}{2}(P - Q) \qquad \ldots \textbf{A1.34}$$
$$\cos P \ - \cos Q = - \ 2 \sin \tfrac{1}{2}(P + Q) \sin \tfrac{1}{2}(P - Q) \qquad \ldots \textbf{A1.35}$$

The sine of a small angle

Certain approximations suggest themselves when the angle is small.

In Fig. A1–11, AOB is a small angle θ, measured in radians. AB is the arc of a circle which subtends this small angle. The radius of a circle is r, and BC is perpendicular to OA at C.

On page 582 it was stated that the length of arc of a circle is equal to the radius multiplied by the angle subtended in radians. That is:

$$AB = r \times \theta$$

$$\text{or} \quad \theta = \frac{AB}{r}$$

$$\text{But} \quad \sin \theta = \frac{BC}{r}$$

Therefore, when θ is sufficiently small for AB to approximate to BC:

$$\sin \theta = \theta$$

If there are x minutes in this small angle of θ radians, then there must be $\frac{x}{\theta}$ minutes in one radian. But one radian is equal to $\frac{360°}{2\pi}$ or 3437.7468 minutes of arc:

$$\text{hence} \quad \frac{x}{\theta} = 3437'.7468$$

$$\text{i.e.} \quad \theta = \frac{x}{3437'.7468}$$

The relation $\sin \theta = \theta$ therefore becomes:

$$\sin x' = \frac{x}{3437'.7468}$$

Since this relation holds for any value of x that is small:

$$\sin 1' = \frac{1}{3437'.7468}$$

$$\therefore \sin x' = x \sin 1' \qquad \qquad \dots \textbf{A1.36}$$

These adjustments are important when practical results have to be obtained from theoretical calculation, as in the construction of the ex-meridian tables described in Volume II of this revised edition of the manual.

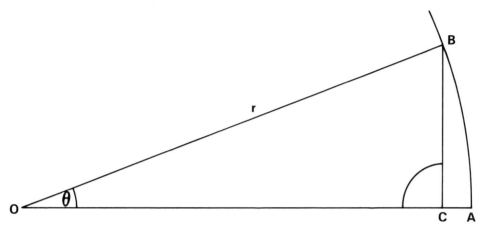

Fig. A1–11.   The sine of a small angle

The cosine of a small angle

Fig. A1–11 shows that, when θ is small, OC approximates to OA, which is the same as OB. But:

$$\cos \theta = \frac{OC}{OB}$$

Therefore, when θ is small, $\cos \theta$ is equal to 1.

A second approximation can be obtained if $\cos \theta$ is expressed in terms of the half-angle, for then:

$$\cos \theta = 1 - 2 \sin^2 \tfrac{1}{2}\theta$$

$$\text{i.e.} \quad \cos \theta = 1 - 2(\tfrac{1}{2}\theta)^2$$

$$\therefore \cos \theta = 1 - \tfrac{1}{2}\theta^2 \qquad \qquad \dots \textbf{A1.37}$$

APPENDIX 2
A Summary of Spherical Trigonometry

Spherical trigonometry is the science of trigonometry (Appendix 1) applied to the triangles marked on the surface of a sphere by planes through its centre.

DEFINITIONS

The sphere

A sphere is defined as a surface, every point on which is equidistant from one and the same point, called the *centre*. The distance of the surface from the centre is called the *radius* of the sphere.

Great circle

The intersection of the spherical surface with any plane through the centre of a sphere is known as a *great circle*.

Small circle

When a plane cuts a sphere but does not pass through its centre, its intersection with the spherical surface is called a *small circle*.

Spherical triangle

A three-sided figure, *ABC* in Fig. A2–1, formed by the minor arcs of three great circles on the spherical surface is known as a *spherical triangle*.

The side of a spherical triangle is the angle it subtends at the centre of the sphere and may be measured in degrees and minutes, or radians.

In Fig. A2–1, *ABC* is a spherical triangle formed by the minor arcs of three great circles, *AB*, *AC* and *BC*. The length a of the side *BC* is equal to the angle subtended at the centre of the sphere, that is, *BOC*. Similarly, b and c are equal to the angles *AOC* and *AOB*.

Spherical angles

In a spherical triangle (Fig. A2–1), the angle A is the angle between the planes containing the great circles *AB* and *AC*, that is, the angle between the plane *AOB* and the plane *AOC*. Similarly, the angle B is the angle between the planes *AOB* and *COB*, and the angle C is the angle between the planes *AOC* and *COB*.

In a spherical triangle *ABC*, it is customary to refer to its angles as A, B and C

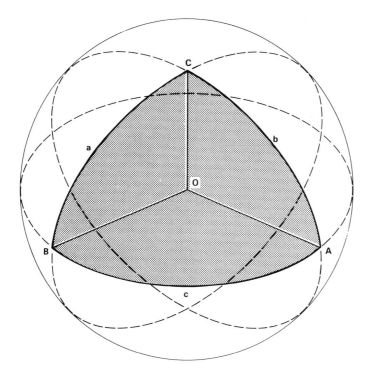

Fig. A2–1.   The spherical triangle

and to the sides opposite these angles as *a*, *b* and *c*. This is analogous to the conventions adopted in a plane triangle and set out in Appendix 1.

Properties of the spherical triangle

Certain properties of a spherical triangle are equivalent to those of a plane triangle. For example, the largest angle is always opposite the largest side, and the smallest angle is always opposite the smallest side. One side is always less than the sum of the other two sides, e.g. $c < a + b$ in Fig. A2–1. There is, however, one very important difference between spherical and plane triangles. The sum of the three angles of the spherical triangle, $A + B + C$, is *always greater* than 180° (π radians). The sum is always less than 540° (3π). The sum of the three sides of the spherical triangle, $a + b + c$, is always less than 360° (2π).

THE SOLUTION OF THE SPHERICAL TRIANGLE

There are six things to be known about a spherical triangle: the sizes of its three angles and the lengths of its three sides. Various formulae connect these angles and sides so that, if sufficient of them are given, the rest can be found. The common problems are those of finding the third side when two sides and their included angle are known, and finding a particular angle when the three sides are known.

The cosine and sine formulae

Cosine formula

In Fig. A2–2, O is the centre of the sphere of radius R. AB, BC and CA are the minor arcs of three great circles forming the spherical triangle ABC on the surface of the sphere. $OA = OB = OC = R$.

CD is the perpendicular from C to the plane OAB.
CE is the perpendicular from C to the line OB.
$\therefore$ DE is perpendicular to OB,
and angle CED = spherical angle at B.

Similarly, CG, is the perpendicular from C to the line OA
$\therefore$ DG is perpendicular to OA,
and angle CGD = spherical angle at A.
    angle $BOC = a$ angle $AOC = b$ angle $BOA = c$

GH is the perpendicular from G on to OB, and DJ is the perpendicular from D on to GH. JD is parallel and equal to HE. Angle $JGD = c$.

In the triangle COE, which is right-angled at E:

$$\frac{OE}{OC} = \cos a$$

$$\therefore OE = R \cos a$$

$$\text{but } OE = OH + HE$$

$$= OG \cos c + GD \sin c$$

$$= R \cos b \cos c + CG \cos A \sin c$$

$$= R \cos b \cos c + R \sin b \cos A \sin c$$

$\therefore$ (COSINE RULE) $\cos a = \cos b \cos c + \sin b \sin c \cos A$ ... **A2.1**

Similarly:

$$\cos b = \cos c \cos a + \sin c \sin a \cos B \qquad \text{... } \textbf{A2.2}$$

$$\cos c = \cos a \cos b + \sin a \sin b \cos C \qquad \text{... } \textbf{A2.3}$$

Thus, if any two sides and their included angle are given, the third side may be found, this side being the one opposite the only spherical angle in the formula. Such formulae are analagous to the cosine formulae for the plane triangle set out in Appendix 1.

When all three sides of the spherical triangle are known, the angle may be found by transposing the relevant cosine formula. For example, from **(A2.1)**:

$$\cos A = \frac{\cos a - \cos b \cos c}{\sin b \sin c} \qquad \text{... } \textbf{A2.4}$$

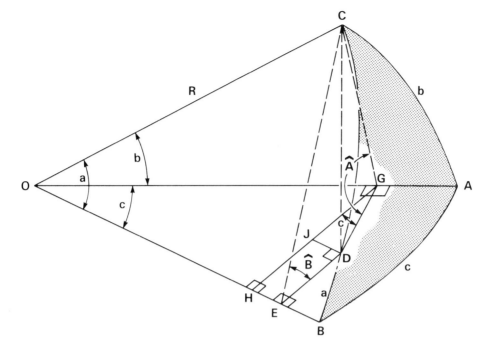

Fig. A2–2.   Spherical trigonometry: the cosine and sine formulae

Sine formula

In the triangles CED and CGD, both right-angled at D:

$$\frac{CD}{CE} = \sin B \text{ and } \frac{CD}{CG} = \sin A$$

thus $CE \sin B = CD = CG \sin A$

$$\therefore R \sin a \sin B = R \sin b \sin A$$

i.e. $\quad\dfrac{\sin a}{\sin A} = \dfrac{\sin b}{\sin B}$

and, by symmetry:

$$(\text{SINE RULE}) \quad \frac{\sin a}{\sin A} = \frac{\sin b}{\sin B} = \frac{\sin c}{\sin C} \qquad \dots \textbf{A2.5}$$

The sine formula for the spherical triangle is analogous to the sine formula for the plane triangle set out in Appendix 1, and has the same limitation in that ambiguity arises if it is used to solve the triangle when two sides and one angle are given. It must be remembered that as $\sin \theta = \sin (180° - \theta)$, there is no way of knowing from the formula alone whether the quantity found is greater or less than $90°$.

Suppose (Fig. A2–3) that a is 66°, b is 50° and B is 40°. From the formula:

$$\sin A = \frac{\sin a}{\sin b} \times \sin B$$

$$= \sin a \, \sin B \, \operatorname{cosec} b$$

$$= \sin 66° \, \sin 40° \, \operatorname{cosec} 50°$$

$$= 0.76657$$

$$A = 50°02'.8 \text{ or } 129°57'.2$$

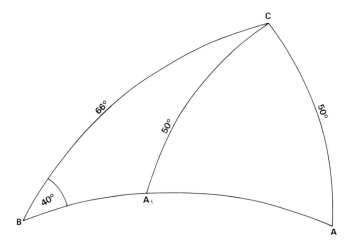

Fig. A2–3.   Spherical trigonometry — ambiguity in sine formula

Fig. A2–3 shows that ABC and A_1BC are possible triangles. The ambiguity, however, may often be resolved in practice and the formula is easier and quicker to use on a calculator than the cosine formula. The sine formula may therefore often be used to find the great-circle course, having found the distance.

The sine rule is a useful cross-check against the accuracy of the workings when the complete solution of the spherical triangle is found using the cosine formula: $\dfrac{\sin a}{\sin A}$, $\dfrac{\sin b}{\sin B}$ and $\dfrac{\sin c}{\sin C}$ must all equal the same value.

Polar triangles

In the same way as the equator is related to the Earth's axis, which cuts the Earth's surface at the North and South Poles, so every great circle has an axis and two poles.

The polar triangle $A_1B_1C_1$ of the spherical triangle ABC (Fig. A2–4) is formed as follows:

A_1 is the 'pole' of the great circle BC on the same side of BC as A. OA_1 is perpendicular to the plane of the great circle through BC.

B_1 is the 'pole' of the great circle AC. OB_1 is perpendicular to the plane of the great circle through AC.

C_l is the 'pole' of the great circle AB. OC_l is perpendicular to the plane of the great circle through AB.

The two triangles ABC and $A_lB_lC_l$ are mutually polar.
In the polar triangle $A_lB_lC_l$,

$$a_l = \pi - A \qquad A_l = \pi - a$$
$$b_l = \pi - B \qquad B_l = \pi - b$$
$$c_l = \pi - C \qquad C_l = \pi - c$$

If these values are substituted in the cosine rule (formula **A2.1**), the following formula is obtained:

$$\text{(POLAR COSINE RULE)} \quad \cos a = \frac{\cos A + \cos B \cos C}{\sin B \sin C} \qquad \ldots \textbf{A2.6}$$

Such a formula may be used to calculate a side of the spherical triangle given all three angles. It may also be used to calculate an angle given the other two angles and the opposite side.

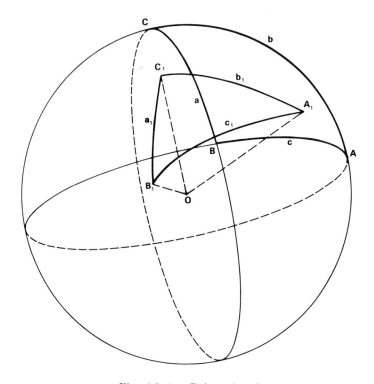

Fig. A2–4.   Polar triangles

The four-part formula

This is a formula the terms of which are four consecutive angles and sides of any spherical triangle.

In Fig. A2–5, the four parts to be considered are C, a, B and c. The angle B, contained by the two sides a and c, is called the 'inner angle' or 'I.A.'. The side a, common to the angles B and C, is called the 'inner side' or 'I.S.'. The others are the 'other angle' C, denoted by 'O.A.', and the 'other side' c, denoted by 'O.S.'.

The four-part formula states that:

$$\cos (\text{I.S.}) \cos (\text{I.A.}) = \sin (\text{I.S.}) \cot (\text{O.S.}) - \sin (\text{I.A.}) \cot (\text{O.A.}) \qquad \ldots \textbf{A2.7}$$

It may be proved thus:

$$\cos b = \cos c \cos a + \sin c \sin a \cos B$$

$$\cos c = \cos a \cos b + \sin a \sin b \cos C$$

By substituting for $\cos b$:

$$\cos c = \cos a \,(\cos c \cos a + \sin c \sin a \cos B)$$
$$+ \sin a \sin b \cos C$$

i.e. $$\cos c = \cos c \,(1 - \sin^2 a) + \sin a \cos a \sin c \cos B$$
$$+ \sin a \sin b \cos C$$

Therefore, since $\cos c$ cancels out and $\sin a$ is common to the remaining terms:

$$\sin a \cos c = \cos a \sin c \cos B + \sin b \cos C$$

i.e. $$\sin a \,\frac{\cos c}{\sin c} = \cos a \cos B + \frac{\sin b \cos C}{\sin c}$$

Hence, by the sine formula:

$$\sin a \cot c = \cos a \cos B + \frac{\sin B \cos C}{\sin C}$$

i.e. $$\cos a \cos B = \sin a \cot c - \sin B \cot C$$

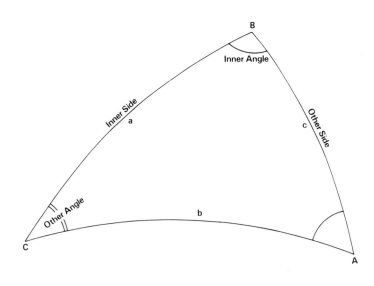

Fig. A2–5.   The four-part spherical triangle

The four-part formula may be used to find the initial or the final course direct from the latitude and longitude without first finding the great-circle distance.

Right-angled triangles

If one angle of a spherical triangle is a right angle, the formulae for solving the triangle are greatly simplified.

Thus, if the angle C in the triangle ABC is a right angle (Fig. A2–6), the cosine formula **(A2.3)** becomes:

$$\cos c = \cos a \cos b \qquad \qquad \dots \textbf{A2.8}$$

and the sine formula **(A2.5)** becomes:

$$\frac{\sin a}{\sin A} = \frac{\sin b}{\sin B} = \sin c \qquad \qquad \dots \textbf{A2.9}$$

The numerous formulae thus obtainable are best summarised by Napier's rules.

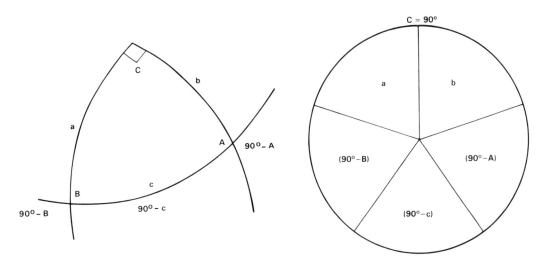

Fig. A2–6.   Napier's right-angled triangles

Napier's mnemonic rules for right-angled triangles

The triangle ABC is 'extended' as shown in Fig. A2–6, to form the symbolic five quantities, a, b, $(90° - A)$, $(90° - c)$, $(90° - B)$, displayed clockwise around the triangle. These quantities may also be shown as the sectors of a circle having a vertical radius that represents the right angle at C.

If any one of these quantities is taken as the 'middle' quantity, two of the other four quantities become 'adjacent' and the remaining two quantities become 'opposite'.

Napier's rules are:

$$\text{sin middle} = \text{products of tans of adjacents} \qquad \dots \textbf{A2.10}$$
$$= \text{products of cosines of opposites} \qquad \dots \textbf{A2.11}$$

In the triangle ABC, right-angled at C, Napier's rules give the ten formulae in Table A2–1, which may also be derived from the various formulae described earlier.

Table A2–1

MIDDLE	FORMULA	DERIVED FROM
a	$\sin a = \tan b \cot B$	Four-part formula
	$\sin a = \sin c \sin A$	Sine rule
b	$\sin b = \tan a \cot A$	Four-part formula
	$\sin b = \sin c \sin B$	Sine rule
$(90° - A)$	$\cos A = \tan b \cot c$	Four-part formula
	$\cos A = \cos a \sin B$	Polar cosine rule
$(90° - c)$	$\cos c = \cot A \cot B$	Polar cosine rule
	$\cos c = \cos a \cos b$	Cosine rule
$(90° - B)$	$\cos B = \tan a \cot c$	Four-part formula
	$\cos B = \cos b \sin A$	Polar cosine rule

Right-angled spherical triangles may be used as follows:

1. To find the position of the vertex on the great circle.
2. To solve an isosceles triangle where two points are in the same latitude, by bisecting the triangle.
3. To find where a great circle cuts the equator.
4. To solve the composite track.

Quadrantal triangles

A quadrantal triangle is a spherical triangle where one side is equal to 90°, e.g. c in Fig. A2–7.

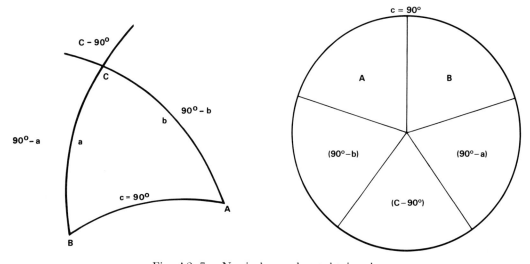

Fig. A2–7. Napier's quadrantal triangles

As with the right-angled triangle, the quadrantal triangle may be 'extended' and a five-part figure constructed. The symbolic five quantities are now A, B, $(90° - a)$, $(C - 90°)$, $(90° - b)$. These quantities may also be combined in accordance with Napier's rules (**A2.10** and **A2.11**), for example:

$$\sin A = \tan B \cot b$$
$$\sin A = \sin a \sin C$$
$$\cos a = \cos A \sin b$$

(etc.)

The haversine

When using logarithmic tables instead of a calculator, it is more convenient to solve the spherical triangle using a function called the *haversine* of the angle.

This function is half the versine—hence the name haversine—and the versine of an angle is defined as the difference between its cosine and unity, that is:

$$\text{versine } \theta = 1 - \cos \theta \qquad \qquad \text{...} \textbf{A2.12}$$

and it follows that:

$$\text{haversine } \theta = \tfrac{1}{2}(1 - \cos \theta) \qquad \qquad \text{...} \textbf{A2.13}$$

The haversine of an angle is thus always positive, and it increases from 0 to 1 as the angle increases from 0° to 180°. Fig. A2–8 shows the haversine curve in relation to the cosine curve from which it is derived. *Norie's Tables* give the values of the haversine for angles between 0° and 360°.

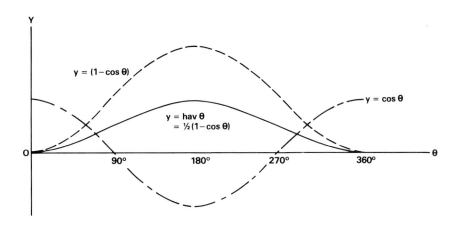

Fig. A2–8. The haversine curve

The usefulness of the haversine formula is confined to situations where a solution has to be found from logarithmic tables. If calculators or computers are available, the previous formulae (cosine rule, sine rule, etc.) should be used in preference.

The haversine formula

To express the cosine rule in terms of haversines instead of cosines, substitute for the appropriate cosines their values in terms of the haversine. Thus $\cos A$ can be written $(1 - 2 \text{ hav } A)$, and the formula becomes:

$$\cos a = \cos b \cos c + \sin b \sin c \, (1 - 2 \text{ hav } A)$$

i.e. $\quad \cos a = \cos b \cos c + \sin b \sin c - 2 \sin b \sin c \text{ hav } A$

$$= \cos (b \sim c) - 2 \sin b \sin c \text{ hav } A$$

Similar substitutions for $\cos a$ and $\cos (b \sim c)$ give:

$$1 - 2 \text{ hav } a = 1 - 2 \text{ hav } (b \sim c) - 2 \sin b \sin c \text{ hav } A$$

i.e. $\quad \text{hav } a = \text{hav } (b \sim c) + \sin b \sin c \text{ hav } A \qquad \dots \textbf{A2.14}$

The half log haversine formula

This formula, which gives one of the angles when the three sides are known, is derived from the cosine rule by making substitutions similar to those used in building the haversine formula.

As before, the first substitution gives:

$$\cos a = \cos (b \sim c) - 2 \sin b \sin c \text{ hav } A$$

$$2 \sin b \sin c \text{ hav } A = \cos (b \sim c) - \cos a$$

By the rule for the subtraction of two cosines this equation becomes:

$$2 \sin b \sin c \text{ hav } A = 2 \sin \tfrac{1}{2} \left[a + (b \sim c) \right] \sin \tfrac{1}{2} \left[a - (b \sim c) \right]$$

Therefore, by division:

$$\text{hav } A = \text{cosec } b \text{ cosec } c \sin \tfrac{1}{2} \left[a + (b \sim c) \right] \sin \tfrac{1}{2} \left[a - (b \sim c) \right]$$

But, from the definition of the haversine:

$$\text{hav } x = \tfrac{1}{2} (1 - \cos x) = \tfrac{1}{2} \left[1 - (1 - 2 \sin^2 \tfrac{1}{2} x) \right]$$

$$= \sin^2 \tfrac{1}{2} x$$

Therefore, by analogy:

$$\sin \tfrac{1}{2} \left[a + (b \sim c) \right] = \sqrt{\text{hav } \left[a + (b \sim c) \right]}$$
$$\sin \tfrac{1}{2} \left[a - (b \sim c) \right] = \sqrt{\text{hav } \left[a - (b \sim c) \right]}$$

By substitution:

$$\text{hav } A = \text{cosec } b \text{ cosec } c \sqrt{\text{hav } \left[a + (b \sim c) \right] \text{hav } \left[a - (b \sim c) \right]}$$

In logarithmic form this is:

$$\log \text{hav } A = \log \text{cosec } b + \log \text{cosec } c + \tfrac{1}{2} \log \text{hav } \left[a + (b \sim c) \right]$$
$$+ \tfrac{1}{2} \log \text{hav } \left[a - (b \sim c) \right] \qquad \dots \textbf{A2.15}$$

The haversine solution to the example on page 39 is set out below.

A ship steams from position F (45°N, 140°E) to T (65°N, 110°W). Find the great-circle distance and the initial course.

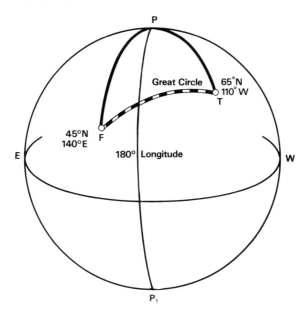

Fig. A2–9.   A great-circle problem

Great-circle distance

It is required to find the great-circle distance between two points, F and T, with known latitudes and longitudes. The haversine formula **(A2.14)** then becomes:

$$\text{hav } FT = \text{hav } FPT \sin PF \sin PT + \text{hav } (PF \sim PT)$$
$$= \text{hav (d.long) } \sin (90° - \text{lat F}) \sin (90° \pm \text{lat T})$$
$$+ \text{hav } [(90° - \text{lat F}) \sim (90° \pm \text{lat } T)]$$

This applies to F in either north or south latitudes.

i.e. hav dist = hav d.long cos lat F cos lat T

$$+ \text{hav (co-lat } F \sim \text{co-lat } T) \qquad \qquad \dots \textbf{A2.16}$$

$$= \text{hav } 110° \cos 45° \cos 65° + \text{hav } (45° \sim 25°)$$
$$= \text{hav } 110° \cos 45° \cos 65° + \text{hav } 20°$$

log hav 110°	$\overline{1}$. 82673
log cos 45°	$\overline{1}$. 84949
log cos 65°	$\overline{1}$. 62595

$\overline{1}$. 30217	0.20053
hav 20°	0.03015
hav 57°24′.5	0.23068

∴ G.C. distance $= 3444′.5$

Great-circle bearing

When it is necessary to find the great-circle bearing of one point on the Earth's surface from another (or the initial course when sailing on a great-circle track from one point to another), the half-log haversine formula **(A2.15)** is applied. Thus, the bearing of T from F is given by:

hav PFT

$$= \text{cosec } PF \text{ cosec } FT \sqrt{\text{hav } [PT + (PF \sim FT)] \text{ hav } [PT - (PF \sim FT)]}$$

or

$$\log \text{hav } PFT = \log \text{cosec } PF + \log \text{cosec } FT + \tfrac{1}{2} \log \text{hav } [PT + (PF \sim FT)]$$
$$+ \tfrac{1}{2} \log \text{hav } [PT - (PF \sim FT)]$$

i.e. log hav initial course

$$= \log \text{cosec co-lat } F + \log \text{cosec distance}$$
$$+ \tfrac{1}{2} \log \text{hav}[\text{co-lat } T + (\text{co-lat } F \sim \text{distance})]$$
$$+ \tfrac{1}{2} \log \text{hav}[\text{co-lat } T - (\text{co-lat } F \sim \text{distance})] \qquad \dots \textbf{A2.17}$$
$$= \log \text{cosec } 45° + \log \text{cosec } 57° \ 24'.5$$
$$+ \tfrac{1}{2} \log \text{hav}[25° - 12° \ 24'.5]$$
$$+ \tfrac{1}{2} \log \text{hav}[25° + 12° \ 24'.5]$$
$$= \log \text{cosec } 45° + \log \text{cosec } 57° \ 24'.5$$
$$+ \tfrac{1}{2} \log \text{hav } 12° \ 35'.5 + \tfrac{1}{2} \log \text{hav } 37° \ 24'.5$$

log cosec 45°	0.150515
log cosec 57° 24′.5	0.074414
$\tfrac{1}{2}$ log hav 37° 24′.5	$\overline{1}$.506074
$\tfrac{1}{2}$ log hav 12° 35′.5	$\overline{1}$.040056
log hav PFT	$\overline{2}$.771059

$$\text{initial course} = \text{N28° } 07'.3\text{E}$$
$$= 028°$$

APPENDIX 3
The Spherical Earth

MERIDIONAL PARTS FOR THE SPHERE

As was explained in Chapter 4, the meridional parts of any latitude are the number of longitude units in the length of a meridian between the parallel of that latitude and the equator. A longitude unit is the length on the chart representing one minute of arc in longitude.

Fig. A3–1. Construction of the mer. part formula

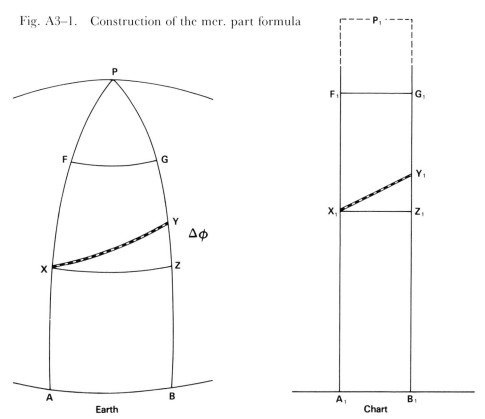

Earth   Chart

Construction of the mer. part formula for the sphere

In Fig. A3–1, X is any point on the Earth in latitude ϕ, and Y is a neighbouring point differing from it in latitude by the small amount $\Delta\phi$. X_1 and Y_1 are the corresponding points on the Mercator chart where, since all meridians are straight lines at right angles to the equator, A_lB_l is equal to X_lZ_l.

The ratio that the chart length A_lB_l bears to the geographical distance AB decides the longitude scale of the chart. That is, when AB and A_lB_l are expressed in the same units, A_lB_l is some fraction of AB or, what is the same thing, AB is equal to kA_lB_l where k is some constant. If, for example, AB is 1 minute of arc and A_lB_l is 1 mm, 1 mm on the chart is equivalent to 1 minute of arc or approximately 1,853,300 mm on the Earth, and k is 1,853,300. The value of k thus determines the size of the chart. For the actual measurement of meridional parts, however, it is sufficient to know the chart unit that represents 1 minute of arc along the equator.

In the example-quoted, where 1 mm represents 1 minute, the meridional parts of X_l are simply the number of millimetres in X_lA_l.

To calculate this chart length and so determine the number of minutes of arc along the equator to which it is equivalent, consider the distortion that occurs away from the equator.

XZ is the parallel through X, and XY the rhumb line joining X to Y. On the chart X_lZ_l is the parallel and X_lY_l the rhumb line, both lines being straight. Then, if all lengths XZ, AB, A_lB_l . . . are measured in the same units:

$$XZ = AB \cos \phi \text{ (from formula } \textbf{2.1}\text{)}$$
$$= kA_lB_l \cos \phi$$
$$= kX_lZ_l \cos \phi$$
$$\text{i.e. } X_lZ_l = \frac{1}{k} XZ \sec \phi$$

Any arc of a parallel, the latitude of which is ϕ, is thus represented on the chart by a line proportional to the actual length of the arc multiplied by sec ϕ, a quantity greater than unity. The distance scale along the parallel is therefore stretched.

Again, if Y is taken sufficiently close to X for XYZ to be considered a plane triangle right-angled at Z:

$$\frac{Z_lY_l}{ZY} = \frac{X_lZ_l}{XZ}$$
$$= \frac{1}{k} \sec \phi$$
$$\text{i.e. } Z_lY_l = \frac{1}{k} ZY \sec \phi$$

Any small element of a meridian in the neighbourhood of latitude ϕ is thus represented on the chart by a line proportional to the actual length of the element multiplied by sec ϕ, and the distance scale along the meridian is therefore stretched.

The actual distance between Z and Y on the Earth, being $\Delta\phi$ in circular measure, is $\dfrac{180 \times 60}{\pi} \Delta\phi$, or 3437.747 $\Delta\phi$ minutes of arc. Hence:

$$Z_I Y_I = \frac{1}{k} \, 3437.747 \, \sec \phi \, \Delta\phi$$

in minutes of arc.

But 1 minute of arc is equal to k millimetres, or whatever the scale units are. Therefore:

$$Z_I Y_I = \left(\frac{1}{k} \, 3437.747 \, \sec \phi \, \Delta\phi\right) k$$

in millimetres or scale units.

The actual chart length of $Z_I Y_I$ in millimetres, or whatever the scale units are, is thus:

$$3437.747 \, \sec \phi \, \Delta\phi$$

The chart length of any particular parallel from the equator, measured along a meridian is clearly the sum of all the component elements of which the expression just found is typical. If the latitude of the parallel is L_F, this sum, in the chosen units, is given by:

$$3437.747 \int_O^{L_F} \sec \phi \, d\phi$$

That is, the number of meridional parts or longitude units (a longitude unit being the length on the chart that represents 1 minute of arc in longitude) in the length of a meridian between latitude L_F and the equator is:

$$3437.747 \, \log_e \tan (45° + \tfrac{1}{2} L_F°)$$

Evaluation of the mer. part formula

The actual evaluation of this formula may be accomplished more easily if the logarithm is expressed to base 10. Thus, if y is the number of meridional parts:

$$y = 3437.747 \, \log_{10} \tan (45° + \tfrac{1}{2} L_F°) \, \log_e 10$$
$$= 7915.7045 \, \log_{10} \tan (45° + \tfrac{1}{2} L_F°) \qquad \ldots \textbf{(4.1)}$$

Suppose the latitude is 40°. Then:

$$y = 7915.7045 \, \log_{10} \tan 65°$$
$$= 7915.7045 \times 0.33132745$$
$$= 2622.69$$

CORRECTED MEAN LATITUDE FOR THE SPHERE

On page 28 it was made clear that, given certain circumstances, the mean latitude must not be used to determine d.long by means of formula **(2.5)**, but a correction to that mean latitude must first be applied.

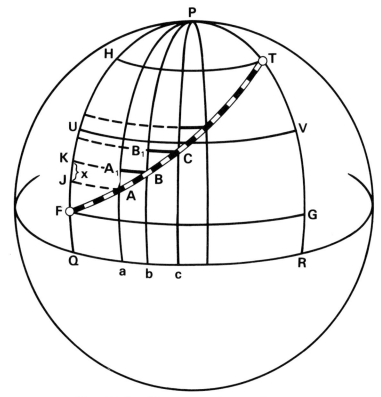

Fig. A3–2.   The corrected mean latitude

In Fig. A3–2, a ship steams from F to T. Since the departure is greater than HT and less than FG, it must be exactly equal to the arc of some parallel UV. The latitude of this parallel is called the corrected mean latitude, and if it is denoted by L, then:

$$QR = UV \sec L$$

i.e.   d.long = departure $\sec L$

This is an accurate formula, but L must be known before it can be used. The problem is therefore to find L.

The latitudes of F and T may be denoted by L_F and L_T, and the difference of latitude between them, FH, divided into n equal parts of length x. JK is one of these parts. Then:

$$\text{d.lat} = nx = L_T - L_F$$

If parallels of latitude are now drawn through the points $J, K \ldots$, intersecting the rhumb line FT in A, B, etc. and the meridians through these points of intersection in A_1, B_1, etc., n small triangles are formed. Moreover, these triangles are equal because in each the side of which AA_1 is typical is x; the angle at A_1 is 90°; and the angle at A is the course, which is constant between F and T. The length of the arc of which A_1B is typical is thus the same for each triangle and, if the triangles are made sufficiently small (that is, if n is made sufficiently large) for the conditions for evaluating an accurate departure to be realised, the departure between F and T is the sum of the elements A_1B. Thus:

$$\text{departure} = ny$$

where y is the length of A_1B. Also, the d.long corresponding to the element A_1B is ab and:

$$ab = A_1B \sec (\text{latitude } B)$$

$$ab = y \sec (\text{latitude } K)$$

By adding all these elements ab, bc, etc. the d.long is obtained, the formula being:

$$\text{d.long} = y[\sec (L_F + x) + \sec (L_F + 2x) + \ldots + \sec L_T]$$

Or, since the departure is equal to ny:

$$\text{d.long} = \text{departure} \, \frac{\sec (L_F + x) + \sec (L_F + 2x) + \ldots + \sec L_T}{n}$$

But the corrected mean latitude L is given by:

$$\text{d.long} = \text{departure} \sec L$$

Hence, by equating these two values of the d.long:

$$\sec L = \frac{1}{n} [\sec (L_F + x) + \sec (L_F + 2x) + \ldots + \sec L_T]$$

The quantity $\sec L$ is thus the mean of the secants of the latitudes of the successive parallels.

Written in the integral form in order that the value of $\sec L$ may be found, the equation is:

$$\sec L = \frac{1}{nx} [\sec (L_F + x) + \sec (L_F + 2x) + \ldots + \sec L_T]x$$

$$= \frac{1}{(L_T - L_F)} [\sec (L_F + x) + \sec (L_F + 2x) + \ldots + \sec L_T]x$$

Then, as n becomes larger, x grows progressively smaller and, in the limit:

$$\sec L = \frac{1}{\text{d.lat}} \int_{L_F}^{L_T} \sec L \, dL \ldots$$

$$= \frac{1}{\text{d.lat}} \left[\log_e \tan \left(\frac{\pi}{4} + \frac{L}{2} \right) \right]_{L_F}^{L_T} \quad \text{if d.lat is expressed in radians}$$

$$= \frac{1}{\text{d.lat}} \times \frac{180 \times 60}{\pi}$$

$$\times \log_e 10 \, [\log_{10} \tan (45° + \tfrac{1}{2}L_T°) - \log_{10} \tan (45° + \tfrac{1}{2}L_F°)]$$

if d.lat is expressed in minutes of arc.

It may be seen that:

$$\frac{180 \times 60}{\pi} \times \log_e 10 \left[\log_{10} \tan (45° + \tfrac{1}{2}L_T°) - \log_{10} \tan (45° + \tfrac{1}{2}L_F°)\right]$$

corresponds to the meridional parts formula **(4.1)** and is equal to the difference of meridional parts (DMP). Thus:

$$\sec L = \frac{\text{DMP}}{\text{d.lat (minutes of arc)}} \qquad \qquad \dots (2.7)$$

APPENDIX 4
Projections

This appendix deals with the following:

1. The conical orthomorphic projection on the sphere.
2. The deduction of the mer. part formula for the sphere.
3. The position circle on the Mercator chart.
4. The modified polyconic projection.
5. The polar stereographic projection.
6. The gnomonic projection.
7. The transverse Mercator projection—conversion from geographical to grid co-ordinates and vice versa.

THE CONICAL ORTHOMORPHIC PROJECTION ON THE SPHERE

On projections of the simple conical type, all meridians are equally spaced straight lines meeting in a common point beyond the limits of the chart or map. The parallels are concentric circles, the common centre of which is the point of intersection of the meridians. This is illustrated in Fig. A4–1. The cone AVG is tangential to the sphere along the standard parallel $AFGH$; AV is the radius r_O of the standard parallel at latitude ϕ_O on the projection, co-latitude Z_O, and is equal to $R \tan Z_O$ where R is the radius of the sphere; the angles EVF and WVF on the projection are equal, each representing $180°$ of longitude on the sphere.

The scale

The meridians and parallels of this projection intersect at right angles and thus angles are preserved. Although this is a necessary condition for orthomorphism, it is not sufficient. To make the projection orthomorphic, the scale along the meridian must be equal to the scale along the parallel at any point on the projection.

In Fig. A4–2, $ABCD$ is an infinitely small quadrilateral on the sphere, while $A_1B_1C_1D_1$ is its plane representation on the conical projection. The small change in the meridian on the projection, $d\theta$, is only a fraction of the equivalent change in the meridian on the sphere, $d\lambda$, and this fraction may be referred to as:

$$n, \text{ the constant of the cone}$$
$$\text{where } d\theta = nd\lambda \qquad \qquad \dots \textbf{A4.1}$$

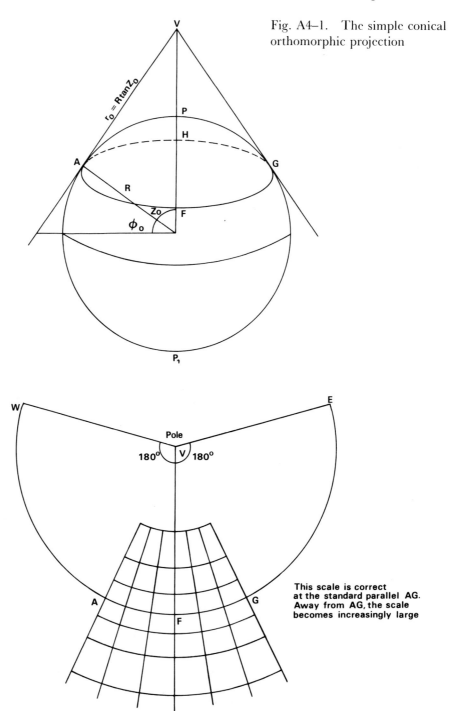

Fig. A4–1. The simple conical orthomorphic projection

The scale along the meridian at A_1 is the relationship:

$$\frac{A_1B_1}{AB} = \frac{-\mathrm{d}r}{R\mathrm{d}\phi} = \frac{\mathrm{d}r}{R\mathrm{d}Z} \qquad \qquad \ldots \mathbf{A4.2}$$

The negative sign must be allocated to dr if ϕ is used, because r increases as ϕ decreases, and the positive sign must be allocated if Z is used, when r increases as Z increases.

The scale along the parallel at A_I is the relationship:

$$\frac{A_ID_I}{AD} = \frac{rd\theta}{R\cos\phi\,d\lambda}$$

$$= \frac{rd\theta}{R\sin Z\,d\lambda} = \frac{nr}{R\sin Z} \qquad \ldots \mathbf{A4.3}$$

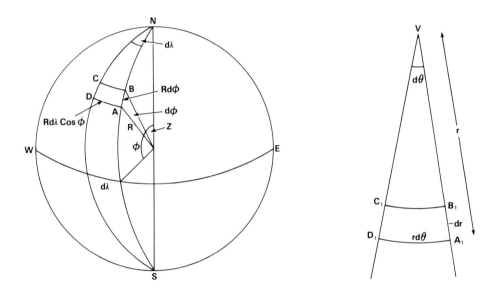

Fig. A4–2.   Scale on the conical orthomorphic projection

To be orthomorphic, these two scales must be equal:

i.e. $$\frac{dr}{R\,dZ} = \frac{nr}{R\sin Z}$$

$$\frac{1}{r}dr = n\,\mathrm{cosec}\,Z\,dZ$$

i.e. $$\int \frac{1}{r}dr = \int n\,\mathrm{cosec}\,Z\,dZ$$

$$\log_e r = n\log_e \tan\frac{Z}{2} + C$$

$$= n\log_e \tan\frac{Z}{2} + \log_e k$$

$$r = k\left(\tan\frac{Z}{2}\right)^n \qquad \ldots \mathbf{A4.4}$$

where k is a constant defining the scale.

The general properties of a system of conformal conical projections may be defined by this formula **(A4.4)**.

The constant of the cone

From Fig. A4–1, it may be seen that the length of the standard parallel $AFGH$ is $2\pi R \cos \phi_O$, whilst the radius of the parallel on the projection is $R \tan Z_O$ or $R \cot \phi_O$. When this conical shape is displayed for the whole 360° of longitude for the Earth, the angle on the projection represents 2π. Thus:

$$R \cot \phi_O \, d\theta = 2\pi R \cos \phi_O$$

$$d\theta = 2\pi \sin \phi_O$$

but, in this case, $\quad d\lambda = 2\pi$

so, from **(A4.1)**, $\quad 2\pi n = 2\pi \sin \phi_O$

$$\therefore n = \sin \phi_O = \cos Z_O \qquad \qquad \ldots \textbf{A4.5}$$

Thus for the simple conical projection, the constant of the cone, n, equals $\sin \phi_O$, the sine of the standard parallel.

Conical orthomorphic projection with two standard parallels

Since the scale at any point not on the standard parallel is too large, two standard parallels may be chosen, where the scale is correct. This is illustrated in Fig. A4–3. Between the two parallels, the scale of the chart is too small, while beyond them the scale is too large. This projection is known as Lambert's conical orthomorphic projection.

DEDUCTION OF THE MER. PART FORMULA FOR THE SPHERE

The formula giving the meridional parts of any latitude may be derived from the general formula for the cone **(A4.4)**.

If Z_O is the co-latitude of the standard parallel, the radius of the parallel on the projection is given by **(A4.4)**.

$$r_O = k \left(\tan \frac{Z_O}{2} \right)^n$$

The distance between the standard parallel and any other parallel is given by:

$$r_O - r = k \left[\left(\tan \frac{Z_O}{2} \right)^n - \left(\tan \frac{Z}{2} \right)^n \right]$$

$$\simeq kn \left(\log_e \tan \frac{Z_O}{2} - \log_e \tan \frac{Z}{2} \right)$$

an approximation obtained by expanding the right-hand side in its exponential form, given that n ultimately tends to zero.

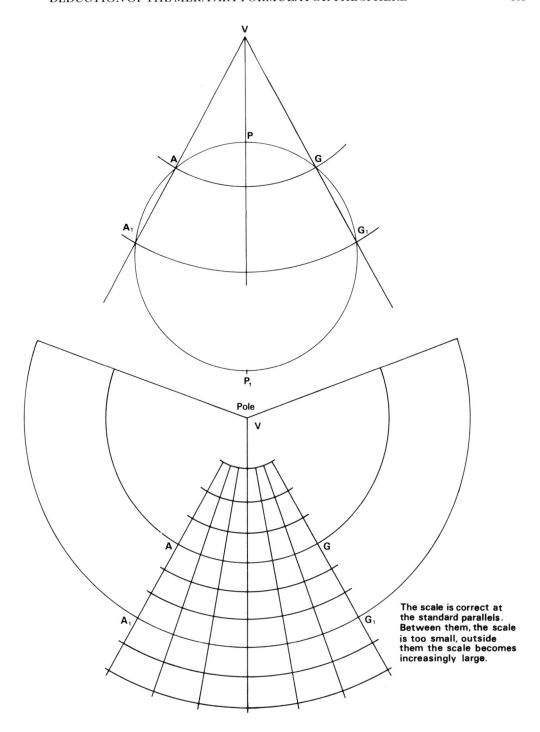

Fig. A4–3. Lambert's conical orthomorphic projection, two standard parallels

The value of k follows at once from the fact that $r_O \cos Z_O$ is equal to $R \sin Z_O$ and is given by:

$$k = \frac{R \sin Z_O}{\cos Z_O} \times \frac{1}{\left(\tan \dfrac{Z_O}{2}\right)^n}$$

and since $\qquad n = \cos Z_O$

$$kn = \frac{R \sin Z_O}{\left(\tan \dfrac{Z_O}{2}\right)^n}$$

When the cone becomes a cylinder, the standard parallel becomes the equator, this being the Mercator projection, Z_O becomes $90°$ and:

$$kn = R$$

The value of $(r_O - r)$, which is now the chart length of a parallel in latitude ϕ from the equator, measured along a meridian, is therefore given by:

$$r_O - r = -R \log_e \tan \frac{Z}{2}$$

$$= R \log_e \cot \frac{Z}{2}$$

$$= \frac{10800}{\pi} \log_e \tan \left(\frac{\pi}{4} + \frac{\phi}{2}\right)$$

$$= 3437.747 \log_e \tan \left(45° + \frac{1}{2} \phi°\right)$$

$$= 7915.7045 \log_{10} \tan \left(45° + \frac{1}{2} \phi°\right) \qquad \ldots \textbf{(4.1)}$$

THE POSITION CIRCLE ON THE MERCATOR CHART

A position circle is a circle drawn on the Earth's surface with the geographical position of the heavenly body as centre. It is a small circle. When plotted on a Mercator chart, this curve of position will no longer be a circle, and the problem is to find the equation of the resulting curve.

Fig. A4–4 shows the relative positions of the pole P, the observer Z, and the geographical position of the heavenly body U, when the true altitude (obtained from a sextant reading) is a, and the declination is d. The latitude of Z is ϕ. Then, if X and x are the easterly longitudes of Z and U, the hour angle of the heavenly body is $(x - X)$.

The cosine formula applied to the spherical triangle PZU gives:

$$\cos UZ = \cos PU \cos PZ + \sin PU \sin PZ \cos UPZ \qquad \ldots \textbf{(A2.1)}$$

i.e. $\qquad \sin a = \sin d \sin \phi + \cos d \cos \phi \cos (x - X)$

or $\cos (x - X) = \sin a \sec d \sec \phi - \tan d \tan \phi \qquad \ldots \textbf{A4.6}$

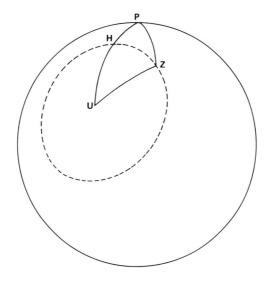

Fig. A4–4.   Position circle

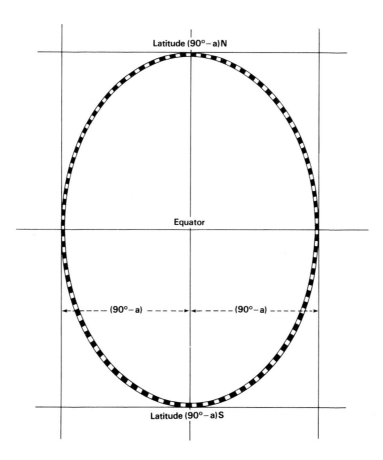

Fig. A4–5.   Position circle plotted on a Mercator chart, declination zero

If the co-ordinates of Z on the chart are x and y, x is given by this equation, and y by:

$$\sec \phi = \tfrac{1}{2}(e^y + e^{-y})$$
$$\text{and } \tan \phi = \tfrac{1}{2}(e^y - e^{-y})$$

Hence, by substitution:

$$2 \cos (x - X) = e^y (\sin a \sec d - \tan d)$$
$$+ e^{-y} (\sin a \sec d + \tan d) \qquad \qquad \text{...} \mathbf{A4.7}$$

This is the general equation of the curve on the chart that represents the position circle, and the curve itself is defined by the values of a, d and X.

Fig. A4–5 shows the curve as it appears on a Mercator chart when the declination is zero, and Fig. A4–6 shows three typical curves representing position circles for three values of the altitude when the geographical position is in latitude 40°N, longitude 60°W.

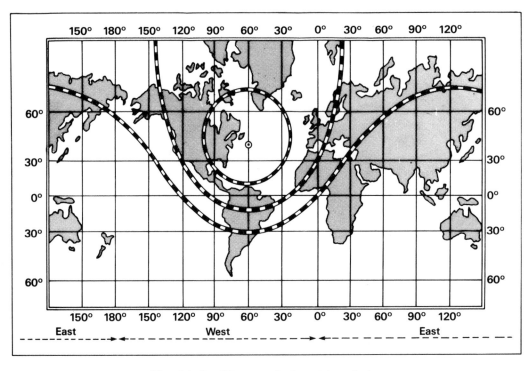

Fig. A4–6.   Three typical position circles

THE MODIFIED POLYCONIC PROJECTION

Although new charts on a scale 1:50 000 or larger are now drawn on the transverse Mercator projection, there are still many harbour plans and approaches in general use traditionally described on the chart as being gnomonic. In fact these plans have been drawn on a modified form of the polyconic projection.

In the polyconic projection, the central meridian alone is straight and the distances between consecutive parallels are made equal to the real distances along the surface of the spheriod, to the scale required for the chart. Each parallel is constructed as if it were the standard parallel of a simple conical projection. This means (*see* Chapter 4) that the circular arcs in which the parallels are developed are not concentric, but their centres lie on the central meridian. The other meridians are concave towards the central meridian and, except near the corners of maps or charts showing large areas, they intersect the parallels at angles differing only slightly from right angles.

In practice on Admiralty charts, all meridians are drawn as straight lines and to this extent the polyconic projection has been modified, although the normal curvature of the limiting meridians would be extremely small in any case, having regard to the scale of the chart.

The co-ordinates (x, y) of any point Q on the projection (Fig. A4–7) may be found from the formulae:

$$x = \nu \, \Delta\lambda \, \cos \phi \qquad \qquad \ldots \textbf{A4.8}$$

$$y = \tfrac{1}{4} \nu (\Delta\lambda)^2 \sin 2\phi \qquad \qquad \ldots \textbf{A4.9}$$

where ϕ is the latitude of the parallel,

$\Delta\lambda$ is the difference of longitude from the central meridian,

ν is the radius of curvature at right angles to the meridian* at latitude ϕ.

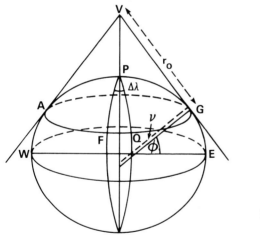 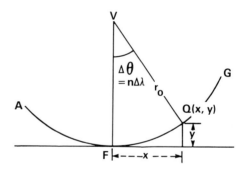

Fig. A4–7.   The modified polyconic projection

These formulae are accurate for projections covering 2° of latitude and 1° of longitude. The projection may be extended to 2° of longitude without any appreciable inaccuracy by laying off co-ordinates from each of the extreme meridians, to cover a further 30 minutes of longitude.

---

* This radius of curvature is sometimes referred to as the transverse radius of curvature and should not be confused with the meridional radius of curvature ρ described in Chapter 3. For any spheroid, $\nu = \dfrac{a}{(1 - e^2 \sin^2 \phi)^{1/2}}$

THE POLAR STEREOGRAPHIC PROJECTION

The polar stereographic projection (Fig. A4–8) is a perspective conformal projection on a plane tangential to the sphere at the pole, obtained by projecting from the opposite pole. Angles are correctly represented; parallels of latitude are represented by circles radiating outwards from and centred on the pole. Meridians appear as straight lines originating from the pole.

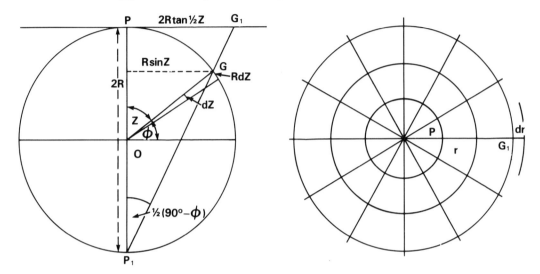

Fig. A4–8.   The polar stereographic projection

If R is the Earth's radius and ϕ the latitude of G, the angle PP_IG_I is $\frac{1}{2}(90° - \phi°)$ and the radius PG_I of the projected parallel is $2R \tan \frac{1}{2}(90° - \phi°)$.

If the radius PG_I is r, and the co-latitude of ϕ is Z, the scale along the parallel at G_I is:

$$\frac{r}{R \sin Z} = \frac{2R \tan \frac{1}{2}Z}{R \sin Z} = \sec^2 \tfrac{1}{2}Z$$

The scale along the meridian at G_1 where dr is a small increase in r and dz a small increase in Z is:

$$\frac{dr}{R dz} = \frac{2R \frac{1}{2} \sec^2 \frac{1}{2}Z}{R} = \sec^2 \tfrac{1}{2}Z$$

The scale is the same in each direction; thus the orthomorphic property is established.

GNOMONIC PROJECTION

Principal or central meridian

The plane on which the parallels and meridians are projected is a tangent plane and, to avoid distortion, the tangent point K should be chosen in the centre of the area to be shown. In Fig. A4–9, its latitude is 20°N.

Since the gnomonic projection is a perspective projection, the point on the tangent plane that corresponds to a point on the sphere that represents the Earth is found by producing the radius at the point until it cuts the tangent plane. Thus p corresponds to P, the pole, and all points on the meridian PK project into the straight line pK. PK is known as the principal or central meridian.

If B is any point and ABC any great circle through it, the arc AB projects into the straight line ab.

The meridian through B is PBL and, since it is part of a great circle, pbl is also a straight line. The meridians on the gnomonic graticule are thus straight lines radiating from p.

The straight line Kl corresponds to the great-circle arc KL.

If ϕ_K and ϕ_A are the latitudes of K and A, then:

$$KP = 90° - \phi_K = KOP$$

and $$AP = 90° - \phi_A = AOP$$

Since Kp lies in a plane tangential to the sphere at K, OK, the radius of length R, is perpendicular to Kp. Therefore:

$$\frac{Kp}{OK} = \tan KOp = \tan KOP$$

i.e. $$Kp = R \cot \phi_K$$

Also $$KOA = KOP - AOP$$
$$= \phi_A - \phi_K$$

and $$\frac{Ka}{OK} = \tan KOa = \tan KOA$$

i.e. $$Ka = R \tan (\phi_A - \phi_K) \qquad \ldots \textbf{A4.10}$$

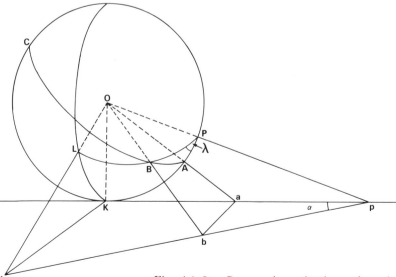

Fig. A4–9. Gnomonic projection—the principal meridian

The chart distances of the pole (Kp) and any point on the central meridian (Ka) from the tangent point are thus known, and it is clear from Fig. A4–9 that, if the latitude of A is greater than that of K, a will lie on the line Kp between K and p. If the latitude of A is less, a will lie beyond K on pK produced.

Angle between two meridians on the chart

The difference of longitude between the meridians PBL and PAK in Fig. A4–9 is the angle LPK, denoted by λ, and this angle is projected into the angle lpK, denoted by α.

Suppose the great circle ABC is chosen so that it cuts the meridian PK at right angles. Its projection ab will then be at right angles to Kp and, from the plane right-angled triangle pab:

$$ab = ap \tan \alpha$$

Also, if the plane of the great circle KLM is made to cut the central meridian at right angles, the angle pKl is a right angle and, from the plane right-angled triangle pKl:

$$Kl = Kp \tan \alpha$$

From the plane right-angled triangles lKO and pKO:

$$Kl = OK \tan KOL$$

and $\qquad Kp = OK \tan KOP = R \cot \phi_K$

By Napier's rules applied to the spherical triangle LKP, right-angled at K:

$$\tan KL = \sin KP \tan \lambda$$

Hence, by combining these relations:

$$\tan \alpha = \sin \phi_K \tan \lambda \qquad \qquad \ldots \textbf{A4.11}$$

From this relation it is apparent that when ϕ_K is $90°$—that is, when the pole is the tangent point—α is equal to λ and there is no distortion in the chart angles between the meridians: they are equal to exact differences of longitude. When the tangent point is not at the pole, there is distortion and the angles between the meridians are not represented correctly on the chart.

If the distance ab is required, it can be found by substitution. Thus:

$$
\begin{aligned}
ab &= ap \tan \alpha \\
&= (Kp - Ka) \sin \phi_K \tan \lambda \\
&= R[\cot \phi_K - \tan (\phi_A - \phi_K)] \sin \phi_K \tan \lambda \\
&= R \tan \lambda \cos \phi_A \sec (\phi_A - \phi_K) \qquad \qquad \ldots \textbf{A4.12}
\end{aligned}
$$

Parallels of latitude

Since the parallels of latitude are not great circles, they form a series of curves on the gnomonic graticule.

In Fig. A4–10 ABC is a parallel in latitude ϕ, and b is the projection of B. As B moves along the parallel, b describes a path which is not a straight line. The

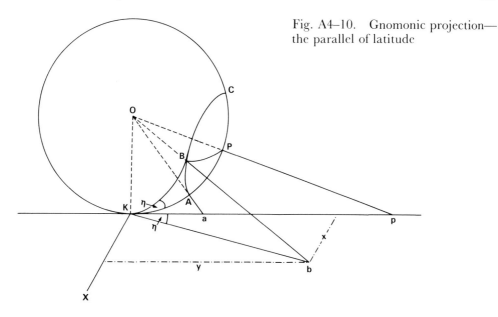

problem is to find the equation of the path, and this can be done by referring b to the rectangular axes KX and Kp.

If the angle AKB is denoted by η, the angle bKp will also be η because the great circles KB and KP can be regarded as 'meridians' radiating from 'pole' K which is a tangent point. There is thus no distortion when this angle is projected. Hence, if x and y are the co-ordinates of b:

$$x = Kb \sin \eta$$
$$\text{and} \quad y = Kb \cos \eta$$
$$\text{and} \quad x^2 + y^2 = Kb^2$$

From the plane right-angled triangle KOb:

$$Kb = OK \tan KOb$$

From the spherical triangle PBK, by the cosine formula:

$$\cos PB = \cos KB \cos KP + \sin KB \sin KP \cos \eta$$

i.e. $\quad \sin \phi \sec KB = \sin \phi_K + \tan KB \cos \phi_K \cos \eta$

For convenience take the radius of the sphere as unity. Then:

$$\sin \phi \sec KB = \sin \phi_K + y \cos \phi_K$$
$$\text{and} \quad \tan^2 KB = x^2 + y^2$$

i.e. $\quad \sec^2 KB = 1 + x^2 + y^2$

$$\therefore \sin^2 \phi (1 + x^2 + y^2) = \sin^2 \phi_K + 2y \sin \phi_K \cos \phi_K + y^2 \cos^2 \phi_K$$

i.e. $x^2 \sin^2 \phi + y^2 (\sin^2 \phi - \cos^2 \phi_K) - 2y \sin \phi_K \cos \phi_K$

$$= \sin^2 \phi_K - \sin^2 \phi \qquad \ldots \textbf{A4.13}$$

For all points on the parallel ABC, ϕ is constant. ϕ_K is also constant. This equation is therefore the equation of the curve that represents the parallel ABC on the chart.

To construct a gnomonic graticule

When the tangent point is on the equator or at the pole, the graticule admits of simple geometrical construction. When the tangent point is elsewhere, the formula just established must be employed.

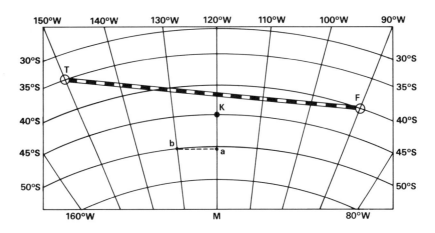

Fig. A4–11.   Gnomonic graticule

Fig. A4–11 shows the graticule when the tangent point is in latitude 45°S, longitude 120°W. *MK* is the central meridian, and the other meridians are inclined to it at angles given by:

$$\tan \alpha = \sin \phi_K \tan \lambda$$

where ϕ_K is 45° and λ has successive values 10°, 20°, 30°, etc. The position of the pole (not shown in the figure) is given by:

$$Kp = OK \cot \phi_K$$

Kp can therefore be marked according to the chosen scale, and the meridians drawn as lines radiating from *p* at the angles discovered.

Again, if *b* is the point corresponding to latitude 50°S, longitude 130°W, and *ba* is the perpendicular from *b* to *MK*, the length of *Ka* in the chosen scale is given by:

$$Ka = \tan (\phi_A - \phi_K)$$

in which ϕ_A is the latitude of *A*, the point that *a* represents on the chart (Fig. A4–10).

If ϕ_B is the latitude of *B*, the point that *b* represents on the chart, Napier's rules applied to the triangle *PBA* give:

$$\tan \phi_A = \tan \phi_B \sec \lambda$$

where λ is the difference of longitude between *A* and *B*. This formula gives ϕ_A since ϕ_B is 50° and λ is 10°. Hence *Ka* can be found. Also, in the chosen units:

$$ab = \tan \lambda \cos \phi_A \sec (\phi_A - \phi_K)$$
$$\text{i.e.} \quad ab = \tan 10° \cos \phi_A \sec (\phi_A - 45°)$$

The point b, corresponding to latitude 50°S, longitude 130°W, can therefore be plotted with other points where this parallel cuts the meridians.

In this way all the parallels can be inserted.

Equatorial gnomonic graticule

When the tangent point is on the equator, ϕ_K is zero, and the general formulae are simplified considerably. The graticule, however, lends itself to a geometrical construction.

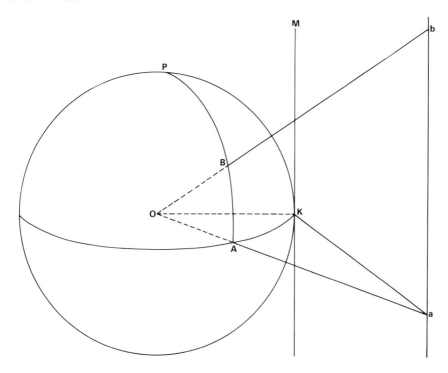

Fig. A4–12. Gnomonic projection—the equatorial graticule (1)

In Fig. A4–12 the central meridian is KP, and this is represented on the chart by KM which is at right angles to OK. The equator KA projects into the straight line Ka at right angles to KM, and any other meridian, AP, projects into a line at right angles to Ka and therefore parallel to KM.

The distance between the projected meridian ab and the central meridian is given by:

$$Ka = OK \tan KOA$$
$$= R \tan (\text{d.long between } K \text{ and } A)$$

The positions of the meridians can thus be decided.

If B is any point on the meridian AP in latitude ϕ, B projects into b, and ab represents this latitude on the chart. Fig. A4–13 shows the geometrical construction for finding the position of b.

The plane of projection is represented by *MKa* in the plane of the paper, and *Ka* is a tangent to the equatorial circle at *K*. *A* is fixed on this circle by its exact difference of longitude from *K*, and it projects into *a*. If ab_l is now drawn at right angles to *Oa*, so that the angle aOb_l is equal to the latitude of *B*, the triangle aOb_l is equal in all respects to the triangle *aOb* in Fig. A4–12. The position of *b* can thus be marked merely by marking *ab* equal to ab_l.

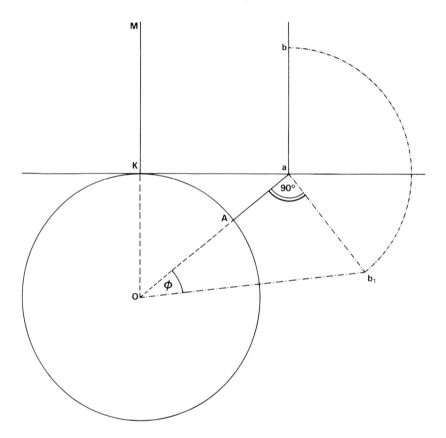

Fig. A4–13.   Gnomonic projection—the equatorial graticule (2)

Other points on the projection of the parallel through *B* can be found in the same way. Since, however, a graticule is usually drawn for equal angular intervals of latitude and longitude, the work can be shortened by drawing radials at the required interval and using them for both d.long and latitude as shown in Fig. A4–14.

This same construction can be used for finding the position of the vertex and the latitude of any point on a great circle, the longitude of which is known.

Any great circle projects into a straight line. Also, a great circle cuts the equator in two points 180° apart. In Fig. A4–15, *Q* is one of these points, and *q* its projection. Then, since the longitude of the vertex is 90° from the longitude of *Q*, the position of the vertex *v* is found merely by making the angle *QOU* a right angle.

The angle uOv_l measures the latitude of the vertex.

If the latitude of any point x is required, it can be found in the same way, that is, by drawing xy at right angles to uq and yx_l at right angles to Oy, and making yx_l equal to xy. The angle yOx_l then measures the latitude of the point X on the Earth to which x corresponds on the chart.

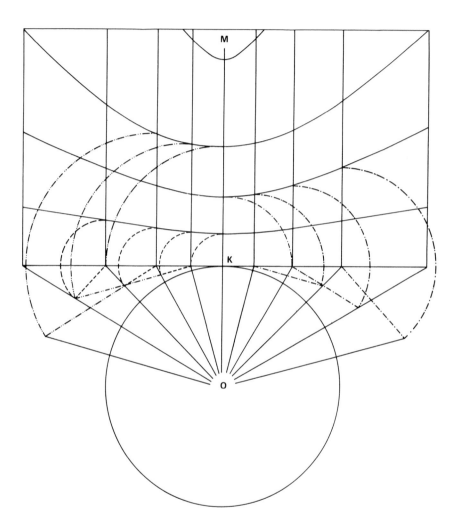

Fig. A4–14. Gnomonic projection—the equatorial graticule (3)

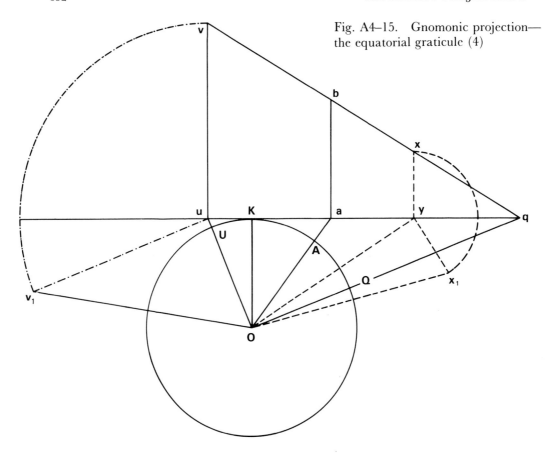

Fig. A4–15. Gnomonic projection—
the equatorial graticule (4)

THE TRANSVERSE MERCATOR PROJECTION

Conversion from geographical to grid co-ordinates and vice versa

The formulae to be used in the appropriate computer program for the
conversion of geographical position to grid co-ordinates and vice versa on the
transverse Mercator projection are set out below.

Symbols

The symbols used in these formulae, which correspond to those in use in the
Hydrographic Department, are set out below.

a = semi-major axis of spheroid (metres)

b = semi-minor axis of spheroid (metres)

e = eccentricity of spheroid

$n = \dfrac{a - b}{a + b}$

ϕ = latitude (radians)

λ = longitude (radians)

λ_O = longitude of central meridian (CM) of grid (radians)

$\Delta\lambda$ = $\lambda - \lambda_O$

t = $\tan\phi$

ρ = radius of curvature of meridian (metres)

$$= \frac{a(1 - e^2)}{(1 - e^2 \sin^2\phi)^{3/2}}$$

ν = radius of curvature at right angles to meridian (metres)

$$= \frac{a}{(1 - e^2 \sin^2\phi)^{1/2}}$$

η^2 = $\dfrac{\nu}{\rho} - 1 = \dfrac{e^2 \cos^2\phi}{(1 - e^2)}$

S_ϕ = length of meridian arc from equator to latitude ϕ (metres)

$$\theta = \frac{S_\phi}{b(1 + n)\left(1 + \dfrac{5n^2}{4} + \dfrac{81n^4}{4}\right)}$$

ϕ_I = 'footpoint' latitude

$\left.\begin{array}{l} t_I \\ \rho_I \\ \nu_I \\ \eta_I \end{array}\right\}$ variables, defined above, corresponding to ϕ_I

E = grid easting (metres)

N = grid northing (metres)

FE = 'false' easting of true origin

FN = 'false' northing of true origin

E' = 'true' easting = E − FE (points east of CM) or FE − E (points west of CM)

N' = 'true' northing = N − FN

k_O = scale factor on CM (= 0.9996 for UTM)

To find the length of the meridional arc given the latitude

This is already set out in formula **(5.19)** on page 94 and in Appendix 5 (page 643 et seq.), but is repeated here for convenience, in a slightly different form.

$$S_\phi = a(1 - e^2)\left[-\frac{35}{3072}e^6 \sin 6\phi + \left(\frac{15e^4}{256} + \frac{105e^6}{1024}\right)\sin 4\phi\right.$$
$$-\left(\frac{3e^2}{8} + \frac{15e^4}{32} + \frac{525e^6}{1024}\right)\sin 2\phi$$
$$\left.+ \left(1 + \frac{3e^2}{4} + \frac{45e^4}{64} + \frac{175e^6}{256}\right)\phi\right]$$

To find the 'footpoint' latitude, given the true grid co-ordinates

If S_O is the length of the meridian arc from the equator to the true origin, then:

$$S_{\phi_I} = S_O \pm \frac{N'}{k_O} \quad (+ \text{ in N hemisphere}, \ - \text{ in S hemisphere})$$

and ϕ_I can be found from S_{ϕ_I} using the formula:

$$\phi_I = \frac{8011}{2560} n^5 \sin 10\theta_I + \frac{1097n^4}{512} \sin 8\theta_I$$

$$+ \left(\frac{151n^3}{96} - \frac{417n^5}{128}\right) \sin 6\theta_I$$

$$+ \left(\frac{21n^2}{16} - \frac{55n^4}{32}\right) \sin 4\theta_I$$

$$+ \left(\frac{3n}{2} - \frac{27n^3}{32} + \frac{269n^5}{512}\right) \sin 2\theta_I + \theta_I \qquad \ldots \textbf{A4.14}$$

ϕ_I being the latitude of the foot of the perpendicular drawn from a point on the projection to the CM.

To convert from geographical to grid co-ordinates

$$\frac{E'}{k_O\nu} = \Delta\lambda \cos \phi + \frac{\Delta\lambda^3 \cos^3 \phi}{6} (1 - t^2 + \eta^2)$$

$$+ \frac{\Delta\lambda^5 \cos^5 \phi}{120} (5 - 18t^2 + t^4 + 14\eta^2 - 58t^2\eta^2)$$

$$+ \frac{\Delta\lambda^7 \cos^7 \phi}{5040} (61 - 479t^2 + 179t^4 - t^6) \qquad \ldots \textbf{A4.15}$$

and:

$$\frac{N'}{k_O\nu} = \frac{S_\phi}{\nu} + \frac{\Delta\lambda^2}{2} \sin \phi \cos \phi + \frac{\Delta\lambda^4}{24} \sin \phi \cos^3 \phi (5 - t^2 + 9\eta^2 + 4\eta^4)$$

$$+ \frac{\Delta\lambda^6}{720} \sin \phi \cos^5 \phi (61 - 58t^2 + t^4 + 270\eta^2 - 330t^2\eta^2)$$

$$+ \frac{\Delta\lambda^8}{40\,320} \sin \phi \cos^7 \phi (1385 - 3111t^2 + 543t^4 - t^6) \qquad \ldots \textbf{A4.16}$$

If an accuracy of $\pm$ 0.01 m is acceptable, terms containing $\Delta\lambda^6$ and higher powers of $\Delta\lambda$ may be ignored.

To convert from grid to geographical co-ordinates

$$\frac{\phi}{t_I} = \frac{\phi_I}{t_I} - \frac{(E')^2}{2k_O^2\rho_I\nu_I} + \frac{(E')^4}{24k_O^4\rho_I\nu_I^3}(5 + 3t_I^2 + \eta_I^2 - 9t_I^2\eta_I^2 - 4\eta_I^4)$$

$$- \frac{(E')^6}{720k_O^6\rho_I\nu_I^5}(61 + 90t_I^2 + 45t_I^4 + 46\eta_I^2 - 252t_I^2\eta_I^2 - 90t_I^4\eta_I^2)$$

$$+ \frac{(E')^8}{40\ 320k_O^8\rho_I\nu_I^7}(1385 + 3633t_I^2 + 4095t_I^4 + 1575t_I^6)$$

$$\ldots \mathbf{A4.17}$$

and:

$$\Delta\lambda \cos\phi_I = \frac{E'}{k_O\nu_1} - \frac{(E')^3}{6k_O^3\nu_I^3}(1 + 2t_I^2 + \eta_I^2)$$

$$+ \frac{(E')^5}{120k_O^5\nu_I^5}(5 + 28t_I^2 + 24t_I^4 + 6\eta_I^2 + 8t_I^2\eta_I^2)$$

$$- \frac{(E')^7}{5040k_O^7\nu_I^7}(61 + 662t_I^2 + 1320t_I^4 + 720t_I^6) \qquad \ldots \mathbf{A4.18}$$

If an accuracy of $\pm\ 0''.001$ is acceptable, terms containing $(E')^7$ and higher powers of E' may be ignored.

636

APPENDIX 5
The Spheroidal Earth

This appendix deals with the following:

1. The equation of the ellipse.
2. Geodetic, geocentric and parametric latitudes.
3. The length of one minute of latitude.
4. The length of the meridional arc.
5. Meridional parts for the spheroidal Earth.
6. The length of the Earth's radius in various latitudes.

THE EQUATION OF THE ELLIPSE

When a point M (Fig. A5–1) moves so that its distance from a fixed point S (the focus) is always in a constant ratio e (less than unity) to its perpendicular distance from a fixed straight line AB (the directrix), the locus of M is called an ellipse of eccentricity e.

The equation of the ellipse takes its simplest form when the co-ordinates of S are $(-ae, 0)$ and the directrix AB is the line:

$$x = -\frac{a}{e}$$

In Fig. A5–1, by defintion:

$$MS = eMC$$

$$MC = x + \frac{a}{e}$$

$$(MS)^2 = y^2 + (x + ae)^2$$

$$\therefore e^2 \left(x + \frac{a}{e}\right)^2 = (x + ae)^2 + y^2$$

i.e. $(1 - e^2)x^2 + y^2 = a^2 (1 - e^2)$

This may be written in the form:

$$\frac{x^2}{a^2} + \frac{y^2}{b^2} = 1 \qquad \qquad \text{...A5.1}$$

$$\text{where} \qquad b^2 = a^2 \left(1 - e^2\right) \qquad\qquad \dots \textbf{A5.2}$$

$$\text{i.e.} \qquad e = \left(\frac{a^2 - b^2}{a^2}\right)^{1/2} \qquad\qquad \dots \textbf{(3.2)}$$

The ellipse corresponds to a cross-section of the Earth, where a is the equatorial and b the polar radius. As b is less than a, the Earth is 'flattened' in the polar regions.

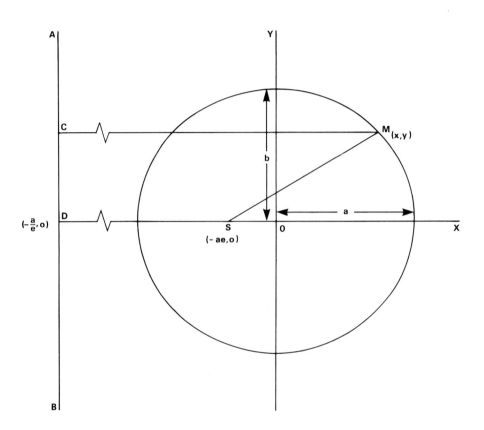

Fig. A5–1.   The ellipse

The flattening or ellipticity of the Earth may be defined by a quantity f where:

$$f = \frac{a - b}{a} \qquad\qquad \dots \textbf{(3.1)}$$

From **(3.1)** and **(3.2)**:

$$e = \left(2f - f^2\right)^{1/2} \qquad\qquad \dots \textbf{(3.3)}$$

The quantities a, e and f are used regularly in the solution of rhumb-line and great-circle sailing problems on the spheroid.

GEODETIC, GEOCENTRIC AND PARAMETRIC LATITUDES

Geodetic and geocentric latitudes

In Fig. A5–2, as explained in Chapter 3, ϕ is the geodetic and θ the geocentric latitude of M.

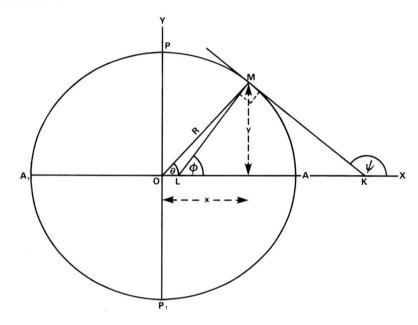

Fig. A5–2.   Geodetic and geocentric latitudes

If the distance of the point M from the polar axis OP is x, and its distance from the major axis OA is y, these distances or co-ordinates are connected by the equation of the ellipse on which M lies; that is:

$$\frac{x^2}{a^2} + \frac{y^2}{b^2} = 1$$

$$\frac{y^2}{b^2} = 1 - \frac{x^2}{a^2}$$

$$y^2 = b^2 - \frac{x^2 b^2}{a^2}$$

By differentiation: $$2y \frac{\mathrm{d}y}{\mathrm{d}x} = -2x \frac{b^2}{a^2}$$

$$\frac{\mathrm{d}y}{\mathrm{d}x} = -\frac{x}{y} \frac{b^2}{a^2}$$

If ψ is the angle which the tangent MK makes with the X-axis then, since the slope of the tangent is measured by the differential coefficient:

$$\tan \psi = \frac{dy}{dx} = -\frac{b^2}{a^2}\frac{x}{y}$$

But ψ is equal to $(\phi + 90°)$ since ML is perpendicular to MK:

hence $\quad \tan \psi = -\cot \phi$

$$\therefore \cot \phi = \frac{b^2}{a^2}\frac{x}{y} \qquad\qquad \dots \textbf{A5.3}$$

$$= \frac{b^2}{a^2} \cot \theta$$

ϕ and θ are connected by the formulae:

$$\tan \theta = \frac{b^2}{a^2} \tan \phi \qquad\qquad \dots \textbf{(3.4)}$$

$$= (1 - f)^2 \tan \phi \qquad\qquad \dots \textbf{(3.5)}$$

$$= (1 - e^2) \tan \phi \qquad\qquad \dots \textbf{(3.6)}$$

The difference between the geodetic and geocentric latitudes is zero at the equator and the poles and has a greatest value when $\phi = 45°$. For the International (1924) Spheroid where $f = 1/297$, the greatest value of the angle OML $(\phi - \theta) \simeq 11.6$ minutes of arc.

The parametric latitude

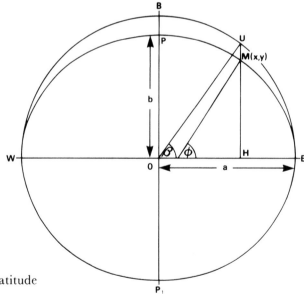

Fig. A5–3. Parametric latitude

In Fig. A5–3, as explained in Chapter 3, β is the parametric latitude of M.
If the co-ordinates of M are (x, y) and WBE is a semi-circle of radius a, centre O.

$$OH = OU \cos \beta$$

i.e. $\quad x = a \cos \beta$

From **(A5.1):**

$$\frac{y^2}{b^2} = 1 - \frac{x^2}{a^2}$$

$$= 1 - \cos^2 \beta$$

$$y^2 = b^2 (1 - \cos^2 \beta) = b^2 \sin^2 \beta$$

$$y = b \sin \beta$$

$$\therefore \frac{y}{x} = \frac{b}{a} \tan \beta$$

From Fig. A5–2:

$$\frac{y}{x} = \tan \theta$$

which, from **(3.4):**

$$= \frac{b^2}{a^2} \tan \phi$$

$$\therefore \tan \beta = \frac{b}{a} \tan \phi \qquad \ldots \textbf{A5.4}$$

$$= (1 - f) \tan \phi \qquad \ldots \textbf{A5.5}$$

The difference between the geodetic and parametric latitudes is zero at the equator and at the poles and has a greatest value when $\phi = 45°$. For the International (1924) Spheroid where $f = 1/297$, this amounts to 5.8 minutes of arc approximately.

THE LENGTH OF ONE MINUTE OF LATITUDE

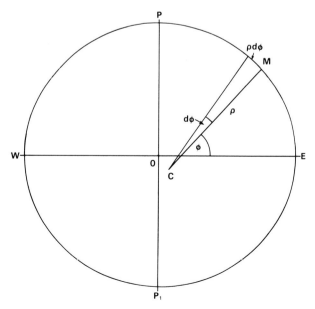

Fig. A5–4. The length of one minute of latitude (1)

The length of the sea mile (one minute of latitude on the spheroid) may be found from the general formula $\rho d\phi$ (Fig. A5–4) where ρ is the radius of curvature in the meridian and $d\phi$ a small increase (in radians) in the geodetic latitude ϕ.

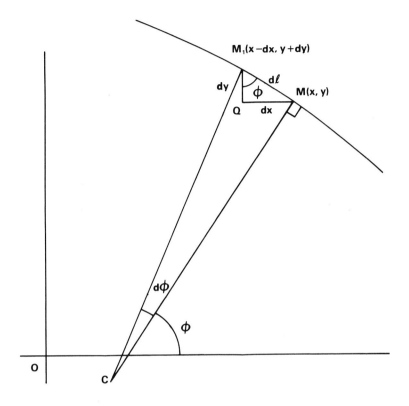

Fig. A5–5.   The length of one minute of latitude (2)

Fig. A5–5 shows an expanded version of Fig. A5–4, where $d\phi$ is a very small increase in ϕ. The co-ordinates of M are (x, y); those of M_1, representing this small increase, are $(x - dx)$, $(y + dy)$.

The triangle MQM_1 may be considered plane and, if the length of MM_1 is denoted by $d\ell$ then:

$$\frac{d\ell}{dx} = -\frac{1}{\sin \phi}$$

But, as $d\ell = \rho d\phi$

$$\frac{d\ell}{d\phi} = \rho$$

$$= \frac{dx}{d\phi} \times \frac{d\ell}{dx}$$

$$\therefore \rho = -\frac{1}{\sin \phi} \times \frac{dx}{d\phi} \qquad \qquad \ldots \textbf{A5.6}$$

$\dfrac{dx}{d\phi}$ may be found as follows:

From **(A5.3)**:

$$y = \frac{xb^2}{a^2} \tan \phi$$

which, from **(A5.2)**:

$$= x(1 - e^2) \tan \phi$$

If this value of y is substituted in the general equation of the ellipse **(A5.1)** and the value of b from **(A5.2)** also substituted, then:

$$\frac{x^2}{a^2} + \frac{x^2 (1 - e^2)^2 \tan^2 \phi}{a^2 (1 - e^2)} = 1$$

$$x^2 + (1 - e^2)x^2 \tan^2 \phi = a^2$$

$$x^2 (1 + \tan^2 \phi - e^2 \tan^2 \phi) = a^2$$

$$x^2 (\sec^2 \phi - e^2 \tan^2 \phi) = a^2$$

$$x^2 \left[\frac{1}{\cos^2 \phi} - \frac{e^2 \sin^2 \phi}{\cos^2 \phi} \right] = a^2$$

$$x = \frac{a \cos \phi}{(1 - e^2 \sin^2 \phi)^{1/2}}$$

$$= a \cos \phi \, (1 - e^2 \sin^2 \phi)^{-1/2} \qquad \dots \text{A5.7}$$

Differentiating:

$$\frac{dx}{d\phi} = \frac{-a(1 - e^2) \sin \phi}{(1 - e^2 \sin^2 \phi)^{3/2}}$$

Substituting in **(A5.6)**:

$$\rho = \frac{a(1 - e^2)}{(1 - e^2 \sin^2 \phi)^{3/2}} \qquad \dots \text{(3.8)}$$

Thus, when $d\phi$ equals $1'$ of arc:

$$1' \text{ of latitude} = \frac{a(1 - e^2)}{(1 - e^2 \sin^2 \phi)^{3/2}} \sin 1' \qquad \dots \text{(3.9)}$$

This is the theoretical expression for the sea mile. The expression may be expanded as follows:

$$1' \text{ of latitude} = a \sin 1'(1 - e^2) \left(1 + \frac{3e^2}{2} \sin^2 \phi + \frac{15e^4}{8} \sin^4 \phi + \dots \right)$$

Disregarding terms of e^4 $(10^{-5} \times 4.5)$ and higher powers:

$$1' \text{ of latitude} = a \sin 1' \left(1 + \frac{3e^2}{2} \sin^2 \phi - e^2\right)$$

$$= a \sin 1' \left[1 - e^2 + \frac{3e^2}{4}(1 - \cos 2\phi)\right]$$

$$= a \sin 1' \left(1 - \frac{e^2}{4} - \frac{3e^2}{4} \cos 2\phi\right)$$

$$= a \sin 1' \left[1 - \frac{e^2}{4}(1 + 3 \cos 2\phi)\right]$$

When figures for a and e for the International (1924) Spheroid are given:

$1'$ of latitude $= 1852.28 - 9.355 \cos 2\phi$ metres ...**A5.8**

which gives a solution for the sea mile correct to the order of 0.001%.*

THE LENGTH OF THE MERIDIONAL ARC

The distance ℓ along a meridian between two latitudes ϕ_1 and ϕ_2 may be found as follows:

$$\ell = \int_{\phi_1}^{\phi_2} \rho\, d\phi \qquad \qquad ...(5.17)$$

$$= a(1 - e^2) \int_{\phi_1}^{\phi_2} \frac{1}{(1 - e^2 \sin^2 \phi)^{3/2}}\, d\phi \qquad ...(5.18)$$

Expanding by the binomial theorem:

$$= a(1 - e^2) \int_{\phi_1}^{\phi_2} \left(1 + \frac{3e^2}{2} \sin^2 \phi + \frac{15e^4}{8} \sin^4 \phi + \frac{35e^6}{16} \sin^6 \phi + \dots\right) d\phi$$

Each term in the integral may now be integrated separately where:

$$\int \sin^2 \phi\, d\phi = \int \left(\tfrac{1}{2} - \tfrac{1}{2} \cos 2\phi\right) d\phi$$

$$= \frac{\phi}{2} - \frac{\sin 2\phi}{4} + c$$

$$\int \sin^4 \phi\, d\phi = \int \left(\frac{3}{8} - \frac{\cos 2\phi}{2} + \frac{\cos 4\phi}{8}\right) d\phi$$

$$= \frac{3\phi}{8} - \frac{\sin 2\phi}{4} + \frac{\sin 4\phi}{32} + c$$

$$\int \sin^6 \phi\, d\phi = \int \left(\frac{10}{32} - \frac{15 \cos 2\phi}{32} + \frac{3 \cos 4\phi}{16} - \frac{\cos 6\phi}{32}\right) d\phi$$

$$= \frac{10\phi}{32} - \frac{15 \sin 2\phi}{64} + \frac{3 \sin 4\phi}{64} - \frac{\sin 6\phi}{192} + c$$

(etc.)

---

* By comparison with NP 240, *Spheroidal Tables*, formula **(A5.8)** gives a solution which is correct at the equator, 0.001% in error at latitude 45° and 0.002% in error at latitude 90°.

$$\ell = a(1 - e^2) \left[\phi + \frac{3e^2}{2} \left(\frac{\phi}{2} - \frac{\sin 2\phi}{4} \right) \right.$$

$$+ \frac{15e^4}{8} \left(\frac{3\phi}{8} - \frac{\sin 2\phi}{4} + \frac{\sin 4\phi}{32} \right)$$

$$\left. + \frac{35e^6}{16} \left(\frac{10\phi}{32} - \frac{15\sin 2\phi}{64} + \frac{3\sin 4\phi}{64} - \frac{\sin 6\phi}{192} \right) + \ldots \right]_{\phi_1}^{\phi_2}$$

This may be expanded in the form:

$$\ell = a \left[A_0\phi - A_2 \sin 2\phi + A_4 \sin 4\phi - A_6 \sin 6\phi + \ldots \right]_{\phi_1}^{\phi_2}$$

$$\ldots \textbf{(5.19)}$$

$$\ell = a \left[A_0 (\phi_2 - \phi_1) - A_2 (\sin 2\phi_2 - \sin 2\phi_1) \right.$$

$$\left. + A_4 (\sin 4\phi_2 - \sin 4\phi_1) - A_6 (\sin 6\phi_2 - \sin 6\phi_1) + \ldots \right]$$

$$\ldots \textbf{A5.9}$$

where ϕ is measured in radians and

$$A_0 = 1 - \frac{1}{4} e^2 - \frac{3}{64} e^4 - \frac{5}{256} e^6 - \ldots$$

$$A_2 = \frac{3}{8} \left(e^2 + \frac{1}{4} e^4 + \frac{15}{128} e^6 + \ldots \right)$$

$$A_4 = \frac{15}{256} \left(e^4 + \frac{3}{4} e^6 + \ldots \right)$$

$$A_6 = \frac{35}{3072} e^6 + \ldots$$

A computer is ideal for this calculation, and may be programmed to carry out the computation to as many terms as the user wishes.

Such a calculation may be determined reasonably quickly, and to a high degree of accuracy, using a pocket calculator and disregarding terms of e^6 ($10^{-7} \times 3.1$) and higher powers. In this case, the meridional arc distance ℓ from the equator to latitude ϕ may be found from the formula:

$$\ell = a \left[\phi - \frac{e^2\phi}{4} - \frac{3e^2}{8} \sin 2\phi - \frac{3e^4}{64}\phi - \frac{3e^4}{32} \sin 2\phi + \frac{15e^4}{256} \sin 4\phi \right]$$

$$\ldots \textbf{(5.24)}$$

Tables may be constructed from the general formula **(5.19)** as the user desires by means of a desk-top computer, giving the length of the meridional arc for any latitude at, say, minute of arc intervals. This may be computed for any spheroid and may be expressed in metres, n miles, etc. depending on the unit used for a. The length of the meridional arc between the two different latitudes can then be measured and the course and distance computed between two positions using formulae **(5.22)** and **(5.23)** (*see* the example on page 95). Conversely, if the course, distance and initial positions are known, the final latitude may be computed from the length of the meridional arc and the final longitude from the difference of meridional parts.

EXAMPLE

A ship in position 2°N, 25°W, steers a course of 060° for 600 miles. What are her latitude and longitude at the end of the run?

If no allowance is made for the spheroidal shape of the Earth, the latitude and longitude of the final position may be found from formulae **(2.3)** and **(5.3)** respectively:

$$\text{d. lat} = \text{distance cos course} = 600' \cos 60° = 5°N$$

$$\text{d. long} = \text{DMP tan course (DMP for the sphere)}$$

which, from formula **(4.1)**:

$$= 301.03 \tan 60° = 521'.4E = 8° \, 41'.4E$$

$$\text{final position} = 7°N, \, 16° \, 18'.6W$$

On the International (1924) Spheroid, from **(5.23)**:

$$\ell = \text{distance cos course} = 300 \text{ n miles}$$

$$\ell_1 \text{ for } 2°N = 119.412 \text{ n miles}$$

$$\therefore \ell_2 = 419.412 \text{ n miles}$$

which, from a table constructed for the spheroid, may be seen to be the equivalent of:

$$7° \, 01'.46N \text{ latitude}$$

$$= 7° \, 01'.5N$$

$$\text{d. long} = \text{DMP tan course}$$

which, from NP 239:

$$= 300.515 \tan 60° = 520'.5E = 8° \, 40'.5E$$

$$\text{final position} = 7° \, 01'.5N, \, 16° \, 19'.5W$$

If a computer-produced table for the length of the meridional arc against latitude is not available, an approximate final latitude may be obtained from **(A5.8)**, where:

$$l = \text{d. lat} \left(\frac{1852.28 - 9.355 \cos 2 \, (\text{mean lat})}{1852} \right) \dots \textbf{A5.10}$$

In the above example, using a mean latitude of $4\frac{1}{2}°N$:

$$\text{d. lat} = 5° \, 01'.5N$$

$$\text{final latitude} = 7° \, 01'.5N$$

This final latitude can now be tested against **(5.24)** and adjusted as necessary. The longitude may now be determined using DMP for the spheroid.

The difference beween the two latitudes (1'.5 in this case) illustrates the error which can arise from the assumption that a distance in n miles can be said to equate to a d. lat measured in minutes of arc or sea miles. For the practical navigator, little account need be taken of this difference between the n mile and the sea mile except when precise distances, particularly near the equator or the poles, are required, as the maximum error in this assumption is of the order of 0.5%.

MERIDIONAL PARTS FOR THE SPHEROIDAL EARTH

Certain books of tables (e.g. NP 239, *Table of Meridional Parts based on the International (1924) Spheroid*, or *Norie's Tables* (Clarke 1880 spheroid) make an allowance for the oblate spheroidal shape of the Earth.

The table of meridional parts which cartographers use to compute the graticules for Mercator charts is the table of *spheroidal* meridional parts; its use is thus consistent with the use of the chart. Astronomical observations at sea are made with reference to a horizon which is part of the spheroidal surface of the Earth; thus, tables of spheroidal meridional parts are consistent with the co-ordinates of positions found from astronomical observations.

In Fig. A5–6, the elliptic meridional section of the Earth may be expressed by the equation:

$$\frac{x^2}{a^2} + \frac{y^2}{b^2} = 1$$

where $x = a \cos \beta$

$y = b \sin \beta$

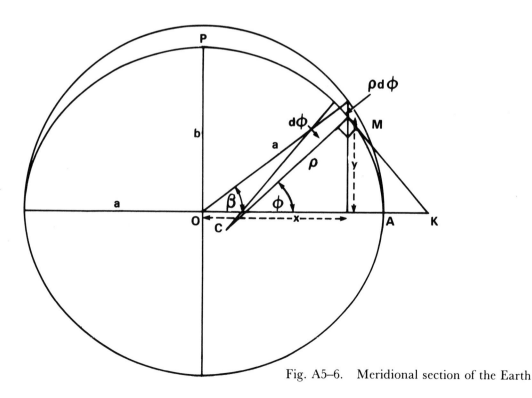

Fig. A5–6.   Meridional section of the Earth

At a point M which has co-ordinates (x, y) with reference to O, the centre of the ellipse, let the geographical latitude be ϕ. If the radius of curvature at M is ρ, the length of an element of the meridian is $\rho d\phi$.

In order to measure the meridional parts of ϕ, the element $\rho d\phi$ must be expressed in terms of the length of 1 minute of longitude at latitude ϕ. Now the longitude scale for this latitude is x/a times the longitude scale at the equator, and the unit of longitude at the equator is the length of that equatorial element which subtends an angle of 1 minute of arc at the centre of the Earth. The length of this element is a divided by the number of minutes in 1 radian, that is:

$$\frac{a\pi}{10800}$$

The length of a minute of longitude at latitude ϕ is thus:

$$\frac{x}{a} \times \frac{a\pi}{10800} \qquad \text{or} \qquad \frac{x\pi}{10800}$$

and the number of longitude units in the meridional element $\rho d\phi$ is:

$$\rho d\phi \div \frac{x\pi}{10800} \qquad \text{or} \qquad \frac{10800}{\pi} \times \frac{\rho}{x} \ d\phi$$

The meridional parts at latitude L are given by the equation:

$$\text{mer. parts } L = \frac{10800}{\pi} \int_O^L \frac{\rho}{x} \ d\phi$$

which, from **(3.8)** and **(A5.7)**:

$$= \frac{10800}{\pi} \int_O^L \frac{a\ (1-e^2)}{(1-e^2 \sin^2 \phi)^{3/2}} \times \frac{1}{a \cos \phi \ (1-e^2 \sin^2\phi)^{-1/2}} \ d\phi$$

$$= \frac{10800}{\pi} \int_O^L \sec \phi \ \left(\frac{1-e^2}{1-e^2 \sin^2 \phi}\right) d\phi \qquad \ldots \text{A5.11}$$

$$= \frac{10800}{\pi} \int_O^L \sec \phi [1 - e^2 \cos^2 \phi \ (1 + e^2 \sin^2 \phi + e^4 \sin^4 \phi$$

$$+ \ e^6 \sin^6 \phi + \ldots)] d\phi$$

$$= \frac{10800}{\pi} \int_O^L (\sec \phi - e^2 \cos \phi - e^4 \sin^2 \phi \cos \phi$$

$$- \ e^6 \sin^4 \phi \cos \phi - \ldots) d\phi$$

$$= \frac{10800}{\pi} \left[\log_e \tan \left(45° + \frac{L°}{2}\right) - e^2 \sin L - \frac{1}{3} e^4 \sin^3 L \right.$$

$$\left. - \frac{1}{5} e^6 \sin^5 L - \ldots \right] \qquad \ldots \textbf{(5.21)}$$

For the International (1924) Spheroid, a suitable numerical formula giving the meridional parts correct to three decimal places is:

$$\text{mer. parts} = 7915.7045 \, \log_{10} \tan \left(45° + \frac{L°}{2}\right)$$
$$- 23.1108 \sin L - 0.052 \sin^3 L \qquad \qquad \text{...A5.12}$$

THE LENGTH OF THE EARTH'S RADIUS IN VARIOUS LATITUDES

In Fig. A5–2 the required geocentric radius is OM and, if this length is denoted by R, it follows that x is $R \cos \theta$ and y is $R \sin \theta$. Hence, by substituting for x and y in the equation of the ellipse:

$$\frac{R^2 \cos^2 \theta}{a^2} + \frac{R^2 \sin^2 \theta}{b^2} = 1$$

but as $b^2 = a^2 (1 - f)^2$

$$R^2[(1 - f)^2 \cos^2 \theta + \sin^2 \theta] = a^2 (1 - f)^2$$

When terms in f^2 ($10^{-5} \times 1.1$) are neglected, this equation becomes:

$$R^2 (1 - 2f \cos^2 \theta) = a^2 (1 - 2f)$$

$$R = a \left(\frac{1 - 2f}{1 - 2f \cos^2 \theta}\right)^{1/2}$$

When the right-hand side is expanded by the binomial theorem, terms in f^2 and higher powers again being omitted, the equation becomes:

$$R = a(1 - f) (1 + f \cos^2 \theta)$$
$$= a(1 - f \sin^2 \theta)$$

Since θ varies from ϕ by a small quantity, R may be expressed in terms of the geodetic latitude (page 638) without appreciable error by direct substitution:

i.e. $R = a(1 - f \sin^2 \phi)$ \qquad \qquad \text{...A5.13}

APPENDIX 6
Vertical and Horizontal Sextant Angles

VERTICAL SEXTANT ANGLES

Base of the object below the observer's horizon

A position line may be obtained from the observation of the vertical sextant angle (VSA) such as a distant mountain peak where the base is below the observer's horizon.

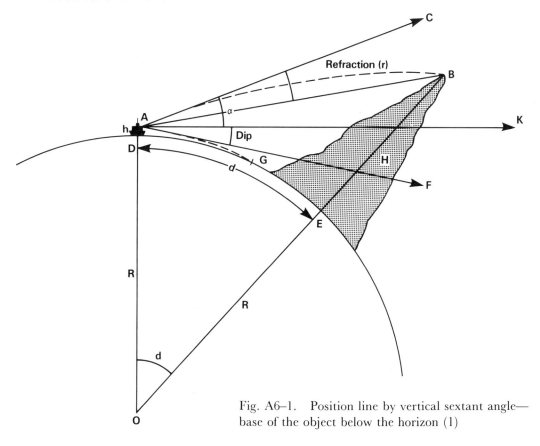

Fig. A6–1. Position line by vertical sextant angle—base of the object below the horizon (1)

This situation is illustrated in Fig. A6–1. O is the centre of the Earth, which has radius R. AD is the height of eye h. B is the summit of a mountain whose height BE is H above sea level. DE is the required distance d, while the angle measured between the mountain top and the observer's horizon is represented by the angle CAF. This takes account of the terrestrial refraction r, which 'bends' the ray of light as it proceeds through the atmosphere between object and observer. Thus, the top of the mountain B is seen in the direction AC, while the horizon G is seen in the direction AF. These two lines AC and AF are tangential to their respective curved rays of light (pecked in Fig. A6–1).

AK is the horizontal at the observer's position and the angle KAF is known as the angle of *dip*, which may be defined as the angle between the horizontal plane through the eye of the observer and the apparent direction of the visible horizon. It is always present when the observer's eye is above sea level.

Dip is tabulated in the *Nautical Almanac* and in *Norie's Tables*. Terrestrial refraction amounts to approximately 1/13 of the distance in n miles of the object, expressed in minutes of arc. Dip and refraction are explained fully in Volume II of this manual; both must be subtracted from the observed altitude of the summit to obtain the true altitude.

Provided that an estimated distance of the object is available, a position line may be obtained.

The apparent altitude of B as measured from the sea horizon, when reduced by dip, is the angle CAK, α. The true altitude of B, the angle BAK, is $(\alpha - r)$, where r is the amount of refraction CAB.

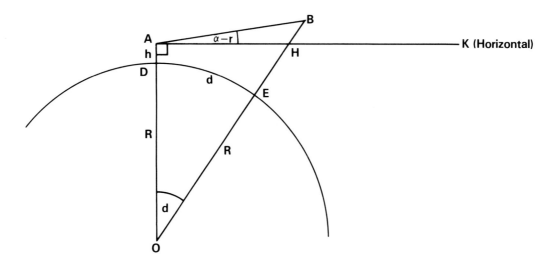

Fig. A6–2.   VSA. Base of the object below the horizon (2)

In the triangle OAB (Fig. A6–2):

$$OA = R^* + h$$
$$OB = R + H$$

* R may be found from the formula $R = a(1 - f \sin^2 \phi)$ (*see* formula **A5.13**) where a is the equatorial radius, f is the compression (flattening) of the spheroid and ϕ is the mean latitude between observer and object.

$$OAB = 90° + \alpha - r$$

$$OBA = 180° - (d + 90° + \alpha - r)$$

$$= 90° - d - \alpha + r$$

$$\frac{\sin OBA}{\sin OAB} = \frac{R + h}{R + H}$$

$$\frac{\sin 90° - (d + \alpha - r)}{\sin 90° + (\alpha - r)} = \frac{R + h}{R + H}$$

$$\frac{\cos (d + \alpha - r)}{\cos (\alpha - r)} = \frac{R + h}{R + H}$$

$$\cos (d + \alpha - r) = \frac{R + h}{R + H} \cos (\alpha - r) \qquad \ldots \textbf{A6.1}$$

The distance d may easily be found from evaluating formula **(A6.1)** on a hand-held calculator, as shown by the following example.

EXAMPLE

A mountain 1646 m (5400 ft) high is observed at a range of about 25 miles. Mean latitude between observer and object is 41° 27′. Height of eye is 7.6 m (25 ft). The vertical sextant angle of the summit is 1° 59′.3. Index error of the sextant is −1′.3. What is the range of the mountain?

observed angle	1°59′.3
index error	−1′.3
	1°58′.0
dip	−4′.9
apparent altitude (α)	1°53′.1
refraction correction (r) (25/13 = 1′.9)	−1′.9
true altitude ($\alpha - r$)	1°51′.2 (1°.8533)

$$R = 3438.9726 \text{ n miles}$$
$$H = 0.8889 \text{ n miles}$$
$$h = 0.0041 \text{ n miles}$$

$$\cos (d + 1°.8533) = \frac{3438.9767}{3439.8615} \cos 1°.8533$$

$$d = 2°.2634 - 1°.8533$$
$$= 0°.4101$$
$$= 24.6 \text{ n miles*}$$

If the estimated distance if found to be much in error, a second approximation will be necessary.

---

* This distance may be taken for all practical purposes as sea miles. The maximum error in so doing varies between zero at about latitude 45° and 0.5% at the equator and the poles.

Long-range position lines obtained in this way are of little value if different from normal refraction (*see* Volume II of this manual) is suspected. Abnormal refraction is likely to be present when the temperature of the water and that of air differ considerably.

This method of obtaining a position line has a limited application and while useful in giving a reasonably satisfactory long-range position line on a single isolated peak, e.g. Tenerife in the Canaries, it should not be used with a mountain peak which forms part of a mountain chain unless it has been positively identified.

HORIZONTAL SEXTANT ANGLES

Rapid plotting without instruments

To enable fixes obtained by horizontal sextant angles to be plotted rapidly without instruments, a lattice of HSA curves may be constructed on a chart. Each curve gives the constant angle between a pair of suitably placed fixing marks, and is in fact an arc of a circle. If a set of curves is plotted for each of two pairs of marks, then, having observed the angle between each pair simultaneously, the navigator can plot the resultant fix immediately at the intersection of the two curves corresponding to the two angles. A sufficient number of curves must be drawn to enable the observed angles to be plotted conveniently by interpolation between the lattice lines.

Preparing a lattice for plotting HSA fixes

This is illustrated in Fig. A6–3.

Consider the pattern of arcs which may be generated from one pair of objects *A* and *B*. Three arcs are shown: *AEB*, *ADB*, *ACB*. Their centres *O*, *P*, *Q* respectively, all lie along the perpendicular bisector *FQ*, of the base line *AB*. Consider one arc *AEB*. Let *OQ*, the distance of the centre of the arc from the base line, be *x*. Then:

$$x = \tfrac{1}{2}d \cot \theta \qquad \qquad \text{. . . A6.2}$$

where *d* is the length of the base line and θ is the angle subtended by the chord *AB* on the circumference of the circle through *AEB*.

This formula may now be used to construct the lattice for all required angles.

Fixing objects within the boundaries of the chart

Chart D6472, Diagram for Facilitating the Construction of Curves of Equal Subtended Angles, issued by the Hydrographer with the miscellaneous charts and diagrams folio 317 (*see* page 126) enables the Navigating Officer to plot his own lattice of curves on any chart or plotting sheet, provided that all the fixing objects lie within the boundaries of the chart. Full instructions as to how to use Chart D6472 are printed on it.

Fixing objects outside the boundaries of the chart

If the fixing objects do not lie within the area of the chart, the following procedure will enable the Navigating Officer to plot his own lattice.

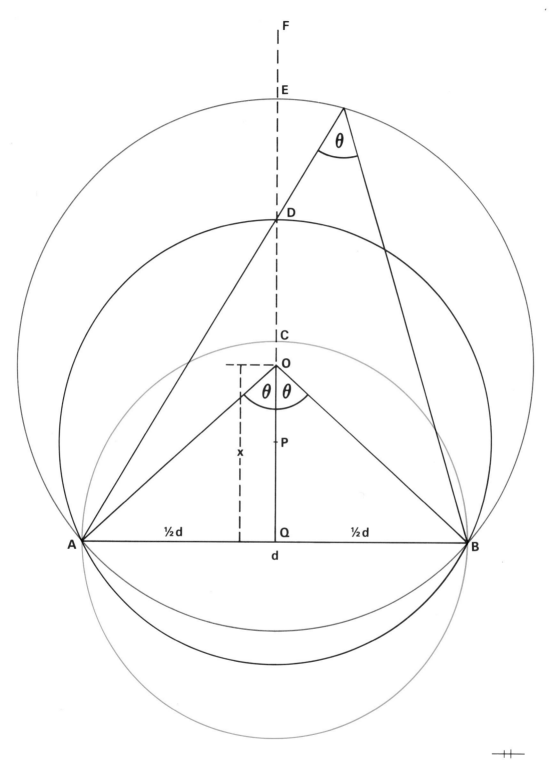

Fig. A6–3. Pattern of arcs generated from one pair of objects

1. Lay out on an appropriate space, such as the floor or deck, the chart or plotting sheet on which the lattice is required. Represent the HSA marks with pins placed in their correct relative positions.

2. From the largest scale navigational chart which shows the fixing marks, measure, as accurately as possible, the distance between them. Convert these distances to the desired scale of the lattice to obtain the distances between the pins on the floor. The simplest method for this scaling up is to find a multiplication factor, e.g. if the navigational chart has a natural scale of 1:50,000 and the lattice is to have a scale of 1:10,000, then all chart lengths taken off the former must be multiplied by $\dfrac{50,000}{10,000} = 5$.

   In this case, if two objects, A and B, are found to be 150 mm apart of the navigational chart, the pins should be placed $(150 \times 5) = 750$ mm apart on the floor.

3. Measure the angle between the base lines (α in Fig. A6–4) and lay this off on the floor. Measure the appropriate floor lengths and mark the position of the

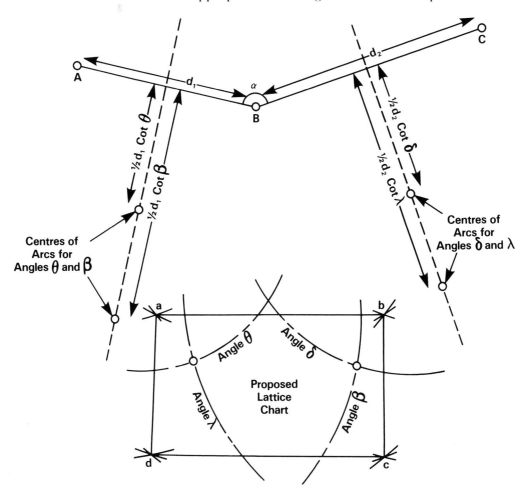

Fig. A6–4.   Construction of the HSA lattice

third object *C*. If the grid co-ordinates of the fixing marks are known, the accuracy of all these measurements should be checked by calculation.

4. Next, the exact position on the floor for the lattice chart must be found. On the largest scale navigational chart which shows both the lattice area and the fixing marks, draw in the limits of the lattice chart. Measure the distances from each of the fixing marks to all four corners of the lattice (*Aa, Ab, Ad, Ac, Ba, Bb*, etc.). Scale up these distances by the multiplication factor found as described above, and then, by striking off arcs on the floor, fix the positions of the corners of the lattice. Pin down the outline lattice chart in this position.

5. On the floor draw the base lines and their perpendicular bisectors.

   Note: Where the floor surface is unsuitable for drawing, tightly stretched thread can be used.

6. On the perpendicular bisectors of the base lines mark the centres of the arcs to be drawn ($\frac{1}{2}d \cot \theta$ from the base line).

   Strike off two arcs from each pair of objects giving an intersection at each end of the lattice area. As a check, compare for accuracy the geographical positions of the intersections thus obtained with fixes plotted by station pointer using the same angles on a navigational chart which shows the objects and lattice area. This will reveal any inaccuracy in the construction of the lattice.

7. Finally, complete the lattice, using red ink for the curves generated from the left-hand angles as viewed from seaward, and green for the right-hand angles. On large-scale lattices an alteration of firm and pecked lines in each pattern

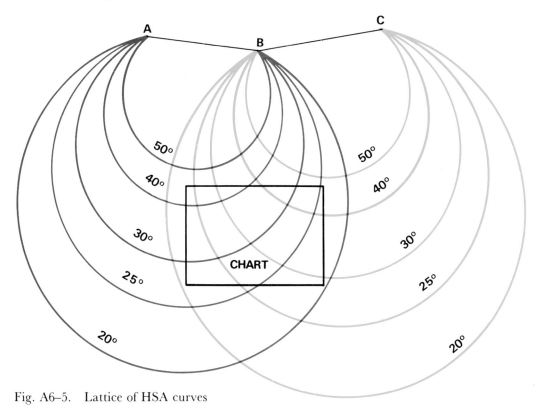

Fig. A6–5. Lattice of HSA curves

may improve the clarity of the lattice. If the curves do not cut at a satisfactory angle or are too widely spaced in any part of the chart, other objects can be taken and the curves generated from them drawn in the appropriate area, colours other than red or green being used. The general form of the completed lattice is shown in Fig. A6–5.

APPENDIX 7
Errors in Terrestrial Position Lines

Chapter 16 and the annex to that chapter discuss how navigational errors (faults, systematic and semi-systematic errors and random errors) may be recognised and dealt with. This appendix sets out to quantify particular errors in terms of distance, given certain parameters: for example, the displacement in a fix given the angle of cut between the position lines, the distance apart of the objects, and an assumed constant (or maximum) value in the error in the bearing of each position line. Errors in terrestrial bearings and in horizontal sextant angles are quantified in terms of the distance between the true and the obtained positions. The appendix concludes with a discussion on how the position is obtained when doubling the angle on the bow in a current or tidal stream.

SEXTANT ERRORS

Whenever a sextant is used, whether for measuring an altitude or a horizontal angle, there is a possibility of an error which may be significant. Index error is easily found, reduced if necessary, and allowed for, but the failure to eliminate *perpendicular error*, *side error* and *collimation error* may easily give rise to an unknown error when an observation is made.

In addition to this error, there is the limitation of the sextant itself, depending on the accuracy aimed at in the observation. The ordinary sextant reads to the nearest $0'.2$.

Personal error

Personal error, as the name suggests, is peculiar to the observer himself, and affects all his observations. Unless it is abnormal it is of no practical importance when bearings are measured, but it may be when altitudes are measured because the precision required is then considerable.

ERRORS IN TAKING AND LAYING OFF BEARINGS

In practical chart work involving observations of terrestrial objects, there is the possibility that the lines of bearing are plotted inaccurately or to a degree of accuracy less than that with which the observations were made.

Bearings taken with a magnetic compass are particularly liable to error because the deviation is not constant and, although it may be practically eliminated when the compass is corrected, it may not be negligible or even accurately known several days later. The effect of sub-permanent magnetism, the heating of funnels, and change in latitude all combine to vary the deviation.

The diameter of the card in the standard magnetic compass is 16.5 cm, and a degree is represented by two lines on the circumference approximately 1.5 mm apart. It is not easy, therefore, to take a bearing with certainty, and if the ship is unsteady the difficulty is further increased.

In the gyro-compass there is the possibility of an unknown residual error in the compass itself.

When these sources of error are borne in mind, it is seen that the resulting error in the line of bearing drawn on the chart may easily reach $\frac{1}{2}°$, and this may lead to an appreciable displacement of the fix.

Displacement of fix when the same error occurs in two lines of bearing

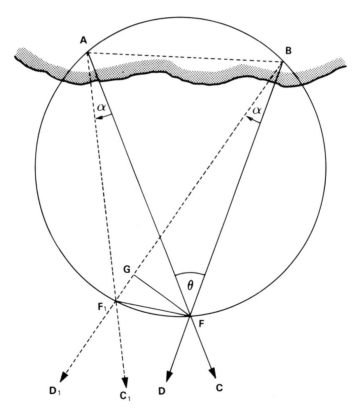

Fig. A7–1.   Errors in two lines of bearing

The fix by two lines of bearing from terrestrial objects is one of the simplest methods of finding a ship's position. In Fig. A7–1, A and B are these objects and AC and BD the two accurate lines of bearing intersecting F, the ship's true position.

If the errors in the position lines drawn on the chart are the same in magnitude and sign—that is, the angle CAC_1 is equal to the angle DBD_1—these position lines may be represented by AC_1 and BD_1, and F_1, their point of intersection, is the fix obtained. The displacement is FF_1.

Let the error in the bearing be denoted by α and the true angle of cut AFB by θ. Then the angle of cut actually obtained is also θ since these angles are in the same segment of which FF_1 is the base.

Hence, if errors in the two position lines are the same in magnitude and sign, F_1 will lie on a circle passing through A, B and F.

To find FF_1, draw FG perpendicular to BF_1. Then:

$$BF \sin GBF = FF_1 \sin BF_1F$$

$$\text{i.e.} \quad FF_1 = \frac{BF \sin GBF}{\sin BF_1F}$$

But the angles BF_1F and BAF are equal, and from the rule of sines:

$$\frac{BF}{\sin BAF} = \frac{AB}{\sin AFB}$$

$$\text{therefore} \quad FF_1 = \frac{AB \sin GBF}{\sin AFB}$$

$$= \frac{AB \sin \alpha}{\sin \theta}$$

If α, which is a small angle, is now expressed in radians, the displacement is given in the form:

$$FF_1 = \frac{\alpha AB}{\sin \theta} \qquad \ldots \textbf{A7.1}$$

Formula **(A7.1)** shows that the error in the fix resulting from a constant error in the observation is least when θ is 90°, and increases as θ decreases, this increase becoming rapid after θ has reached about 30°. When θ is 30°, the error is αAB cosec 30°, or twice the error when the angle of cut is 90°.

EXAMPLE

It is required to find the errors in the fix obtained when the true bearings of two points, A and B, 14 miles apart, are (1) 060° and 030°, (2) 010° and 100°, and the errors in the observed bearings are each 1°.

1. The angle of cut, being the difference of the true bearings, is 30°, and the error in each bearing is $\frac{2\pi}{360}$ radians.

Hence the displacement of the fix is given by:

$$FF_1 = 14' \times \frac{2\pi}{360} \times \text{cosec } 30°$$

$$= 0'.5 \text{ (approximately)}$$

2. The angle of cut is 90°, and the displacement is given by:

$$FF_1 = 14' \times \frac{2\pi}{360} \times \operatorname{cosec} 90°$$

$$= 0'.25 \text{ (approximately)}$$

The cocked hat

When the lines of bearing from three objects, observed simultaneously, are drawn on the chart, it is usually found that they do not meet in a point but form a *cocked hat* as explained in Chapter 9.

The cocked hat results from:

1. The unknown and therefore uncorrected error of the compass which may be as much as 1°.
2. The error in observation resulting from the limitations of the compass, which may be $\frac{1}{4}°$.
3. The error in the actual plotting of the lines of bearing, which may also be $\frac{1}{4}°$.

Of these errors (2) and (3) are fortuitous and may have either sign. That is, the plotted results could be up to $\frac{1}{2}°$ high or $\frac{1}{2}°$ low on what the bearings should be. The remaining error (1), however, has a definite sign and, although it may be high or low, it is the same in each plotted bearing. It is thus convenient to investigate this error first.

The cocked hat arising from the same error in three lines of bearing

In Fig. A7–2, F is the true position, and A, B and C are three objects, the true bearings of which are observed. Suppose these bearings are 221°, 276° and 313°.

If the bearings are taken and laid off correctly, the three position lines intersect in F, but if there is an unknown compass error of 1° low, say—it is shown in the figure as 10° for the sake of clarity—the bearings plotted on the chart are AZ (220°), BX (275°) and CY (312°), and they form the cocked hat XYZ.

Since the difference between the bearings of A and B will be the same whether the compass error is applied or not, the angle AZB must be equal to the angle AFB, and Z, the point of intersection of the two bearings AZ and BZ, must lie on the circle through A, B and F. Similarly X, the point of intersection of the two bearings BX and CX, must lie on the circle through B, C and F; and Y, the point of intersection of the two bearings AY and CY, must lie on the circle through A, C and F.

The true position F, can be seen to lie *outside* the triangle XYZ.

The distances of F from the vertices of the triangle are given by formula **(A7.1)** on page 659. Thus, if α is the constant error of the bearings in radians and θ_1, θ_2 and θ_3 are the angles between the bearings of A and B, B and C, and C and A:

$$FZ = \frac{\alpha AB}{\sin \theta_1} \qquad \qquad \text{... A7.2}$$

$$FX = \frac{\alpha BC}{\sin \theta_2} \qquad \dots \textbf{A7.3}$$

$$FY = \frac{\alpha CA}{\sin \theta_3} \qquad \dots \textbf{A7.4}$$

The distances AB, BC and CA can be taken from the chart. If, for example, they are respectively 2′, 5′, and 7′ and the values of θ_1, θ_2 and θ_3 are 30°, 90° and

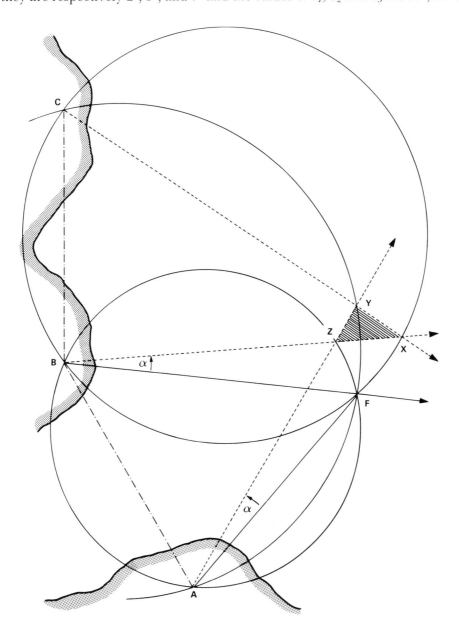

Fig. A7–2. Errors in three lines of bearing (1)

120°, while the constant error is 1°, the separate displacements of F are given by the above formulae as:

$$FZ = 0.7 \text{ cables}$$
$$FX = 0.9 \text{ cables}$$
$$FY = 1.4 \text{ cables}$$

When the cocked hat results from an inaccuracy in the assumed value of the compass error (i.e. a constant error), the amount and sign of the error may be obtained approximately from Fig. A7–2. In this figure Z is the intersection of the position lines through A and B, and F lies on the circle through A, B and Z. For similar reasons, F lies on the circles through B, C and X, and C, A and Y. F is therefore the point of intersection of the three circles.

In this case, the position of F, obtained by this construction, is the true position of the ship.

It must be borne in mind that the three circles drawn in Fig. A7–2, irrespective of the number of errors involved and of the differences in magnitude and sign that may exist between them, will always intersect in one point. This point, however, will only be the true position of the ship when the amount and sign of the error are the same on each bearing, i.e. a compass error as previously explained.

EXAMPLE

It is required to find the compass error when the bearings of three objects, carefully taken by gyro-compass, are such that the difference between the bearings of A and B is 45°. AB is 6′ and FZ, as measured on the chart, is 0′.4.

From formula **(A7.2)**:

$$FZ = \frac{\alpha AB}{\sin \theta_1}$$

$$\alpha = \frac{0.4 \sin \frac{1}{4}\pi}{6} \text{ radians}$$

$$= 2°.7$$

The sign of α can be obtained from the chart.

The cocked hat in general

When errors of observation and plotting are included with the compass error, the resulting errors in the position lines may all differ, and a cocked hat is formed as shown in Fig. A7–3.

The constant error α is now replaced by separate and unequal errors α_1, α_2 and α_3. In this example α_1 and α_2 have the same sign, which is opposite to that of α_3.

As before, F is the true position of the ship, and AZ, BX and CY are the lines of bearing actually plotted and forming the cocked hat XYZ.

Unless the errors α_1, α_2 and α_3 are definitely known, it is impossible to locate the position of F from this cocked hat.

The value and sign of α_3 may cause the plotted line of bearing CY to pass through Z. Z is then the fix by observation, but it is still a distance FZ in error. It is thus clear that, even when all three lines of bearing intersect in a single point, the resultant fix may be considerably in error. The best estimate of the true position F can be arrived at using the least squares solution (*see* page 492).

In the practice of navigation, when a cocked hat is obtained, it is customars to place the ship's position on the chart in the most dangerous position that can be derived from the observations because the existence of the cocked hat is evidence that the observations are inaccurate and, by interpreting them to his apparent disadvantage, the navigator gives himself a margin of safety which he might not otherwise have.

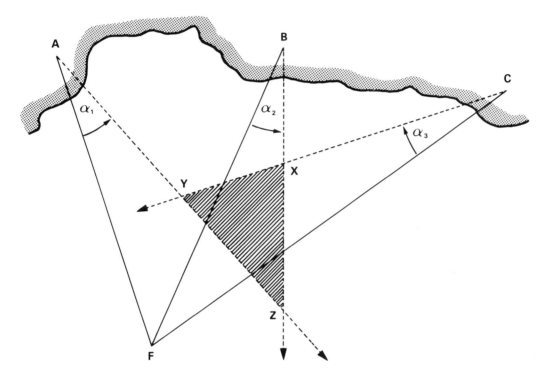

Fig. A7–3.   Errors in three lines of bearing (2)

ERRORS IN HSA FIXES

When the horizontal angle subtended by two objects at an observer is measured, it tells him that his position lies on the arc of a circle passing through the points. If the angle subtended by one of these objects and a third object is now measured, a second position circle is obtained, intersecting the first position circle at the common object. The other point of intersection is the observer's position. These position circles can be plotted directly, or the angles can be set on a station pointer. But, whatever method is used for finding the observer's position, there will be a possibility of error in the position found owing to:

1. Error in the measurement of the angles.
2. Plotting error, or the instrumental error inherent in the station pointer.
3. Error arising from the fact that, in general, the three objects and the observer will not lie in a horizontal plane.

In Fig. A7–4, AFB and BFC are the accurate position circles and AF_1B and BF_1C are those obtained by observation and plotting. F is the true position of the observer, and F_1 is that obtained.

X is the point in which the circles BFC and AF_1B intersect, and BX produced cuts the circle AFB in Y.

It is assumed that each horizontal angle has the same error α. That is, the plotted angle AF_1B is equal to the true angle AFB plus the error α. The error α is equal to the angle XAY. Similarly, the plotted angle BF_1C is equal to $(BFC + \alpha)$.

r_1 is the ratio of the observer's distance from the first object A to the distance of A from B, the middle object, i.e.

$$r_1 = \frac{AF}{AB}$$

similarly $$r_2 = \frac{CF}{CB}$$

θ is the acute angle of cut between the two circles AFB and BFC; that is to say, θ is the acute angle between the tangents to the two circles at the point of intersection F.

The distance between the true position F and the plotted position F_1 (i.e. the error in position F_1) may be found from the formula:

$$FF_1 = \frac{\alpha FB}{\sin \theta} \sqrt{r_1^2 + r_2^2 + 2r_1r_2 \cos \theta} \qquad \ldots \mathbf{A7.5}$$

where α is measured in radians.

Maximum errors in the HSA fix

Formula ($\mathbf{A7.5}$) shows that FF_1 varies directly as α and the distance of the fix from the object common to both observations, and inversely as $\sin \theta$; FF_1 also depends on the values of the ratios r_1 and r_2.

When θ is small, $\operatorname{cosec} \theta$ and $\cos \theta$ are both large, and FF_1 is large.

When θ is equal to $90°$, $\operatorname{cosec} \theta$ is unity, and $\cos \theta$ is zero, and FF_1 is given by:

$$\alpha FB \sqrt{r_1^2 + r_2^2}$$

For values of r_1 and r_2 not exceeding 5, and for values of $\frac{1}{2}(r_1 + r_2)$ less than 3, the mean ratio $\frac{1}{2}(r_1 + r_2)$ can be used instead of each separate ratio without appreciably altering the maximum error, and when this is done, and the value of α is taken as $\frac{1}{2}°\left(\dfrac{30}{3438} \text{ radians}\right)$, formula ($\mathbf{A7.5}$) can be adjusted to give a still

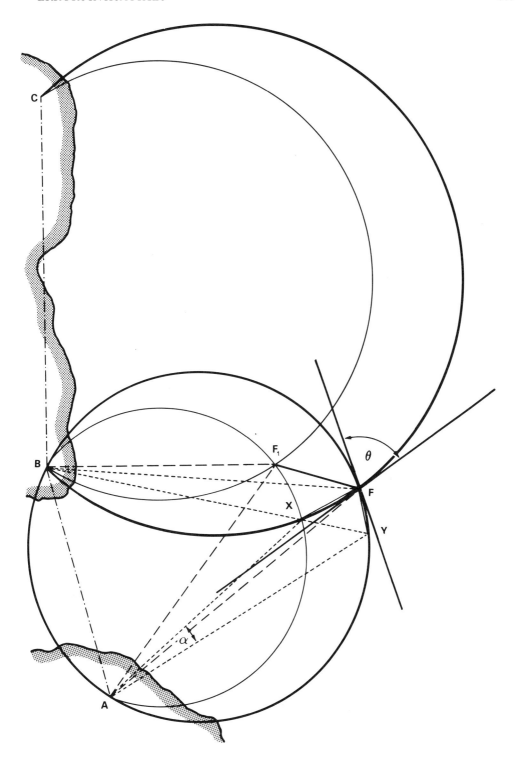

Fig. A7–4. Errors in horizontal sextant angles

more approximate value of the maximum error. Thus:

$$FF_1 \text{ max} = \frac{\alpha FB}{\sin \theta} \ \sqrt{\tfrac{1}{2} (r_1 + r_2)^2 (1 + \cos \theta)}$$

$$= \frac{\alpha FB}{\sin \tfrac{1}{2}\theta} \times \left(\frac{r_1 + r_2}{2} \right)$$

$$= \frac{30FB}{3438 \sin \tfrac{1}{2}\theta} \times \left(\frac{r_1 + r_2}{2} \right)$$

$$= \frac{FB}{\theta°} \left(\frac{r_1 + r_2}{2} \right) \text{ in miles (approximately)}$$

$$= \frac{\text{distance of middle object}}{\text{acute angle of cut in degrees}} \times \text{mean ratio} \quad \ldots \textbf{A7.6}$$

If the distance FB is taken as unity, a table may be constructed in terms of θ and the mean ratio, giving the values of FF_1, and from this table the error for any other value of FB can be found by multiplying the tabulated error by that value. The error itself is tabulated in cables instead of decimals of a mile.

Table A7–1.   Maximum error in cables of an HSA fix, for each mile of distance from the middle object and for values of θ and the mean ratio, when the error in each angle observed is $\tfrac{1}{2}°$

ACUTE ANGLE OF CUT	MEAN RATIO $\tfrac{1}{2}$	MEAN RATIO 1	MEAN RATIO 1$\tfrac{1}{2}$	MEAN RATIO 2	MEAN RATIO 2$\tfrac{1}{4}$
10°	0.5	1.0	1.5	2.0	2.5
20°	0.3	0.5	0.8	1.0	1.3
30°	0.2	0.3	0.5	0.7	0.8
40°	0.1	0.3	0.4	0.5	0.6
50°	0.1	0.2	0.3	0.4	0.5
60°	0.1	0.2	0.3	0.3	0.4
70°	0.1	0.1	0.2	0.3	0.4
80°	0.1	0.1	0.2	0.2	0.3
90°	0.1	0.1	0.2	0.2	0.3

In Fig. A7–5, A, B and C are three objects. The circles of position corresponding to the horizontal sextant angles have been drawn, and it is seen that they intersect at an angle of about 40°. It is also seen that the ratios r_1 and r_2, being FA/AB and FC/BC, are about 1 and 2. The mean ratio is thus about 1$\tfrac{1}{2}$.

If, for example, FB is 3′, the maximum error in the fix corresponding to an error of $\tfrac{1}{2}°$ in observation and plotting, is 1.2 cables.

Reliability of HSA fixes

Formula **(A7.6)** makes it possible to set out rules for deciding whether a station-pointer fix is reliable or not, and for indicating the extent of its reliability.

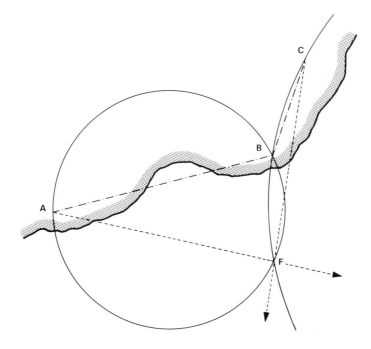

Fig. A7–5. Maximum error in the HSA fix

There are three factors to consider: the acute angle of cut θ, the distance of the fix from the middle object or object common to both observations, and the mean of the ratios r_1 and r_2. The formula shows that the error in the fix will be least when three conditions are fulfilled:

1. The distance of the fix from the middle object is as small as possible. That is, the nearest of the three objects should be chosen as the middle object when practicable.
2. The angle of cut should be as near as 90° as possible.
3. The mean ratio should be as small as possible.

As a rule it is unlikely that all three conditions can be fulfilled at any one time, but it does happen that a reliable fix results even when only two are fulfilled. The fulfilment of a single condition is not sufficient to determine the reliability of a fix. The angle of cut, for example, may be 90°, but the other two factors can easily outweigh this advantage. On the other hand if, in addition to an angle of cut equal to 90°, the distance from the middle object is small, the resulting error will be small.

The angle of cut

In order to ensure that the angle of cut shall not be too small, it is desirable to have an approximate idea of what it will be before the observations are made. This can be obtained by considering the angle subtended at the middle object by the other two objects.

In Fig. A7–6, FL and FM are tangents at F to the position circles. Then θ is the angle LFM.

Since FL is a tangent to the circle BFC at F, the angle LFB is equal to the angle BCF. Similarly, the angle MFB is equal to the angle BAF. Hence:

$$\theta = BAF + BCF$$
$$= 180° - (AFB + ABF) + 180° - (BFC + CBF)$$
$$= 360° - (AFC + ABC)$$

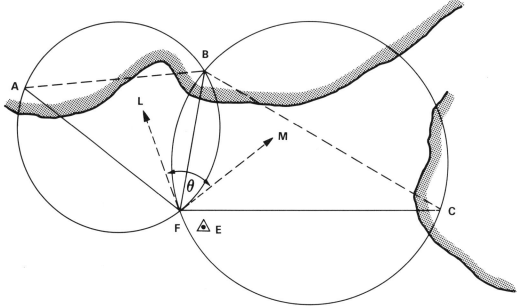

Fig. A7–6.   The angle of cut in an HSA fix

Of these angles, ABC can be measured or estimated from the chart. Also if E is the estimated position of the ship at the time the observations will be made, the angles AEC and AFC will be approximately equal (assuming that E and F are reasonably close together), so that:

$$\theta \simeq 360° - (AEC + ABC) \qquad \qquad \text{...} \textbf{A7.7}$$

The angle AEC can also be estimated from the chart, and a value of θ obtained before the observations are taken. A glance at Table A7–1 will then give some idea of the reliability that can be attached to the fix when it is obtained.

As it stands, formula **(A7.7)** is not general because θ must be less than 90°, and the sum of the angles AEC and ABC will not always be greater than 270°. When they are not, it can be shown, by adjusting the positions of A, B, C and F, that:

$$\theta = (AEC + ABC) - 180°$$
$$\theta = 180° - (AEC + ABC)$$

The rule giving θ is therefore: add the angles AEC and ABC and subtract the sum from 360° or 180°, or subtract 180° from the sum, so as to obtain a value of θ less than 90°.

Examples of satisfactory HSA fixes

In the two examples that follow, E denotes the estimated position of the ship at the time the fix is obtained.

In Fig. A7–7(a), the angle ABC is estimated to be 170°, and the angle AEC 160°. The angle of cut is therefore given by:

$$360° - (170° + 160°)$$
$$= 30°$$

The ratio r_1, being FA/AB or EA/AB approximately, is about $\frac{3}{4}$; and r_2 is about $\frac{5}{4}$. The mean ratio is therefore about unity. Suppose FB is 2', and that the error in each angle observed is $\frac{1}{2}°$. Table A7–1 shows that the possible error in the fix is 2×0.3 or 0.6 cables.

In Fig. A7–7(b), the angle ABC is estimated to be 100°, and the angle AEC 190°. The angle of cut is therefore 70°. Also, r_1 and r_2 are both about $\frac{3}{4}$, and the mean ratio is therefore about $\frac{3}{4}$. If the distance FB in this example is 7', the possible error in the position when the error in each angle observed is $\frac{1}{2}°$, is seen from Table A7–1 to be 7×0.1 or 0.7 cables.

The small and apparently unfavourable angle of cut in the first example is counterbalanced by the small value of FB. In the second example FB is large,

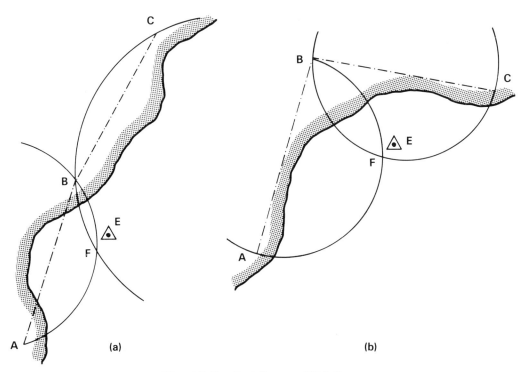

Fig. A7–7.   Satisfactory HSA fixes

but θ is 70°. The two fixes are thus widely separated in their angle of cut, yet their reliability is practically the same, and both would be regarded as satisfactory.

Example of an unsatisfactory fix

When the middle object lies near the circle passing through the other two objects and the fix, the fix cannot fail to be unreliable because, in the limiting position when the middle object lies on that circle, it is impossible to obtain a fix.

Fig. A7–8 shows the middle object badly placed. The angle ABC is about 100° and the angle AEC 60°. The angle of cut is therefore 180° − (100° + 60°) or 20°.

Also, r_1 and r_2 are each about $1\frac{3}{4}$. The mean ratio is therefore about $1\frac{3}{4}$. If FB is 6′, the error in the fix resulting from an error of $\frac{1}{2}°$ in each angle observed is 6 × 0.9 or 5.4 cables, an error sufficiently large to render the fix unreliable.

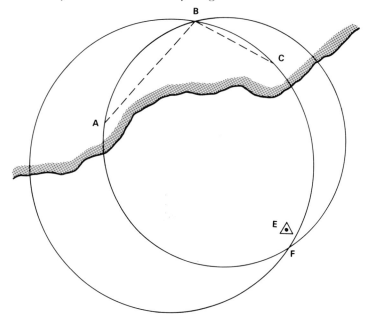

Fig. A7–8.   An unsatisfactory HSA fix

DOUBLING THE ANGLE ON THE BOW AND THE EFFECT OF CURRENT OR TIDAL STREAM

It is apparent that if a ship holds a steady course until the bearing of an object on her bow is doubled, the position at which this occurs forms an isosceles triangle with the first position and the object, and it is distant from the object by an amount equal to the run between the observations. If the ship experiences a current or tidal stream in the meantime, it must be allowed for in order to avoid an error in her final position.

In practice, it will usually be more convenient to solve a problem of this type by plotting it on the chart and transferring the position lines as necessary. The following theory, however, may be regarded as general.

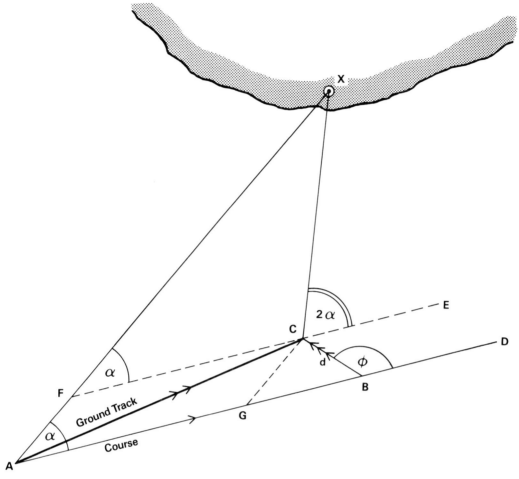

Fig. A7–9.   Doubling the angle on the bow in a tidal stream

In Fig. A7–9, AB is the course of the ship, and BC is the tidal stream. AB and BC combine to give the ground track, AC.

Suppose X is some object observed from the ship. When the ship is at A, the angle on the bow is XAB, denoted by α. When the ship is at C, it is assumed for the purpose of this problem that the angle on the bow has been doubled. At this point the fore-and-aft line is in the direction CE, parallel to AD, and the angle XCE is thus 2α.

EC produced meets AX in F. The angle CFX is therefore equal to the angle CXF, and FC is equal to CX.

CG is drawn parallel to XA. The angle CGB is therefore equal to α, and, since $FAGC$ is a parallelogram:

$$CX = AG = AB - GB$$

AB, the distance resulting from the ship's known speed and the duration of the run, can be found at once, but GB must be calculated from the triangle GCB.

Thus:

$$\frac{GB}{BC} = \frac{\sin GCB}{\sin BGC}$$

i.e. $\quad GB = BC\, \dfrac{\sin GCB}{\sin \alpha}$

If BC is denoted by d (the amount of drift during the run) and the angle CBD by ϕ, the angle GCB is $(\phi - \alpha)$ and:

$$CX = AB - \frac{d \sin (\phi - \alpha)}{\sin \alpha} \quad \dots (\phi > \alpha) \qquad \dots \textbf{A7.8}$$

If ϕ is less than α, CX is given by:

$$AB + \frac{d \sin (\alpha - \phi)}{\sin \alpha} \qquad \qquad \dots \textbf{A7.9}$$

These formulae suffice when the current or tidal stream carries the ship to port, and the object is also to port. They also suffice when the ship is carried to starboard and the object is to starboard. When, however, the ship moves to starboard and the object is to port or vice versa, it can easily be shown that CX is given by:

$$AB + \frac{d \sin (\phi + \alpha)}{\sin \alpha} \qquad \qquad \dots \textbf{A7.10}$$

The distance of the ship from the object at the instant of the second observation can therefore be found.

EXAMPLE

At 1000 an object is seen to bear 040° to an observer on board a ship steaming 075° at 16 knots in a tidal stream setting 300° at 3 knots. At 1030 the same object bears 005°. How far is the ship from the object at 1030?

At 1000 the angle on the port bow is $(075° - 040°)$ or 35°. At 1030 the angle is $(075° - 005°)$ or 70°. Also, the angle ϕ is $(75° - 300° + 360°)$ or 135°.

The ship's run in 30 minutes is 8′, and d is 1′.5.

Both the set of the tidal stream and the object are to port. The distance of the ship from the object at 1030 is therefore (formula **A7.8**):

$$8' - \frac{1'.5 \sin (135° - 35°)}{\sin 35°}$$

$$= 8' - \frac{1'.5 \sin 100°}{\sin 35°}$$

$$= 8' - 2'.6$$

$$= 5'.4$$

The position of the ship at 1030 is thus fixed by a bearing and distance of 005° and 5′.4, and it is necessary to plot only the true bearing.

If the set had been in the opposite direction, 120°, ϕ would have been equal to $(120° - 75°)$ or 45°, and the distance would have been (formula **A7.10**):

$$8' + \frac{1'.5 \sin (45° + 35°)}{\sin 35°}$$
$$= 8' + 2'.6$$
$$= 10'.6$$

Effect of the tidal stream when ϕ has particular values

The general formula is simplified considerably when ϕ has certain values. These values and adjustments are:

1. When ϕ is equal to zero. This means that the direction of the current or tidal stream is the same as the course steered. Then, by substitution:

$$CX = AB + d$$

2. When ϕ is equal to 180°. The set is now in a direction opposite to the course steered, and:

$$CX = AB - d$$

3. When ϕ is equal to α. This means that the direction of the current or tidal stream is that of the first true bearing, and:

$$CX = AB$$

4. When ϕ is equal to $(180° - \alpha)$. The set is now in a direction opposite to the first true bearing, and again:

$$CX = AB$$

5. When ϕ is equal to 2α. This means that the direction of the current or tidal stream is that of the second true bearing, and:

$$CX = AB - d$$

6. When ϕ is equal to $(180° - 2\alpha)$. The set is now in a direction opposite to the second true bearing, and:

$$CX = AB + d$$

Bibliography

The following books, publications, pamphlets, etc. have been consulted during the writing of Volume I of the *Admiralty Manual of Navigation*. These are in addition to those references from RN sources (e.g. the *Admiralty Sailing Directions*), which are not included below.

Aeronautical Chart and Information Centre. *Geodetic Distance and Azimuth Computations for Lines Over 500 Miles*. ACIC Technical Report No. 80. US Air Force, August 1957.

Anderson, E. W. *The Principles of Navigation*. Hollis and Carter, 1966.

Anderson, N. M. 'Computer-assisted cartography in the Canadian Hydrographic Service', *International Hydrographic Review*, July 1981.

Appleyard, S. F. *Marine Electronic Navigation*. Routledge and Kegan Paul, 1980.

Blance, A. G. *Norie's Nautical Tables*. Imray, Laurie, Norie and Wilson, 1979.

Bomford, G. *Geodesy*. 3rd edition. Oxford University Press, 1971.

Bowditch, N. *American Practical Navigator*, Volumes I and II. Defence Mapping Agency Hydrographic Centre, 1977 (Volume I), 1975 (Volume II).

Bulmer, B. F. *Meteorology for Mariners*. Met O.895. HMSO, 1978.

Clarke, G. M., and Cooke, D. *A Basic Course in Statistics*. Edward Arnold, 1981.

Cotter, C. H. *The Elements of Navigation and Nautical Astronomy*. Brown, Son and Ferguson, 1977.

Crenshaw, J. R. *Naval Shiphandling*. United States Naval Institute Press, 1975.

Cross, P. A., and Walker, A. S. *Statistical and Computational Aspects of Multi-position Line Fixing (MPLF)*. North East London Polytechnic/RN Hydrographic School, *HMS Drake*, 1984.

Fifield, L. W. J. *Navigation for Watchkeepers*. Heinemann, 1980.

Glansdorp, C., Goldsten, G. H., Kluytenaar, P. A., and Wepster, A. *Round the Horn or Through Magellan*. Report No. R109. Netherlands Maritime Institute (undated but probably 1978/79).

HM GOVERNMENT PUBLICATIONS

Department of Trade. *A Guide to the Planning and Conduct of Sea Passages*. HMSO, 1980.

——*International Convention on Standards of Training, Certification and Watchkeeping for Seafarers, 1978*. Command Paper 7543, *Shipping Misc.* No. 6. HMSO, 1979.

——*Marine Radar Performance Specification, 1982*. HMSO, 1982.

——Merchant Shipping 'M' Notices. HMSO, 1971 to June 1983 (*see also* Department of Transport).

——Statutory Instruments (*Merchant Shipping: Safety* series):

SI 1975 No. 700, *The Merchant Shipping (Carriage of Nautical Publications) Rules 1975.* HMSO, 1975.

SI 1980 No. 530, *The Merchant Shipping (Navigational Equipment) Regulations 1980.* HMSO, 1980. As amended by SI 1981 No. 579, *The Merchant Shipping (Navigational Equipment) (Amendment) Regulations 1981.* HMSO, 1981.

SI 1980 No. 534, *The Merchant Shipping (Navigational Warnings) Regulations 1980.* HMSO, 1980. As amended by SI 1981 No. 406, *The Merchant Shipping (Navigational Warnings) (Amendment) Regulations 1981.* HMSO, 1981.

SI 1982. No. 1699, *The Merchant Shipping (Certification and Watchkeeping) Regulations 1982.* HMSO, 1983.

SI 1983 No. 708, *The Merchant Shipping (Distress Signals and Prevention of Collisions) Regulations 1983.* HMSO, 1983.

Department of Transport. Merchant Shipping 'M' Notices. HMSO, from July 1983 (*see also* Department of Trade).

SI 1984 No. 1203, *The Merchant Shipping (Navigational Equipment) Regulations 1984.* HMSO, 1984. As amended by SI 1985 No. 659, *The Merchant Shipping (Navigational Equipment) (Amendment) Regulations 1985.* HMSO, 1985.

Steering Committee on Pilotage. *Marine Pilotage in the United Kingdom.* HMSO, 1974.

International Association of Lighthouse Authorities. *Maritime Buoyage System.* IALA, 1980.

International Chamber of Shipping. *Bridge Procedures Guide.* Wetherby, 1977.

International Maritime Organisation. *Recommendation on Basic Principles and Operational Guidance Relating to Navigational Watchkeeping.* IMO, 1974.

——*Ships' Routeing.* 5th edition. IMO, 1984, incorporating amendments 1–6.

Kreyszig, E. *Introducing Mathematical Statistics — Principles and Methods.* John Wiley and Sons, 1970.

Maling, D. H. *Coordinate Systems and Map Projections.* George Philip and Son, 1973.

Maloney, E. S. *Dutton's Navigation and Pilotage.* 13th edition. US Naval Institute Press, 1978.

Moody, A. B. *Navigation Afloat.* Hollis and Carter, 1980.

Moss, W. D. *Radar Watchkeeping.* Maritime Press, 1973.

Nautical Institute. *Nautical Review* (including Seaways and Nautical Briefings), Volume 1 No. 1, March 1977, to Volume 4 No. 2, February 1980.

——*Seaways*, March 1980 to December 1985.

Nautical Institute/Royal Institute of Navigation. *The Selection and Display of Navigational Information.* Proceedings of seminar, December, 1981. Nautical Institute, 1982.

——*Aspects of Navigational Safety.* Proceedings of seminar, December 1982. Nautical Institute, 1983.

Nautical Institute/National Maritime Institute/College of Nautical Studies, Warsash, Southampton. *Ship Operations and Safety.* Proceedings of conference, April 1981. Nautical Institute, 1981.

Racal–Decca. *The Decca Navigator Operating Instructions and Marine Data Sheets*, Volumes 1 and 2. Decca Navigator Company, 1973 (up to and including Amendment No. 8).

——*The Decca Navigator Marine Data Sheets.* Racal–Decca Navigator Ltd, 1985.

——*The Decca Navigator Mark 21 Operating Instructions.* Racal–Decca Navigator Ltd, 1986.

Royal Institute of Navigation. *The Journal of the Institute of Navigation*, Volume I No. 1, 1948; Volume IX No. 4, 1956; Volume 23 No. 2, 1970, to Volume 24 No. 4, 1971.

——*The Journal of Navigation*, Volume 25 No. 1, 1972, to Volume 38 No. 3, 1985.

——*Navigation Equipment and Training Standards*. Proceedings of conference, April 1985. RIN, 1985.

Royal Institute of Navigation/Royal Institute of Naval Architects. *Marine Traffic Engineering*. Proceedings of conference, May 1972. RIN/RINA, 1973.

Skolnik, M. I. *Introduction to Radar Systems*. McGraw-Hill/Kogakusha, 1962.

Smart, W. M. *On a Problem in Navigation*. Royal Astronomical Society, 1946.

Tranter, C. J., and Lambe, C. G. *Advanced Level Mathematics (Pure and Applied)*. 3rd edition. Hodder and Stoughton, 1973.

Troup, Sir James A. G. *On the Bridge*. Hutchinson, 1950.

Vogel, T. J. 'Horizontal datum for nautical charts', *International Hydrographic Review*, July 1981.

Wylie, F. J. *Choosing and Using Ship's Radar*. Hollis and Carter, 1970.

——*The Royal Institute of Navigation's 'The Use of Radar at Sea'*. 5th revised edition. Hollis and Carter, 1978.

Index

Printed in the United Kingdom for Her Majesty's Stationery Office
Dd 737667 11/87 C75 GP 3936 12521